GEOLOGICAL SOCIETY SPECIAL REPORT NO. 23

A revised correlation of Quaternary deposits in the British Isles

Edited by

D. Q. BOWEN

GW00771765

Contents

List of Authors

Bowen, D. Q.
Department of Earth Sciences, Cardiff University, Cardiff, CF1 3YE, Wales, UK (e-mail: BowenDQ@cardiff.ac.uk)

Lewis, S. G.
Department of Geology & Geography, Cheltenham and Gloucester College of Higher Education, Cheltenham, GL50 4AZ (e-mail: Slewis@chelt.ac.uk)

Maddy, D.
Department of Geography, University of Newcastle, Newcastle-upon-Tyne, NE1 7RU (e-mail: Darrel.Maddy@newcastle.ac.uk)

Gibbard, P. L.
Department of Geography, Cambridge University, Cambridge, CB2 3EN (e-mail: PLG1@cus.cam.a-c.uk)

Preece, R. C.
Department of Zoology, Cambridge University, Cambridge, CB2 3EJ (e-mail: rcp1001@cus.cam.a-c.uk)

Campbell, S.
Earth Science Division, Countryside Council for Wales, Bangor, Gwynedd LL57 2LQ (e-mail: S.Campbell@ccw.gov.uk)

Thomas, G. S. P.
Department of Geography, Liverpool University, Liverpool, L69 3BX (e-mail: Thoma@liverpool.a-c.uk)

Sutherland, D. G.
Placer Deposits, 2 London Street, Edinburgh, EH3 6NA

McCabe, A. M.
Department of Environmental Sciences, University of Ulster, Coleraine, Northern Ireland, BT52 1SA

Cameron, T. D. J.
British Geological Survey, Murchison House, West Mains Road, Edinburgh EH9 3LA

Holmes, R. A.
British Geological Survey, Murchison House, West Mains Road, Edinburgh EH9 3LA

Preface

Although this report includes some Holocene stratigraphical units, it should be noted, as mentioned in Chapter 1, that it was thought inappropriate to deal with the biostratigraphical complexity of Devensian late-glacial and Holocene subdivision. Such data could well form the basis of a separate report.

Thanks are due to the Stratigraphy Commission of the Geological Society of London for their support, especially the Chairman, Professor Peter Rawson, as well as John Gregory who steered the report through its various stages. David Ogden and his colleagues at the Geological Society Publishing House are also thanked for their unfailing and swift help.

The American Geophysical Union is thanked for permission to reproduce Figures 2 and 3. Finally, the two internal reviewers of the Geological Society Stratigraphy Commission and the two external reviewers are thanked for their valuable comments.

Chapter 1

On the correlation and classification of Quaternary deposits and land–sea correlations

D. Q. BOWEN

The correlation and classification of Quaternary deposits is desirable for three principal reasons. First, as an exercise in lithostratigraphy, the basis of all stratigraphy and the means for understanding geological history. Second, to establish the stratigraphical relationship of units from which inferences may be drawn about palaeoclimate. This provides information for understanding the past, present and possible future climate system. Third, to provide standardized geological information for different users. The first of these is largely self-evident. The second is less so. But some success in the correlation of terrestrial deposits with ocean sediments and ice-cores from Greenland has made a fundamental contribution to describing the climate system and an emerging understanding of the leads and lags in the coupled ocean–atmosphere–hydro(cryo)-sphere–biosphere system. This has placed new and exacting requirements of terrestrial data for correlation hitherto only available on long time-scales from relatively few sites with the necessary high degree of resolution. To that extent the second edition of this report a quarter of a century since its first edition benefits from the explosion of new data, new methods of geochronology and better awareness of the importance of the wider picture.

The third reason is to provide standardized information about superficial deposits for users such as the environmental protection and nature conservation agencies, for water authorities and civil engineers. That said, it is recognized that most of the information in this volume is specialized and not invariably well suited to the needs of everyone (see 'How to use this report').

Subdivision of the Quaternary of the British Isles

The base of the Quaternary, as defined by the International Union of Geological Sciences (IUGS), occurs just below the top of the Olduvai magneto-subchron at Vrica in Italy (Aguirre & Passini 1985). Its age, on an astronomically tuned time-scale, is estimated as 1.905 Ma (Shackleton *et al.* 1990). On this definition, the shallow-water deposits of East Anglia (Red Crag and Norwich Crag Formations) are late Pliocene in age. They are included in this report, however, because: (1) the base of the Quaternary in Britain was placed at the base of the Red Crag on the recommendation of the 1948 International Geological Congress in Britain (Mitchell *et al.* 1973); (2) evidence from northwest Europe shows a major faunal change at about 2.5 Ma (Zagwijn 1974; Gibbard *et al.* 1991*b*); and (3) a wide range of evidence suggests that the IUGS boundary was placed at an inappropriate horizon and that an age of 2.5 Ma is more appropriate. The Stratigraphy Commission of the International Union for Quaternary Research (INQUA) is currently seeking a suitably defined boundary stratotype. If an age of 2.5 Ma is secured on a sound lithostratigraphical basis, then it will coincide with the first appearance of *Homo habilis* (Africa), the dominant genus of the Quaternary; the appearance of loess in the stratigraphical record in China; and the first evidence of substantial ice-rafting in the north Atlantic

(Rockall Basin).

Subdivision of the Quaternary of the British Isles into a Pleistocene and Holocene Series has long been standard. But subdivision of the Pleistocene into Lower, Middle and Upper has not been formally proposed. Elsewhere, many place the base of the Middle Pleistocene at the Matuyama–Brunhes reversal (Richmond 1996). This has not yet been identified in the British Isles and its position may only be inferred approximately on the basis of correlations with the continent. Informally, the base of the Upper Pleistocene is drawn at the oxygen isotope stage 6/sub-stage 5e boundary in deep-sea cores. In Britain, there is general agreement that oxygen isotope sub-stage 5e corresponds broadly with the Ipswichian. Pending formal agreement by IUGS such definitions are only informal and no formal subdivision is proposed in this report.

The correlation and classification of Quaternary deposits in the British Isles may be traced back to Ramsay (1852) and Reid (1882). W. B. Wright (1914, 1937) proposed an 'older drift' and a 'newer drift' division for the glacial deposits of the British Isles. He was followed by Charlesworth (1928, 1929, 1957) who delimited their respective provinces and thus, unintentionally, provided an interpretative but potentially misleading geomorphological base-line for subsequent stratigraphical work. Other schemes of classification and their correlation were provided by Zeuner (1945, 1959), Arkell (1943) and Wills (1951). The immediate forerunner to modern classification, however, was Baden-Powell (1948) who recognized Lowestoft and Gipping glaciations in East Anglia. These appeared to be confirmed by West & Donner (1956) on the basis of till fabric work. Following pollen analysis of the deposits at Hoxne (West 1956) and Bobbitshole (West 1957), West (1958) proposed that the Hoxnian post-dated the Lowestoft glaciation, the Ipswichian post-dated the Gipping glaciation, and the Hunstanton glaciation post-dated the Ipswichian. This was re-stated by West (1963) and it subsequently became the basis of classification (Table 1) for the first edition of this report (Mitchell *et al.* 1973). Thus identification of such standard interglacial marker horizons in regions beyond East Anglia were then used to fix other deposits in time elsewhere (Mitchell *et al.* 1973). The pre-Cromer forest Bed deposits of the Norwich Crag and the Red Crag were subdivided biostratigraphically (pollen and foraminifera) to recognize the pre-Ludhamian, Ludhamian, Thurnian, Antian, and Baventian (Funnell & West 1962; Funnell 1961). Subsequently, West & Wilson (1966) defined the Beestonian and Pastonian, and West (1980) added the Pre-Pastonian and Brammertonian.

By the time the first edition of this report was published (Mitchell *et al.* 1973) two major developments had taken place, one local and provincial, the other global in its implications. The first was the demonstration by officers of the Geological Survey that there was no lithostratigraphical evidence in East Anglia for the Gipping glaciation: that is, for glacial deposits intermediate in age between the Hoxnian and the Ipswichian (Bristow & Cox 1973). Second, the full impact and implica-

Table 1. *Classification table of proposed British Quaternary Stages in 1973 (from Mitchell et al. 1973)*

STAGE	STRATOTYPE	NOTES
Flandrian		Begins 10 ka (14C) Base: base of pollen zone IV
Devensian	Four Ashes, Staffs (SJ914082)	<u>Late</u>: 26 to 10 ka (14C) _Middle_: 50 to 26 ka (14C): includes Upton Warren interstadial complex <u>Early</u>: Preceding 50 ka (14C): includes Chelford interstadial ~ 60 ka (14C)
Ipswichian	Bobbitshole, Ipswich (TM 148414)	Base at beginning of pollen zone I I
Wolstonian	Wolston, Warwicks (SP 411748)	Includes Baginton-Lillington gravels Baginton sand, Wolston series, Dunsmore gravels. (Base: bottom of B-L gravels)
Hoxnian	Hoxne, Suffolk (TM543977)	Base at beginning of pollen zone H I
Anglian	Corton cliff, Suffolk (TM 543977)·	Lowestoft Till Corton Sands Norwich Brickearth/Cromer Till Base at bottom of lower till
Cromerian	West Runton, Norfolk (TG 188432)	Upper Fresh-water Bed Base at base of pollen zone C 1
Beestonian	Beeston, Norfolk (TG 169433)	Arctic Fresh-water Bed. Base at base of pollen zone P I
Pastonian	Paston, Norfolk (TG 341352)	Gravels, sands and silts Base at base of pollen zone Be I
Baventian	Easton Bavents, Suffolk (TM 518787)	Marine silt Base at base of pollen zone L 4
Antian Thurnian Ludhamian	Ludham, Norfolk Borehole at TG385199	Marine shelly sand. Base at base of pollen zone L3 (forams: L v) Marine silt. Base at base of pollen zone L2 (L m: forams) Shelly sand. Base at base of pollen zone L 1 (L 1 forams)
Waltonian	Walton-on-the-Naze, Essex (TM 267237)	Older Red Crag. Base at base of Crag at Walton

tions of Emiliani's (1955, 1957) work on the oxygen isotope stratigraphy of deep-sea deposits was, by now, fully appreciated in some quarters in that it pointed to far greater potential complexity in the classification of terrestrial sequences than had hitherto been appreciated (Shackleton & Opdyke 1973; Evans 1971).

The problem of the missing post-Hoxnian but pre-Ipswichian glaciation (Gipping) was anticipated by Mitchell *et al.* (1973) who, while not accepting the conclusions of Bristow & Cox (1973) about the absence of a post-Hoxnian, pre-Ipswichian, glaciation in East Anglia (Shotton, *in* Mitchell *et al.* 1973), were convinced of that event in the west Midlands at Nechells and Quinton (Shotton *ibid.*) where interglacial deposits correlated with those at Hoxne separated upper and lower glacial deposits. They did not, however, locate their 'type-locality' there, but at Wolston in Warwickshire (Table 1) which consisted of deposits representing a cold climate 'cycle from cold protoglacial, through full glacial to a period of ice-retreat' (Shotton *ibid.*). The 'type-locality' at Wolston was, however, 'unrelated to any interglacial marker horizon' (Bowen 1978) — the fundamental basis of the 1973 classification (Mitchell *et al.* 1973). Since then a variety of evidence has been adduced to demonstrate that the Wolstonian type-locality, proposed as the post-Hoxnian, pre-Ipswichian glaciation, is pre-Hoxnian and is correlated with the Lowestoft Formation (Anglian) of East Anglia (Perrin *et al.* 1979; Maddy *et al.* 1991; Sumbler 1983a). The discovery of organic deposits, correlated with the Hoxnian, on the surface of the Wolstonian deposits, at Froghall, appears to have settled this controversy (Midlands, Chapter 3; and Keen *et al.* 1997) in as conclusive a manner as Bristow & Cox (1973) showed that evidence for a Gipping glaciation in East Anglia did not exist. At the present time, the only lithostratigraphical evidence adduced to support a post-Hoxnian, but pre-Ipswichian, glaciation of East Anglia comes from the Nar Valley in Norfolk (Eastern England, Chapter 2), where gravels interpreted as outwash overlie the marine clays (Nar Member) of the Nar Valley Formation; but no till was identified (Gibbard *et al.* 1991a, 1992).

A further problem with the classification of 1973 was implicit in its stratigraphical tables and commentaries: that is, the standard stages based in East Anglia and at Wolston, Warwickshire, were incapable of recognition much beyond these regions, other than by fitting local evidence, sometimes arbitrarily, into the standard classification. Thus, in Wales and Scotland, it was not possible to make correlations with East Anglia farther back than the Ipswichian.

Mitchell *et al.* (1973) 'accepted climatic fluctuation as the guiding principle for defining the stages of the British Quaternary'. Thus at the outset it inevitably followed that a classification of cold and temperate stages would form the basis of the model. With the exception of the Wolstonian in Warwickshire and the Devensian in Staffordshire, it was based entirely in East Anglia. The 1973 scheme rested primarily on a number of biostratigraphically defined fixed points in time, when pollen analysis indicated the development of mixed oak deciduous forest (Table 1). These temperate events, or interglacials, when combined with intervening cold stages that sometimes recorded glaciations, formed a continuum of climatically inferred events. Mitchell *et al.* (1973) were aware of the drawbacks of this approach, not least because of the diachronous nature of the vegetational response during the temperate stages (interglacials), influenced by 'variations in altitude and latitude as exist between southern England and northern Scotland' Mitchell *et al.* (1973). But they believed

that pollen analysis 'is still the best tool for zonation, though it may not necessarily remain so for all time' (Mitchell *et al.* 1973). Subsequent pollen analysis on the Holocene of the British Isles, assisted by radiocarbon ages, has shown some of the difficulties that attend the description of previous interglacials. Pollen biozone boundaries are diachronous and regional vegetational variability is considerable so that different vegetational assemblages of the same age occurred. This is compounded further for the interglacials because individual interglacial events were not based on first appearances, acme development and extinctions of tree and plant species, but rather on biofacies controlled by climate. Thus because of the probability that 'similar constellations of species were repeated several times in the Pleistocene' this could lead to misidentification of standard (temperate) stages (Bowen 1978).

The problems arising from the use of climate controlled biofacies was recognized by Mitchell *et al.* (1973) thus: 'we can often define biozones, they are essentially assemblage zones' (Mitchell *et al.* 1973). Subsequently it was recognized that this approach may have left some important events unrecognized (Bowen 1978; Shotton *et al.* 1983; Bowen *et al.* 1986). One of these was at Stanton Harcourt in Oxfordshire (Briggs *et al.* 1985).

New geochronological methods confirmed that additional events were recorded in the Quaternary deposits of the British Isles. These include uranium-series ages on stalagmite and wood, thermoluminescence (TL) on mineral grains and burnt flint, optically stimulated luminescence (OSL) on mineral grains, electron spin resonance (ESR) dating on fossil tooth enamel, amino acid dating of marine and non-marine bivalves and gastropods and cosmogenic chlorine-36 rock exposure dating. For the late Devensian and the Holocene, the use of accelerator mass spectrometry in radiocarbon dating has enabled the use of smaller samples, thus minimizing problems of contamination and opening up new avenues for the investigation of subdivision on millennial time-scales.

Analytical problems and sample integrity attend all of these methods, but used in combination and with lithostratigraphical, and sometimes geomorphological control, have provided major tools for dating and correlation. Just as radiocarbon dating is widely and reliably applicable in space and time back to about 20 000 radiocarbon years ago (some would claim older applicability), amino acid dating of bivalves and gastropods is applicable back at least as far as the Waverley Wood site in Warwickshire which, on this basis, is pre-Cromerian (West Runton) and some 600 ka ago. Using the time-dependent epimerization of the protein amino acid isoleucine' (L-Ile) to its non diastereoisomer alloisoleucine (D-aIle) in the proteinaceous residue in fossil shells, the D-aIle/L-Ile ratio increases with increasing age. It thus provides a relative dating tool that may be used for correlation (aminostratigraphy). When calibrated by methods that provide an independent geochronology it provides an amino acid geochronology applicable beyond the calibration site (Table 2) Bowen *et al.* (1989). D-aIle/L-Ile ratios are cited throughout the notes in this report and they form an important additional means of correlation, although geochronologically they are ultimately dependent on the accuracy of independent calibration.

All these, however, have given anomalous results. For example: (1) D-aIle/L-Ile ratios on shells from West Runton and Purfleet at first gave anomalously old ages; subsequent analyses gave more acceptable ratios; (2) TL ages for the Swanscombe Member were anomalously young; (3) U-series

Table 2. *Relationship between the classification of the first edition (Mitchell et al. 1973), selected lithostratigraphical units in this report, Aminozones and their characteristic D-aIle/L-Ile ratios, aminozone geochronology and correlation with oxygen isotope stratigraphy and polarity. All the data is referenced in the text except for the D-aIle-L-Ile ratio for Grace in the Somme Valley which represents samples collected from sediments with reversed magnetism (Bates 1993) and dated by ESR (Laurent et al. 1998)*

1st Edition (1973)	Lithostratigraphy	Aminozone	D-aIle/L-Ile	Age (ka)	δ^{18}O & polarity
Devensian	Halling Member Stockport Formation Δ	Halling	0.036 ± 0.01 (3)	10.9 ± 0.12 (^{14}C)	2
	Upton Warren Member	Upton Warren	0.07 ± 0.007 (5)		3
	Cassington Member	Cassington	0.08 ± 0.009 (6)	~ 80 (OSL)	5a
Ipswichian	Trafalgar Square Member	Trafalgar Square	0.1 ± 0.001 (11)	124 ± 5.4 (U) *	5e
Wolstonian	Ridgacre Formation Δ Kidderminster Member			159.5 ± 13 (^{36}Cl)	6
	Strensham Court Bed	Strensham	0.17 ± 0.01 (14)	~ 200 (OSL) *	7
	Bushley Green Member				8
Hoxnian	Hoxne Formation	Hoxne	0.26 ± 0.02 (9)	319 ± 38 (ESR)	9
	Spring Hill Member				10
	Swanscombe Member	Swanscombe	0.3 ± 0.017 (34)	~ 400 (U) * 471 ± 15 (TL) *	11
Anglian	Lowestfoft Formation Δ				12
Cromerian	West Runton Member	West Runton	0.35 ± 0.01 (9)	~ 500 (ESR)	13
	Waverley Wood Member	Waverley Wood	0.38 ± 0.026 (15)		15
	Kenn Formation Δ				16
	Grace Formation	Grace	0.43 ± 0.02 (4)	810 ± 140 (ESR)	21

*age established at another locality of the aminozone.

ages for the Nar Member conflict with age based on D-aIle/L-Ile ratios (North West Norfolk, note 9) but are in agreement for the West Stow Formation (Central East Anglia, note 28). The discovery of new methods and improvements in existing ones may amplify or change current interpretations.

Correlations with the climate system

The implications of Emiliani's (1955, 1957) measurements of oxygen isotope ratios in the tests of planktonic and benthonic foraminifera was to have a global and provincial impact (Fig. 1). These showed that systematic variations in palaeotemperature occurred throughout the Quaternary and although initially Emiliani attempted to correlate them with the then standard four-fold sequence of 'Alpine' glaciations, it was not until Shackleton & Opdyke (1973) showed they represented high continental ice volume (ice-ages) and low ice volume (interglacial) events, later coupled with variability in orbital parameters (Hayes *et al.* 1976), that the full implications of Emiliani's pioneering work was revealed. Time-scales are

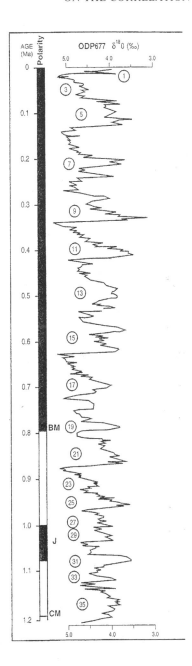

Fig. 1. Oxygen isotope record and polarity from ODP 677 (Shackleton *et al.* 1990) and Shackleton (*pers. comm.*).

geochronology on shorter ones, but the standard means of effecting such correlations is by making correlations with the oxygen isotope stratigraphic scale derived from ocean sediments. This, of course, is not a standard stratigraphical scale, nor are oxygen isotope stages chronostratigraphical ones in the sense of formal stratigraphy (Salvador 1994). Yet, such land–sea correlations using oxygen isotope stages as the scale, possibly a 'floating-scale' in some instances, currently offers a means of addressing Earth history on 10 000 to 100 000 year time-scales. These are the bands at which orbital frequencies appear to operate in driving sedimentation cycles through the forcing function of variability in the climate system. It is difficult to understand changing depositional environments and the changing biota without this wider framework. In turn, a better understanding of terrestrial environments contributes to progress in understanding the coupled ocean–atmosphere–biosphere system, as well as integrating data into a wider appreciation of the evolution of the climate system. There are emerging indications that this will also apply on millennial time-scales (Alley & Clark in press) (Fig. 2).

Quaternary climate variability took place within boundary conditions set by the configuration of the oceans, seaways, and mountain and plateau building caused by plate movements (Raymo *et al.* 1988). Internal variability in each of these components caused feed-backs of different kinds. For the last million years or so the main boundary conditions in which the climate system operated may be regarded as more or less fixed. The last twenty years have seen major advances in the understanding of how orbital forcing has been translated into climate change within the complex ocean–atmosphere system (Imbrie *et al.* 1992, 1993) within which the thermohaline circulation of the oceans and the fluxes of greenhouse gases between oceans, biosphere and atmosphere are major factors.

Evidence from ocean sediments in the northeast North Atlantic, such as oxygen isotope variability, an index of continental ice-sheet volume, ice-rafted sediments, calcium carbonate variability, and sea surface temperatures from planktonic fossils, has shown that north of 45–50°N, ice-sheets bordering the Atlantic Ocean reduced temperatures in the ocean at the 41 000-year and 100 000-year orbital bands. Both signals were 'transferred' from the ice-sheets to the ocean, via the atmosphere, with little or no time-lag (Ruddiman 1987). A temporal relationship between the atmosphere–ocean system and that of terrestrial ice volume is thus clear. North Atlantic sites such as: V23–81 (54° N 16° W), DSDP 607 (41° N 32° W), DSDP 609 (49° W 24° N) and DSDP 552 (Rockall Trough) (56° N 23° W), do not differ significantly from composite and global signals such as the 'global stratigraphic synthesis' (GSS97) of Raymo (1997) (Fig. 3).

For the last two major ice-age cycles events at sub-orbital frequencies occur, sometimes on millennial time-scales (e.g. Bond & Lotti 1995) that allow insight into the detailed nature of climate system interactions. A similar record is now emerging from the Vostok ice-core in Antarctica over the last four glacial cycles. On the continents, however, the record is less complete, and it remains a challenge to correlate terrestrial lithostratigraphical units with the oxygen isotope record in order to provide a framework for interpreting and understanding the biostratigraphical record as part of global biogeochemical fluxes. Some progress is being made with the Devensian of the British Isles and the Heinrich events of the North Atlantic, correlated with Greenland ice-cores, may be correlated with lithostratigraphy and glacial geology in the Irish Sea Basin (McCabe & Clark 1998).

revised from time to time (Shackleton *et al.* 1990) and new data compels revision of existing data sets and theory (Raymo 1997), while the discovery and widespread correlation of millennial events from ice-cores, ocean sediments and some high sedimentation terrestrial sequences has caused a revolution in both understanding and the need to provide high-resolution correlation (Alley & Clark in press). Since the first edition of this report a major international effort has been attempting to correlate the deep-sea record (oxygen isotope stratigraphy) with that of the continents (Kukla 1977; Bowen 1978, 1994*a*; Sibrava *et al.* 1986).

Hemispheric and global correlations in the Quaternary may be made using magnetostratigraphy on longer time-scales, or

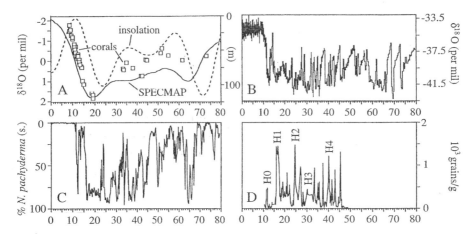

Fig. 2. Climate records for the last 800 000 calendar years. A: Insolation (June, 60° N) with a range from 450 to 515 W/m²); SPECMAP stack of global ice-volume signal (δ^{18}O per mil) and U-Th ages on corals from Barbados and New Guinea. B: GISP2 δ^{18}O record. C: Changes in the percentage of *N. pachyderma* (s.) from North Atlantic core VM23-081. D: Lithic grain concentration (numbers of grains >150 μm gram, from VM23-081 showing Heinrich Events (H). (Reproduced with permission from Alley & Clark, *Mechanisms of Millennial Climate Change* (American Geophysical Union Monograph), in press).

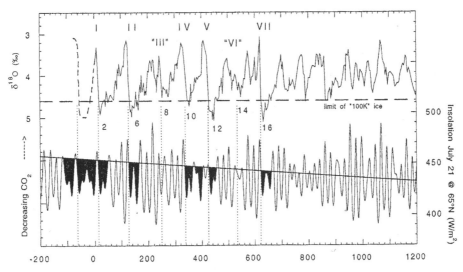

Fig. 3. Benthic δ^{18}O data from Pacific Site 849 plotted to the 'global stratigraphic synthesis timescale' (GSS97) of Raymo (1997). Mid-points of Terminations I to VII are shown by the vertical lines. The horizontal dashed line represents long-term downdraw of atmospheric pco_2 levels indicates the level below which '100 ka' ice is observed. The insolation record (bottom) is from Laskkar *et al.* 1993). Below the slanted line '100 ka' ice can nucleate and be stable (shaded). The interval between 400 and 385 ka followed closley on a termination and peak interglacial conditions and may not have been long enough for '100 ka' ice to have grown. Timescale is in ka. (Reproduced with permission from Raymo 1997).

Subdivision correlation and classification

The close temporal relationship demonstrated between ice-sheets and climate might be taken as a vindication of the former system of classification based on climate cycles (climate-stratigraphy). This, however, would be illusory, and while a primarily climatic element is inevitably part of any classification of Quaternary deposits, there is no good reason why their classification should differ from other Phanerozoic ones. Informal usage of terms such as *interglacial, interstadial,* or *stadial,* imply climatic inference that is not always unambiguous. Failure to distinguish between the deposits, their lithostratigraphy and biostratigraphy, and inferences drawn from them and their contents may cause needless confusion and erroneous conclusions. Further misunderstanding is promoted by both authors and editors in persisting to

regard 'chronostratigraphy' as being synonymous with 'geochronology'.

Stratigraphical approaches to Quaternary rocks is no different to earlier ones: (1) description (and interpretion); (2) correlation (by all possible means); and (3) classification (chronostratigraphy). This report, however, is principally an exercise in the first two. It was the majority view of the contributors to this report that the time was premature to designate additional stages as they were defined in the first edition (Mitchell *et al.* 1973). Thus this report presents a synthesis of what stratigraphical units exist and proposes their mutual correlation before further to wider correlations through oxygen isotope stratigraphy. Discussion and agreement of some of these may lead to proposals for chronostratigraphical classification. It was also agreed that the detailed complexities of the Devensian late-glacial as well as the

Table 3. *Comparison of the views of Bridgland (1994) and Gibbard (1994 and Chapter 5 of this report) on the subdivison, correlation and geochronology of part of the Lower Thames Valley sequence*

δ¹⁸O	1973	P. L. GIBBARD	D. R. BRIDGLAND	δ¹⁸O
5e	Ipswichian	Aveley Member Trafalgar Square Member Purfleet member	Trafalgar Square Member	5e
11 or 9 to 6	Wolstonian	Spring Gardens Member Mucking Member	Mucking Gravel (part)	6
			Aveley interglacial deposits	7
			Mucking Gravel (in part) Corbets Tey Gravel (in part)	8
			Purfleet interglacial deposits	9
		Corbets Tey Member Orsett Heath Member	Corbets Tey Gravel (in part) Orsett Heath Gravel (in part)	10
9 or 11	Hoxnian	Swanscombe Member	Swanscombe interglacial deposits	11
12 ?	Anglian	Dartford Heath Member Hornchurch Member	Orsett Heath Gravel (part) Dartford Heath Gravel Hornchurch Till	12

Holocene required separate treatment as a separate work. Thus subdivision and correlation of the late-glacial and Holocene is only general.

Thus the main object is to describe, define and correlate the Quaternary deposits. The lithological lateral and vertical variability in many of the deposits is considerable, but their geometry as stratigraphical units and their relationship with other ones is a main tool in these correlations. The recommendations of the International Subcommission on Stratigraphic Classification of the International Union of Geological Sciences International Commission on Stratigraphy (Hedberg 1976), and its latest revision (Salvador 1994), have been adopted. The spirit of the Salvador (1994) version in providing recommendations, rather than a 'code', to be followed as mandatory, is accepted. Thus: 'no individual, organization, or nation should feel constrained to follow it, or part of it, unless convinced of its logic and value.... its purpose is to inform, suggest and to recommend' (Salvador 1994 p xv).

Following the correlation of the terrestrial deposits further correlation is made with a global oxygen isotope stratigraphy. This is possible primarily by geochronological means but it is important to recognize the general nature of such correlations. Thus the terrestrial rock units so correlated probably only fall within oxygen isotope stages of longer duration (Bowen 1978). With AMS ^{14}C dating, however, high-resolution correlation is possible for the time-range that method covers.

The main lithostratigraphical unit used in these correlations is the formation which is the fundamental unit in lithostratigraphical classification, its main characteristic being that it is a mappable unit. Formations are subdivided into members, which are always part of a formation, with properties that distinguish them from adjacent parts of that formation. Some members may extend from one formation into another. The proliferation of many, often thin, formations is deemed undesirable (Salvador 1994), something especially relevant to the wealth of detail that is often available for Quaternary deposits.

This is exemplified by a disagreement that has emerged in the case of the Thames Valley (Table 3). Two views have emerged. On the one hand a large number of formations has been proposed (Bridgland 1994), while on the other, considerably fewer formations are proposed with a large number of members (Gibbard 1985, 1994). But such different approaches are not the cause of the disagreement between Bridgland (1994) and Gibbard (1994) on the correlation of the Thames Valley sequences. Similar debate obtains on the age of glaciation: it is argued by some that the major glaciation of the Midlands and East Anglia corresponds to oxygen isotope stage 10 (Sumbler 1995). But where, then, is the glaciation corresponding with stage 12? Others argue that the 'interglacial' sites of Swanscombe and Hoxne are the same age and not, as indicated by D-aIle/L-Ile means separate and correlated respectively with oxygen isotope stages 11 and 9.

Such a view, however, then poses questions for the significance of subsequent events recognized from the stratigraphical and geomorphological evidence.

Lithostratigraphical classification should depend on the place of a stratigraphical unit in a regional hierarchy and not on its inferred significance as an indicator of palaeoclimate. Thus some units that allow inference of a temperate ('interglacial') climate during their deposition are sometimes accorded different lithostratigraphical status on the basis of their relative importance in the regional stratigraphical architecture: for example, in Ireland, the 'interglacial' peat at Newtown is accorded bed status (Ireland: Western Irish Sea Basin, note 1); organic lake sediments at Hatfield are accorded member status (Thames Valley: Middle Thames and Vale of St. Albans, note 26); while lake deposits at Hoxne are accorded formation status (Eastern England, South and East Suffolk, note 29).

Because of the large number of units proposed in this volume and the high degree of variability within the units many details are best acquired from the references cited. Whenever possible, a stratotype (holostratotype) at a specific locality is used, although sometimes the actual deposits are not exposed today. Sometimes it is necessary to refer to an auxiliary or auxiliary reference sections (parastratotypes), for a fuller characterization of a unit: for example, in the case of formations of glacial deposits, defined in a type-region.

In the naming of lithostratigraphical units local geographical features have been used. In general the recommendations of the ISSC code (Salvador 1994) are followed in avoiding the use of a genetic and lithologic term. Genesis is sometimes ambiguous and there is often rapid vertical and lateral changes in the lithofacies of some Quaternary deposits. Given the previous existence of many lithostratigraphic units with informal and often inappropriate names, new and effective ones had to be established. A major difficulty in so doing is the inadequacy, or absence, of designated stratotypes. Thus the new lithostratigraphical names are proposed provisionally. Many of them can be tied to a stratotype or unit stratotype, or potential ones, and a definitive reference in the literature. But others, as indicated in the notes on the stratigraphical tables, await full definition. Some long-standing historical names have been retained because no good purpose is achieved in re-naming them: e.g. the Norwich Crag Formation. In time it is likely that proposals for a large number of separate units will become subsumed under fewer names.

The correlations presented in the stratigraphical tables in each chapter are based on the subdivision of the deposits in each region, area or locality. Correlation within each region and with others is by all possible means. These are similar but sometimes additional to those used to correlate earlier Phanerozoic deposits (Bowen 1978). One distinguishing characteristic is the use of several dating methods to accomplish correlation in the absence of other means. The Quaternary lithostratigraphical record is usually fragmentary and sometimes highly dissected. While some units are correlated by lateral continuity in the field, others are correlated by comparability of depositional style in similar geomorphic settings. Some complicated lithostratigraphical relationships occur when younger units outcrop altitudinally below older ones as in valley aggradations where alternate deposition and incision has taken place as driven by climate change or uplift (Maddy 1997). The separation of stratigraphical units in this way, however, offers advantages over regions where the record is mainly in the sub-surface, as in the

Netherlands.

As has been mentioned a majority of the authors agreed that it was premature to propose further stages on the 1973 model, nor to use the standard stage names of Mitchell *et al.* (1973) on the correlation charts because correlation was uncertain. Some convergence of majority and minority authors is seen on the charts for the Thames Valley and South and South East England, where some standard stages of the earlier classification (Mitchell *et al.* 1973) and an oxygen isotope stage scale appear side by side. But major disagreements continue.

Use of the term 'Wolstonian' is still debated vigorously. The deposits of the type-area in Warwickshire have been shown to be correlated with the Lowestoft Formation (Anglian) thus formally rendering the name Wolstonian redundant (Maddy *et al.* 1991; Sumbler 1983*a*; Keen *et al.* 1997) Instead the name is continued as the Wolston Formation (Chapter 3) and correlated with the Lowestoft Formation of East Anglia (Chapter 2). In an attempt at compromise. Gibbard & Turner (1988) suggested that the 'Wolstonian' may be defined as represented by all the deposits between the end of the Hoxnian and the base of the Ipswichian, an unacceptable proposal to the majority of contributors to this volume.

Ultimately it is debatable whether these should be based on inferences of climate change. It is undeniable that inference of climate change is a pervasive feature of this volume as is explicitly expressed in the introduction to the first edition (Mitchell *et al.* 1973). General international practice also continues to be pervasive. A proper chronostratigraphical alternative would be to propose large bodies of Quaternary deposits with more or less consistent, although variable, lithology, within which climatic fluctuations would be recognized from other means, including biostratigraphy, lithology or by means of correlation with oxygen isotope stratigraphy, from ocean and well as ice-cores. Such larger bodies of rock could consist of all those currently broadly recognized as: Early Pleistocene; those associated with the major glaciations and cold episodes of lowland England; and those of the last glacial cycle and Holocene. Each of these four major bodies of sediment are distinctive and unique in different ways. Coincidentally they also correspond to global events inferred from other sources. Not least, however, they would allow an escape from the confusion of the past and allow a real chronostratigraphy based on actualities to emerge, with an inferential climate-stratigraphy to derive from it.

How to use this volume

The regions used in this report correspond broadly with those used in the first edition (Mitchell *et al.* 1973), but in addition, correlations are made with the Quaternary deposits of the continental shelf surrounding the British Isles. The first edition was based on the designation of British Standard Stages defined at 'type-localities'. Correlations were then made with these for nine principal regions in the British Isles: Eastern England, English Midlands, Northeast England, Northwest England, Southwest England, Southeast England, Scotland, Wales, and Ireland.

The present report is subdivided into 11 chapters including the introduction. Correlations are made within each region using all possible means. The further correlations, again by all possible means, are made with the timescale provided by oxygen isotope stratigraphy thus relating the British evidence to an international standard, a practice increasingly adopted by national geological surveys following the ground-breaking work of the United States Geological Survey in 1986 (Richmond & Fullerton in Sibrava *et al.* 1986).

A minority of authors prefer to retain the stages proposed in the first edition of this report (Mitchell *et al.* 1973) and an additional column appears on their correlation tables: for example, in the case of the Thames Valley (Chapter 4) and South and Southeast England (Chapter 5). Chapter 11, which deals with the continental shelf, has a column showing the 1973 British stages as well as some Dutch chronostratigraphical nomenclature. This arises, especially for the Dutch correlations, because of joint work between the British Geological Survey and the Dutch Geological Survey, that made readier correlations with the Dutch sequence, especially for the early Pleistocene. Schematic charts for the continental shelf are presented because of the nature of the extensive seismo-stratigraphical information involved. In these cases (Chapters 4 & 5) the oxygen isotope stratigraphy is indicated but the correlations made are more general. The case of the Thames Valley has already been referred to (Table 3). Thus the reader may be able to relate these chapters to others where the correlations made are more precise.

Formations, members and beds are shown on the correlation tables, with formations in bold. The stratigraphical units are numbered as are the notes that refer to them in the text. It is not possible to include all the detailed information for each unit and further information may be gleaned from the reference list of over two thousand items. The regional maps only indicate the approximate location of stratotypes, but national grid references are included in the notes.

Many of the stratigraphical units proposed are not amenable to systematic and widespread mapping away from their stratotypes. Nor were the subdivisions proposed in the first edition of this report (Mitchell *et al.* 1973) as is evident on the 'ten-mile' British Geological Survey (BGS) maps of Quaternary Deposits in the British Isles published in 1977. Some of the units propose are only indicative at present in that they point to potentially new units for detailed mapping or, by their nature, are incapable of being shown as mappable units on maps. They are, however, important subdivisions of the Quaternary succession and are in no way diminished in status for all that.

The correlations proposed are intended to generate debate and to secure agreement. By the time the next edition appears it is probable that widespread correlation on millennial time-scales will be standard in which some of the stratigraphical units proposed here may figure.

Chapter 2

Eastern England

S. G. LEWIS

With contributions from: D. T. Aldiss, P. Allen, N. M. Ashton, S. Boreham, D.Q. Bowen, A. Brandon, D. A. Cheshire, P. L. Gibbard, P. M. Hopson, A. M. McCabe, M. G. Sumbler, C. Turner, C. A. Whiteman & J. J. Wymer

Marine deposition dominated the Early Pleistocene and parts of the early Middle Pleistocene. The region experienced glaciation on at least two occasions; during the Anglian and Late Devensian. There may also be some localities that show evidence of additional glacial episodes (Gibbard et al. 1991a, 1992). Evidence of fluvial activity is significant, with major reorganization of the drainage system as a result of glaciation during the Anglian.

Early Pleistocene deposits are mainly marine in origin, and were deposited at the margins of the southern North Sea basin. The Red Crag and Norwich Crag Formations occur in the southern and eastern parts of East Anglia. Coastal sections together with boreholes through the deeper Crag basins provided reference sections for Early Pleistocene stages defined by Mitchell et al. (1973). These provide lithostratigraphical and biostratigraphical information for correlation of the British sequence with those of the Netherlands (Gibbard et al. 1991b). These correlations reveal a gap of about 1 Ma in the British sequence.

The early Middle Pleistocene is represented by the uppermost Cromer Forest-bed Formation, that consists of marine and freshwater deposits on the northeast coast of Norfolk. Coeval terrestrial sedimentation is represented by the Kesgrave Formation of the Thames and deposits of its tributary rivers.

The extensive chalky till in Eastern England provides an important stratigraphical marker in the region. When Mitchell et al. (1973) published the first edition of this report the existence of two till sheets of different ages was being questioned (Bristow & Cox 1973). Since then, research has led to a widespread acceptance that there is only one regionally extensive chalky till, deposited during the Anglian (Perrin et al. 1979). During the Anglian the Lowestoft Formation was deposited by British-based glaciers and the North Sea Drift Formation by a Scandinavian ice-sheet that impinged upon parts of northeast Norfolk, inland as far as Diss, Suffolk.

The later Middle Pleistocene is known from numerous localities where temperate-phase organic sequences have been identified as at Hoxne (Hoxnian) and Bobbitshole (Ipswichian). Fluvial deposition during the later Middle and Late Pleistocene produced gravel and sand aggradations under a cold climate, and their extensive terrace features.

In the Nar Valley on the eastern margin of the Fen Basin the sequence is: (i) Lowestoft Formation, (ii) Nar Member and (iii) Tottenhill Member. The fluvial gravels of the Tottenhill Member are thought to be outwash and thus represent a glaciation later than that represented by the Lowestoft Formation (Anglian) but before the Late Devensian (Gibbard et al. 1991a, 1992).

Glaciation during the Devensian deposited tills and associated outwash in north west Norfolk, as represented by the Hunstanton Formation and along the coast of Lincolnshire.

These overlie raised beaches correlated with the Ipswichian (oxygen isotope sub-stage 5e), and glaciation has been further constrained by radiocarbon dating.

Eastern England contains a large number of localities with evidence of human occupation (Wymer 1985). The close association of Quaternary geology and Palaeolithic archaeology is evident from the number of multi-disciplinary investigations that have taken place over the last two decades.

The correlation of Quaternary rocks in Eastern England has been made with regionally extensive lithostratigraphical units, such as the till of the Lowestoft Formation. Geochronological ages have also assisted correlation. Among these, the aminostratigraphical model for southern Britain revealed a more complex record than that based on pollen biostratigraphy, and its calibration by independent age estimates enabled correlation with oxygen isotope stratigraphy (Bowen et al. 1989). Arising from this, the Anglian is correlated with oxygen isotope stage 12. This poses some problems because it identifies two events of temperate climate after the Anglian: that recorded at Swanscombe (oxygen isotope stage 11) and that at Hoxne (oxygen isotope stage 9).

Holderness and Lincolnshire

(1) Bytham Formation. Stratotype: Thunderbolt pit, Castle Bytham [SK 998184]. It extends from Castle Bytham east through Witham-on-the-Hill towards the Fen edge south of Bourne (Rose 1989; Lewis 1993). It consists of fluvial gravels overlain by sands in a steep-sided W–E valley as identified from boreholes (Wyatt 1971; Wyatt et al. 1971; Rose 1987, 1989). Sedimentary structures show west to east palaeoflow.

(SGL)

(2) Castle Bytham Member. Stratotype: Thunderbolt pit, Castle Bytham [SK 998184]. Limestone/quartzite sands and gravels overlying Jurassic bedrock (Lewis 1993). Also present at Witham-on-the-Hill [TF 030177]. The gravels are generally 3–4 m thick and dominated by limestone and ironstone with significant quantities of Triassic quartzite and quartz and Carboniferous chert.

(SGL)

(3) Witham Member. Stratotype: Castle Bytham [SK 998184]; also at Witham-on-the-Hill [TF 030177] and continuously between the two. It overlies the Castle Bytham Member and consists of cross-stratified, reddish brown to brown sands, derived from the Triassic sandstones of the Midlands (Bateman & Rose 1994), with some thin clay laminae deposited in a fluvial environment. Palaeoflow is towards the east. Formerly called the Bytham sand (Rose 1987, 1989; Lewis 1989, 1993).

(SGL)

(4) Little Bytham Bed. A fossiliferous sequence of sandy silts (1.12 m) from a borehole at Witham-on-the-Hill (Rose 1989).

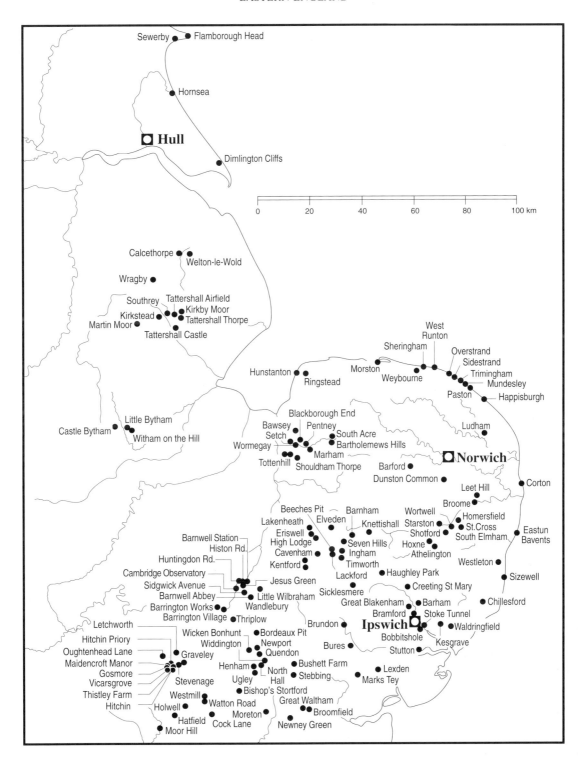

Fig. 4. Localities in Eastern England.

It lies between the Castle Bytham and Witham Members, toward the northern edge of the buried valley. Pollen indicates development of boreal forest dominated by *Pinus* and *Picea* in cool temperate climate (Gibbard & Peglar 1989).

(SGL)

(5) Lowestoft Formation. (Central East Anglia 12). Straw (1979, 1983) considered that the glacial deposits of Lincoln-shire were Wolstonian, but they are regarded as Anglian by Mitchell *et al.* (1973) and Perrin *et al.* (1979).

(SGL)

(6) Wragby Member. Stratotype: Wragby [TF 133781]. It consists of the Wragby Till of Straw (1966, 1983). The definition includes all chalk-bearing tills with a matrix derived predominantly from Upper Jurassic mudstones, notably the

Table 4. *Correlations between Lincolnshire, Holderness. the Proto-Trent east of the Lincoln Gap, the Bain Valley and Northeast Norfolk and oxygen isotope stratigraphy*

$\delta^{18}O$	LINCS & HOLDERNESS	PROTO-TRENT	BAIN VALLEY	NORTHEAST NORFOLK
1	**FENLAND FORMATION** (21)	Trent Member (9)	Bain Member (6)	**FENLAND FORMATION** (27)
2	**HOLDERNESS FORMATION** (12) Flamborough Member (20) Hornsea Member (19) Withernsea Member (18) Mill Hill Member (17) Skipsea Member (16) Dimlington Bed (15) Bridlington Member (14)	**TRENT VALLEY FORMATION** (6)	**BAIN VALLEY FORMATION** (1)	
3		Kirkstead Member (8)	Castle Member (5)	
5				
5e	Sewerby Member (13)		Tattershall Bed (4)	
6	**WELTON-LE-WOLD FORMATION** (9) Welton Member (11) Welton Beck Member (10)	Southrey Member (7)	Thorpe Member (3)	
7			Kirkby Bed (2)	
8				
9				
10				
11	**KIRMINGTON FORMATION** (8)			**DUNSTON COMMON FORMATION** (26) **BARFORD FORMATION** (25) **SIDESTRAND CLIFF FORMATION** (24)
12	**LOWESTOFT FORMATION** (5) Calcethorpe Member (7) Wragby Member (6)	**LOWESTOFT FORMATION** (1) Kirkby Moor Member (5) Martin Member (4) Tattershall Airfield Member (3) Wragby Member (2)		**LOWESTOFT FORMATION** (22) Weybourne Town Member (23) **NORTH SEA DRIFT FORMATION** (12) Beacon Hill Member (21) Trimingham Member (20) Cromer Member (19) Stow Hill Member (18) Mundesley–Trimingham Member (17) Marl Point Member (16) Walcott Member (15) Ostend Member (14) Happisburgh member (13)
pre-12	**BYTHAM FORMATION** (1) Little Bytham Bed (4) Witham Member (3) Castle Bytham Member (2)			**CROMER FOREST-BED FORMATION** (5) Mundesley Member (10) Bacton Member (11) West Runton Member (9) Runton Member (8) Paston Member (7) Sheringham Member (6) **NORWICH CRAG FORMATION** (3) Sidestrand Member (4) **RED CRAG FORMATION** (1) Ludham Member (2)

Oxford, Kimmeridge and Ampthill clay formations. Occurs principally in Lincolnshire, between the Lincolnshire Limestone outcrop of Lincoln Heath, and the Chalk Wolds. It includes lithofacies variability Straw (1966, 1983), notably part of the Heath Till east of Grantham, which passes westwards into the Oadby (till) Member (Wolston Formation) characterized by a matrix derived from Lias mudstone.

(MGS)

(7) Calcethorpe Member. Stratotype: Calcethorpe House [TF 240887]. Based on the Calcethorpe Till of Straw (1966, 1983), but extended to include his Belmont Till. A variety of chalk-bearing till characterized by a significant proportion of Lower Cretaceous material in the matrix and as erratic clasts. Occurs chiefly in the Horncastle district [TF 260695] of east Lincolnshire (Straw 1983).

(MGS)

(8) Kirmington Formation. Stratotype: old brickpit at Kirmington [TA 102116]. The sequence consists of up to 9 m of clays, sands and flinty gravel thought to be glacial deposits at the base, overlain by 10 m of clays and sands thought to be interglacial (Boylan 1966). The sequence is capped by 5 to 6 m of estuarine silts ('warp') containing estuarine shells, with a thin peat at its base with freshwater shells and 2.5 m of flint shingle interpreted as a storm beach deposit (Penny et al. 1972). The top of the estuarine silts lies at 25 m O.D. The top of the shingle lies at 27 m O.D. (Penny et al. 1972). The sequence was correlated by Watts (1959a) with the Hoxnian (oxygen isotope stage 9) on the basis of pollen from the peat (Watts 1959a). The elevation of the estuarine deposits, however, makes comparison with Swanscombe and the Nar Valley (stage 11) more likely.

(DQB)

(9) Welton-le-Wold Formation. This is of part of the glacial sequence of the Lincolnshire Wolds in the vicinity of Welton-le-Wold [TF 282884] where a sequence of gravels and tills was identified in quarry workings (Alabaster & Straw 1976). The glacigenic Welton Member was suggested to represent a glaciation intermediate between the Anglian and Devensian glaciations (Bowen et al. 1986). This continues to be its current status although it could equally be the same age as the Lowestoft Formation and thus Anglian. Thus correlation with oxygen isotope stage 6 is only tentative.

(SGL)

(10) Welton Beck Member. Formerly the Welton gravels (Alabaster & Straw 1976), they underlie the Welton Member at Welton-le-Wold [TF 282884] and consist of a lower series of bedded gravels, sands and silts overlain by an upper sequence of flint gravel with some silty facies (Alabaster & Straw 1976). The upper part of these gravels have yielded a mammalian fauna including straight-tusked elephant, horse, and red deer (Alabaster & Straw 1976). Four crude derived bifaces also came from these gravels (Wymer & Straw 1977). The presence of horse and the occurrence of artefacts of Acheulian type has been used to constrain the age of this member and the overlying glacigenic Welton Member (Alabaster & Straw 1976; Bowen et al. 1986). But see the comment on the uncertain age of the Welton Formation above.

(SGL)

(11) Welton Member. Seen at quarry at Welton-le-Wold [TF 282884], where it consists of a calcareous, greyish-brown, sandy silty clay diamict containing abundant chalk and flint together with some igneous and Carboniferous erratics (Alabaster & Straw 1976). Up to 13m in thickness, it rests on the Welton Beck Member and is overlain by the Holderness

Formation in the southern part of the quarry and by the solifluced Calcethorpe Member (Lowestoft Formation) in the northern part. Madgett & Catt (1978) correlated it with the Bridlington Member (Basement till) of Holderness.

(SGL)

(12) Holderness Formation. Type-area: Holderness, East Yorkshire. Except for the Sewerby Member it consists of a succession of diamict, gravel, sand, silt and clay about 70 m thick interpreted as glacial in origin. The inclusion of the Sewerby Member is justified because the Holderness Formation constitutes the mappable unit. Its base overlies Chalk about 30 m below sea level. Nine members are proposed on the basis of the stratigraphical position, vertical and lateral facies change, sediment geometry, colour variations, erratic and mineral suites and macro and micro-fabrics (Catt & Penny 1966; Madgett & Catt 1978; Bisat 1932, 1939, 1940, 1948; Derbyshire et al. 1984).

(AMM & DQB)

(13) Sewerby Member. Stratotype: Sewerby [TA 199686]. It consists of beach gravel containing an interglacial faunal assemblage (Ipswichian) overlain by blown sand, colluvium and coombe rock (Catt & Penny 1966; Catt 1991).

(AMM & DQB)

(14) Bridlington Member. Stratotype: Dimlington Cliff [TA 376237]. Formerly the 'Basement Till' of Catt & Penny (1966). Poorly-defined Bed of muddy diamict containing inclusions of fossiliferous marine mud and glauconitic sand (Reid 1885; Bell 1917; Catt & Penny 1966; Catt 1991). The Bed is contorted, streaked-out, sheared and overthrust. D-aIle/L-Ile data shows a mixed fauna but the youngest ratios (0.065) indicate a Late Devensian age (Eyles et al. 1994), although Catt (1991) suggested it was Wolstonian. Lamplugh (1890) wrote that the it 'overlies the fossiliferous Sewerby cliff Bed'. The inclusions of 'Bridlington Crag' are fossiliferous and D-aIle/L-Ile ratios of 0.60 ± 0.097 (5) and 0.62 ± 0.135 (4) on Mya truncata and Mya sp. points to an Early Pleistocene age (Bowen unpublished).

(AMM & DQB)

(15) Dimlington Bed. Stratotype: Dimlington Cliff [TA 376237]. It is preserved in hollows on the surface of the Bridlington Member and consists of delicately laminated and rippled sand-silt containing detrital Arctic moss remains (Bisat & Bell 1941) with radiocarbon dates of $18\,500 \pm 400$ and $18\,240 \pm 250$ (Penny et al. 1969).

(AMM & DQB)

(16) Skipsea Member. Stratotype: Dimlington Cliff [TA 376237]. Formerly the 'Drab Till' of Catt & Penny (1966). A lithologically variable, regionally extensive fine-grained diamict characterized by a banded structure, multiple stacked Bed, chaotic clusters, stratified interBed, deformed Bed and evidence of pervasive shears and attenuation structures (Catt & Penny 1966; Madgett & Catt 1978; Derbyshire et al. 1984; Catt 1991; Eyles et al. 1994).

(AMM & DQB)

(17) Mill Hill Member. Stratotype: Dimlington Cliff [TA 376237]. A shoestring body of gravel containing a diverse marine macrofauna and invertebrate remains (Lamplugh 1925; Catt & Penny 1966). It overlies the Skipsea Member and it has been eroded by the overlying Withernsea Member (Eyles et al. 1994).

(AMM & DQB)

(18) Withernsea Member. Stratotype: Dimlington Cliff [TA 376237]. Formerly the 'Purple Till' of Catt & Penny (1966). A massive, fine-grained diamict (Bisat 1939, 1940; Reid 1885)

that overlies the Skipsea Member. The junction is marked by stratified deposits and shear planes (Catt 1991).

(AMM & DQB)

(19) Hornsea Member. Type-area: east Holderness. Glacial deposits forming a belt of hummocky topography (Valentin 1957; Catt & Penny 1966).

(AMM & DQB)

(20) Flamborough Member. Type area: Flamborough Head. It consists of laterally extensive flat lying gravel that truncates the Skipsea Member.

(AMM & DQB)

(21) Fenland Formation. Includes all the marine alluvium and peats of the Fenland Basin together with all other peat deposits in the region (Ventris 1985).

The Proto-Trent (east of the Lincoln Gap) and Bain Valleys

(1) Lowestoft Formation (Central East Anglia 12).
(2) Wragby Member (Lincolnshire and Holderness 6).
(3) Tattershall Airfield Member. Stratotype: Tattershall Airfield pit [TF 218617]. Up to 7 m of sand and gravel overlying irregular Wragby Till surface between Woodhall Spa and Kirkby on Bain. Forms terrace declining southwestwards, from c. 15 m to c. 8 m, before passing beneath the Thorpe Member. To the east there is a c. 3 m step down to Thorpe Terrace. It is correlated, in part, with part of the Martin Terrace deposits of Straw (1958). It is believed to be outwash (Brandon & Sumbler unpublished).

(AB & MGS)

(4) Martin Member. Type area around Martin Moor [TF 1059]. It corresponds with the Martin Terrace deposits of Straw (1958). It comprises up to c. 3 m of flint and quartzite rich sand and gravel overlying the glaciogenic Wragby Member. It is considered to be outwash; the downstream equivalent of the Eagle Moor Member (Brandon & Sumbler unpublished).

(AB & MGS)

(5) Kirkby Moor Member. Stratotype: sand pit [TF 228627] east of Kirkby on Bain. Up to c. 10 m of generally gravel-free, well-bedded sands form high ground of Kirkby Moor up to c. 27 m above O.D. that is, c. 12 m above Thorpe Terrace. Its relationship to the Tattershall Airfield Member unclear. It corresponds with the Kirkby Moor sands of Straw (1958). Inferred to be distal sandur (Worsley 1991; Brandon & Sumbler unpublished).

(AB & MGS)

(6) Trent Valley Formation. (Trent valley upriver of Nottingham). Although Straw (1958) described deposits now included in the Martin and Southrey Members as 'Witham Terraces', the deposits are placed in the Trent Valley Formation because the River Witham used the Lincoln Gap only from Late Devensian times onwards, initially as a tributary of the combined Trent/Devon at Lincoln. All deposits older than the Late Devensian east of Lincoln Gap were deposited by the combined Trent-Devon alone. When that river diverted northwards into the Humber valley during the deposition of the Holme Pierrepont Member (Late Devensian) (Brandon & Sumbler 1988), only the Witham continued to use the Lincoln Gap until the present day.

(AB & MGS)

(7) Southrey Member. Type area: Woodhall Spa-Kirkstead Bridge area [TF 1862]. Quartzite-rich to flint-rich sandy gravels up to 6 m thick, distributed along the north side of the present Witham valley from Southrey [TF 1366] to Kirkstead [TF 1960] (where it merges with the Thorpe Member of the Bain) as a series of much dissected outliers with a surface falling from c. 8 m to c. 5 m O.D. (i.e. 6 m to 3 m above the Witham floodplain). It equates in part only with the Southrey Terrace of Straw (1958), which is a composite unit. Correlated by altitude with the Balderton Member (oxygen isotope stage 6). Silts deposited under temperate climate conditions occur at two sites in association with the Southrey Member.

(AB & MGS)

(8) Kirkstead Member. Stratotype: British Geological Survey borehole [TF 1630 6114] near Kirkstead (Jackson 1982). A 5–10 m thick extensive sheet of quartzite-rich sandy gravels deposited by the Trent (penetrated by many boreholes beneath the Fen alluvium of the modern Witham valley). It is thought to be coeval with the Castle Member of the Bain and, at least in part, with the lower part of the Holme Pierrepont Member of the Trent west of the Lincoln Gap. It is thought to be Early to Late Devensian in age (oxygen isotope stages 4 to 2).

(AB & MGS)

(9) Trent Member (Proto Trent 9). Valley alluvium throughout the region (Posnansky 1960; Clayton 1953, 1957a).

The Bain Valley

(1) Bain Valley Formation. This is proposed to include all the post-Anglian glaciation fluvial deposits of the River Bain valley.
(2) Kirkby Bed. Stratotype: Tattershall Thorpe [TF 22466040]. Up to 3.3 m of mainly grey silt infill a palaeochannel cut into Wragby Till beneath the Thorpe Member. It is correlated with the Ipswichian (oxygen isotope sub-stage 5e) using molluscs and pollen (Holyoak & Preece 1985). D-aIle/L-Ile ratios indicate an oxygen isotope stage 7 age. It contains a temperate fauna and flora and molluscs (including *Corbicula fluminalis*), beetles, pollen and large mammals (including *Palaeoloxodon antiquus*).

(AB & MGS)

(3) Thorpe Member. Stratotype: Tattershall Thorpe gravel pit [TF 225603]. It is distributed along the west side of Bain valley from Kirkby on Bain to Tattershall beyond which it merges with the Southrey Member (7) of the Trent Valley Formation. Its terrace declines from c. 13 m to c. 5 m O.D. Distinct step of c. 2 m down to Castle Terrace (Ussher et al. 1888). It comprises about 6 m of sand and gravel with intraformational and post-depositional ice wedge casts. The upper 2 m is affected by soil formation (Hykeham soil) as rubified zones subsequently disturbed by cryogenic involutions and ice wedge casting. The deposit has yielded a cold stage large mammalian fauna previously thought to be Devensian (Rackham 1978) but similar to that of the Balderton Member of the same age. TL ages of 148 ± 34 ka were obtained from lower part (Perkins & Rhodes 1994). ESR ages were obtained from mammoth molars of 140 ka (Grün, in Brandon & Sumbler unpublished). Radiocarbon dating gives mid-Devensian ages (Girling 1977, 1980; Holyoak & Preece 1985). Work on stratigraphy, sedimentology, biostratigraphy (beetles and large mammalia), and dating indicate an oxygen isotope stage 6 age (Brandon and Sumbler unpublished).

(AB & MGS)

(4) Tattershall Bed. Stratotype: gravel pit at Tattershall Castle [TF 211571] (Holyoak & Preece 1985) – the only known locality. They infill a palaeochannel cut into the Wragby

Member and comprise *c.* 2 m of grey silt and detrital mud. These contain a temperate fauna and flora including molluscs and pollen (Holyoak & Preece 1985) and a few large mammals (*Palaeoloxodon antiquus*) (Rackham 1981). D-aIle/L-Ile ratios indicate an oxygen isotope sub-stage 5e or oxygen isotope stage 7 age (Holyoak & Preece 1985) or oxygen isotope sub-stage 5e age (Bowen *et al.* 1989). U-Series ages on *Cepaea nemoralis* are 76 000–101 000 years; TL dating of calcareous silt gives 114 000 years. It was thought to be Ipswichian by Holyoak & Preece (1985).

(AB & MGS)

(5) Castle Member. Stratotype: former gravel pits [TF 211571] at Tattershall Castle. It forms an extensive terrace along the Bain valley from Kirkby on Bain (at *c.* 15 m above O.D.) southwards to Tattershall Castle (at *c.* 4.m O.D.), south of which it passes beneath the Witham floodplain deposits. Although separated by a distinct step from the Thorpe Terrace (Ussher *et al.* 1888), it has been confused with the latter by many workers. It comprises mainly sand and gravel up to *c.* 8 m thick with some silts in channel infills and with syndepositional ice wedge casts but no post-depositional casts or cryogenic involutions are known. Radiocarbon ages of enclosed silts of 42–44 ka (Girling 1974, 1980) are probably minimum ages. TL ages of 21 ± 8.5 ka (Perkins & Rhodes 1994) indicate an oxygen isotope stage 2 age. It is thought to be Early to Late Devensian in age but mostly the latter. Grey organic silts ('upper temperate silts') occur in a channel within the Castle Member in a gravel pit between [TF 209570] and [TF 210570]. Temperate beetle fossils are ascribed to the Upton Warren Interstadial (Girling 1974, 1977, 1980). An ESR age estimate on bison teeth is 34 ± 3 ka (Perkins & Rhodes 1994). A fauna of large mammals mainly of *Rangifer tarandus* and *Bison* sp. may be mid-Devensian (Rackham 1978).

(AB & MGS)

(6) Bain Member. Valley alluvium throughout the region.

Northeast Norfolk

(1) Red Crag Formation (South and East Suffolk 1)

(2) Ludham Member. Stratotype: Ludham borehole [TG 385199] (Funnell 1961). It consists of about 44 m of fossiliferous grey sands, silts and clays overlying London Clay. It contains pollen and foraminifera used to subdivide the sequence (West 1961*a*; Funnell 1961). Pollen assemblages indicate a fluctuating climate, with two temperate and two cold episodes (West 1961*a*).

(SGL)

(3) Norwich Crag Formation (South and East Suffolk 4).

(4) Sidestrand Member. Stratotype at Sidestrand [TG 255405]. It was considered to be part of the Norwich Crag Formation by Funnell & West (1977) and West (1980), but the microtine rodent assemblage is similar to that of the later members of the Cromer Forest-bed Formation (Mayhew & Stuart 1986). Thus the possibility that the Sidestrand Member should be re-assigned to the Cromer Forest-bed Formation was considered by Gibbard & Zalasiewicz (1988). It consists of marine laminated clays, sands and gravels up to *c.* 13 m thick, overlying older Crag deposits. Its pollen assemblage shows high levels of non-arboreal pollen, with an absence of thermophilous trees.

(SGL)

(5) Cromer Forest-bed Formation. It consists of freshwater and marine deposits, up to 8 m in thickness, exposed along the coast of Norfolk and Suffolk, from Weybourne to Kessingland. It overlies Chalk and is overlain by Anglian glaciogenic sediments. The sequence was first described by Reid (1882) and was given formation status by Funnell & West (1977). The lithostratigraphy and biostratigraphy of the deposits is described in detail by West (1980).

(SGL)

(6) Sheringham Member. Stratotype: Beeston [TG 169434] where freshwater clays, sands and muds up to 2.5 m thick overlie Chalk (West 1980). The pollen evidence suggests severe climate conditions, with a herb-dominated assemblage (West 1980).

(SGL)

(7) Paston Member. Stratotype: Paston [TG 330355]. It consists of *c.* 3 m of tidal silts and clays and marine shelly sands (Funnel & West 1977; West 1980). It was subdivided by Funnell & West (1977) and West (1980) to recognize the Paston Bed, West Runton clay and West Runton sand.

(SGL)

(8) Runton Member. Stratotype: West Runton [TG 189431]. It consists of *c.* 3 m of beach gravels and was subdivided into a number of beds by Funnell & West (1977) and West (1980): the Beeston Bed (freshwater muds), shelly marine sand and gravel (Woman Hythe gravel) and laminated freshwater clays (Woman Hythe clay). The climate during deposition was cold, with pollen assemblages dominated by herbaceous vegetation, and with evidence of contemporaneous periglacial activity (West 1980).

(SGL)

(9) West Runton Member. Stratotype: West Runton [TG 189431] (West 1980). It consists of *c.* 2 m of freshwater muds and alluvial clays that occur along the Norfok and Suffolk coasts. It includes the West Runton freshwater bed (Upper Freshwater Bed of Reid 1882) and the Corton Rootlet Bed. The Bed were deposited under temperate climate conditions.

(SGL)

(10) Mundesley Member. Stratotype: Mundesley (TG 319363). It comprises *c.* 2.5 m of marine laminated clays and sands and beach sands and gravels (West 1980). The unit includes the *Yoldia* (*Leda*) *Myalis* Bed, which occurs at West Runton (Reid 1882) and the Mundesley Clay.

(SGL)

(11) Bacton Member. Stratotype: at Mundesley [TG 319363]. It comprises the Arctic Freshwater Bed (Reid 1882) which consists of about 1.5 m of clays and muds, found between Trimingham and Bacton. The climate as indicated by high NAP frequencies was cold, with evidence for contemporaneous periglacial conditions (West 1980).

(SGL)

(12) North Sea Drift Formation. Type area: between Cromer and Happisburgh, where it unconformably overlies the Cromer Forest-bed Formation. It extends inland possibly as far as Diss, Norfolk. It consists of glacial diamicts, sands, gravels and associated fine laminated and massive lacustrine sediments predominantly derived from the North Sea region. Deposited predominantly from an ice sheet that entered the area from SW Scandinavia as indicated by erratic rocks from Oslofjord. Large glaciotectonic structures, at various scales, including bedrock schollen and nappe-like injections, give rise to the term 'Contorted Drift' for parts of the sequence. This term and the term North Sea Drift were proposed by Reid (1882). It has been studied by Banham (1988), Hart & Boulton (1991) and Lunkka (1994). The subdivision presented here follows Lunkka (1994).

(PLG)

(13) Happisburgh Member. Stratotype: [TG 3632] coastal sections between Happisburgh and Walcott and can be traced to Trimingham. Mainly unbedded, silty sand diamict, relatively poor in clasts. Clast fabric shows significant orientation from NE to SW. Rests unconformably on the Cromer Forest-bed Formation.

(PLG)

(14) Ostend Member. Stratotype: [TG 3632]. Comprises sorted sands, silts and clays of meltwater origin. It rests conformably on fluted surface of Happisburgh Member. Shows fining-upward sequence from ripple-bedded sands into laminated and massive clays and silty clays. It represents a glaciolacustrine environment.

(PLG)

(15) Walcott Member. Stratotype: [TG 3632]. It overlies the Ostend Member or Cromer Forest-bed Formation. It may also occur within the 'Contorted Drift'. It is distinguished from other diamicts by its silt matrix and high carbonate content. Orientation measurements from deformation structures indicate pressure from the northwest.

(PLG)

(16) Marl Point Member. Stratotype: coastal sections around Mundesley [TG 3037] consisting of sands and associated silt and clays of deltaic origin. Two subunits can be recognized; the Lower Sands Bed subunit may be continuous from underlying Ostend Member, where the Walcott Member is missing. This represents a prograding delta from the SE. The Upper Sand Bed also represents input from the SE, after input of the Walcott Member, but includes sands derived from the NW in more northerly sections.

(PLG)

(17) Mundesley-Trimminham Member. Stratotype: coastal sections in the Walcott area [TG 3632] and Mundesley–Trimingham area, where it is over 10 m thick. At all localities it overlies the Marl Point Member. It is heterogeneous and is composed of sandy diamict lenses and sands and unbedded or laminated fines. Deformation structures are common. It is interpreted as a glaciolacustrine waterlain till complex in a freshwater environment.

(PLG)

(18) Stow Hill Member. Stratotype: coastal sections between Bacton and Mundesley [TG 3235]. It comprises current-bedded medium to coarse-grained sands, with gravel at the base, that rest unconformably on the Mundesley Member. Palaeocurrent measurements indicate deposition ranging from N to NW. Represents delta foreset facies.

(PLG)

(19) Cromer Member. Stratotype: coastal sections at Cromer and Overstrand [TG 2441]. It occurs only NW of Little Marl Point where it reaches 10 m thick. The base is sharp and erosional. There is much disturbance of the junction with the underlying units. Clast fabric indicates movement from NW–SE direction. Northwest of Sidestrand it forms part of the 'Contorted Drift'. Large-scale deformation and injected 'chalk rafts' are associated with the ice movement that emplaced this unit. These are thrust belts formed at ice margin and beneath marginal zone of the glacier.

(PLG)

(20) Trimingham Member. Stratotype: coastal sections around Trimingham [TG 2739]. It is restricted to the Trimingham area where it rests on the Cromer Member; but in places it also underlies it. Maximum thickness is over 20 m. Interpreted as glaciolacustrine.

(PLG)

(21) Beacon Hill Member. Stratotype: coastal sections around Trimingham [TG 2739]. It discontinuously overlies either the Trimingham or Cromer Members, and may grade up from the former locally. It ranges in thickness from 15–23 m. Current bedded sands are in places interbedded with thin silt layers. It includes syndepositional deformation structures, and may coarsen upwards into gravels locally. It was deposited by water from the north. In places, it occurs in 'sand basins' up to 100 m wide and 30 m thick resulting from large-scale loading. Meltwater deposits are disposed into prograding foresets that represent a series of deltas.

(PLG)

(22) Lowestoft Formation (Central East Anglia 12)
(23) Weybourne Town Member. Stratotype: Weybourne Town Pit [TG 114431]. It comprises white, highly calcareous diamict up to 4 m thick. Mainly massive but somely faintly stratified. Its base is markedly erosional and represents basal till. Its fabric and structural measurements indicate input by ice from the south west (Ehlers *et al.* 1987, 1991).

(PLG)

(24) Sidestrand Cliff Formation. Stratotype: coastal sections at Trimingham [TG 269397 to TG 266397]. Up to 5 m of lake or pond sediments filling a hollow in gravel and sand. Palynology indicates correlation with the late Anglian – earliest Hoxnian (Hart & Peglar 1990).

(PLG)

(25) Barford Formation. Stratotype: Barford, Norfolk [TG 111069]. Boreholes have proved a deep channel (up to −34.7 m O.D. cut into Chalk and infilled with chalky Lowestoft till on which rests an extensive spread of lacustrine organic clay-mud, up to 9 m in thickness. Pollen analysis (Phillips 1976) has shown that these represent the early and middle parts of an interglacial succession, strongly linked to that at Hoxne by the presence of the characteristic high non-tree pollen phase in the middle of the succession.

(CT)

(26) Dunston Common Formation. Stratotype: Institute of Geological Sciences borehole at Dunston Common [TG 227026]. The Bed lie in a deep channel cut into the Chalk. 13.4 m of organic lacustrine sediments deposits were recorded down to −8.8 m O.D. (base not reached). Pollen analysis (Phillips 1976) shows it represents the upper part of an interglacial sequence.

(CT)

(27) Fenland Formation (Lincolnshire & Holderness 21). Named the Breydon Formation locally by Arthurton *et al.* 1994 who described up to 22 m of silt and clay of estuarine origin with at least three peat Bed. The formation infills valleys around the Norfolk Broads.

(SGL)

Northwest Norfolk

(1) Lowestoft Formation (Central East Anglia 12). Members of the Lowestoft Formation in the Nar valley (2–7) were considered to be part of the Nar Valley Formation by Ventris (1985). They are included here in the Lowestoft Formation because they are units intimately associated with glacial activity during the Anglian (Ventris 1985).

(SGL)

(2) Woodlands Farm Member. Stratotype: from a borehole at [TF 643116] (Ventris 1985). A lodgement till with a characteristic Jurassic clay matrix, thickness is highly variable, with up

Table 5. *Correlations between Northwest Norfolk and Central East Anglia and oxygen isotope stratigraphy*

$\delta^{18}O$	NORTHWEST NORFOLK		CENTRAL EAST ANGLIA	
1	FENLAND FORMATION (19)		FENLAND FORMATION (49)	
2	**NAR VALLEY FORMATION** (8) Marham Member (14) Pentney Member (13)	**HUNSTANTON FORMATION** (15) Ringstead Member (18) Holkham Member (17)	**LARK VALLEY FORMATION** (32) Lackford Member (38) Cavenham Member (37)	**CAM VALLEY FORMATION** (39) Barnwell Station Member (48) Sidgwick Avenue Member (47) Barnwell Abbey Member (46)
3				
4				
5				Barrington Member (45) Histon Road Member (44)
5e	Pentney Priory Bed (12) Wormegay Member (11)	Morston Member (16)	Kentford Member (36)	
6	Tottenhill Member (10)		Fornham Member (35)	Huntingdon Road Member (43) Little Wilbraham Member (42)
7			Eriswell Member (34)	Bordeaux Pit Member (41)
8				
9			Sicklesmere Member (33)	North Hall Member (40)
10				
11	Nar Member (9)		Icklingham Tufa Bed (29) **WEST STOW FORMATION** (28)	**ELVEDEN FORMATION** (31) **BARNHAM FORMATION** (30)
12	**LOWESTOFT FORMATION** (1) South Acre Member (7) Blackborough End Member (6) Bartholomews Hills Member (5) Setch Member (4) Bawsey Member (3) Woodlands Farm Member (2)		**LOWESTOFT FORMATION** (12) Wandlebury Member (23) Wicken Bonhunt M (22) Henham Member (21) Widdington Member (20) Newport Member (19) Quendon Member (18) Barrington Works M (17) Observatory Member (16) Pleasure Gardens Member (15) Oulton member (14) Lowestoft Till Member (13)	**NORTH SEA DRIFT FORMATION** (24) Starston Member (27) Leet Hill Member (26) Corton Member (25)
> 12			**SHOULDHAM FORMATION** (1) High Lodge Member (5) Lakenheath Member (4) Fodderstone Member (3) Shouldham Thorpe Member (2)	**THRIPLOW FORMATION** (11) **INGHAM FORMATION** (6) Timworth Member (10) Knettishall Member (9) Ingham Farm Member (8) Seven Hills Member (7)

to c. 50 m deposited in over-deepened tunnel-valleys (Ventris 1985, 1986).

(SGL)

(3) Bawsey Member. Stratotype: at quarries near Bawsey [TF 679193] (Ventris 1986). A pale-coloured, calcareous till, with a high content of Cretaceous lithologies, c. 1 m in thickness, lying in depressions in the underlying Woodlands Farm Member (Ventris 1986). It may be a flow till (Evans 1975).

(SGL)

(4) Setch Member. Stratotype: borehole [TF 638145] (Ventris 1985, 1986). Formerly referred to as the Setch laminated clays, it consists of glaciolacustrine laminated clays, deposited in a pro-glacial lake in the lower Nar valley during decay of the Anglian ice sheet. It overlies the Woodlands Farm Member in the N3 borehole (Ventris 1986).

(SGL)

(5) Bartholomews Hills Member. Stratotype: gravel pit [TF 817131] (Ventris 1985). Head gravel and sand with chalk up to 5 m in thickness, on the south side of the Nar valley at c.40 m O.D. Associated with Palaeolithic artefacts of Levallois type (Wymer 1985).

(JJW)

(6) Blackborough End Member. Stratotype: gravel pits near Blackborough End [TF 679151] (Ventris 1985). It consists of up to c. 8 m of fluvial sand and gravels and head gravels deposited during decay of the Anglian ice-sheet (Ventris 1985, 1986). The lower part of the unit is associated with steep-sided channels cut into the underlying Carstone.

(SGL)

(7) South Acre Member. Stratotype: gravel pit near South Acre [TF 802150] (Ventris 1985). It consists of fluvial sands and gravels c. 10 m thick (thought to be outwash Ventris 1985, 1986) overlying the Bawsey Member.

(SGL)

(8) Nar Valley Formation. Type area: the valley of the River Nar in northwest Norfolk. It incorporates the post-Anglian part of the Nar Valley Formation as defined by Ventris (1985, 1986).

(SGL)

(9) Nar Member. Stratotype: borehole [TF 643166] (Ventris 1985). The sequence is also exposed at Tottenhill gravel pit [TF 632114]. It consists of the Nar Valley freshwater Bed including a compressed wood peat and the Nar Valley clays, blue grey shelly silty clay that indicate a sea-level of 23 m O.D. Ventris (1985, 1996). Pollen and molluscs indicate a temperate climate and Ventris (1985, 1986, 1996) correlates the sequence with the Hoxnian. U-series ages on the compressed wood peat suggest correlation with stage 9 (Rowe et al. 1997). But D-aIle/L-Ile ratios from the freshwater sands near the base of the sequence of 0.289 ± 0.026 (3) shows that it is older than the type-site for the Hoxnian. It has been correlated with oxygen isotope stage 11 (Bowen et al. 1989).

(SGL)

(10) Tottenhill Member. Stratotype: the Tottenhill gravels pits [TF 632114]. It consists of about 10 m of medium to coarse cross-stratified sands and gravels, dominated by flint, and overlying the Nar Valley Member (Ventris 1985, 1986). Its palaeoflow was to the south west. The sequence has been interpreted as sub-aquatic deltaic sediments by Gibbard et al. (1991a, 1992) and Lewis & Rose (1991a), possibly deposited from an adjacent ice sheet some time between oxygen isotope stage 11 and oxygen isotope sub-stage 5e. The uppermost part of the Tottenhill Member is a brown silty clay with red mottles and conspicuous involutions. Micromorphological analysis

suggests a phase of soil formation under temperate climate conditions followed by disruption by periglacial active layer processes during the Ipswichian and Devensian (Lewis & Rose 1991a).

(SGL)

(11) Wormegay Member. Stratotype: at Wormegay [TF 655131] (Ventris 1985, 1986). It consists of up to 2.5 m of sand and gravel overlying the Nar Valley Member, and represents fluvial deposition following a period of incision after the deposition of the Tottenhill Member. The unit forms the Wormegay Terrace in the areas between Wormegay and Narborough.

(SGL)

(12) Pentney Priory Bed. Deposits at Pentney [TF 707131]. Comprises about a metre of organic detritus muds that accumulated under low energy conditions in a fluvial system. The pollen assemblage indicates vegetation development from boreal forest through to mixed oak forest. The deposits are correlated with the Ipswichian (Ventris 1985, 1986).

(SGL)

(13) Pentney Member. Stratotype: gravel pit near Pentney [TF 707131] (Ventris 1985, 1986). It consists of about 3.5 m of fluvial sand and gravels deposited after a period of incision through the Wormegay Member. Contemporary cold climate conditions are suggested by the sedimentology of these deposits, the presence of ice-wedge casts within the gravels and the occurrence of organic silt lenses containing an open vegetation assemblage (Ventris 1985, 1986). Radiocarbon ages on mosses contained within the sands and gravels give an age of 21 000 years $\pm$ 1000 (Ventris 1985)

(SGL)

(14) Marham Member. Stratotype: gravels up to a metre in thickness near Marham [TF 717114] (Ventris 1985, 1986). Pingo remnants, infilled with Holocene (Flandrian) deposits, occur on its surface (Sparks et al. 1972).

(SGL)

(15) Hunstanton Formation. This the basal Morston Member that is included because the Hunstanton Formation is the mappable unit, but mostly the tills and associated sands and gravels on the northwest Norfolk coast that are correlated with the Late Devensian (Straw 1960).

(SGL)

(16) Morston Member. Comprises the Morston raised beach deposits (type section: TF 987441, Gale et al. 1988) where c. 2.3 m of rounded flint cobbles and gravel are considered to be interglacial high sea-level deposits (Solomon 1931, 1932; Gale et al. 1988). Pollen from finely laminated mud beneath the beach gravel suggests warm climate conditions (Gale et al. 1988). It overlies Lowestoft Formation and is overlain by the Hunstanton Formation. Similar raised beach deposits may be present at Old Hunstanton [TF 681425] (Gallois 1978).

(SGL)

(17) Holkham Member. Formerly the Hunstanton till, it is a dull reddish-brown sandy clay, containing chalk and flint pebbles together with Carboniferous and Triassic material and a variety of igneous and metamorphic rocks (Gallois 1978). It is up to 10 m in thickness, and occurs as a continuous outcrop from Heacham to Brancaster, then as a discontinuous deposit to Morston (Straw 1960). It is well known from cliff sections at Hunstanton [TF 673413] which constitute the stratotype; sections are also known in Holkham Park brick-pit [TF 863428].

(SGL)

(18) Ringstead Member. Glaciofluvial sediments of variable thickness and character associated with the Holkham Member around Heacham, Ringstead, Hunstanton and Holkham (Straw 1960). Landforms associated with meltwater deposition include the Hunstanton esker in Old Hunstanton Park [TF 206940].

(SGL)

(19) Fenland Formation (Lincolnshire & Holderness, note 21).

Central East Anglia (and part of Cambridgeshire)

(1) Shouldham Formation. Deposits identified from Should-ham Thorpe, Norfolk [TF 657085] southwards along the eastern margin of the Fens. Additional members are defined based upon the sequence recognized at High Lodge, Milden-hall and Lakenheath, Suffolk. Its type area is along the eastern Fen margin south from Shouldham Thorpe to the Lark valley (Lewis 1993).

(SGL)

(2) Shouldham Thorpe Member. Stratotype: Shouldham Thorpe, Norfolk [TF 657085] where 3 m of gravel, containing abundant quartzite, quartz and flint, overlies Lower Cretac-eous at 24 O.D. Similar deposits along the Fen edge, for example at Northwold [TL 739976] and Methwold [TL 750922], may be correlated with this member (Rose 1987; Lewis 1991, 1993).

(SGL)

(3) Fodderstone Member. Stratotype: Shouldham Thorpe, Norfolk [TF 657085]. It consists of up to 3 m of cross-stratified and horizontally bedded sand with gravelly beds of similar clast lithology to the underlying Shouldham Thorpe Member. Palaeoflow direction toward south-southeast, a trend con-sistent with the underlying gravels (Rose 1987; Lewis 1991, 1993).

(SGL)

(4) Lakenheath Member. Stratotype: the Summit of Maid-scross Hill, Lakenheath [TL 727825] as described by Rose (1987) and Lewis (1993). It consists of c. 3 m of quartzite and quartz-rich, fluvial sands and gravels, observed overlying Chalk (Flower 1869) at an elevation of about 30 m O.D. The gravels are distinguished from the Shouldham Thorpe Member on altitudinal grounds (Lewis 1993).

(SGL)

(5) High Lodge Member. Stratotype: High Lodge, Mildenhall, Suffolk [TL 739754]. These overlie chalky diamict as the result of glaciotectonic deformation (Lewis 1992). They consist of lower and upper brown and intervening grey clayey silt, with thin sand laminae developed within the lower brown clays. Pollen from the High Lodge Bed includes *Pinus* and *Picea* (Hunt 1992) and indicate a boreal forest vegetation. Together with a coleopteran assemblage this suggests cool temperate conditions. A sparse mammalian fauna includes *Dicerorhinus etruscus* (Stuart 1992) now renamed *Stephanorhinus hunsdhei-mensis* The archaeology consists of cores, flakes and flake tools (Ashton 1992). The High Lodge Member is thought to be Cromerian.

(NMA)

(6) Ingham Formation. Stratotype: Ingham, Suffolk [TL 855715] where quartzite and quartz rich gravels were first described by Clarke & Auton (1982, 1984) and named the Ingham sand and gravel. The Ingham Formation is recognized over a wide area of central East Anglia, from the Lark valley in the west to Knettishall in the Little Ouse valley and across the Little Ouse-Waveney watershed, where gravels of Ingham-type composition have been identified from boreholes (Auton 1982;

Auton *et al.* 1985; Wilcox & Stanczyszyn 1983).

(SGL)

(7) Seven Hills Member. Stratotype: borehole at Seven Hills, north of Ingham [TL 863745] at an altitude of c. 50 m O.D. (Lewis & Bridgland 1991; Lewis 1993). It overlies Chalk and is 4 m thick. The gravel is dominated by quartzite and quartz, with lesser amounts of flint. Carboniferous chert is also present. The gravels are probably of fluvial origin. 3 km to the southwest [TL 845716], a thin, heavily dissected deposit west of Ingham is considered to be part of the same member.

(SGL)

(8) Ingham Farm Member. Stratotype: at [TL 855715] gravels overlie Chalk bedrock heavily disturbed by solution processes causing localized collapse of the gravels into the resulting hollows (Clarke & Auton 1982, 1984; Lewis 1993; Lewis & Bridgland 1991). The gravel is 4–5 m thick and consist mainly of far-travelled quartzite and quartz, with flint as a minor constituent. The base of the gravels lies at c. 40 m O.D. at the type section, and the upper surface at c. 44 m O.D.

(SGL)

(9) Knettishall Member. Stratoype: Knettishall, Suffolk [TL 951798] where gravels overlie Chalk and are composed mainly of quartzite, quartz, Carboniferous chert and flint. The member is at an elevation of 25.2 m O.D. with the top of the gravels at 31.8 m O.D. Palaeoflow direction was towards the northeast (Lewis & Rose 1991*b*; Lewis 1993).

(SGL)

(10) Timworth Member. Stratotype: Timworth [TL 853692]. Up to 10 m of gravels containing quartzite, quartz, flint and chalk overlie Chalk at 12–18 m O.D. (Lewis & Bridgland 1991; Lewis 1993).

(SGL)

(11) Thriplow Formation. Stratotype: at [TL 445447]. It consists of gravel remnants north of the Chalk escarpment (Sparks 1957) that may represent pre-Anglian river courses, or Anglian meltwater gravels. In the latter case it would be a member of the Lowestoft Formation.

(SGL)

(12) Lowestoft Formation. It forms a widespread series of glaciogenic and associated deposits. The sequence has been investigated since the early work of Trimmer (1851). Baden-Powell (1948) introduced the term Lowestoft boulder clay, and the term Lowestoft till is now used widely to refer to the chalky tills of Eastern England (Perrin *et al.* 1979). Perrin *et al.* (1979) used the term 'Lowestoft till group' as an informal term to include 'the Lowestoft Till (including the Chalky Boulder Clay of the east Midlands), the Wragby Till and the 'Lowestoft-type' Marly Drift' (Perrin *et al.* 1979). Bridge & Hopson (1985) and Hopson & Bridge (1987) formally defined the Lowestoft Till Group. The term Lowestoft Formation proposed here, is based on the definition of Mathers *et al.* (1987), and it comprises 'an extensive sheet of chalky boulder clay [till], together with outwash sands and gravels, silts and clays' (Mathers *et al.* 1987). The sequence at Corton, Suffolk [TM 543977] is the stratotype for this unit (Baden-Powell 1948). The Lowestoft Formation is recognized over a wide area of East Anglia and the East Midlands. The regional distribution and variability of the Lowestoft Till was examined by Perrin *et al.* (1979). It overlies a range of rocks from Chalk, Kimmeridge Clay, Jurassic limestone, Lias clay to older Quaternary sediments. At numerous localities it is overlain by temperate organic deposits: for example, at Hoxne (West 1956), Mark's Tey (Turner 1970), the Nar Valley (Ventris 1985, 1986, 1996), Hitchin (Kerney 1959; Gibbard 1974), Hatfield (Sparks *et al.*

1969), East Farm, Barnham (Ashton *et al.* 1994*a*) and Beeches Pit, West Stow (Kerney 1976; Preece *et al.* 1991). The Lowestoft Formation consists mainly of chalky tills, with associated outwash deposits, with a clast and mineral assemblage derived dominantly from Cretaceous and Jurassic rocks to the north and west. The Lowestoft Formation consists of numerous lithological units, which are all associated with the glacial episode responsible for the deposition of the Lowestoft Till. The stratotype is also described by Arthurton *et al.* (1994).

(SGL)

(13) Lowestoft Till Member. Stratotype: Corton, Suffolk [TM 543977]. This was commonly referred to as the Chalky Boulder Clay, for example by Harmer (1909) prior to the investigations of Baden-Powell (1948). Harmer (1909) described several lithofacies in the chalky boulder clay, including the 'chalky-Kimmeridgian' and the 'chalky-Oxfordian' boulder clays. The Lowestoft Till of Baden-Powell (1948) was the lower of two chalky boulder clays which several authors believed could be recognized in East Anglia, the upper unit being called the Gipping boulder clay (Baden-Powell 1948). The Lowestoft Till was defined by Baden-Powell (1948) as chalky tills with a dark, Jurassic rich matrix identifiable across much of East Anglia. Subsequent reinvestigations have indicated that there is only one chalky till sheet in East Anglia (Bristow & Cox 1973; Perrin *et al.* 1973, 1979) of distinctive lithology and mineralogy. It covers a wide area: its southern limit runs from the Ipswich area in the east, to north London, into Hertfordshire and Bedfordshire. The work of Perrin *et al.* (1979) is a regional synthesis of the lithology and mineralogy of the Lowestoft Till. The character of the Lowestoft till varies according to the nature of the substrate over which the ice passed, but overall the unit has distinctive lithological properties that indicate derivation from an ice sheet flowing down the eastern margin of the British Isles and entering East Anglia through the area now occupied by the Wash and Fen basin. It is generally correlated with oxygen isotope stage 12.

(SGL)

(14) Oulton Member. It overlies the Lowestoft Till Member at the type locality of Corton [TM 543977] as a sequence of laminated silts and clays (Banham 1971; Arthurton *et al.* 1994) that represent proglacial lacustrine deposition associated with the ice sheet that deposited the Lowestoft Till Member. It is *c.* 5 m in thickness.

(SGL)

(15) Pleasure Gardens Member. Stratotype: the type sections at Corton [TM 543977] where it consists of a chalky deposit of variable thickness (*c.* 2 m). It is interpreted as a flow till consisting of redeposited Lowestoft Till Member (Banham 1971).

(SGL)

(16) Observatory Member. Stratotype: gravels at [TL 431601]. It appears to be the earliest evidence of the Cam system, but may be mostly glacial meltwater gravels (Marr 1920). It may also be a downstream equivalent of the sediments occupying the glacial tunnel valley of the Cam (Baker 1977). It is apparently aligned through the Oakington gap in the Lower Greensand outcrop.

(SB)

(17) Barrington Works Member. Stratotype: at [TL 393512]. Formerly the Barrington Till and associated meltwater sediments (Hoare & Connell 1981). It forms a plateau west of Cambridge and caps the Chalk escarpment to the south and east.

(SB)

(18) Quendon Member. Stratotype: [TL 524320]. The Lower Till Complex of Baker (1977). It may be the equivalent of the Barrington Works Member.

(SB)

(19) Newport Member. Stratotype: proglacial lake sediments at [TL 340518] (Baker 1977).

(SB)

(20) Widdington Member. Stratotype: sands and gravels at TL 531308. The outwash sands and gravels of Baker (1977).

(SB)

(21) Henham Member. Stratotype: till filling a buried channel [TL 523300] (Baker 1977). It may be the equivalent of the Barrington Works Member.

(SB)

(22) Wicken Bonhunt Member. Stratotype: glaciolacustrine clays and silts filling a buried channel [TL 513336] (Baker 1977). It may be the equivalent of the Newport Member.

(SB)

(23) Wandlebury Member. Stratotype: gravel and sand [TL 495535]. It is derived from the Lowestoft Formation Till. It may be equivalent to (the upper) part of the Observatory Member.

(SB)

(24) North Sea Drift Formation (North East Norfolk 12)

(25) Corton Member. Stratotype: Corton, Suffolk [TM 548965]. Referred to as the Corton Bed by Banham (1971) and as the Corton Sands by Hopson & Bridge (1987). It consists of up to 10 m of fine to medium grained sands, with ripples, horizontal lamination and tabular cross-sets deposited by flow from the north west (Bridge & Hopson 1985). Three fining-upwards cycles have been recognized within the unit. It is interpreted as outwash of the North Sea Drift ice sheet.

(SGL)

(26) Leet Hill Member. Stratotype: pit at Leet Hill [TM 378929]. These sands and gravels were recognized by Hopson & Bridge (1987) in the lower Waveney valley. They are glaciofluvial deposits up tp 5 m thick associated with the North Sea Drift ice sheet and are characterized by a distinctive suite of igneous lithologies which include rhomb porphyries and granitic and metamorphic rock types.

(SGL)

(27) Starston Member. Stratotype: Starston, Norfolk, [TM 243844], Lawson 1982). The name was introduced by Lawson (1982) to refer to brown sandy diamicts and laminated sediments mainly beneath chalky tills of the Lowestoft Formation. It consists of clayey sand and sandy clay, containing flint gravel and a few chalk pebbles, commonly displaying fine laminations. The unit is up to *c.* 7 m in thickness (Auton *et al.* 1985). The Starston till includes deposits classified as the basal brown sandy till in the Redgrave area (Clarke & Auton 1982). It includes the brown sandy diamict at Knettishall (Lewis & Rose 1991*b*; Lewis 1993) which overlies the Ingham Formation and occurs as lenses within the overlying Leet Hill Member.

(SGL)

(28) West Stow Formation. Fine-grained deposits overlying chalky diamict and underlying a flint-rich clayey gravel at Beeches Pit, West Stow [TL 798719] (Whitaker *et al.* 1891; Kerney 1976; Holyoak *et al.* 1983; Preece *et al.* 1991; Bridgland & Lewis 1991). It includes pale-coloured calcareous silts and clays and grey to black layers (the carbonaceous seams described by Skertchly in Whitaker *et al.* 1891) containing abundant bone fragments. The deposits contain a diverse molluscan and vertebrate fauna, indicative of temperate climate conditions, and a Lower Palaeolithic core, flake and biface assemblage (Gowlett 1994). U-series dating of the tufa by Holyoak *et al.* (1983) yielded age estimates of 300 ka. D-aIle/L-Ile ratios (Bowen unpublished), U-series (Atkinson unpublished) and TL dating of burnt flint (Lewis unpublished) all suggest correlation with oxygen isotope stage 11.

(SGL)

(29) Icklingham Tufa Bed. This occurs within the sequence at Beeches Pit, West Stow [TL 798719] and is a fragmentary tufa contained within a detrital silt and clay deposit, overlying chalky diamict and lying beneath and interdigitating with the grey to black clay facies. It has yielded a rich molluscan assemblage, containing woodland species indicating temperate forested conditions (Kerney 1976, Preece *et al.* 1991). The assemblage includes elements from western, central and south east Europe. *Laminifera* cf. *pauli*, a species now restricted to the western Pyrenees occurs. This is the type locality of the extinct land snail *Retinella* (*Lyrodiscus*) *skertchlyi* (Kerney 1976); the modern distribution of this subgenus is confined to the Canary Islands.

(SGL)

(30) Barnham Formation. Stratotype: fossiliferous silts and clays in an old brick-pit near East Farm, Barnham [TL 875787]. It overlies glaciofluvial sands and gravels and till (Ashton *et al.* 1994a). Vertebrate and molluscan fauna indicates temperate climate conditions, associated archaeology includes core and flake assemblage and biface assemblage (Ashton *et al.* 1994b; Wymer 1985). D-aIle/L-Ile ratios on *Bythinia tentaculata* of 0.31 and 0.29, and *Valvata piscinalis* of 0.26 and 0.28, indicate correlation with Swanscombe and oxygen isotope stage 11 (Ashton *et al.* 1994a).

(SGL)

(31) Elveden Formation. Stratotype: Elveden, Suffolk [TL 809804] (Ashton & Lewis unpublished; Paterson & Fagg 1940). It consists of over 4 m of grey clays and up to 3.5 m of brown sandy clays in a channel cut into chalky till. Fragmentary molluscan and vertebrate remains suggest temperate climate conditions. The associated archaeology is a Lower Palaeolithic core, flake and biface assemblage.

(NMA)

(32) Lark Valley Formation. Comprises the post-Anglian fluvial and associated deposits in the River Lark valley. Five terraces were identified by Clayton (1983), though only the lowest two terraces (1st and 2nd) form substantial spreads of sand and gravel. The lower terraces are also present further up the Lark valley towards Bury St Edmunds (Hawkins 1981). Deposits within the Lark valley at Beeches Pit, West Stow are also included within this formation.

(SGL)

(33) Sicklesmere Member. Stratotype: Sicklesmere [TL 874609] where a sequence of organic muds overlying chalky till is identified in boreholes (West 1981). The pollen assemblage indicates forest vegetation correlated with the sequence at Hoxne (West 1981)

(SGL)

(34) Eriswell Member. A small remnant of gravelly sand, *c.* 1.6 m thick at [TL 730790], mapped as terrace 5 by the British Geological Survey (Clayton 1983).

(SGL)

(35) Fornham Member. Best developed around Fornham, where it is generally up to 4.0 m in thickness, and overlies Chalk or glacial silts. The stratotype is near Kentford [TL 710667]. Mapped as terrace 4 by the British Geological Survey

(Clayton 1983).

(SGL)

(36) Kentford Member. Stratotype: borehole at [TL 706675]. Deposits of sand and gravel around Kentford have been mapped as terrace 3 of the River Lark (Clayton 1983). The deposits are about 4 m in thickness. They also occur around Timworth (Bristow 1990).

(SGL)

(37) Cavenham Member. Stratotype: Cavenham [TL 763708] as described by Bristow (1990). Deposits of sand and gravel mapped as terrace 2 of the River Lark (Clayton 1983, Bristow 1990) occur around Sicklesmere, Timworth and Hengrave and are particularly extensive around Cavenham, and between Tuddenham and Culford. The deposits consist of sandy gravel up to *c.* 13 m in thickness, but more typically around 4 m thick. In places the gravels overlie a grey fine grained unit mapped as 'glacial silt' (Bristow 1990).

(SGL)

(38) Lackford Member. Stratotype: 4.5 m of sand and gravel at [TL 799709] (Bristow 1990), although it can reach about 10 m. It is mapped as terrace 1 of the River Lark (Clayton 1983, Bristow 1990). It occurs around Hawstead Green and between Mildenhall and Icklingham, but is best developed around Lackford.

(SGL)

(39) Cam Valley Formation. This is characterized by gravels and sands dominated by predominantly angular flint, quartz and minor exotic lithologies, and associated sediments. Its members are associated with the River Cam and tributaries.

(SGL)

(40) North Hall Member. Stratotype: lacustrine sediments in the upper Cam at [TL 524303]. Pollen assemblages indicate correlation with the first half of the Hoxnian (Baker 1977).

(SB)

(41) Bordeaux Pit Member. Stratotype: gravels of the upper Cam valley at [TL 512416] (Sparks 1955). It may be the equivalent of the Thriplow Member, or the Little Wilbraham Member.

(SB)

(42) Little Wilbraham Member. Stratotype: gravel at [TL 546587]. It is found east of Cambridge (Penning & Jukes-Browne 1881), and was defined as the 4th Terrace by the British Geological Survey.

(SB)

(43) Huntingdon Road Member. Stratotype: gravel at [TL 437604] north of Cambridge (Marr & King 1932) Mapped as the 4th Terrace by the British Geological Survey.

(SB)

(44) Histon Road Member. Stratotype: predominantly fine-grained fluvial deposits at [TL 444610]. Pollen assemblages and fauna indicate correlation with the Ipswichian (Sparks & West 1959). Mapped as part of the 3rd Terrace by the British Geological Survey.

(SB)

(45) Barrington Village Member. Stratotype: predominantly fluvial deposits at [TL 404498]. Formerly the Barrington Bed. Pollen assemblages and fauna indicate correlation with the Ipswichian (Gibbard & Stuart 1975).

(SB)

(46) Barnwell Abbey Member. Stratotype: gravel at [TL 463588] (Marr 1920). Mapped as the 3rd Terrace by the British Geological Survey.

(SB)

(47) Sidgwick Avenue Member. Stratotype: gravel at [TL

443580] (Lambert *et al.* 1963). Mapped as the 2nd Terrace by the British Geological Survey.

(SB)

(48) Barnwell Station Member. Stratotype: gravel at [TL 472598] (Bell & Dickson 1971). Mapped as the 1st Terrace by the British Geological Survey.

(SB)

(49) Fenland Formation (Lincolnshire & Holderness, note 21). Stratotype: peat and associated alluvial deposits at TL 453593.

(SB)

South and East Suffolk

(1) Red Crag Formation. This term was first used by Funnell and West (1977). It consists of a sequence of basal pebbles overlain by shelly sands, distributed over parts of Essex and south east Suffolk, deposited by inter- and sub-tidal sedimentation. It is divided in the deeper parts of the Crag basin into two members (Mathers & Zalasiewicz 1988). It is typically 10–40 m in thickness and lies between elevations of +40 to −40 m O.D. (Mathers & Zalasiewicz 1988).

(SGL)

(2) Sizewell Member. Stratoype: borehole [TM 471622] of the Aldeburgh-Sizewell transect between −47.6 and −34.3 m O.D. (Zalasiewicz *et al.* 1988). It consists of shelly sands with clay lenses up to 13 m in thickness at the base of the Red Crag Formation (Zalasiewicz *et al.* 1988).

(SGL)

(3) Thorpeness Member. Stratotype: within borehole [TM 471622] of the Aldeburgh-Sizewell transect between −34.3 and −13.3 m O.D. (Zalasiewicz *et al.* 1988). It consists of 20–30 m of fine to medium sands and shelly sands with thin clay laminae (Zalasiewicz *et al.* 1988). On the basis of its pollen it is pre-Ludhamian.

(SGL)

(4) Norwich Crag Formation. This term was first used by Funnell & West (1977). It consists of a sequence of mainly marine sediments, ranging from gravels to clays.

(SGL)

(5) Chillesford Church Member. Stratotype: at the Chillesford Church pit, Suffolk [TM 382523]. It was formerly the Chillesford Sand Member (Mathers & Zalasiewicz 1988). It is typically 5–10 m (somely up to 15 m) of yellow-orange fine- to medium-grained well sorted sands with silty clay layers of marine origin (Zalasiewicz & Mathers 1985; Mathers & Zalasiewicz 1988). It overlies the Red Crag Formation or older rocks.

(SGL)

(6) Chillesford Member. Stratotype: at [TM 382523]. It was formerly the Chillesford Clay Member (Zalasiewicz & Mathers 1985; Mathers & Zalasiewicz 1988; Zalasiewicz *et al.* 1991). It was originally assigned to the Norwich Crag Formation by Funnell and West (1977). It consists mostly of unfossiliferous pale grey silty clay, with rare sand laminae forming localised bodies on top of the Chillesford Church Member. Locally, it includes pollen, foraminifera and molluscs that indicate deposition during the cold climatic conditions of the Baventian-Pre-Pastonian, and is correlated with the Easton Bavents clay to the north (Zalasiewicz *et al.* 1991).

(SGL)

(7) Creeting Member. Stratotype at Creeting St Mary [TM 0955]. It consists of well-sorted fine- to medium- micaceous sand in exposures of up to about 11 m thick but reaching more than 80 m in the Stradbroke Trough (Allen 1984). Its

sedimentology indicates an origin as inter-tidal sand. It is overlain locally by the College Farm Member at Great Blakenham [TM 110503]. Deposition occurred at the southern limit of the Stradbroke Trough at Creeting St Mary, in a shallow marine embayment at Great Blakenham (Allen 1984; Gibbard *et al.* 1996) and in the main Crag Basin at sites such as Valley Farm [TM 116433] and Kesgrave [TM 228465] (Spencer 1967, 1971; Dixon 1978). The Creeting Sands and the College Farm Silty Clay formerly consituted the Creeting Formation (Allen 1984), although they are here incorporated into the Norwich Crag Formation (Zalasiewicz & Mathers 1985; Mathers & Zalasiewicz 1988).

(PA)

(8) College Farm Member. Stratotype: Great Blakenham [TM 102500]. Formerly known as the College Farm Silty Clay (Allen 1984; Gibbard *et al.* 1996). It occurs only locally, as at the stratotype and Creeting St Mary. It comprises massive or brecciated Bed of silty clay or interlayered sand and silty clay, representing mud flats associated with sand flats of the Creeting Member. Plant macrofossil evidence indicates a freshwater environment (Field 1992). Early pollen work by Holyoak (Allen 1984) suggested an Early Pleistocene cool period, refined by Field (1992) and Gibbard *et al.* (in press) as late within the Antian-Bramertonian Stage, equivalent to the Tiglian TC3 of the Netherlands on the basis of the occurrence of *Azolla tegeliensis*.

(PA)

(9) Easton Bavents Member. Stratotype: coastal exposures at Easton Bavents [TM 518787]. It comprises *c.* 2 m of blue-grey clay with sands laminae, overlying sands and overlain by the Westleton Member exposed along the Suffolk coast north of Southwold (Funnell & West 1962). The sediments have yielded a pollen assemblage of cold aspect and a marine foraminifera and mollusc fauna (Funnell & West 1962, Norton & Beck 1972).

(SGL)

(10) Westleton Member. The type locality is at Westleton Common [TM 445687] although the deposits are also well exposed at Wangford [TM 470777] (Hey 1967a). It consists of flint-rich gravels, found along the coast and inland around Easton Bavents and Covehithe, Suffolk. They are typically *c.* 10 m in thickness, and consist of shallow south east dipping gravels. On the coast they overlie the Easton Bavents Member. The Westleton Member is interpreted as a beach deposit (Hey 1967a; Mathers & Zalasiewicz 1996). It comprises a gravel beach facies, shoreface facies and rip channel facies forming a gravel beach and rip channel system (Mathers & Zalasiewicz 1996).

(SGL)

(11) Kesgrave Formation. Stratotype: Kesgrave [TM 228465]. It is a series of gravel and sand bodies representing terrace aggradations along an early course of the River Thames in southern East Anglia, traced and defined by continuity of outcrop, composition, clast lithology and sedimentary structures (Hey 1965, 1980; Rose *et al.* 1976; Rose & Allen 1977; Bridgland 1988a, 1994; Whiteman 1992). The surface of the gravels is commonly affected by pedogenesis. The Valley Farm Soil is a rubified and clay-enriched pedogenic horizon affecting the topmost 1.0–1.5 m of various members of the Kesgrave Formation. The rubification indicates formation in dry, most probably warm interglacial conditions (Rose & Allen 1977) but detailed examination shows the soil to have a long and complex history, varying according to position (Kemp 1985a, 1987a). Its stratotype is the (now infilled)

Table 6. *Correlations between South and East Suffolk, Hertfordshire and Western Essex and Eastern Essex and oxygen isotope stratigraphy*

δ¹⁸O	SOUTH & EAST SUFFOLK		EASTERN ESSEX	HERTS & WESTERN ESSEX
1	FENLAND FORMATION (39)		Staines Member (14)	Staines Member (26)
2		**WAVENEY VALLEY FORMATION** (35) Shotford Member (38)		
3				
4				
5				
5e	**BOBBITSHOLE FORMATION** (34)	Wortwell Member (37)	Lexden Member (13)	
6		Broome Member (36)		
7	**BRUNDON** (32) **STUTTON** (33) & **STOKE TUNNEL** (31) **FORMATIONS**			
8				
9		**ATHELINGTON FORMATION** (30)		Hatfield Member (25)
10				
11	**ST CROSS SOUTH ELMHAM** (28) **& HOXNE FORMATIONS** (29)		**MARKS TEY FORMATION (12)**	**HITCHIN FORMATION** (23) Hitchen Tufa Bed (24)
12	**LOWESTOFT FORMATION** (17)	Homersfield Member (27) Haughey Park Member (26) Blakenham Member (25) Bramford Member (24) Broomwalk Member (23) Creeting Hill Member (22) Sandy Lane Member (21) Shrubland Member (20) Skeet`s Green Member (19) Whitelodge Farm Member (18)	**LOWESTOFT FORMATION** (6) Great Waltham Member (11) Newney Green Member (10) Shrubland Member (9) Belsteads Member (8) Broomfield Member (7)	**LOWESTOFT FORMATION** (4) Hertford Member (22) Gravely Member (21) Vicarsgrove Member (20) Maydencroft Member (19) Gosmore Member (18) Charlton Member (17) Thistley Farm Member (16) Stevenage Member (15) Priory Member (14) Ugley Green Member (13) Hoddesdon Member (12) Cock Lane Member (11) Wadesmill Member (10) Ugley Member (9) Stortford Member (8) Ware Member (7) Moor Mill Member (6) Watton Road Member (5)
>12	**KESGRAVE FORMATION** (11)	Waldringfield Member (16) Moreton Member (15) Bures Member (14) Stebbing Member (13) Bushett Member (12)	**KESGRAVE FORMATION (1)** Moreton Member (5) Bures Member (4) Stebbing Member (3) Bushett Member (2)	Holwell Bed (3) Westmill Member (2)
	NORWICH CRAG FORMATION (4)	Westleton Member (10) Easton Bavents Member (9) College Farm Member (8) Creeting Member (7) Chillesford Member (6) Chillesford Church M (5)		**LETCHWORTH FORMATION** (1)
	RED CRAG FORMATION (1)	Thorpeness Member (3) Sizewell Member (2)		

Valley Farm pit [TM 116433] (Rose & Allen 1977). The Barham soil, stratotype at Barham [TM 133515] is a complex pedogenically reorganised horizon affecting the topmost 1.0–1.5 m of various members of the Kesgrave Formation and the Valley Farm Soil. Widespread throughout East Anglia (Rose *et al.* 1985).

(PA)

(12) Bushett Member (Eastern Essex, note 2)

(13) Stebbing Member (Eastern Essex, note 3)

(14) Bures Member (Eastern Essex, note 4))

(15) Moreton Member (Eastern Essex, note 5)

(16) Waldringfield Member. Stratotype: Waldringfield [TM 258447] (Allen 1984). It consists of up to 5.3 m of sand and gravel, comprising only durable, mostly angular and sub-angular lithologies, particularly flint. Compared to older members of the Kesgrave Formation, quartzites are less commonly colourless and it has more flint. Palaeoflows are to the NE.

(PA)

(17) Lowestoft Formation (Central East Anglia 12). In this region the formation consists of a number of tills, dominated by a lodgement facies, with associated fluvioglacial complexes of gravels, sands and silts related to both the advance and decay of the ice sheet. Large scale variation in the composition of the glacial deposits is described by Perrin *et al.* (1979), and local variation in southern East Anglia by Rose and Allen (1977) and Allen *et al.* (1991). An alternative view of both till genesis and variation is given by Hart (1994).

(PA)

(18) Whitelodge Farm Member. Stratotype: periglacial cover-sand found within the cores of involutions at Barham [TM 133515], and infilling sand wedges, as at Great Blakenham [TM 102500]. Heavy minerals, such as epidote, garnet and chlorite, particularly softer varieties such as actinolite, apatite and biotite, distinguish it from the underlying members of the Kesgrave Formation. Formerly called the Barham Coversand (Rose *et al.* 1976).

(PA)

(19) Skeet's Green Member. Stratotype: calcareous silt at Barham [TM 133515]. A loess, sometimes reworked. It has a comparable heavy mineral assemblage to the Shrubland Member, linking them with the Lowestoft Formation. Formerly called the Barham Loess (Rose & Allen 1977; Allen 1984)

(PA)

(20) Shrubland Member. Stratotype: sands and gravels at Barham [TM 133515] (Rose & Allen 1977). It is comparable in composition with the underlying Kesgrave Formation, but with erratics from the tills, including *Rhaxella* chert. Its maximum thickness is 3.5 m. Palaeoflow direction usually to the south east. It is interpreted as ice-distal outwash, but incorporating reworked Kesgrave Formation material. Formerly called the Barham Sand and Gravel.

(PA)

(21) Sandy Lane Member. Stratotype: up to 1.8 m of chalk-rich gravels and sands at Barham [TM 133515] (Rose & Allen 1977). Contains some lenses of silt, found beneath till of the Lowestoft Formation.

(PA)

(22) Creeting Hill Member. Stratotype: former pit at Creeting St Mary [TM 096558]. Formerly known as the Creeting Till (Allen *et al.* 1991), a brown or brownish yellow till, varying from sandy to silty, occurring in lenses up to 0.5 m thick within the Sandy Lane or Shrubland Members. Regarded as flow till.

lenses within outwash.

(PA)

(23) Broomwalk Member. Stratotype: at Barham [TM 133515]. Formerly called the Barham Till (Allen *et al.* 1991): a sandy till, commonly banded, with strong preferred orientations of clasts and rich in lithologies from the gravels lying immediately below. A basal till, rarely more than 1 m thick, usually found beneath the Bramford Member, but may be found beneath the Blakenham Member.

(PA)

(24) Bramford Member. Stratotype: Bramford quarry [TM 131483]. Till of variable colour and composition, usually more sandy and brown in colour than the Blakenham Member. Typically found in valley-side locations. Associated with melt-out from stagnant ice (Allen *et al.* 1991)

(PA)

(25) Blakenham Member. Stratotype: quarry at Great Blakenham [TM 102500]. Up to 13 m of massive, clay-rich dark grey lodgement till (Rose & Allen 1977). It is typical of plateau areas in Suffolk. It is continuous with the Bramford and Broomwalk Members (below) regarded as lithofacies variants within the one till sheet (Allen *et al.* 1991).

(PA)

(26) Haughley Park Member. Stratotype: Haughley Park pit [TL 997624] (Allen 1984). It comprises up to 12 m of chalk-rich, ice-proximal gravels, usually overlying till of the Low-estoft Formation.

(PA)

(27) Homersfield Member. Stratotype: gravels at Homersfield [TM 285854]. It forms the highest terrace 5–7 m above the Waveney floodplain between Wortwell and Bungay (Sparks & West 1968). The sedimentology and lithology of these deposits showed that the gravels are associated with chalky 'flow tills' and are glaciofluvial in origin (Coxon 1979, 1984). A mammalian fauna occurs at Flixton (Funnell 1955; Coxon 1984).

(SGL)

(28) St Cross South Elmham Formation. Stratotype: former brick pit at St Cross South Elmham, Norfolk [TM 303840]. Up to 10 m of lacustrine clay-mud infill a depression in the surface of chalky till. Pollen analysis by West (1961*b*) and further studies by Coxon (Singer *et al.* 1993) show that the deposits represent the first half of an interglacial sequence which is correlated with the Hoxnian.

(CT)

(29) Hoxne Formation. Stratotype: Oakley Park pit, Hoxne, Suffolk [TM 176769] (West 1956; Gladfelter 1993). Stratotype of the Hoxnian (Mitchell *et al.* 1973). Up to 15 m of fluviatile sands, silts and gravels overlying interglacial peats and lacustrine clays above till of the Lowestoft Formation, and overlain by head gravel. The pollen biostratigraphy suggests an age for the lacustrine sediments.immediately after the Anglian glaciation (oxygen isotope stage 11). However, D-aIle/ L-Ile ratios indicate correlation with oxygen isotope stage 9 (Bowen *et al.* 1989). Palaeolithic artefacts are associated with the fluvial sequence.

(JJW)

(30) Athelington Formation. Stratotype: former brick pit at Athelington, Suffolk [TM 222710]. Up to 11 m of lacustrine clay and clay-mud infill a depression in the surface of chalky till. Pollen analysis by Coxon (1985) records an interglacial succession which is correlated with the Hoxnian (West 1956).

(CT)

(31) Stoke Tunnel Formation. Stratotype: southern end of the railway tunnel in Ipswich [TM 162434]. 13 m of head gravel overlie richly fossiliferous silts, sands and loams with base at 7 m O.D. (Wymer 1985). It extends at least 0.5 km south to Maidenhall. Pollen indicates a temperate climate. Horse and mammoth dominate the mammalian assemblage.

(JJW)

(32) Brundon Formation. Stratotype: pits near Sudbury, Suffolk [TL 863417]. It consist of sands and gravels, with lenses of chalky till in the lower part and a layer of clay in the middle of the sequence (Wymer 1985), and represent deposition by the River Stour. A rich molluscan fauna from the grey clay (stratum 4 of Moir & Hopwood 1939) includes *Corbicula fluminalis* and *Belgrandia marginata*, and indicates a temperate climate. Deposits above this level have yielded a mammalian fauna including *Mammuthus primigenius* and *Equus caballus*, *Bos primegenius* and *Bison priscus* are also common (Wymer 1985). Palaeolithic artefacts from this site are of Levallois type (Wymer 1985). U-series dates on bones of *M. primigenius* of 230 ± 30 ka and 174 ± 30 ka (Szabo & Collins 1975) suggest correlation with oxygen isotope stage 7.

(SGL)

(33) Stutton Formation. Stratotype: a site on the Stour estuary at [TM 150330] (Wymer 1985). Predominantly fine sands and silts with some gravel facies. The deposits have yielded a molluscan fauna including *Corbicula fluminalis*, indicative of temperate conditions, together with a mammalian fauna that includes mammoth, straight-tusked elephant, rhinoceros and horse, while the palaeobotany suggests an Ipswichian age (Sparks & West 1963), whereas D-aIle/L-Ile ratios suggest correlation with oxygen isotope stage 7 (Bowen *et al.* 1989). The limited archaeological assemblage is Palaeolithic and may include Levallois artefacts (Wymer 1985; Roe 1968).

(SGL)

(34) Bobbitshole Formation. Stratotype: Bobbitshole near Ipswich, Suffolk [TM 148414] (West 1957). The stratotype of the Ipswichian (Mitchell *et al.* 1973). It consists of up to c, 3.5 m of lacustrine silts and clay-mud, which pollen analysis has shown to represent the earlier part of an interglacial succession (West 1957). The molluscan fauna has been investigated by Sparks (1957) and the coleoptera by Coope (1974). D-aIle/L-Ile ratios of 0.09 ± 0.01 (6) indicate correlation with oxygen isotope sub-stage 5e (Bowen *et al.* 1989)

(CT)

(35) Waveney Valley Formation. Sands and gravels and associated fine-grained organic Bed deposited by the River Waveney (Coxon 1979, 1984, 1993a).

(SGL)

(36) Broome Member. Stratotype: fluvial sands and gravels at Broome Heath [TM 348915]. It forms a terrace along the River Waveney between Wortham and Broome Heath (Sparks & West 1968). It has ice wedge casts and silty lenses with pollen indicating a cold climate.

(SGL)

(37) Wortwell Bed. Stratotype: organic deposits beneath gravels at Wortwell [TM 275844] Sparks & West (1968). They consist of sands and muds, containing pollen, plant macrofossils and molluscs, deposited in a low energy backwater environment. They are truncated by overlying gravels. Correlation is with Ipswichian pollen zones IpIa - IpIIb (Sparks & West 1968).

(SGL)

(38) Shotford Member. Stratotype: gravels at Shotford [TM 246813]. It occurs underlying the floodplain of the River Waveney occur along much of the river from Lopham to

Ellingham (Sparks & West 1968; Coxon 1979, 1984). It has yielded *Coelodonta antiquitatis* and *Mammuthus primigenius* (Coxon 1984).

(SGL)

(39) Fenland Formation (Lincolnshire & Holderness, note 21).

Eastern Essex

(1) Kesgrave Formation (South and east Suffolk 10). The fullest sequence in eastern England of gravels and sands representing an early course of the River Thames (Whiteman 1992). Its members have been separated into an upper grouping with more complex development of the Valley Farm Soil (Kemp 1985a, 1987a, b) and a higher quartz + quartzite :- flint ratio in the gravels (described in this section); and a lower grouping (described in the Thames section).

(CAW)

(2) Bushett Member. Stratotype: borehole at Bushett Farm [TL 672288] (Hopson 1981). It showed 10.7 m of sandy gravel, gravelly sand and sand with evidence of the Valley Farm Soil in the upper 1–2 m. The mean quartzite:quartz ratio is 0.41 (16–32 mm fraction). Its outcrop is about 10 km wide, trending SW–NE between Bishop's Stortford and the Essex-Suffolk border at a gradient of *c*. 0.53 m km^{-1} (Whiteman 1992).

(CAW)

(3) Stebbing Member. Stratotype: Cowlands Farm quarry, Stebbing [TL 669233] (Whiteman 1992). It consists of some 10 m of sandy gravel, sand and silt in three sub-units with evidence of the Valley Farm Soil in the upper 2–3 m. Mean gradient of the Member is 0.47 m km^{-1}, and it trends in a SW–NE direction.

(CAW)

(4) Bures Member. Stratotype: sand pit 1 km west of Bures [TL 896342] (Whiteman 1992). Ellison & Lake (1987) recorded up to 10 m of mostly fine to coarse sand including trough cross-bedded sets up to 2.5 m thick, but sandy gravels have also been observed. Hopson (1981) logged 5 m of sand with a few gravel lags overlain by 4.5 m of cross-bedded and horizontally bedded sands alternating with massive or weakly bedded gravels. Mean gradient of the Member is 0.42 m km^{-1}, trending SW–NE.

(CAW)

(5) Moreton Member. Stratotype: Moreton [TL 534073] (Whiteman 1992). Millward *et al.* (1987) recorded up to 9 m of sediment in three sub-units of variable thickness consisting of sand with gravel layers, sandy clay and sandy gravel. Mean gradient of the Member is 0.42 m km^{-1}, trending SW–NE.

(CAW)

(6) Lowestoft Formation (Central East Anglia 12). The glacial sequence of Essex has been attributed to two or three separate events (Clayton 1957b, 1960), and to the Saalian (Wolstonian) by Bristow & Cox (1973). But, Perrin *et al.* (1979) and Mitchell *et al.* (1973) regarded it as Anglian. It includes tills at Maldon (Whitaker 1889; Allen *et al.* 1991) and Hornchurch (Lower Thames Valley) (Holmes 1892; Allen *et al.* 1991). Two till members are recognized in Essex though up to five till members have been identified in adjacent areas to the west and east.

(CAW)

(7) Broomfield Member. Stratotype: Broomfield, Essex [TL 723114] (Rose *et al.* 1976). It consists of up to 0.3 m of well sorted medium and fine-grained sand with some polished pebbles and few thin discontinuous lenses of dark grey clayey sand (Barham and Valley Farm Soils). The sand is interpreted as coversand (Rose & Allen 1977) and was formerly known as the Barham coversand (Allen 1984) with a type locality at Barham, Suffolk [TM 133515].

(CAW)

(8) Belsteads Member. Stratotype: Broomfield, Essex [TL 723114] (Rose *et al.* 1985; Whiteman 1990). Consists of *c.* 0.4 m of slightly calcareous laminated silty sand with a few gravel stringers. It contains dark grey gravelly, silty clay lenses especially near the base where they are traceable into the underlying Barham and Valley Farm Soils. Interpreted as a periglacial gelifluction deposit.

(CAW)

(9) Shrubland Member (South and east Suffolk 20). Formerly named the Barham sand and gravel from the stratotype at Barham [TM 133515]. Locally up to *c.* 5 m of sands and gravels similar in composition to the Kesgrave Formation but with distinctive erratics from the tills of the Newney Green and Great Waltham Members.

(CAW)

(10) Newney Green Member. Stratotype: Newney Green [TL 645066]. Generally reddish-brown, structurally complex, commonly banded, sand-rich, silty clay tills up to 2 m thick of predominantly local provenance occurring invariably at the base of the till sequence (Allen *et al.* 1991). Widespread in East Anglia especially south of the Chalk outcrop and correlated with the Broomwalk Member. It overlies the Shrubland Member.

(CAW)

(11) Great Waltham Member. Stratotype: Great Waltham [TL 687122]. Part of widespread, dark to medium grey, massive, silty and clayey tills up to 4 m thick extending over much of East Anglia. Clast component dominantly striated chalk, in a matrix of Jurassic clays (Allen *et al.* 1991). A thin sand lens sometimes separates a lower dark, and a lighter upper, sub-unit, as at Great Waltham and Broomfield.

(CAW)

(12) Marks Tey Formation. Stratotype: Marks Tey brickworks at Marks Tey, Essex [TL 912242]. Up to 35 m of lacustrine sediments overlie till and glacial gravel in a deep channel cut down into the London Clay (Ellison & Lake 1987). The lower part of the lacustrine sediments, in part with diatomaceous laminations, has yielded a late-glacial and complete interglacial pollen sequence with *Pterocarya* present; the upper part consisting of laminated grey silts contains cold-climate plant remains (Turner 1970). The interglacial pollen record closely resembles that at Hoxne and it is regarded as a parastratotype of the Hoxnian. Correlation with pollen records from France suggest an oxygen isotope stage 11 age. These lacustrine Bed also outcrop at the adjacent site at Copford [TL 927244] and similar deposits occur at Rivenhall End, Kelvedon [TL 839165] (Turner 1970).

(CT)

(13) Lexden Member. Stratotype: former brick pit at Lexden, Essex [TL 978253]. In the 1860s a channel filled with fossiliferous peat and organic clay was exposed below brickearth in the terrace deposits of the River Colne. Shotton *et al.* (1962), studied mammalian, beetle and pollen fossils from museum collections and concluded they were interglacial. Ordinarily it would be classified as a member of a formation defined for the Colne Valley; but in the absence of such a definition it is technically part of the regional and local Lowestoft Formation.

(CT)

(14) Staines Member (Middle Thames Valley 37)

Hertfordshire and West Essex

(1) Letchworth Formation. Stratotype: borehole near Fairfield Hospital [TL 205350] where it caps a small hill at *c.* 70 m O.D. (Hopson *et al.* 1996). It is restricted in distribution to the north-west of Letchworth. It consists of pebbly sands and sandy gravels, containing abundant rounded quartzite, quartz and sandstone, and some flint. It probably pre-dates the glacial deposits of the district (Hopson *et al.* 1996) and represents a pre-Anglian drainage line running from the Midlands towards the Thames basin (Hopson *et al.* 1996; Smith & Rose 1997). It may correlate with the lower aggradations of the Kesgrave Formation (Hopson *et al.* 1996)

(PMH)

(2) Westmill Member (Middle Thames & the Vale of St. Albans note 17). Formerly the Westmill Lower Gravel (Gibbard 1977; Cheshire 1986a; Bridgland & Cheshire 1994). Part of the Middle Thames Formation (8).

(DAC)

(3) Holwell Bed. Stratotype: Holwell Hyde quarry, Welwyn Garden City [TL 363116]. It consists of a moderately well-sorted sand with N-S palaeocurrents in a tributary position equivalent to the upper part of the Westmill Member (Cheshire 1986a). Part of the Middle Thames Formation (8).

(DAC)

(4) Lowestoft Formation (Central East Anglia, note 12).
(5) Watton Road Member (Middle Thames & the Vale of St. Albans note, 19).

(DAC)

(6) Moor Mill Member (Middle Thames & the Vale of St. Albans 20). Parastratotype at Moor Mill SSSI [TL 147027]. 2.6 m of laminated clay lake Bed formed in the proglacial Moor Mill Lake (Gibbard 1977), formed by the damming of the proto-Thames in the Vale of St Albans by the ice that deposited the Ware Member (Cheshire 1986a; Bridgland & Cheshire 1994). Gibbard (1977) attributed the damming to a later advance that deposited the till of the Eastend Green Member.

(DAC)

(7) Ware Member. Stratotype: Westmill Quarry, Ware [TL 346154]. Parastratotype: Downfield Farm SSSI [TL 349163]. It is up to 3 m in thickness and is the oldest till in the Vale of St. Albans (Gibbard 1977; Cheshire 1986a).

(DAC)

(8) Stortford Member. Stratotype: borehole at Bishop's Stortford [TL 479195] where it is 12 m thick. It was deposited by the second advance of the Lowestoft Till ice sheet into the Hertfordshire and west Essex area (Cheshire 1986a; Allen *et al.* 1991) and has a widespread distribution, extending south to Finchley and Hornchurch.

(DAC)

(9) Ugley Member. Stratotype: Ugley quarry SSSI [TL 520280]. It was deposited by the least extensive ice advance in this area. It is up to 7 m thick and contains more chalk and flint than the two earlier till members (Cheshire 1986a; Allen *et al.* 1991; Cheshire & Bridgland 1994).

(DAC)

(10) Wadesmill Member. Stratotype: Westmill quarry [TL 346154]. It was formerly named the Westmill Till (Cheshire 1986a, Allen *et al.* 1991, Bridgland & Cheshire 1994). It is up to 4 m thick and is the uppermost member of the Lowestoft Formation in this area. It is similar to the Ugley Member, but is more extensive. It extends southwestwards to Hatfield. It is interpreted as part of the Eastend Green Till by Gibbard

(1977) in the Hertford–Ware area (Middle Thames & the Vale of St. Albans 22).

(DAC)

(11) Cock Lane Member. Stratotype: Cock Lane quarry, Hoddesdon [TL 354077]. It lies between the Ware Member and the Stortford Member above. It is the lower part of the Hoddesdon gravel, formerly recognized by Cheshire (1986a) and Bridgland & Cheshire (1994).

(DAC)

(12) Hoddesdon Member. Stratotype: Cock Lane quarry, Hoddesdon [TL 354077]. It lies above the Stortford Member and below the Ugley Member. It is the upper part of the Hoddesdon Gravel, formerly recognized by Cheshire (1986a) and Bridgland & Cheshire (1994).

(DAC)

(13) Ugley Green Member. Stratotype: gravel at Ugley quarry SSSI [TL 520280]. It lies between the Ugley Member and the Wadesmill Member. It is rich in chalk and represents ice-proximal meltwater sediments (Cheshire 1986a; Cheshire & Bridgland 1994).

(DAC)

(14) Priory Member. Stratotype: borehole [TL 184288] in the grounds of Hitchin Priory. A lodgement till, up to 10 m; also present in boreholes south of Hitchin within a presumed 'tunnel valley' (Woodland 1970).

(DTA)

(15) Stevenage Member. Stratotype: borehole for the Little Wymondley bypass [TL 221270]. It is the oldest till unit in the Stevenage channel. It is a dark grey silty clay, up to 10 m, containing chalk pebbles (Aldiss 1992b). It is not known outside the Stevenage channel, although it is similar to the Priory Member of the Hitchin channel (Hopson et al. 1996).

(DTA)

(16) Thistley Farm Member. Stratotype: Thistley Farm [TL 190266]. It consists of c. 2 m of pale brown, laminated clayey silt (Hopson et al. 1996), and is the glaciolacustrine facies associated with the Hitchin and Stevenage channels (Hopson et al. 1996).

(DTA)

(17) Charlton Member. Stratotype: Maydencroft Manor borehole [TL 182276]. It consists of diamict known from the valley of the River Hiz, south west of Hitchin. It overlies glaciofluvial deposits which separate it from the underlying Priory Member. Generally c. 3 m in thickness, it is correlated with units in boreholes that are up to 10 m (Hopson et al. 1996). Interpreted as flow tills and waterlain tills, is also recognized in the Stevenage channel south east of Hitchin (Aldiss 1992b; Hopson et al. 1996).

(DTA)

(18) Gosmore Member. Stratotype: Gosmore borehole [TL 187276] proved 12.4 m of sandy gravels, containing flint and chalk and an erratic suite typical of Anglian glaciofluvial sediments (Hopson et al. 1996). Similar deposits are known from other boreholes through the Hitchin and Stevenage channels. It may, in part, correlate with the Westmill Member (Middle Thames Valley and Vale of St. Albans note 16), the Hertford Member of Cheshire (note 22) and is glacial outwash (Hopson et al. 1996). It interdigitates with the Thistley Farm Member (note 16) (Hopson et al. 1996).

(DTA)

(19) Maydencroft Member. Stratotype: borehole [TL183276] near Maydencroft Manor. It consists of dark grey lodgement till c. 7 m in thickness (Hopson et al. 1996).

(DTA)

(20) Vicarsgrove Member. Stratotype: Vicarsgrove pit [TL 178276]. It consists of about 3.5 m of sand that probably passes laterally into glaciolacustrine deposits (Aldiss 1992a).

(DTA)

(21) Graveley Member. Stratotype: borehole [TL 229284]. It is 14.3 m thick and is the the uppermost till of the Stevenage channel (Hopson et al. 1996; Aldiss 1992b).

(DTA)

(22) Hertford Member. (Westmill Member, Lowestoft Formation, Middle Thames note 16). Stratotype: Westmill quarry [TL 346154]. It was formerly recognized by Gibbard (1977) as the Westmill Upper Gravel (Middle Thames & the Vale of St. Albans note 17). Identified as a Lea Valley deposit by Cheshire (1986a) and Bridgland & Cheshire (1994), deposited after the Thames had been diverted from the Vale of St Albans. It is correlated with the Black Park Member (Middle Thames & the Vale of St. Albans note 25). Together with the Smug Oak Member (Middle Thames & the Vale of St. Albans note 23) it is the first post-diversion glaciofluvial-fluvial deposit in the Vale of St Albans. It interdigitates with the Lowestoft Formation.

(DAC)

(23) Hitchin Formation. Stratotype: north of Gosmore [TL 119277]. It consists of up to 5.8 m of lacustrine silty clay, generally coarser towards the base, containing pollen, plant macrofossils and shell fragments (Boreham & Gibbard 1995). It overlies the Lowestoft Formation. The age of the Hitchin Bed ranges from late Anglian to Hoxnian (Boreham & Gibbard 1995) and are overlain, probably unconformably, by 'brickearth'.

(DAC)

(24) Hitchin Tufa Bed. Stratotype: 1 km north west of Hitchin on Oughtonhead Lane [TL 172299]. It consists of calcareous tufa within a sequence of fine-grained deposits overlying Anglian glaciofluvial sediments. It contains a temperate molluscan assemblage (Kerney 1959).

(SGL)

(25) Hatfield Member (Middle Thames and the Vale of St. Albans note 26).

(DAC)

(26) Staines Member (Middle Thames, note 37).

Chapter 3

English Midlands

D. MADDY

With contributions from: A. Brandon, G. R. Coope, T. D. Douglas, C. P. Green, Cunhai Gao, A. J. Howard, D. H. Keen, A. Richards, J. M. Sinclair, K. A. Smith, M. G. Sumbler & P. Worsley

The Quaternary deposits of the Midlands of England provide an important link between the younger and shorter sequences of deposits in upland Britain with those of the longer largely non-glaciated record of lowland Southern England. Upland glaciation in Wales, the Pennines, the Lake District and Scotland built domes which allowed ice to coalesce and spread southwards across the English Midlands where the ice-sheets deposited extensive spreads of sediment. The thick ice-sheets of largely unconsolidated glacigenic sediment, together with the relatively easily erodible Mesozoic bedrock of Midland England, subsequently allowed extensive river systems to fashion successive 'post-glacial' landscapes.

The most extensive glacigenic deposits are those of the Wolston & Risbury Formations: the former is correlated with the Lowestoft Formation of Eastern England and is thus, by definition, Anglian (oxygen isotope stage 12). These formations overlie the Baginton and Mathon Formations that represent the sediments of two major river systems that were obliterated by the Anglian glaciation. Cut into these extensive marker formations of glacial and fluvial deposits are the younger fluviatile formations of the Wye, Severn, Avon, Trent, Ouse and Nene. They have yielded considerable biostratigraphical information and, importantly, contain materials for dating. Using aminostratigraphy (D-aIle/L-Ile ratios) and U-series, temperate organic deposits in each of these valleys have been variously correlated with oxygen isotope stages 9 and 7, and sub-stage 5e.

In addition to the Anglian glaciation, the English Midlands contains evidence for at least two further major ice advances. Glacigenic deposits in the Birmingham (Ridgacre Formation) area overlie a temperate organic sequence which has been correlated with the Hoxnian on the basis of palynology (Duigan 1956; Turner & Horton unpublished). The Ridgacre Formation has been correlated with oxygen isotope stage 10 by Sumbler (1995), but with oxygen isotope stage 6 by Maddy et al. (1995): the latter using Chlorine-36 rock exposure ages. The Stockport Formation delimits the maximum extent of Late Devensian ice (oxygen isotope stage 2) in the northwest of the region sometime after 30 ka, as shown by radiocarbon ages from Four Ashes by A.V. Morgan (1973).

Lugg Valley

(1) Humber Formation. Stratotype: Pudleston [SO 464592]. Fluvial sands and gravels derived from northerly derived cold stage fluvial system which deposited the Mathon Formation. It includes locally derived Devonian and Triassic, Carboniferous, Precambrian and Lower Palaeozoic clasts from regions to the north and northwest. It caps valley flanks on higher ground

between 140–220 m O.D. is between 2 and 8 m in thickness, and is locally overlain or reworked by glacial deposits of the Risbury Formation.

(AR)

(2) Risbury Formation. Type-area: Risbury area [SO 5453 to 5471]. It is correlated with the Older Drift Deposits of Brandon (1984, 1989). Ice-contact, glaciolacustine, glaciodeltaic and glaciofluvial deposits occur as remnants above 80 m O.D. outside the Late Devensian terminal moraine from Leominster to areas south and east of Hereford (Brandon 1989; Richards 1994). It is locally up to 30 m in thickness. The gravels include locally derived Devonian and northerly derived components reworked from the Humber Formation (1). Members of the Risbury Formation record oscillation of an ice-front during retreat across northeast Herefordshire.

(AB & AR)

(3) Newton Farm Member. Stratotype: Newton Farm [SO 627516]. Glaciotectonized glaciodeltaic sands and gravels up to 26 m thick. It was deposited at margins of a large ice-dammed lake: Glacial Lake Bromyard (Richards 1994). Formerly mapped as Older Fluvioglacial Gravel Deposits (Brandon 1989).

(AR)

(4) Kyre Brook Member. Stratotype: Hall Farm [SO 642624]. Humber Formation gravels reworked by catastrophic drainage from Glacial Lake Bromyard (Richards 1994). Crossbedded sand units and overlying gravel crossbedded up to 6 m thick, form a low terrace from Collington [SO 648597] to Tenbury Wells [SO 680610], with a base at 100 m to 120 m O.D.

(AR)

(5) Stoke Lacy Member. Stratotype: Windmill Hill [SO 606487]. Glaciotectonized sand, gravel and till units up to 15 m in thickness (Richards 1994). Formerly it was mapped as Older Fluvioglacial Gravel Deposits (Brandon 1989).

(AR)

(6) Stoke Prior Member. Type area: Stoke Prior-Steens Bridge-Bowley Court [SO 555524] to [SO 555580]. Glacigenic deposits forming hill cappings between 80 and 140 m O.D. It includes till, glaciolacustrine, glaciofluvial and glaciodeltaic deposits representing ice-marginal deposition and the formation of Glacial Lake Humber during a recessional phase of a pre-Hoxnian glaciation (Richards 1994). Formerly it was mapped as Older Fluvioglacial Gravel Deposits (Brandon 1989).

(AR)

(7) Franklands Gate Member. Stratotype: Franklands Gate [SO 549456]. Channelized glaciotectonized, ice-marginal sands and gravels up to 8 m thick with a base at 80 m O.D. at the type site, 98 m O.D. at Norton Court (SO 538495) to 115 m O.D. at Vennwood [SO 54854900]. Formerly mapped as Older

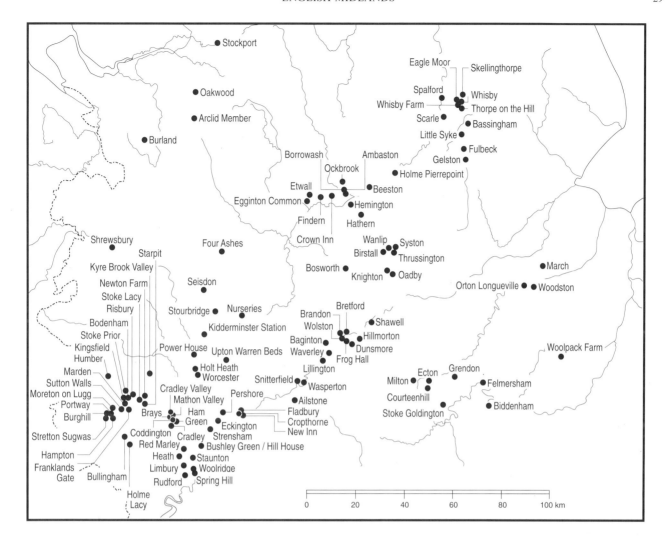

Fig. 5. Localities in the English Midlands.

Fluvioglacial Gravel Deposits (Brandon 1989).

(AR)

(8) Portway Member. Type area: Burghill [SO 488448] (Brandon & Hains 1981). Glaciotectonized, glaciolacustrine and glaciofluvial deposits up to 12 m thick representing ice-marginal fluctuation and deposition during a recessional phase of a pre-Hoxnian glaciation. Gravels of this Member are dominated by locally derived Devonian clasts and the absence of northerly derived components (Brandon 1989; Richards 1994). It occurs beyond or beneath the deposits of the Herefordshire Formation (15). Formerly Portway Sand and Gravel (Brandon & Hains 1981).

(AB & AR)

(9) Starpit Formation. Stratotype: Hewitts Gravel Pit [SO 621485]. Up to 5 m of interbedded sands and gravels channeled into Stoke Lacy Member (5) and Devonian from 125 m O.D. [SO 626516] to 88 m O.D. [SO 442629] on the flanks of the Lodon Valley. The gravels are dominated by locally derived Devonian, with rare low grade metamorphic and igneous clasts from Shropshire.

(AR)

(10) Lugg Valley Formation. Includes all the fluvial terrace deposits in the Lugg Valley (Brandon 1989) down-valley of the Late Devensian terminal moraine at Newton. Intermediate in age between the Risbury (2) and Herefordshire (15) formations. It is found from the Dinmore Hill meander to the confluence with River Wye. In contrast to the glacigenic gravels they contain few local Devonian clasts and abundant fine-grained Silurian (Ludlovian) sandstones (Brandon 1989). Prior to late Devensian glaciation, the River Lugg was joined by the Teme at Aymestrey and by the Onny at Leominster (Pocock 1925; Dwerryhouse & Miller 1930).

(AB)

(11) Sutton Walls Member. Stratotype: Sutton Walls pit [SO 524464] (now infilled: Brandon 1982). It comprises sands and gravels up to 8 m thick. Formerly known as the Sutton Walls or Fourth Terrace Deposits; occurs from Sutton Walls southwards to the confluence with the Wye (Brandon 1989). It is correlated altitudinally with the Holme Lacy Member of Wye (Wye Valley note 5).

(AB)

(12) Kingsfield Member. Type area: Kingsfield [SO 521498]. Largest terrace remnant (Brandon 1982). Comprises sands and gravels forming up to 3 m thick remnants from Dinmore Hill meander to the confluence with the River Wye. Formerly known as the Kingsfield or Third Terrace Deposits. It is correlated, altitudinally with Hampton Member of Wye (Wye Valley note 6) (Brandon 1989).

Table 7. *Correlations between the Lugg Valley, Wye Valley and the valleys west and south of the Malvern Hills and oxygen isotope stratigraphy*

δ¹⁸O	LUGG VALLEY	WYE VALLEY	VALLEYS WEST & SOUTH OF THE MALVERN HILLS
1	Elmore Member (16)	Elmore Member (13)	Elmore Member (18)
2	LUGG VALLEY FORMATION (10) Marden Member (14) / HEREFORDSHIRE FORMATION (15)	WYE VALLEY FORMATION (4) Bullingham Member (7) / HEREFORDSHIRE FORMATION (8) Bodenham (12) Stretton Sugwas (11) Burghill (10) & Hereford (9) Members	CRADLEY VALLEY FORMATION (9) Ham Green Member (12) / GLYNCH VALLEY FORMATION (13) Rudford Member (17) Staunton Member (16)
3			
4			
5			
5e			
6	Moreton on Lugg Member (13)	Hampton Member (6)	Colwell Member (11) / Redmarley Member (15)
7	Kingsfield Member (12)		
8			
9	Sutton Walls Member (11)	Holme Lacy Member (5)	Cradley Bed (10) / Heath Member (14)
10	STARPIT FORMATION (9)		
11		RISBURY FORMATION (1)	RISBURY FORMATION (5) Limbury Member (8) Coddington Member (7) White House Member (6)
12	RISBURY FORMATION (2) Portway(8) Franklands Gate (7) Stoke Prior (6) Stoke Lacy (5) Kyre Brook (4) & Newton Farm members (3)		MATHON VALLEY FORMATION (1) South End Member (4) Mathon Member (3) Brays Bed (2)
13–16	HUMBER FORMATION (1)		

(13) Moreton on Lugg Member. Type area: Moreton on Lugg [SO 505456]. A large terrace remnant (Brandon 1982, 1984). Sands and gravels occur as dissected remnants, up to 2 m thick, from Dinmore Hill meander to the confluence with the River Wye. It was formerly known as the Moreton on Lugg or Second Terrace Deposits. It is correlated, altitudinally, with the Bullingham Member of Wye (Wye Valley note 7) (Brandon 1984, 1989).

(AB)

(14) Marden Member. Type area: Marden [SO 514471]. A large terrace remnant (Brandon 1982, 1984). Sands and gravels occurring as dissected remnants, up to 2 m thick, from Dinmore Hill meander south to Moreton on Lugg. Formerly known as the Marden or Third Terrace Deposits (Brandon 1989). Inferred to be Late Devensian in age because of input of Welsh Silurian greywacke clasts into the Lugg-Teme drainage (Brandon 1989).

(AB)

(15) Herefordshire Formation. (Wye Valley, note 8).

(16) Elmore Member. Valley alluvium (Severn Valley, note 18).

Wye Valley

(1) **Risbury Formation:** (Lugg Valley note 2).
(2) **Newton Farm Member:** (Lugg Valley note 3).
(3) **Portway Member:** (Lugg Valley note 8).
(4) **Wye Valley Formation.** This includes coarse-grained fluvial terrace gravels of the Wye Valley downstream from the Late Devensian terminal moraine at Hereford to the River Lugg confluence. It is intermediate in age between the Risbury (1) and Herefordshire (8) formations. It contains an abundance of Welsh Lower Palaeozoic greywacke clasts and relatively few local Devonian clasts (Brandon & Hains 1981; Brandon 1989). A few terrace remnants occur south of the Lugg confluence as far as Bigsweir (Hey 1991). They are believed to have aggraded mainly under periglacial conditions, although distal outwash episodes from glaciers in central Wales have also been proposed (Hey 1991).

(AB)

(5) Holme Lacy Member. Type area: around Holme Lacy [SO 552356], where the largest, dissected terraced gravel remnants occur. It forms a well defined sheet of dissected fluvial sand and gravel. It was formerly named Third Higher River Terrace(Brandon & Hains 1981) and is correlated altitudinally with the Bushley Green Terrace (Bushley Green Member: Severn Valley note 6) of the Severn Valley (Hey 1991).

(AB)

(6) Hampton Member. Type area: between Hampton Park and Corporation Farm [SO 534401] to 537394] where the largest terraced gravel remnant occurs. Comprises fluvial sands and gravels up to 3 m thick. Formerly named the Second Higher River Terrace (Brandon & Hains 1981). It is correlated altitudinally with the Kidderminster Terrace (Kidderminster Station Member (Severn Valley note 9) of the Severn Valley (Hey 1991).

(AB)

(7) Bullingham Member. Type area: south side of the River Wye at Lower Bullingham [SO 501388 to 529374], Hereford. Comprises sands and gravels up to 5 m thick, with base 4.5-6 m above the River Wye floodplain. Formerly named the First Higher River Terrace (Brandon & Hains 1981). It is correlated altitudinally, with the Main Terrace (Holt Heath Member:

Severn Valley note 11) of the Severn Valley (Hey 1991).

(AB)

(8) Herefordshire Formation. Type area: Herefordshire west of the River Lugg. It comprises westerly derived, generally undissected, tills, ice contact deposits and fluvioglacial outwash containing abundant Welsh Lower Palaeozoic greywacke sandstones and local Devonian nodular calcrete and sandstone clasts. Locally it is up to 30 m thick in valleys. Ascribed to the Late Devensian (Brandon 1989). Formerly known as Herefordshire end-moraine (Charlesworth 1929; Luckman 1970) and Newer Drift Deposits (Brandon 1989).

(AB)

(9) Hereford Member. Type area: Herefordshire west of the River Lugg. It was formerly known as Newer Till (Brandon 1989). A widespread till blanket generally less than 4 m thick and forming smooth topography.

(AB)

(10) Burghill Member. Type area: Burghill [SO 4888] (Brandon & Hains 1981; Brandon 1989). Heterogeneous, coarse-grained, cobbly, bouldery gravels, tills and sands forming a narrow ridge, typically 200 m wide at the maximum extent of the Late Devensian glaciation. The deposits are up to 12 m thick and are probably contiguous with the Orleton Moraine of Dwerryhouse & Miller (1930) (Brandon 1989).

(AB)

(11) Stretton Sugwas Member. Type area: Stretton Sugwas pits [c. SO 455423]. It comprises slumped, contorted, mainly coarse-grained, ill-sorted gravels, with tills and glaciolacustrine clays, deposited at ice contact. It gives rise to a kame and kettle topography, especially along the Wye valley west of Stretton Sugwas. It was formerly known as kettle-kame moraine (Brandon & Hains 1981; Brandon 1989).

(AB)

(12) Bodenham Member. Type area: Lugg valley from Newton [SO 512540] to Lugg Bridge [SO 530417]. Comprises partly sub-alluvial, undeformed, sheet-like, coarse-grained valley sandur sands and gravels up to 14 m thick, beneath low terraces along the River Lugg. It also occurs in other valleys such as that of the proto-Wye at Hereford and that of the River Arrow. Formerly known as Newer Fluvioglacial Terrace Deposits (Brandon 1989).

(AB)

(13) Elmore Member. Valley alluvium (Severn Valley, note 18)

Valleys West and South of Malvern Hills

(1) Mathon Valley Formation. Type area : Mathon [SO 731443]. It includes all fluvial deposits of the pre-Risbury Formation Mathon Valley. It is well preserved, up to 9 m thick, in a palaeovalley in the Mathon to Clencher's Mill area with dissected remnants to north and south (Barclay *et al.* 1992).

(AB)

(2) Brays Bed. Stratotype: The Brays Pit, Mathon, Herefordshire [SO 729441] – the only known site (Gibbard *et al.* unpublished). Temperate silts about 1 m thick, filling bedrock palaeochannel below the Mathon Member. The fossil fauna and flora indicates deposition under post-temperate conditions of an interglacial event of Middle Pleistocene, pre-Anglian, age.

(AB)

(3) Mathon Member: Stratotype: The Brays Pit, Mathon, Herefordshire [SO 729441]. Sands and gravels typically 3–5 m thick. The lower unit is coarse-grained river sand and gravel.

The upper unit with lacustrine clay clasts and coal input probably includes distal outwash component (Brandon *et al.* unpublished). Formerly lower the part of the Mathon Sand and Gravel (Barclay *et al.* 1992). Its distribution is the same as the Mathon Valley Formation.

(AB)

(4) South End Member. Type locality: The Brays Pit, Mathon, Herefordshire [SO 729441]. Typically about 4 m of reddish brown, trough cross-bedded, braid-plain sands. Distributed from the South End to Clencher's Mill. It was formerly known as the upper part of the Mathon Sand and Gravel (Barclay *et al.* 1992).

(AB)

(5) Risbury Formation. (Lugg Valley note 2). It comprises the glacigenic deposits described by Barclay *et al.* (1992), infilling palaeochannel west of the Malvern Hills. It is up to 25 m thick in this area and known to be Anglian on the basis of the underlying Brays Bed (2) and overlying Cradley Bed (10)

(AB)

(6) White House Member. Stratotype: The Brays Pit, Mathon, Herefordshire [SO 729441]. It is correlated with the White House Silts (Hey 1959). It consists of reddish brown, laminated, glaciolacustrine clays and silts, up to 23 m thick, occurring in a palaeovalley from Mathon to Clencher's Mill (Barclay *et al.* 1992).

(AB)

(7) Coddington Member. Type area: around Coddington [SO 7343]. It comprises up to 10 m of reddish brown tills with northern provenance including a significant Triassic quartzite and quartz component. Malvernian clasts increase in abundance south of Clencher's Mill around Eastnor (Barclay *et al.* 1992). The more southerly occurrences were formerly called the Eastnor Clay (Hey 1959). Correlation with tills of the Lugg Valley was suggested by Richards (1994).

(AB & AR)

(8) Limbury Member. Type area: Limbury Hill [SO 777253]. Comprises a few metres of Triassic quartzite-rich sand and gravel which cap several hills in the lower Leadon valley area. The flint component increases southwards. It was named the Limbury gravels and probably has a glaciofluvial origin (Barclay *et al.* 1992).

(AB)

(9) Cradley Valley Formation. Type area: Cradley Brook valley from near South End [SO 7477] upstream to headwaters [SO 7339]. It includes post-Anglian heterogeneous deposits of the Cradley valley described by Barclay *et al.* (1992).

(AB)

(10) Cradley Bed. Stratotype: Augerhole at Colwall [SO 73814000], at the head of the Cradley Brook valley. It is the only known site and is correlated with the Cradley Silts. It is up to 1 m thick and contains temperate molluscs and pollen indicating an environment from sub-arctic scrub with *Hippophae* (late Anglian) to early temperate *Betula* woodland with *Quercus* and *Ulmus* (early Hoxnian) (Barclay *et al.* 1992).

(AB)

(11) Colwall Member Type Section: Colwall [SO 73814000]. In the upper reaches of the Cradley valley around Colwall [SO 7441], the deposit, 2 to 4 m of mainly yellow-brown diamict, forms an extensive, dissected, solifluction terrace. It overlies the Cradley Bed at the type section and is, therefore, post-Hoxnian. It is correlated with the Colwall Gelifluctate and is believed to be oxygen isotope stage 6 in age (Barclay *et al.* 1992).

(AB)

(12) Ham Green Member. Type area: Colwall to Ham Green [SO7442 to 7444]. It consists of undissected sheets of diamict flooring western tributary valleys to Cradley Brook and, therefore, is inferred to be Late Devensian in age. It is correlated with the Younger Gelifluctate of Barclay *et al.* (1992).

(AB)

(13) Glynch Valley Formation. It includes all the fluvial deposits in the valleys of the Leadon and its tributaries Glynch, Ell and Moor End brooks as described by Worssam *et al.* (1989). These sand and gravel terrace deposits were previously allocated numbers, unnamed, and correlated altitudinally with those of the Severn and Avon rivers.

(AB)

(14) Heath Member. Type area: Heath Bungalow area [SO 766305] of Glynch Brook valley, where the largest terrace remnant occurs. Sands and gravels equate with the Fifth Terrace Deposits and are correlated with the Bushley Green Terrace (Bushley Green Member: Severn Valley, note 6) (Worssam *et al.* 1989).

(AB)

(15) Redmarley Member. Type area: Redmarley d'Abitot [SO 763320] of the Glynch Brook valley, where one of the largest terrace remnants occurs. Sands and gravels equate with the Fourth Terrace Deposits and correlated with the Kidderminster Terrace of the Severn (Kidderminster Station Member: Severn Valley note 9) of the Severn Valley (Worssam *et al.* 1989).

(AB)

(16) Staunton Member. Type area: Staunton area [SO 780285] of the Glynch Brook valley where a large terrace remnant occurs. Sands and gravels are equated with the Third Terrace Deposits and correlated with the Main Terrace (Holt Heath Member: Severn Valley, note 11) of the Severn Valley (Worssam *et al.* 1989).

(AB)

(17) Rudford Member. Type area: Rudford [SO 778218] of the Leadon valley as a small terrace remnant. Sands and gravels equate with the Second Terrace Deposits and are correlated with the Worcester Terrace (Worcester Member: Severn Valley note 14) of the Severn Valley (Worssam *et al.* 1989).

(AB)

(18) Elmore Member. Valley alluvium (Severn Valley, note 18)

Cheshire, Shropshire and Staffordshire Lowlands

P. Worsley

(1) Seisdon Formation. A glacigenic sequence beneath the Trysull Bed, which, if the latter are *in situ*, are probably Anglian in age (Worsley 1991).

(2) Trysull Member. Silts below the Stockport Formation (Wolverhampton Till) and above the Seisdon Formation, at Lowe's Pit [SJ 847950] and Cooper's Pit [SJ 848946] (A. V. Morgan 1973). Pollen analysis (Morgan A. V. 1973) and D-aIle/L-Ile ratios indicate correlation with the Hoxnian (Bowen 1991).

(3) Oakwood Formation. Glacigenic sequence including the Oakwood till lying beneath the Chelford Formation at Oakwood Quarry, Chelford [SJ 824717] (Worsley *et al.* 1983). It is likely to be of the same age as the till beneath the Arclid Member at Arclid Quarry. It is possible that the Oakwood Formation is Anglian (Worsley 1991), but could be

Table 8. *Correlations between the Cheshire-Shropshire-Staffordshire Lowlands, the Birmingham Region and the Severn Valley and oxygen isotope stratigraphy*

δ¹⁸O	CHESHIRE STAFFORDSHIRE	SHROPSHIRE LOWLANDS	BIRMINGHAM REGION	SEVERN	VALLEY
1	Elmore / Fenns Whixall	Member (13) / Member (12)	Elmore Member (5)	Elmore	Member (18)
2	STOCKPORT FORMATION (10)	SHREWSBURY FORMATION (11)	STOCKPORT FORMATION (4)	SEVERN VALLEY FORMATION (6) — Power House Member (17), Worcester Member (16), Holt Heath Member (15)	STOCKPORT FORMATION (14)
3	CHELFORD FORMATION (5), Burland Member (8),	FOUR ASHES FORMATION (9)		Upton Warren Bed (13)	
4	Farm Wood Member (7),				
5	Arclid Member (6)		RIDGACRE FORMATION (3)	Stourbridge Bed (12)	RIDGACRE FORMATION (10)
5e					
6	OAKWOOD FORMATION (3), Lapwing Bed (4)			Kidderminster Station Member (11)	
7					
8				Bushley Green Member (9)	
9	Trysull Member (2)		QUINTON FORMATION (2)	Hill House Bed (8)	Tryssul Member (5)
10				Spring Hill Member (7)	
11					
12	SEISDON FORMATION (1)		NURSERIES FORMATION (1)	WOLSTON FORMATION (1), Woolridge Member (3), Thrussington Member (2)	SEISDON FORMATION (4)
13-16					

the same age as the Ridgacre Formation of the Birmingham area that is correlated with oxygen isotope stage 6 (Birmingham, note 3) (Maddy *et al.* 1995).

(4) Lapwing Bed. A thin biogenic rich fluvio-lacustrine sequence beneath the Oakwood Formation at Oakwood quarry resting on the Triassic (Worsley *et al.* 1983).

(5) Chelford Formation. Stratotype: Farm Wood Quarry [SJ 810730]. It consists of up to 20 m of white and buff coloured sands. Where entirely buff in colour the term Congleton Sand has been applied by Evans *et al.* (1968). Interpreted as a fluvio-aeolian succession of alluvial fans with a dominantly east-west flow direction (Boulton & Worsley 1965; Worsley 1966). TL dating (Rendell *et al.* 1991) has suggested an age of about 100 ka for the sand adjacent to the Farm Wood Member (U-series: 86 + 26/-21 ka). The lower part of the Chelford Formation probably pre-dates the Ipswichian (oxygen isotope sub-stage 5e). It was previously ascribed to the glacigenic Middle Sands (Simpson & West 1958).

(6) Arclid Member. A complex organic-rich sand sequence proved in a borehole at [SJ 775620]. Originally it was assumed to be part of the Farm Wood Member peat (Worsley 1991). But pollen analysis on organic detritus associated with a molar of *Mammuthus* has suggested an Ipswichian age (Worsley 1992).

(7) Farm Wood Member. Stratotype: Farm Wood Quarry [SJ 810730]. The stratigraphy and palaeobotany of this peat unit, that includes tree stumps of *Pinus sylvestris* in growth position, was described by Simpson & West (1958) who regarded it as part of the now redundant Middle Sands (Worsley 1966, 1967). It was interpreted by Simpson & West (1958) as an early Devensian interstadial. The Farm Wood Member was later used by Worsley (1966) to divide the Chelford (Sands) Formation. The history of radiocarbon dating has been assessed by Worsley (1980) who concluded that the ^{14}C ages indicate minimum dates. This is confirmed by the U-series age of 86, + 26/-21 ka (Heijnis & van der Plicht 1992).

(8) Burland Member. Organic silts and clays with a thin peat in borehole beneath 28 m of Stockport Formation [SJ 602533]. The fossil biota suggests that it is part of the Farm Wood Member (Bonny *et al.* 1986).

(9) Four Ashes Formation. Stratotype: Four Ashes [SJ 916082]. It consists of thin fluvial gravels of local Permo-Triassic rock provenance and is overlain by the Stockport Formation (Worsley 1991). It contains about 50 organic rich lenses (A. Morgan 1973; A.V. Morgan 1973). Palaeoecological data and radiocarbon ages from these suggest that it is partly Ipswichian in age (oxygen isotope sub-stage 5e) and partly Early and Middle Devensian (oxygen isotope sub-stages 5d to oxygen isotope stage 3). It is part of the Devensian stratotype (Mitchell *et al.* 1973).

(10) Stockport Formation. Stratotype: on the northern bank of the River Mersey at [SJ 908915] where the sequence overlies bedrock. It consists of glacigenic sediments that contain Borrowdale volcanic rocks, Eskdale granite and flints. It forms a blanket of material deposited by the Late Devensian glaciers moving south from northwestern England and from the Irish Sea Basin. Trace comminuted marine molluscan faunas and complete shells are, in places common, in its fluvial lithofacies and entire shells may be present (Thompson & Worsley 1967). It replaces the description used to describe the classical tripartite succession of the Geological Survey (Hull 1864) that consisted of Lower Boulder Clay, Middle Sands, and Upper Boulder Clay (Worsley 1966, 1967).

(11) Shrewsbury Formation. Stratotype: abandoned quarry at Mousecroft Lane [SJ 476109]. It comprises the glacigenic sediments composed of Welsh erratics deposited by ice moving eastwards from a source in the Welsh uplands (Worsley 1991). It overlies the Stockport Formation unconformably in the Shrewsbury area; but at some locations, farther north, it may be coeval with it (Worsley 1970).

(12) Fenns Whixall Member (Tregaron Formation, Mid-Wales, note 17). Peats, organic muds and silts (Turner 1964).

(13) Elmore Member. Valley alluvium (Severn Valley, note 18)

The Birmingham Region

(1) Nurseries Formation. Stratotype: Quinton [SO 992847], near Birmingham (Horton 1974). It consists of purplish brown stony clay with abundant erratics of local origin, particularly those derived from Coal Measures.

(DM)

(2) Quinton Formation. Stratotype: Quinton (note 1). Sands, silts and clays containing plant material. Correlated with the Hoxnian by palynology (Kelly 1964; Horton 1989; Turner & Horton unpublished), thus may belong to either oxygen isotope stage 11 or 9.

(DM & MGS)

(3) Ridgacre Formation. Stratotype: Quinton (note 1). It comprises glacigenic sands and till which demonstrably pre-date the Devensian, and overlie the temperate Quinton Bed (2). Although it has been correlated with the Wolston Formation by Shotton (1989) and was correlated with oxygen isotope stage 10 by Sumbler (1995), it is probably oxygen isotope stage 6 in age on the basis of ^{36}Cl ages on glacial boulders on its surface (169±13.1 ka and 150.2±9.2 ka) (Maddy *et al.* 1995).

(DM & MGS)

(4) Stockport Formation. (Cheshire–Shropshire–Staffordshire Lowland, note 10).

(5) Elmore Member. Valley alluvium (Severn Valley, note 18)

Severn Valley

(1) Wolston Formation (Avon Valley, note 6).

(2) Thrussington Member. (Leicestershire note 6). Till beneath the Woolridge Member at Woolridge and present at several other localities in the region. It corresponds with the Eastnor Boulder Clay of Hey (1959, 1963) and Coddington Till of Barclay *et al.* (1992).

(MGS)

(3) Woolridge Member. Stratotype: Woolridge [SO 806 237] (Maddy *et al.* 1995). At its type locality it is generally less than 2 m in thickness and consists of sandy clayey coarse gravels directly on top of till correlated with the Thrussington Member (2) and is an outwash deposit derived from it. It lies beneath the Woolridge Terrace of Wills (1938) which is found on isolated hills above 80 m O.D. south of Tewkesbury.

(DM & MGS)

(4) Seisdon Formation (Cheshire–Shropshire–Staffordshire Lowlands, note 1)

(5) Tryssul Member (Cheshire–Shropshire–Staffordshire Lowlands, note 2)

(6) Severn Valley Formation. It consists of fluviatile sand and gravel members deposited by a river draining the present lower Severn valley (Wills 1938; Maddy *et al.* 1995).

(DM)

(7) Spring Hill Member. Stratotype: Spring Hill [SO 808232]

Table 9. *Correlations between the Severn Valley, Warwickshire Avon Valley and Leicestershire and oxygen isotope stratigraphy*

δ¹⁸O	SEVERN VALLEY	AVON VALLEY	LEICESTERSHIRE
1	SEVERN VALLEY FORMATION (6) — Elmore Member (18)	AVON VALLEY FORMATION (16) — Elmore Member (30)	SOAR VALLEY FORMATION (11) — Soar Member (16)
2	STOCKPORT FORMATION (14); Power House Member (17), Worcester Member (16), Holt Heath Member (15), Upton Warren Bed (13)	Bretford Member (29), Wasperton Member (28)	Syston Member (15)
3			
4			
5			
5e	Stourbridge Bed (12)	Fladbury Bed (27), Eckington Bed (26), New Inn Member (25)	Wanlip Member (14)
6	RIDGACRE FORMATION (10); Kidderminster Station Member (11)	Cropthorne Member (24)	Birstall Member (13)
7	Bushley Green Member (9)	Ailstone Bed (23), Strensham Member (22)	
8	Hill House Bed (8)	Strensham Court Bed (21), Pershore Member (20)	
9	Tryssul Member (5)	Allesborough Bed (19), Frog Member (18)	Knighton Member (12)
10	Spring Hill Member (7)	Frog Hall Member (17)	
11	SEISDON FORMATION (4)		
12	WOLSTON FORMATION (1); Woolridge Member (3), Thrussington Member (2)	WOLSTON FORMATION (6); Dunsmore Member (15), Shawell Member (14), Hillmorton Member (13), Oadby Member (12), Knightlow Member (11), Grounds Farm Member (10), Bosworth Member (9), Thrussington Member (8), Snitterfield Member (7)	WOLSTON FORMATION (5); Eagle Moor Member (10), Oadby Member (9), Wigston Member (8), Bosworth Member (7), Thrussington Member (6)
13 to 16		BAGINTON FORMATION (1); Brandon Member (5), Lillington Member (4), Waverley Wood Member (3), Thurmaston Member (2)	BAGINTON FORMATION (1); Brandon Member (4), Lillington Member (3), Thurmaston Member (2)

(Maddy *et al.* 1995). Comprises fluviatile sand and gravels up to 7.2 m in thickness. It corresponds, at least in part, with the Sixth Terrace deposits of British Geological Survey (Barclay *et al.* unpublished).

(DM & MGS)

(8) Hill House Bed. Stratotype: (see 9). It was formerly called the Bushley Green Bed by Maddy *et al.* (1995). It comprises up to 1.5 m of compact sands and coarse gravelly sands (Bridgland *et al.* 1986). These contain a molluscan fauna of cool temperate aspect. D-aIle/L-Ile ratios of 0.24 ± 0.01 (2) from *Trichia hispida* correlate the Bed with oxygen isotope stage 9 and with the Hoxnian (Bowen *et al.* 1989).

(9) Bushley Green Member. Stratotype: Bushley Green [SO 862351] (Maddy *et al.* 1995). It comprises up to 6.9 m of fluviatile sands and gravels. It can be traced from Lower Broadheath to Apperley. Its upper surface is *c.* 45 m above the present river. It lies beneath the Bushley Green Terrace of Wills (1938) or the Fifth Terrace of British Geological Survey (Worssam *et al.* 1989; Barclay *et al.* in press).

(DM & MGS)

(10) Ridgacre Formation. (Birmingham, note 3). Isolated deposits which are correlated with the Ridgacre Formation are found at Gibbet Hill and Madeley Heath where outwash sands and gravels exceed 50 m in thickness. The Stourport diamict, that lies below the Holt Heath Member (below) at Stourport [SO 795743] (Dawson 1988; Maddy *et al.* 1995), may also be part of this formation.

(DM)

(11) Kidderminster Station Member. Stratotype: Yates's Pit near Kidderminster railway station [SO 839763] (Maddy *et al.* 1995). It comprises up to 7.9 m of sands and gravels that are traced from Kidderminster, in the Stour valley, to Lassington. It underlies the Kidderminster Terrace of Wills (1938), the Fourth Terrace of British Geological Survey (e.g. Worssam *et al.* 1989). It is the oldest lithostratigraphical unit of the Severn Valley Formation to contain significant quantities of Permian Clent Breccia.

(DM & MGS)

(12) Stourbridge Bed. Stratotype: recorded at the base of the Holt Heath Member at Stourbridge [SO 895855] (Boulton 1917). It contained *Hippopotamus*, which is generally regarded as indicating an Ipswichian age (oxygen isotope sub-stage 5e).

(DM)

(13) Upton Warren Bed. Stratotype: Upton Warren [SO 935673] (Coope *et al.* 1961). Radiocarbon ages of $41\,500 \pm 1\,200$ and $41\,900 \pm 800$ suggest correlation with oxygen isotope stage 3. But because D-aIle/L-Ile ratios on *Lymnaea* of 0.066 ± 0.007 (5) were close to those of the Ipswichian stratotype ($0.09 \pm$), it was argued that the unit was older and it was correlated with oxygen isotope sub-stage 5a (Bowen *et al.* 1989). On this interpretation the radiocarbon ages were regarded as minimum ages. Subsequently its (D-aIle/L-Ile) age was revised to about 57 ka (Bowen in press).

(DM)

(14) Stockport Formation (Cheshire–Shropshire–Staffordshire Lowlands, note, 10).

(15) Holt Heath Member. Stratotype: close to Holt Heath [SO 827627] (Dawson & Bryant 1987; Maddy *et al.* 1995). It consists of up to 10 m of sands and gravels that can be traced from Bridgnorth, where it lies approximately 30 m above the present river, to Gloucester, where it passes beneath the modern floodplain. It contains a significant proportion of 'Irish Sea' derived erratics probably introduced by the ice which deposited the Stockport Formation (14). It underlies the

Main Terrace of Wills (1938) or the Third Terrace of British Geological Survey (Worssam *et al.* 1989; Barclay *et al.* in press).

(DM & MGS)

(16) Worcester Member. Stratotype: Grimley [SO 835608] (Dawson 1989). It consists of commonly coarse-grained gravel and sand. Its upper surface lies *c.* 8 m below the Holt Heath Member and is traced from Bewdley to Tewkesbury. It underlies the Worcester Terrace of Wills (1938) or Second Terrace of British Geological Survey maps (Worssam *et al.* 1989; Barclay *et al.* in press).

(DM & MGS)

(17) Power House Member. Stratotype: Wilden [SO 824730] (Shotton & Coope 1983). Up to 12 m of sands and gravels that underlie most of the lower Severn valley (Williams 1968*a*). It outcrops from Bridgnorth to Stourport. Below Worcester it underlies the modern alluvium. The culmination of its deposition was dated at $12\,570 \pm 220$ (Shotton & Coope 1983). It underlies the Power House Terrace of Wills (1938) or the First Terrace of British Geological Survey (Barclay *et al.* in press).

(DM & MGS)

(18) Elmore Member. Valley alluvium throughout the region (Hewlett & Birnie in press).

Avon Valley

(1) Baginton Formation. Stratotype: Baginton [SP 348750], where it ranges in thickness from 5–8 m. It is found between Snitterfield, near Stratford-upon-Avon, to Thurmaston, near Leicester. It consists of the fluviatile Baginton-Lillington Gravel and the Baginton Sand first described by Shotton (1953). Shotton (1953) also described supposed glacial deposits ('Bubbenhall Clay') at the base of the Baginton Formation near Bubbenhall [SP 358708] and at Whitley, Coventry [SP 353770]. But subsequent work (e.g. Sumbler 1983*a*; Old *et al.* 1987) in the Rugby–Coventry–Leamington region has failed to recognize this, nor any evidence for glacial deposits older than the Wolston Formation.

(DM & MGS)

(2) Thurmaston Member. (Leicestershire note 2). Formerly the Baginton Gravel and it replaces the Baginton Gravel Member of Maddy & Lewis (1991)

(3) Waverley Wood Member. Stratotype: Waverley Wood Pit [SP 365715] (Shotton *et al.* 1993). Up to 3 m of fine-grained Bed in a number of channels. They underlie the Thurmaston Member, but at Brandon [SP 384 763] they are intercalated within it (Maddy *et al.* 1994). Its flora and fauna indicate deposition under temperate conditions. D-aIle/L-Ile ratios of 0.381 ± 0.027 (12) from *Bithynia troscheli*, and 0.381 ± 0.025 (3)] from *Trichia hispida* are pre-Cromerian (West Runton) and have been correlated with oxygen isotope stage 15 (Bowen *et al.* 1989).

(DM,MGS & DHK)

(4) Lillington Member. Stratotype: Lillington [SP 328675] (Shotton 1953). It is correlated with the Baginton Gravel (Jurassic facies) of Shotton (1953).

(DM)

(5) Brandon Member. Stratotype: the former site of Pools Farm Pit, Brandon [SP 384763] (Maddy *et al.* 1994). It is correlated with the Baginton Sand of Shotton (1953) and the name replaces the Baginton Sand Member of Maddy & Lewis (1991).

(DM)

(6) Wolston Formation. Stratotype: Wolston [SP 410746]. This comprises the glacigenic sediments of the Wolston Series of Shotton (1953). In its type area it overlies the Baginton Formation and is overlain by the terrace deposits of the River Avon. It was designated as the stratotype of the post-Hoxnian and pre-Ipswichian, Wolstonian Stage by Mitchell *et al.* (1973), even though it was stratigraphically unrelated to deposits of either Hoxnian or Ipswichian age (Bowen 1978). Later, it was correlated with the older (Anglian) Lowestoft Formation of East Anglia (Perrin *et al.* 1979; Sumbler 1983*a*, *b*; Rose 1987). On that basis it is correlated with oxygen isotope stage 12, although recently it has been argued that, in part at least, it may correlate with oxygen isotope stage 10 (Sumbler 1995).

(MGS)

(7) Snitterfield Member. Stratotype: Snitterfield [SP 234596] (Maddy & Lewis 1991). It comprises a lacustrine sand and replaces the Snitterfield Sand Member of Maddy and Lewis (1991).

(DM)

(8) Thrussington Member. (Leicestershire note 6).

(9) Bosworth Member (Leicestershire note 7).

(10) Grounds Farm Member. Stratotype: Wolston [SP 410746] (Shotton 1953; Sumbler 1983*a*; Old *et al.* 1987). It comprises bedded, in some cases laminated, lacustrine clay and silt which, in the type area, overlies the Thrussington Member (8), and is overlain by the Dunsmore Member (15). It corresponds to the Wolston Clay of Shotton (1953). Generally, it is 10 to 20 m thick, but it probably exceeds 30 m in the Brinklow area [SP 4379]. Locally it contains local lenses of sand, including the widespread Knightlow Member (11), that separates it into lower and upper sub-units. In its upper part particularly, it contains sporadic dropstones, mainly of chalk and flints, and bodies of till. It is well developed in the Rugby, Coventry, and Leamington area, with outliers occurring farther south: for example at Snitterfield, Stretton on Fosse [SP 22 38]. North of Stretton under Fosse [SP 45 81], the lower sub-unit passes laterally into the lithologically similar Bosworth Member (Leicestershire, note 7) and the upper sub-unit is replaced by the Oadby Member (Leicestershire, note 9).

(DM)

(11) Knightlow Member. Stratotype: Wolston Pit (3) at the foot of Knightlow Hill. It is developed principally in the Rugby–Leamington area. It corresponds with the Wolston Sand/Sand and Gravel of previous accounts (Shotton 1953; Sumbler 1983*a*; Old *et al.* 1987) and is a lenticular unit of glaciofluvial sand, 1–3 m in thickness, within the Grounds Farm. At the stratotype, it probably correlated with the Wigston Member (Leicestershire note 8), although elsewhere it is likely that similar sand bodies occur at other horizons within the Wolston Formation: for example, in the Stretton under Fosse [SP 45 81] area (Sumbler 1983*a*; Bridge *et al.* in press).

(MGS)

(12) Oadby Member (Leicestershire note 9)

(13) Hillmorton Member. Stratotype: Hillmorton Pit [SP 542737]. It comprises the Hillmorton Sand of Sumbler (1983*a*) and Old *et al.* (1987). It consists of glaciofluvial sand with some gravel lenses, which infills a bedrock channel (probable modified pre-glacial valley) east of Rugby. It is probably up to 50 m thick. It passes westward and northward into the lacustrine Grounds Farm Member (10). At the stratotype it is overlain by Dunsmore Member (15), but southeastwards passes below the major till unit of the Oadby Member (12) near Kilsby [SP 56 71]. It is probably outwash associated with the advance of the ice that deposited the Oadby Member.

(MGS)

(14) Shawell Member. Stratotype: Gibbet Lane Quarry, Shawell [SP 540806]. This is the Shawell Gravel of Sumbler (1983*a*) and Bridge *et al.* (in press). It is a unit of clast-supported flint and limestone-rich gravels and cross-bedded sands, intercalated within the Oadby Member in an area between Rugby and Lutterworth. It is up to about 11 m thick, and it is proximal outwash derived from the ice that deposited the Oadby Member. It is probably slightly younger than the Wigston Member (Leicestershire note 8) and the main bed of the Knightlow Member (11).

(MGS)

(15) Dunsmore Member. Stratotype: Linghall Quarry [SP 449729], Lawford Heath, Rugby. It corresponds with the Dunsmore Gravel of Shotton (1953) and consists of flint-rich, poorly sorted glaciofluvial outwash sand and gravel that caps the glacial succession of the Wolston Formation in the area between Hinckley in the north (overlying Oadby Member) and Leamington Spa in the south (overlying the Grounds Farm Member). Typically, it forms plateaux as at Dunsmore in the Rugby area. Although generally 2 to 4 m thick, its thickness is highly variable because of erosion as indicated by its channelled base. Isopachytes on the Dunsmore Member in the Hinckley–Leamington region show that it is related to the Avon drainage system and it may be regarded as the oldest member of the Avon Valley Formation; thus, by definition, it is restricted to the Avon catchment. Downstream it probably grades into the older part of the Avon fifth terrace (Sumbler 1983*a*, 1989), which may be correlated with the Spring Hill Member of the Severn Valley Formation (Severn Valley note 7).

(MGS)

(16) Avon Valley Formation. It consists of fluviatile sand and gravels of the contemporary valley that post-dates deposition of the Wolston Formation. It is incised into both the Baginton and Wolston Formations.

(DM)

(17) Frog Hall Member. Stratotype: Frog Hall Pit [SP 416736]. It comprises the Frog Hall Sand and Gravel of Sumbler (1989), described as alluvial fan deposits by Old *et al.* (1987), and mistakenly included in the Dunsmore Member by Shotton (1953). It consists of up to 12 m of fluviatile silts, sands and gravels that infill a channel incised into the Dunsmore Member, to which it is lithologically similar.

(DM)

(18) Frog Member. Stratotype: Frog Hall Pit [SP 416736]. It consists of up to 7.2 m of organic silts filling a channel about 300 m wide which is incised up to 25 m below the base of the Dunsmore Member. Pollen, plant macrofossil, coleopteran, molluscan and ostracod data indicate deposition in the first part of a temperate stage. D-alle/L-Ile ratios of 0.24 ± 0.023 (16) on *Bithynia tentaculata*, 0.23 ± 0.011 (7) on *Valvata piscinalis* and 0.24 ± 0.008 (5) indicate correlation with the Hoxnian and oxygen isotope stage 9 (Keen *et al.* 1997).

(MGS & DHK)

(19) Allesborough Bed. Stratotype: Allesborough Hill, Pershore [SO 938464]. It comprises 0.5 m of fossiliferous sands at the base of the Pershore Member (Whitehead 1989). It was formerly the Pershore Fossil Bed of Maddy *et al.* (1991).

(DM)

(20) Pershore Member. Stratotype: Allesborough Hill, Pershore [SO 938464], where it is *c.* 7.2 m thick (Whitehead 1989).

It consists of fluvial sands and gravels that underlies the 5th Terrace of the Avon (Tomlinson 1925; Worssam *et al.* 1989). It is correlated with the Bushley Green Member of the Severn Valley Formation (Maddy *et al.* 1991).

(DM)

(21) Strensham Court Bed. Stratotype: (21). The Bed comprise fossiliferous blue-grey clays with some gravel stringers. Plant and animal remains suggest deposition under temperate climatic conditions. D-aIle/L-Ile ratios of 0.166 ± 0.01 (14), 0.165 ± 0.009 (7) and 0.176 ± 0.016 (8) on *Bithynia tentaculata* indicate correlation with oxygen isotope stage 7 (Bowen *et al.* 1989; de Rouffignac *et al.* 1995). It replaces the Strensham Bed of de Rouffignac *et al.* (1995).

(DM)

(22) Strensham Member. Stratotype: Upper Strensham [SO 904397] Up to 3.9 m of gravels and pebbly sands that underlies a terrace at 43 m O.D. It is 7 m lower than the Pershore Member (19) and 7 m higher than the Cropthorne Member (23) (de Rouffignac *et al.* 1995). It was formerly included in the Pershore Member (Barclay *et al.* in press).

(DM/MGS)

(23) Ailstone Bed Stratotype: Ailstone [SP 211512], where it consists of a basal lag gravel overlain by fossiliferous sands and some compact clayey sandy lenses 0.7 m thick. Its fauna includes *Corbicula fluminalis* and suggests deposition in a temperate climate (Maddy *et al.* 1991). D-aIle/L-Ile ratios of 0.167 ± 0.004 (3) on *Valvata piscinalis* indicate correlation with oxygen isotope stage 7 (Bowen *et al.* 1989)

(DM & DHK)

(24) Cropthorne Member. Borehole at Cropthorne [SP 002450] (Maddy *et al.* 1991) where it is c.5 m thick (Maddy 1989). It comprises fluvially deposited sands and gravels and underlies the Fourth Terrace of the Avon (Tomlinson 1925; Maddy *et al.* 1991). This name replaces the Ailstone Member of Maddy *et al.* (1991).

(DM)

(25) New Inn Member Stratotype: New Inn, Cropthorne [SO 997443] where c.2.5 m of fluvially deposited sands and gravels underlie the Third Terrace of the Avon (Tomlinson 1925; Maddy *et al.* 1991).

(DM)

(26) Eckington Bed. Stratotype: Eckington Railway Cutting [SO 919417] (Keen & Bridgland 1986). It comprises *c.* 1m of sandy gravel resting on Lower Lias Clay at 23.3 m O.D. Keen & Bridgland (1986) report a temperate molluscan fauna with *Hippopotamus*. A similar record of *Hippopotamus* is reported from beneath the New Inn Member at the New Inn (Strickland 1836). D-aIle/L-Ile ratios from Old Fallow, close to the New Inn locality, of 0.116 ± 0.000 (2) on *Pisidium* indicates correlation with oxygen isotope sub-stage 5e (Bowen *et al.* 1989). This name replaces the New Inn Fossil Bed of Maddy *et al.* (1991).

(DM & DHK)

(27) Fladbury Bed. Stratotype: Lower Moor, Fladbury [SO 995462] (Coope 1962). Peat from beneath the Wasperton Member contained a Coleopteran fauna similar to that at Upton Warren and was ^{14}C dated to $38\,000 \pm 700$ years. Broadly correlative deposits have been described from Brandon (SP 390754) (Coope 1968; Kelly 1968; Shotton 1968). The ^{14}C age, however, may be a considerable underestimate of its true age.

(DM & MGS)

(28) Wasperton Member. Stratotype: Wasperton [SP 266588], where it is 3 m thick (Dawson 1987). It comprises fluvially

deposited cold climate sands and gravels that underly the Second Terrace of the Avon (Tomlinson 1925; Old *et al.* 1987).

(DM & MGS)

(29) Bretford Member. Stratotype: Bretford [SP 430771]. It consists of 3–4 m of fluvial sands and gravels beneath the First Terrace of the River Avon. It is best developed in the Upper Avon, above Stratford. Downstream. it is correlated with the Power House Member of the Severn Valley Formation.

(MGS)

(30) Elmore Member. (Severn Valley, note 18)

Leicestershire

(1) Baginton Formation (Avon Valley. note 1).

(2) Thurmaston Member. Stratotype: Thurmaston [SK 615101] (Rice 1968), where it is *c.* 6 m in thickness. It equates with the Baginton Gravel (Triassic facies) of Shotton (1953).

(DM)

(3) Lillington Member (Avon Valley, note 4).

(4) Brandon Member Avon Valley, note 5).

(5) Wolston Formation (Avon Valley, note 6).

(6) Thrussington Member. Stratotype: Thrussington [SK 646162] (Rice 1968). It comprises a largely Trias-derived till with local addition of bluish grey Bed rich in Liassic debris (Rice 1968, 1981) and is generally 3–5 m in thick in the Avon Valley (Old *et al.* 1987). It extends at least to Snitterfield where it overlies the Snitterfield Member (Avon Valley 7). A similar Triassic-derived till in the Lower Severn Valley is correlated with this member (Severn Valley 2) and indicates that it was formerly more extensive (Maddy *et al.* 1995).

(DM)

(7) Bosworth Member. Stratotype: Cadeby Pit [SK 435028]. It comprises lacustrine, commonly laminated clays and silts lying stratigraphically between the Thrussington Member and the Wigston Member. Former names are: the Bosworth Clays and Silts (Shotton 1976; Douglas 1980; Rice 1981; Worssam & Old 1988) the Glen Parva/Rotherby Clays (Rice 1968) and the Wolston Clay (Bridge *et al.* in press). It occurs between Market Bosworth and Leicester, and extends to Stretton Under Fosse in the south, where it passes into the lower sub-unit of the Grounds Farm Member. It reaches over 25 m in thickness in the Wolvey area [SP 4387].

(MGS & TDD)

(8) Wigston Member. Type area: Wigston (southeast Leicester). Stratotype: Cadeby Pit (see 7). Former names are the Wigston Sand and Gravel (Rice 1968), the Cadeby Sand and Gravel (Douglas 1980) and the Wolston Sand and Gravel (Rice 1981; Bridge *et al.* in press). It comprises glaciofluvial sands and gravels; clasts are generally dominated by 'Bunter' pebbles and coal, that suggest derivation from the 'western' ice that deposited the Thrussington Member. It is well developed between Market Bosworth, Leicester and Monks Kirby [SP 46 83]. Farther south it is probably represented by the Knightlow Member (Avon Valley note 11). It is probably over 25 m thick in the area between Leicester and Coventry.

(MGS)

(9) Oadby Member. Stratotype: Oadby [SP 631999] (Rice 1968). This is a till with high Cretaceous chalk, flint and Jurassic limestone content, normally with a Lias clay matrix, but locally the matrix may have high proportions of Mercia Mudstone. It is found over a wide area of the East Midlands from the Wreake Valley to west of Stratford upon Avon and south to Moreton-in-Marsh where an extensive outlier forms most of the Moreton Drift (Tomlinson 1929). As the

Wolvercote Member of the Upper Thames Valley Formation is believed to be associated with the Oadby Member ice-sheet (e.g. Bishop 1958, but disputed by Maddy *et al.* 1991), it has been suggested that the Moreton Drift, and thus part of the Wolston Formation, is oxygen isotope stage 10 in age and not oxygen isotope stage 12 (Sumbler 1995). To the north, however, the Oadby Member is correlated with the Lowestoft Formation that is Anglian (Perrin *et al.* 1979).

(DM & MGS)

(10) Eagle Moor Member. (Trent & Lower Dove Valley note 5). It comprises flint-rich outwash gravels, and includes the 'flinty gravel' of the Coalville district (Worssam & Old 1988), and part of the Anker Sand and Gravel of the Nuneaton area (Bridge *et al.* in press).

(MGS)

(11) Soar Valley Formation. Fluviatile sands and gravels underlying terraces at different heights in the Middle Soar valley.

(DM)

(12) Knighton Member. Type area: the Leicester suburb of Knighton [SK 6001]. A plateau surface between 83 m and 92 m is underlain by up to 1 m of waterlain sand and gravel (Rice 1968).

(DM)

(13) Birstall Member. Type area: around Birstall [SK 5909] where extensive gravels occur (up 2.5 m thick), appoximately 9 m to 12 m above the present alluvium. It is well represented in the Wreake Valley (Rice 1968) as the Older river gravel.

(DM)

(14) Wanlip Member. Stratotype: Wanlip [SK 6010]. Gravel deposits, generally 1.5 to 3 m thick lying 3 m above the present alluvium (Rice 1968).

(15) Syston Member. Stratotype: Syston [SK 6211]. Sand and gravel aggradation with terrace surfaces named the Syston and Quorndon Terraces (Rice 1968).

(DM)

(16) Soar Member. Holocene valley alluvium of the Soar Valley.

Lower Soar Valley

Loughbrough to the Trent

(1) Wolston Formation (Avon Valley, note 6).

(2) Hathern Member. Type locality: Hathern [SK 503214] (Brandon 1995) – the only known locality. Up to 3 m of mainly coarse gravel with base at 53 m O.D. lying between bedrock and the Thrussington Member. It contains abundant Carboniferous Limestone chert and limestone clasts, the latter particularly as angular cobbles. It was probably deposited as outwash along the proto-Derwent Valley.

AB

(3) Thrussington Member. (Leicestershire, note 6). It contains more Carboniferous material than in its type area (Brandon 1994).

AB

(4) Oadby Member (Leicestershire, note 9).

(5) Soar Valley Formation (Leicestershire, note 11).

(6) Knighton Member. (Leicestershire, note 12). This is correlated with the deposits of the Knighton Terrace of Rice (1968). It is not present in the lower Soar valley.

(AB)

(7) Birstall Member. (Leicestershire, note 13). It correlates with deposits beneath the Birstall Terrace of Rice (1968). It is

also correlated altitudinally with the Balderton Member of the Trent Valley (Brandon 1995).

(AB)

(8) Wanlip Member (Leicestershire note, 14). Gravels correlated with deposits beneath the Wanlip Terrace of Rice (1968). Bedrock step of about 2.5–3.5 m above floodplain alluvium in Loughborough area. It is inferred to be Late Devensian. A record of *Palaeoloxodon antiquus* from probably below the Wanlip Terrace at Barrow upon Soar [SK 560170] (Plant 1859) may indicate an Ipswichian age (oxygen isotope sub-stage 5e). It is correlated altitudinally with the Allenton Member of the lower Derwent (Brandon 1995).

(AB)

(9) Syston Member (Leicestershire, note 15). Equates with gravels beneath the Syston Terrace of Rice (1968). Its flora and fauna indicate a Late Devensian age at Syston (Bell *et al.* 1972). It occurs below the alluvium and it forms terraces bordering Soar floodplain. It is correlated with Holme Pierrepont Member of the Trent (Brandon 1995).

(AB)

(10) Soar Member. Holocene valley alluvium throughout the Soar Valley and its tributaries.

Lower Derwent Valley

Derby to the Trent

(1) Wolston Formation (Avon Valley, note 6).

(2) Thrussington Member (Leicestershire, note 6). It contains more Carboniferous material than in its type area (Brandon 1995).

(AB)

(3) Oadby Member (Leicestershire, note 9).

(4) Eagle Moor Member (Proto-Trent, note 3). This occurs at Roy Hill [SK 462345] as a sand and gravel terrace outlier, *c*.2 m thick at 57 m O.D. (Brandon 1996).

(AB)

(5) Derwent Valley Formation. Formulated to include all post-Anglian fluvial sand and gravel deposits of the Derwent Valley. *Hippopotamus* occurs in the Crown Inn Bed (Brandon 1996).

(AB)

(6) Ockbrook Member. Type area: Ockbrook [SK 423348], where it comprises a remnant of a sand and gravel terrace (Brandon 1996).

(AB)

(7) Borrowash Member. Type area: Borrowash [SK 417345]. Up to 5 m of sand and gravel along north side of Derwent valley below Derby. It is correlated with the Balderton Member (Brandon 1996).

(AB)

(8) Crown Inn Member. Stratotype: well at yard of Crown Inn, Allenton [SK 379326]. Consists of about 3 m of clays, silts and gravels (Bemrose & Deeley 1886) with *Hippopotamus* fossils (Brandon 1996). It fills a palaeochannel below the Allenton Terrace (Brandon 1996). Gravels at nearby Boulton Moor are probably from the same palaeochannel (Jones & Stanley 1974).

(AB)

(9) Allenton Member. Type area: Allenton [SK 3732] to Elvaston [SK 4132] southeast of Derby. It is composed of post-depositionally cryoturbated gravels underlying an extensive cryoplanation terrace feature, *c.* 4–6.5 m above the

Table 10. *Correlations between the Lower Soar, Lower Derwent, Trent and Lower Dove, Proto-Trent (to the Lincoln Gap), Devon and oxygen isotope stratigraphy*

δ18O	LOWER SOAR VALLEY	LOWER DERWENT VALLEY	TRENT & LOWER DOVE VALLEYS	PROTO-TRENT	DEVON VALLEY
	SOAR VALLEY FORMATION (5)	**DERWENT VALLEY FORMATION (5)**	**TRENT VALLEY FORMATION (6)**	**TRENT VALLEY FORMATION (4)**	**TRENT VALLEY FORMATION (4)**
1	Soar Member (10)	Derwent Member (12)	Trent Member (12)	Trent Member (12)	Devon Member (8)
2	Syston Member (9)	Ambaston Member (11) Chaddesden Sidings Member (10)	Hemington Member (11) Holme Pierrepoint Member (10)	Spalford Member (11) Holme Pierrepoint Member (10)	Bassingham Fen Member (7)
3					
4	Wanlip Member (8)	Allenton Member (9)	Beeston Member (9)	Scarle Member (9)	Fulbeck Member (6)
5d–5a					
5e					Little Syke Bed (5)
6	Birstall Member (7)	Crown Inn Member (8) Borrowash Member (7)	Egginton Common Member (8)	Whisby Bed (8) Balderton Member (7) Thorpe on the Hill Bed (6)	
7					
8	Knighton Member (6)	Ockbrook Member (6)	Etwall Member (7)	Whisby Farm Member (5)	
9					
10					
11					
12	**WOLSTON FORMATION (1)** Oadby Member (4) Thrussington Member (3) Hathern Member (2)	**WOLSTON FORMATION (1)** Eagle Moor Member (4) Oadby Member (3) Thrussington Member (2)	**WOLSTON FORMATION (1)** Eagle Moor Member (5) Finderm Member (4) Oadby Member (3) Thrussington Member (2)	**WOLSTON FORMATION (1)** Eagle Moor Member (3) Skellingthorpe Member (2)	**WOLSTON FORMATION (1)** Oadby Member (3) Gelston Member (2)

floodplain alluvium, on both sides of Derwent below Derby. Gravels up to 5 m thick. It is probably post-Ipswichian on the basis of *Hippopotamus* in the Crown Inn Bed (Brandon 1996). It is correlated with the Beeston Terrace of the Trent (Swinnerton 1937; Clayton 1953; Posnansky 1960; Jones & Stanley 1974; Brandon 1996).

(AB)

(10) Chaddesden Sidings Member. Type area: Former gravel pit [SK 373350]. These gravels are inferred to form the lower part of the gravel sequence proved by many boreholes penetrating the Ambaston Sand and Gravel and floodplain alluvium in the lower Derwent valley. They are assumed to be Late Devensian in age (Brandon 1995).

(AB)

(11) Ambaston Member. Type area: Ambaston [SK 42 32]. Up to 3.5 m of gravel and overlying silt in a terrace feature about 1–1.5 m above the Derwent floodplain. It is correlated with the older alluvium of Fox-Strangways (1905). It overlies eroded Home Pierrepoint Member near the confluence with the River Trent. Passes laterally into the coeval Hemington Member (Trent Valley note 11) (Brandon 1996).

(AB)

(12) Derwent Member. Holocene valley alluvium in the Lower Derwent Valley and its tributaries.

The Trent and Lower Dove Valleys

(1) Wolston Formation (Avon Valley note 6).
(2) Thrussington Member (Leicestershire, note 6). This contains more Carboniferous material than in the type area.

(AB)

(3) Oadby Member (Leicestershire, note 9).
(4) Findern Member. Stratotype: around Findern, Willington and Chellaston, exposed in sections along Derby Southern Bypass above Oadby Till and below the Etwall Member [e.g. SK 291298]. It consists of up to *c.* 4 m of glaciolacustrine clay and silt (Brandon unpublished.).

(AB)

(5) Eagle Moor Member. (Proto-Trent, note 3). This is the disputed equivalent of part of the Upper Hilton fluvioglacial terrace gravels (Clayton 1953; Posnansky 1960) It forms terrace outliers above the Etwall Member between Etwall and Findern [SK 270320–296308].

(AB & AJH)

(6) Trent Valley Formation. Includes all the fluvial terrace gravels of the Trent valley. It is difficult to correlate terraces upstream of the Trent Trench with those developed along the Proto-Trent downstream, and correlations are made primarily on altitude, degree of dissection, cryoturbation and palaeosol development.

(AB)

(7) Etwall Member. Type area: Hilton–Etwall–Willington [SK 250315–295298]. Up to 3 m of cryoturbated sands and gravels that form dissected terrace remnants at 65–60 m above O.D. along the northern side of the lower Dove into the Trent valley. It is the probable equivalent, in part, with the deposits of the Upper Hilton Terrace (Clayton 1953; Posnansky 1960). It is separated from the lower Egginton Common Member (8) by a 3 m rock step. The rubified temperate Hykeham Palaeosol lies on its surface. It is correlated with the Ockbrook Member (Lower Derwent note 6) of the lower Derwent (Brandon unpublished.).

(AB)

(8) Egginton Common Member. Type area: Helton–Etwall–Willington [SK 252307–290286]. Up to 3 m of cryoturbated sands and gravels that form an extensive terrace on northern side of the lower Dove into the Trent valley at 60–55 m above O.D. It is correlated with the Lower Hilton Terrace (Clayton 1953; Posnansky 1960). It includes the cryoturbated rubified temperate palaeosol **Hykeham Palaeosol** in its type area between Hilton, Etwall and Willington [SK 250315–295298]. The Egginton Common Member is correlated with the Balderton Member (Proto-Trent note 7) (Brandon & Sumbler 1988) downstream, and the Borrowash Member (Lower Derwent note 7) (Brandon 1996) of the lower Derwent.

(AB)

(9) Beeston Member. Type area: Long Eaton to Beeston [SK 480345–530370] where gravels up to 5 m form a dissected terrace about 7 m above the Trent floodplain. It is correlated with that part of the Beeston Terrace of the Trent defined by Clayton (1953) and Posnansky (1960), lying upstream of the Trent Trench. Also correlated with the Scarle Member (Proto Trent note 9) (Brandon & Sumbler 1988) downstream and the Allenton Member (Lower Soar note 9) (Brandon 1995) of the lower Derwent.

(AB)

(10) Holme Pierrepoint Member. Stratotype: Holme Pierrepoint sand and gravel pits [SK 6238], Nottingham (Charsley *et al.* 1990). Formerly termed Floodplain Terrace (Clayton 1953) and Floodplain Sand and Gravel (Brandon & Sumbler 1988). Sandy gravels, up to 10 m thick, form an extensive valley sandur, with syndepositional ice wedge casts, along the Trent valley downstream of the Late Devensian ice margin at Uttoxeter. It occurs beneath the modern alluvium and also forms low terraces *c.* 1–2 m above the floodplain. A fauna of late Pleistocene large mammalia is listed from the deposit (Posnansky 1960).

(AB)

(11) Hemington Member. Stratotype: Hemington Pit [SK 464306]. It forms a terrace, *c.* 1 m above the floodplain from Shardlow to Long Eaton [SK 4330 to 4931]. It overlies the Holme Pierrepoint Member (Salisbury *et al.* 1984) and comprises a lower unit of laterally accreted gravels and an upper unit of overbank silts totalling *c.* 2 m. The basal silts contain late glacial to early Holocene pollen and are radiocarbon dated $10\,320 \pm 160$ B.P. (Coope & Jones 1977). It merges with the Ambaston Member (Lower Derwent note 11) of the lower Derwent (Brandon 1996).

(AB & AJH)

(12) Trent Member. Holocene alluvium in the Trent Valley and its tributaries.

Proto-Trent Valley to Lincoln Gap

(1) Wolston Formation (Avon valley, note 6).
(2) Skellingthorpe Member. Stratotype: British Geological Survey borehole [(SK 912697]) south of Skellingthorpe, Lincs (Jackson 1977), which showed a thickness of 6.6 m of laminated clay and silt. It lies between bedrock and the Eagle Moor Member south of Skellingthorpe. This glaciolacustrine deposit (Brandon & Sumbler 1988) was named Skellingthorpe Clay by Howard (1993).

(AB & MGS)

(3) Eagle Moor Member. Type area: Eagle Moor [SK 890684]. Between Newark and Lincoln, it is a fluvioglacial sandy gravel, up to 6 m thick, that forms terrace outliers from Danethorpe Hill [SK 8457] northwards to Eagle Moor. It contains flint (up to 10%) and quartzite (up to 70%), Carboniferous sandstone,

Triassic sandstone and Rhaxella chert (<1%) and comprises outwash following deposition of the Oadby Member. It is correlated with part of the upper Hilton fluvioglacial terrace gravels of Posnansky (1960) (Brandon & Sumbler 1988, 1991).

(AB, MGS & AJH)

(4) Trent Valley Formation (Trent & Lower Dove Valleys, note 6).

(5) Whisby Farm Member. Stratotype: Pit [SK 925676] near Whisby Farm, between Whisby and Hykeham, Lincoln. Up to 3 m of reddened sand and gravel forming a terrace about 5 m above the Balderton Member and separated from it by a rock step (Brandon & Sumbler 1991). Palaeocurrents show deposition from the northwest into the 'Balderton' course of the Trent valley. It is a head gravel largely derived from the Eagle Moor Member. It is provisionally correlated with oxygen isotope stage 8.

(AB & MGS)

(6) Thorpe on the Hill Bed. Sandy silt with sand and basal gravel up to 1 m thick with base at about 1 m O.D. It occurs in a channel cut in bedrock below the Balderton Member. Its fauna consists of temperate climate large mammals, molluscs, pollen, plant macrofossils and beetles. It occurs below the Balderton Member (oxygen isotope stage 6), and the presence of *Corbicula fluminalis* suggests correlation with oxygen isotope stage 7 (Brandon *et al.* unpublished).

(AB)

(7) Balderton Member. Stratotype: Pit [SK 896663], Whisby, near Thorpe on the Hill, Lincoln. It is found between Newark [SK 7953] and Balderton [SK 8251] to Hykeham [SK 9569], Lincoln. Well exposed sections (Brandon & Sumbler 1991) reveal 7–8.5 m of deposits infilling a 1.5–3 km wide, sinuous palaeovalley heading towards the Lincoln Gap. Its surface falls steadily north-eastwards from 18 m O.D. (about 7 m above Trent floodplain) to about 11 m O.D. It contains cold-climate large mammals dominated by *M. primigenius*, *ABOUT antiquus* and *E. caballus*, molluscs, beetles and pollen. ESR ages on elephant molars and D-aIle/L-Ile ratios from molluscs indicate correlation with oxygen isotope stage 6 (Brandon & Sumber 1991). On its surface is the rubified temperate **Hykeham Soil** (oxygen isotope sub-stage 5e) within Late Devensian ice wedge casts (Howard *et al.* unpublished). It occurs as a line of remanié outliers through Watton [SK 745388] as the Watton sand and gravel, possibly formerly a contiguous tributary deposit of the Balderton Member.

(AB & MGS)

(8) Whisby Bed. Stratotype: Pit [SK 930673], Whisby, Lincoln. Red sand of fluvio-aeolian origin up to 1.5 m thick, that occurs in cores of ice-wedge casts and other Late Devensian cryogenic involutions on top of the Balderton Member. Correlated with oxygen isotope stage 6. It was probably deposited after the Balderton route of the Trent to the Lincoln Gap was abandoned (Brandon & Sumbler 1991).

(AB & MGS)

(9) Scarle Member. Type area: between North Collingham [SK 830620] and North Scarle [SK 840670]. Sands and gravels underlying a terrace 3–4 m above the Trent floodplain with both surface and base of gravel higher than the corresponding levels of the nearby Holme Pierrepoint Member. It probably aggraded when the Trent route to the Lincoln Gap was to west and north of Eagle Moor. It is correlated with the Fulbeck Member originally considered to be Ipswichian (Brandon & Sumber 1988). But like the Fulbeck Member it is probably Early Devensian. It has yielded fossils of *R. tarandus* and *B. priscus* from a pit [SK 855640] at South Scarle (Brandon

unpublished).

(AB & MGS)

(10) Holme Pierrepoint Member. Probably deposited by the Trent, partly en route to the Lincoln Gap via west and north of Eagle Moor and partly after its diversion north to the Humber (Brandon & Sumbler 1988).

(AB & MGS)

(11) Spalford Member. Type area: Spalford [SK 840690], Notts. Spreads of pale brown, fine-grained aeolian sand, up to c. 3 m thick, overlying the Holme Pierrepoint Member. Probably Late Devensian, possibly late-glacial age (Brandon & Sumbler 1988), although Holocene reworking is also indicated (Iron Age and Romano British).

(AB,MGS & AJH)

(12) Trent Member (Trent Valley, note 12).

Devon Valley

(1) Wolston Formation (Avon Valley, note 6).

(2) Gelston Member. Stratotype: Gelston [SK 914451] where up to 10 m of cryogenically involuted quartzite dominant flint-free sands and gravels lie at c. 80 m O.D. (Brandon 1987). Probably glaciofluvial outwash before deposition of the adjoining Oadby Member.

(AB)

(3) Oadby Member (Leicestershire, note 9). Occurs in the Gelston area [SK 9244].

(AB)

(4) Trent Valley Formation. (Trent Valley, note 6). The following two units (5 & 6) were deposited by the River Devon, a tributary of the Trent, included in the Trent Valley Formation. Previously both deposits were included in the Fulbeck Sand and Gravel, inferred to have been deposited by a combined Witham/Devon river en route to the Lincoln Gap during the Ipswichian (Brandon & Sumbler 1988). The Witham river is now thought to have followed a route through the Ancaster Gap until Late Devensian times, when it was diverted westwards to its present course through the Lincoln Gap.

(AB & MGS)

(5) Little Syke Bed. Stratotype: Little Syke drain [SK 896538]. It is found at several other localities in the Fulbeck area close to the western margin of the Fulbeck Member. It consists of cryogenically involuted clayey gravel, c. 0.5 m thick, with abundant large mammal fossils, especially *Hippopotamus* (Brandon & Sumbler 1988) It is correlated with the lower part of Fulbeck Sand and Gravel of Brandon & Sumbler (1988) and is probably Ipswichian.

(AB & MGS)

(6) Fulbeck Member. Type area: Fulbeck Airfield area [SK 8950], Lincs. It consists of cryogenically involuted sandy gravel, up to 3 m thick, infilling a broad, shallow channel from Hougham [SK 8945] northwards to Aubourn [SK 9463]. It is correlated with the upper, Lincolnshire Limestone-rich, part of the Fulbeck Sand and Gravel of Brandon and Sumbler (1988). The deposit extends across the present Witham valley southwards to Woolsthorpe [SK 8435] at 57 m O.D. and to a point where the Devon was diverted into the Trent valley, via Bottesford, during the Late Devensian (Brandon 1991, 1992). It was probably deposited during the Early Devensian (mainly oxygen isotope stage 4). A molar of *M. primigenius* was found near Marston [SK 880419] (Brandon 1991).

(AB & MGS)

(7) Bassingham Fen Member. Stratotype near Bassingham

Table 11. *Correlations between the Nene and Ouse Valleys and oxygen isotope stratigraphy*

$\delta^{18}O$	NENE VALLEY		OUSE VALLEY
1	**NENE VALLEY FORMATION** (4) Nene Member (9)	**FENLAND FORMATION** (11)	**OUSE VALLEY FORMATION** (3) Ouse Member (11)
2			
3	Ecton Member (8)		
4			
5d-5a			Radwell Bed (10) Felmersham Member (9) Ravenstone Member (8) Woopack Farm Bed (7)
5e			
6			Stoke Goldington Member (6)
7	Grendon Member (7)	**MARCH FORMATION** (10)	Hartigans Pit Member (5)
8			
9	Woodston Beds (6) Orton Logueville Member (5)		Biddenham Member (4)
10			
11			
12	**LOWESTOFT FORMATION** (3)		**LOWESTOFT FORMATION** (2)
13 - 16	**MILTON FORMATION** (1) Courteenhall Member (2)		**MILTON FORMATION** (1)

Fen [SK 935600]. It consists of *c.* 2 m of sandy gravel. Lithologically similar to the Fulbeck Member (ie. calcareous Jurassic lithologies), it rests on cryoturbated Lias bedrock and is overlain by 0.5 m of modern alluvium. D-aIle/L-Ile ratios from molluscan remains within the basal silts gave two age estimates: first, oxygen isotope stage 4 for shells of *Lymnaea peregra; second* oxygen isotope sub-stage 5d or 5c for *Valvata piscinalis* (Miller & Hollin, in Howard 1992 unpublished). It is included in the Fulbeck Member by Brandon and Sumbler (1988).

(AJH)

(8) Devon Member. Holocene alluvium.

Nene Valley

(1) Milton Formation. Type-area: it underlies chalky till of the Lowestoft Formation (Central East Anglia note 12) and can be traced in boreholes and excavations to the west and south of Northampton, from Nether Heyford to Preston Deanery. Good exposures occur in the pits at Hill Farm, Rothersthorpe [SP705 575]. It consists of 10 m of well sorted, trough and tabular cross-bedded sands and pebbly sands. Gravels occur at the base and in upper parts as lenses, sheets and channel fills. The gravel is of local provenance (Jurassic limestone and ironstone).

(JS & AS)

(2) Courteenhall Member. Stratotype: landfill site at Courteenhall Grange [SP 758555]. It consists of about 2 m of organic silts and sands with temperate plant macrofossils ostracods and molluscs (K.A. Smith unpublished)

(JS & AS)

(3) Lowestoft Formation (Central East Anglia note 12).

(4) Nene Valley Formation. Type area: the Nene Valley. It consists of sand and gravel members with finer-grained fossiliferous Bed. It overlies the Lowestoft Formation at Hicks Pit, Woodston (Horton *et al.* 1992).

(CPG & DHK)

(5) Orton Longueville Member. Stratotype: Orton Longueville [TL 163964]. Up to 5 m of fluviatile sands and gravels underlying the Third Terrace of the Nene. It is the equivalent of the Third Terrace Gravels of Castleden (1980) at Aldwincle [TL 003810] downstream to beyond Peterborough.

(CPG)

(6) **Woodston Member**. Stratotype: Hicks No. 1 Brickyard [TL 189956]. Fluviatile silts and sand up to a maximum thickness of 3 m yielded pollen, plant macrofossil, coleopteran, molluscan, ostracod and mammalian evidence of deposition under temperate conditions. Pollen analysis suggests correlation with biozone HoIIc of the Hoxnian. D-aIle/L-Ile ratios from *Cepaea* of 0.248 ± 0.095 (2), *Trichia hispida* 0.24 ± 0.023 (2) and *Bithynia tentaculata* of 0.248 ± 0.29 (2) support this and indicate correlation with oxygen isotope stage 9. It is recorded beneath the Third Terrace of the Nene from Orton Waterville [TL 157960] eastward for about 3 km (Horton *et al.* 1992). Brackish mollusca and ostracods (at 11.70 m O.D.) suggest a marine transgression to this elevation.

(DHK & CPG)

(7) **Grendon Member**. Stratotype: Grendon [SP 878617]. Fluviatile sands and gravels up to 7.6 m thick underlying the Second Terrace of the Nene. It is the equivalent of the Second Terrace Gravels of Castleden (1980) from Billing [SP 808621] near Northampton to Stanground [TL 210971] near Peterborough.

(CPG)

(8) **Ecton Member**. Stratotype: Ecton [SP 826617]. Fluviatile sands and gravels underlying the alluvium and the First Terrace of the Nene. Equivalent to the Floodplain Gravels of Castleden (1976). The First Terrace and the Floodplain are separated by a topographic step of 2–3.5 m, but the deposits beneath them are continuous. Middle Devensian fossil assemblages have been described by Holyoak and Seddon (1984).

(CPG)

(9) **Nene Member**. Holocene Nene Valley alluvium.

(10) **March Formation**. Type area: 'islands' on the fen margin of fossiliferous sands and gravels (Keen *et al.* 1990; West *et al.* 1994, 1995) between Eye [TF 230036] and Manea [TL 480895]. Keen *et al.* (1990) proposed that the balance of fluviatile, brackish and marine mollusca, ostracoda and foraminifera indicated deposition in a temperate climate and near-shore environment, with terrestrial and marine-shelf components. Bridgland *et al.* (1991) proposed correlation with oxygen isotope stage 7 on the basis of regional stratigraphal relationships because the deposits appear to form a downstream continuation of the sands and gravels underlying the Second Terrace of the Nene. D-aIle/L-Ile ratios from Somersham were correlated with the Hoxnian (oxygen isotope stage 9) by Bowen (1992). But West *et al.* (1994), however, contended that the pollen and molluscan biostratigraphy suggest the gravels were deposited during the Early Devensian (oxygen isotope stage 4), with reworked Ipswichian marine mollusca (oxygen isotope sub-stage 5e).

(DHK & CPG)

(11) **Fenland Formation**.

Ouse Valley

(1) **Milton Formation**. (Nene Valley, note 1).

(2) **Lowestoft Formation** (Central East Anglia note 12).

(3) **Ouse Valley Formation**. Type area: fluviatile sand and gravel members, preserved as terrace deposits and incorporating a number of generally finer-grained fossiliferous Bed in the Ouse Valley. They contain exotic material from northern and northeastern sources introduced into the area by the ice that deposited the Lowestoft Formation.

(CPG & DHK)

(4) **Biddenham Member**. Stratotype: The Spinney Pit [TL 023503]. Sands and gravels up to 4 m thick that underlie the highest recognised terrace of the River Ouse (Terrace 3). Thin fossiliferous clayey bands within the sequence contain a temperate molluscan fauna including *Belgrandia marginata*. Numerous artefacts of Acheulian type have also been recorded (Prestwich 1861; Harding *et al.* 1991).

(CPG & DHK)

(5) **Hartigans Pit Member**. Stratotype: the former Hartigans Pit. Equivalent to Bed b and c of Green *et al.* (1996). Fossiliferous basal gravel overlain by fossiliferous blue-grey clay. Flora, mollusca, coleoptera and ostracoda indicate temperate climatic conditions. U-series ages of 167 ka (+54/-35) and 208 ka (+44/-33); and D-aIle/L-Ile ratios on *Valvata piscinalis* of 0.146 (3) which suggests correlation with oxygen isotope stage 7.

(CPG & DHK)

(6) **Stoke Goldington Member**. Stratotype: the former Hartigans Pit [SP 853490] (Green *et al.* 1996). Sands and gravels up to 8 m thick underlying Terrace 2 of the Ouse.

(CPG)

(7) **Woolpack Farm Member**. Stratotype: pit 200 m east of Woolpack Farm, Fenstanton [TL 299685]. It consists of 3.6 m of sand and gravel with temperate mammalia, mollusca and coleoptera which together suggest an age equivalent to oxygen isotope sub-stage 5e. Similar sediments which provided the temperate mollusc *Belgrandia marginata* recorded from Galley Hill some 600 m to the east, were also ascribed to oxygen isotope sub-stage 5e (Preece & Ventris 1983).

(CHG, DHK & GRC)

(8) **Ravenstone Member**. Stratotype: Stratotype: the former Hartigans Pit. Equivalent to Bed d-f of Green *et al.* (1996). Fossiliferous clays overlain by chalky gravel in a channel cut into sands and gravels of the Stoke Goldington Member. The flora and fauna indicate cool climatic conditions. D-aIle/L-Ile ratios from *L.truncatula* (4) gave a mean ratio of 0.121 which suggests correlation with the Ipswichian and oxygen isotope sub-stage 5e.

(CPG & DHK)

(9) **Felmersham Member**. Stratotype: former pit near Radwell [TL 006586] (Rogerson *et al.* 1992). Sands and gravels up to 3 m thick underlying Terrace 1 of the Ouse.

(CPG)

(10) **Radwell Member**. Stratotype: former pit near Radwell [TL 006586] (Rogerson *et al.* 1992). Fossiliferous sandy silt and fine gravel up to 0.55 m in thickness, occupying a channel in the Felmersham Member. Plant macrofossils, mollusca, coleoptera and ostracoda suggest deposition in cool temperate conditions. Radiocarbon ages are inconclusive and the material dated (*Abies* wood) suggests age of the member may be late in oxygen isotope stage 5.

(DHK & CPG)

(11) **Ouse Member**. Holocene river alluvium.

Chapter 4

The Thames Valley, its tributary, valleys and their former courses

P. L. GIBBARD

With contributions from D. R. Bridgland, P. Collins & M. G. Sumbler

The Thames is the largest drainage basin in Britain. For convenience it is subdivided into three regions. The Upper Thames occurs upstream of Reading where it crosses gently dipping Jurassic rocks. Its upper catchment includes the Cotswold Hills and south English Midlands. The Middle and Lower Thames occupy the London Basin, where the Thames is a broadly west to east aligned stream along the axis of the basin, with tributaries from the north and south, before it the North Sea through the Thames Estuary.

Deposits of the Thames and its tributaries occur from the tops of the highest hills on the basin margin (*c*.180 m O.D.) to below sea level in the Thames Estuary. The earliest Thames deposits, the Pebble Gravel Formation consists of fragmentary gravels composed predominantly of local materials, particularly flint. They postdate marine sands (Red Crag = ?late Pliocene–earliest Pleistocene) that also occur up to *c*. 180 m O.D. on the margins of the London Basin, that indicate relative uplift of the western end of the basin during the

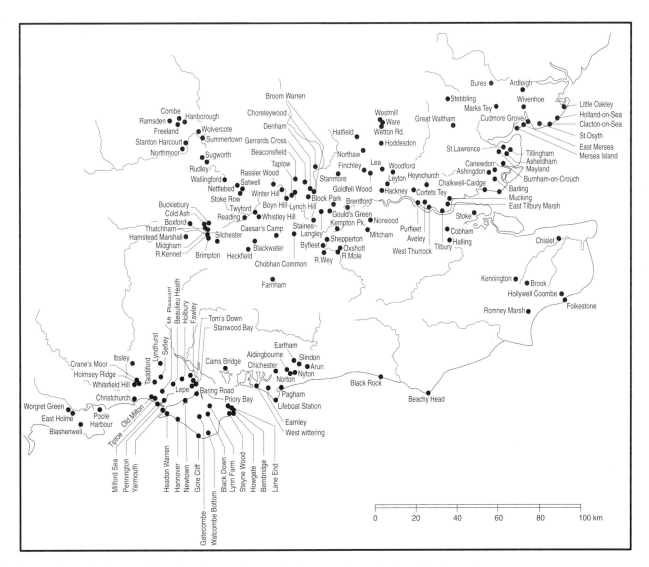

Fig. 6. Localities in the Thames Valley, its tributary valleys and in Southeast Essex, South and Southeast England.

Table 12. *Correlations between the Upper, Middle (and the Vale of St. Albans) and Lower Thames and oxygen isotope stratigraphy*

δ¹⁸O	1973	UPPER THAMES	MIDDLE THAMES & VALE OF ST ALBANS	LOWER THAMES
1	FLANDRIAN	**UPPER THAMES FORMATION** (8) Staines Member (17)	**MAIDENHEAD FORMATION** (24) Staines Member (37)	**LOWER THAMES FORMATION** (11) Tilbury Member (25)
2	DEVENSIAN	Northmoor Member (16)	Shepperton Member (36) Langley Member (35) Kempton Park Member (34) Reading Town Member (33)	Shepperton Member (24) Langley Member (23) East Tilbury Marshes Member (22) West Thurrock Member (21)
3 / 4 / 5		Summertown–Radley Member (15)		
5e	IPSWICHIAN	Wolvercote Channel Member (14)	Trafalgar Square Member (32)	Trafalgar Square Member (20) Aveley Member (19) Spring Gardens Member (18)
6 to ?10	WOLSTONIAN	Daylesford Member (13) Wolvercote Member (12) **WOLSTON FORMATION** (11) Hanborough Member (10)	Spring Gardens Bed (31) Taplow Member (30) Lynch Hill Member (29) Boyn Hill Member (28)	Mucking Member (17) Purfleet Member (16) Corbets Tey (15) Orsett Heath (14)
9 to 11	HOXNIAN	Wallingford Member (9)	Slade Oak Lane Beds (27) Hatfield Member (26)	Swanscombe Member (13)
12?	ANGLIAN		Black Park Member (25) **LOWESTOFT FORMATION** (18) Smug Oak Member (23) Eastend Green Member (22) Ware Member (21) Moor Mill Member (20) Watton Road Member (19)	Dartford Heath Member (12) **LOWESTOFT FORMATION** (8) Robin Hood's Pool Member (10) Hornchurch Member (9)
pre-12	CROMERIAN	Freeland Member (7) Sugworth Member (6) Combe Member (5) **NORTHERN DRIFT FORMATION** (1) Wilcote Member (4) Ramsden Heath Member (3) Waterman's Lodge Member (2)	**MIDDLE THAMES FORMATION** (8) Westmill (17) Winter Hill (16) Rassler (15) Gerrards Cross (14) Beaconsfield (13) Chorleywood (12) Satwell (11) Westland Green (10) & Stoke Row (9) Members **PEBBLE GRAVEL FORMATION** (2) Northaw (7) Stanmore (6) Priest's Hill (5) Netlebed (4) Members & Little Heath Bed (3) **ROTHAMSTED FORMATION** (1)	**PEBBLE GRAVEL FORMATION** (6) Warley Member (7) **EPPING FOREST FORMATION** (1) Woodford Green (5) Buckhurst Hill (4) & Debden Green (3) High Beach (2)

Pleistocene (Gibbard 1988*b*). The Pebble Gravels represent the Thames and tributaries that were established following regression of the sea in the Early Pleistocene (Wooldridge & Linton 1955).

A major change in gravel lithology is present in the next youngest units. They consist of river terrace remnants, characterized by rocks exotic to the present Thames catchment. These are traced from the Upper Thames, where they are aligned parallel to the modern Thames tributary, the Evenlode, downstream through the Middle Thames Valley. Here they diverge from the modern course and pass through Hertfordshire, parallel to the shallow Vale of St. Albans and enter East Anglia where they form terraces, mostly buried beneath tills of the Anglian glaciation (Hey 1976*b*, 1980; Rose & Allen 1977; Rose 1995; Whiteman 1992; Whiteman & Rose 1992).

Glaciation during the Anglian overrode the Thames drainage system in east and central England, damming the Thames and its southbank tributaries north of London. This resulted in the river adopting a new course through present day London (Wooldridge 1938, 1960; Gibbard 1977, 1979, 1985, 1994; Bridgland 1994). Subsequent evolution of the Thames system has been marked by the cyclic development of a sequence of gravel and sand aggradations under periglacial climates during the Middle and Late Pleistocene. These aggradational members show a marked reduction in exotic material, accompanied by an equivalent increase in local lithologies. This change marks a severing of the headwater catchment in the West Midlands.

The Thames Valley also includes a number of important interglacial fossiliferous sequences that provide both stratigraphical control and palaeoenvironmental evidence. East of London, the valley was invaded repeatedly by the sea so that, as today, a substantial estuary developed during periods of high eustatic sea level (interglacials). Submergence of the valley system has meant that offshore of SE Essex, a drowned course of the Thames and its tributaries occurs aligned towards the E and SE (Bridgland 1988*a*; Bridgland & D'Olier 1989). Upstream in the estuary, a thick wedge of Flandrian (Holocene) marsh and mud sediments have accumulated (Devoy 1979). Both in and upstream of the estuary floodplain alluvium overlies Late Devensian gravels.

A major procedural problem is the nature of the status to be accorded to the sand and gravel terrace lithostratigraphical units, as discussed in Chapter 1. Here the individual lithostratigraphical units are accorded member status and the term formation is used to refer collectively to members with broadly unified lithostratigraphical characteristics.

A further debate in the Thames catchment is the means by which chronostratigraphical correlation of individual temperate character deposits is achieved both between sites and between the standard classification (Mitchell *et al*. 1973) and oxygen isotope stratigraphy (Chapter 1). The approach followed here is an attempt to integrate the different means of correlation that have been used.

Upper Thames

P.L. Gibbard & M.G. Sumbler

(1) Northern Drift Formation. Comprises high-level gravels, 1-2 m thick and predominantly comprise quartz and quartzite pebbles in a clay matrix. The assemblage reflects derivation from the west Midlands. Opinion differs over its genesis: some have invoked a glacial origin while others consider they are degraded and decalcified remnants of fluvial accumulations (Shotton *et al*. 1980; Hey 1986). Hey (1986) subdivided the sequence altitudinally and lithologically into five members (units 2–6).

(2) Waterman's Lodge Member. Stratotype: Waterman's Lodge at [SP 3261836]. Thickness not known and recogniton of the unit is based on lithology and altitude. Occurs at over 300 m O.D. in the north Cotswolds and has a high ratio of quartz to quartzites.

(3) Ramsden Heath Member. Stratotype: gravel and sand at Ramsden Heath [SP 345158] (Hey 1986). Unknown thickness. Subdivision based on altitude.

(4) Wilcote Member. Stratotype: exposure at Wilcote [SP 370153]. Unknown thickness. Subdivision based on altitude (Hey 1986).

(5) Combe Member. Stratotype: at [SP 409164]. It was originally identified by Arkell (1947*a*, *b*) as the Combe Terrace (Hey 1986).

(6) Sugworth Member. Stratotype: fossiliferous, fluvial sediment complex of sand, silt and organic mud occupying channels cut into bedrock at [SP 513007]. Detailed investigation concluded was 'Cromerian Complex' in age (Shotton *et al*. 1980). But Gibbard (1985) suggested correlation with the Hoxnian on the basis of terrace projection; this is now thought unlikely (Gibbard *et al*. 1992) but D-aIle/L-Ile ratios of 0.296 ± 0.008 (4), 0.286 ± 0.016 (2), and 0.299 ± 0.002 (3) on *Cepaea* and 0.305 ± 0.001 (2) on *Trichia* suggest correlation with beds at Swanscombe: that is, younger than Cromerian (Bowen *et al*. 1989). Correlation with oxygen isotope stage 11 is advocated by Sumbler (1995).

(7) Freeland Member. Stratotype: at [SP 406121]. Originally identified by Arkell (1947*a*, *b*) as the Freeland Terrace (Hey 1986).

(8) Upper Thames Formation. This is characterized by gravels dominated by local limestone lithologies (Sandford 1924; Briggs *et al*. 1985; Gibbard & Allen 1995). It includes all mainstream Thames units from the Hanborough Member to the Staines Member.

(9) Wallingford Member. Stratotype: gravels and sands at [SP 640890]. It was formed by local stream(s) on the NW side of the Chalk escarpment, then subjected to intense cryoturbation. It includes a fossiliferous unit, the Gould's Green Bed, that includes evidence of subarctic environment. It is correlated with the 'Upper Winter Hill terrace' of the Middle Thames: i.e., the Winter Hill or Black Park Member (Middle Thames notes 16 and 25) by Horton *et al*. (1981)

(10) Hanborough Member. Stratotype: up to 3 m of gravel and sand resting on bedrock at [SP 418136]. First proposed by Sandford (1924), it contains vertebrate remains and rare Palaeolithic artefacts (Arkell 1947*c*). It has been correlated with the Boyn Hill and Lynch Hill Members of the Middle Thames (Gibbard 1985; Bridgland 1994).

(11) Wolston Formation. This consists of the 'Moreton Drift' of Tomlinson (1929) and Bishop (1958) composed of chalky tills and sands and gravels in the vicinity of Moreton-in-Marsh [SP 205323]. Bridgland (1994) and Maddy *et al*. (1991) correlate it with stage 12. But Sumbler (1995) correlated it with stage 10 believing it to be younger than the Hanborough Member.

(MGS)

(12) Wolvercote Member. Stratotype: the former Wolvercote brickpit [SP 498105] where up to 3 m of limestone-rich gravel and sand overlie bedrock [SP 498105]. The gravels contain a proportion of flint that Arkell (1947a, b) and Sumbler (1995) suggested were derived from the 'Moreton Drift'. First proposed by Sandford (1924), it remains unclear whether it overlies or underlies the Wolvercote Channel Member (Bridgland 1994); although it is generally accepted that it underlies it. It has been correlated with the Taplow Member of the Middle Thames (Gibbard 1985).

(13) Daylesford Member. Stratotype: Daylesford gravel pit (disused) [SP 244255]. It was included in the 'Moreton Drift' by Tomlinson (1929) and consists of flint bearing sands and gravels that form terraces in the upper reaches of the Evenlode.

(14) Wolvercote Channel Member. Stratotype: the former Wolvercote brickpit [SP 498105]. It consists of fossiliferous sand, pebbly sand, silt, clay and organic sediment filling a channel excavated into unit 11 and bedrock, that has yielded floral and faunal remains, and Palaeolithic artefacts. Its age is disputed but it is thought to be either Ipswichian or possibly earlier (oxygen isotope stage 9) (Sandford 1924; Bishop 1958; Gibbard 1985; Bridgland 1994).

(15) Summertown-Radley Member. Stratotype: at [SP 523988; parastratotype: at SP 415052] It comprises up to 3 m of gravel and sand resting on bedrock. It was first proposed by Sandford (1924), who recognized two subunits, a lower gravel containing 'cold-climate' Mammalia and an upper subunit that yielded 'warm-climate' remains including *Hippopotamus*. It now appears there are at least three subunits, (1) the principal one comprising cold- climate gravel and sand; (2) fossiliferous sands and associated sediment of temperate origin: the **Eynsham Bed** [SP 429008] of Briggs *et al.* (1985) that is biostratigraphically correlated with the Ipswichian (oxygen isotope sub-stage 5e); and (3) a second fossil-bearing temperate gravel, the **Stanton Harcourt Bed**. The units are not all seen in superposition and, therefore, the relative ages are not unequivocal, particularly that of unit 3. Bridgland (1994) follows Briggs *et al.* (1985) in proposing that unit 3 may be ascribed to oxygen isotope stage 7. This is supported by D-aIle/L-Ile ratios of 0.154 ± 0.007 (3) (*Bithynia*), 0.153 ± 0.014 (6) (*Lymnaea*), 0.163 ± 0.016 (9) (*Corbicula*), and 0.174 ± 0.014 (8) (*Cepaea*) (Bowen *et al.* 1989); but the biostratigraphical evidence is equivocal (Chapter 1, table 2 for a summary of the D-aIle/L-Ile data and geochronological age estimates). The main mass of gravels and sands (including reworked *Hippopotamus*) (unit 2) is probably Devensian in age (Goudie & Hart 1975; Seddon & Holyoak 1985; Gibbard 1985). Thus the Stanton Harcourt Bed could also be Ipswichian, and Sandford's lower gravel unit could be pre-Ipswichian: that is, late Wolstonian.

(16) Northmoor Member. Stratotype: at [SP 430027]. It was first identified as the 'Floodplain Terrace' by Sandford (1924). The term Northmoor Terrace was introduced by Arkell (1947a,b). It comprises gravel and sand underlying modern floodplain, has yielded vertebrate fossils and includes fossiliferous channel fills. Radiocarbon ages obtained from the latter range from 13 500 to 10 500 BP and 40 000 to 29 000 BP (Briggs *et al.* 1985; Aalto *et al.* 1984). It is the upstream equivalent of both the Kempton Park and Shepperton Members of the Middle Thames (Gibbard 1985). River Ray equivalents are the First and Second terrace deposits (Ambrose & Horton 1991).

(17) Staines Member. (Middle Thames note 37). This consists of fine-grained deposits of silt, clay, mud, peat, marl, tufa, sand and gravel that immediately underlie modern floodplain surface throughout main river and tributary valleys (Ambrose & Horton 1991). The sediments are rich in archaeological and fossil material.

Middle Thames Valley and the Vale of St. Albans

P. L. Gibbard

(1) Rothamsted Formation. Stratotype at Rothamsted. Disturbed sandstone in Clay-with-Flints at 132 m O.D. [TL 125132]. It has been suggested that this is a marine Pliocene deposit correlative of the Netley Heath Member (Blackwater-Loddon, note 1) and Suffolk Red Crag in East Anglia (Dines & Chatwin 1930).

(2) Pebble Gravel Formation. The earliest high-level Thames gravels of the south Chilterns-south Hertfordshire-south central Essex area. It occurs as highly dissected remnants that comprise local lithologies predominantly flint (Gibbard 1985; Gibbard & Allen 1995; Bridgland 1994). Bridgland (1994) suggested the distinction of separate a Chiltern Pebble Gravel and a North London Pebble Gravel of Thames and south-bank tributary origin, respectively, but these names should be regarded as informal.

(3) Little Heath Bed. Stratotype: the highest gravel unit on the Chilterns that consists of local lithologies. It is interpreted as a littoral marine or possibly fluvial deposit [TL 017083] (Moffat & Catt 1986; Bridgland 1994). It may be part of the Pebble Gravel Formation.

(4) Nettlebed Member. Stratotype: at Nettlebed [SU 702872]. Between 1 and 2 m of gravel and sand dominated by local lithologies mainly of rounded flints derived from local Tertiary rocks (Gibbard 1985; Bridgland 1994).

(5) Priest's Hill Member. Stratotype: Priest's Hill, Nettlebed [SU 701872]. A fine-grained fluvial or lacustrine sediment up to 3 m thick with temperate climate pollen assemblages spanning the first half of an early Pleistocene interglacial event (Turner 1983; Horton 1977, 1983; Gibbard 1985).

(6) Stanmore Member. Stratotype: at Harrow Weald Common [TQ 147929]. Previously termed the '500 foot' or 'Higher' Pebble Gravel (Wooldridge 1960; Green & McGregor 1978a), ot may, in part, be of Mole-Wey origin (Bridgland 1994)

(7) Northaw Member. Stratotype: at Northaw Great Wood [TQ 281040]. Previously termed '400 foot' or 'Lower' Pebble Gravel (Wooldridge 1960; Avery & Catt 1983). It may, in part, be of Mole-Wey origin (Bridgland 1994); and, in part, correlated with the Westland Green Member.

(8) Middle Thames Formation. Characterized by gravels dominated by flint and substantial lithologies of Midlands origin, particularly vein quartz and quartzite (Gibbard 1985, 1989; Gibbard & Allen 1995). It includes all the mainstream Thames members from Stoke Row to Winter Hill (units 8–16) in the Middle Thames region. Downstream, it is correlated with the Kesgrave Formation in eastern Essex.

(9) Stoke Row Member. Stratotype: at Stoke Row [SU 686834]. High-level gravel remnant, 1 to 2 m thick, rich in vein quartz and quartz material of Midlands origin. Previously included in unit 10 by Hey (1965) and Gibbard (1985).

(10) Westland Green Member. Stratotype: at Westland Green [TL 422215]. A high-level gravel remnant up to 2.5 m thick rich in vein quartz and quartz material of Midlands origin (Hey 1965, 1980; Gibbard 1985).

(11) Satwell Member. Stratotype: up to 2 m of gravel and sand at Satwell [SU 706839] (Gibbard 1985).

(12) Chorleywood Member. Stratotype: sand and gravel at Chorleywood [TQ 023953] (Moffat & Catt 1986; Bridgland 1994).

(13) Beaconsfield Member. Stratotype: up to 6 m of gravel and sand overlying Chalk at Beaconsfield Station [SU 940912]

(Gibbard 1985). Previously termed the 'Higher Gravel Train' (Wooldridge 1938, 1960; Green & McGregor 1978).

(14) Gerrards Cross Member. Stratotype: gravel and sand at Gerrards Cross [SU 940912]; parastratotype: at [TQ 071993] (Gibbard 1985, 1989). Previously termed the 'Lower Gravel Train' (Wooldridge 1938, 1960; Green & McGregor 1978) and Harefield Terrace (Hare 1947). Ascribed to the Leavesden Green Gravel (term discontinued because of duplication) in the Vale of St. Albans by Gibbard (1977).

(15) Rassler Member. Stratotype: at Rassler Wood [SU 822862]. It was originally identified morphologically by Sealy & Sealy (1956). Gibbard (1985) found no evidence for fluvial deposits at the stratotype, nor at the level mapped by Sealy & Sealy (1956). It was therefore, abandoned. Whiteman & Rose (1990) and Bridgland (1994) have readopted the name for gravels apparently intermediate between units 14 and 16 but the basis for this is unclear because the deposits have only been identified on altitudinal criteria.

(16) Winter Hill Member. Stratotype: gravel and sand up to 6 m thick at Winter Hill [SU 880863] (Gibbard 1985, 1989). Previously named the Winter Hill Terrace by Wooldridge (1938) and Hare (1947). It divides into lower (fluvial) and upper (deltaic) subunits in the area north of Slough. The lower subunit was deposited by the Thames before the arrival of the Lowestoft Formation ice sheet. The upper subunit was formed by delta progradation into a ponded Thames.

(17) Westmill Member. Stratotype: at Westmill [TL 342162]. This is the downstream continuation of the Winter Hill Member (16) in the Vale of St.Albans (Gibbard 1977, 1985). Near Ware, the Lower and Upper subunits recognized by Gibbard (1977) are separated by the Ware (Till) Member (Lowestoft Formation – note 21). Gibbard (1977) concluded the Upper subunit was of mixed outwash and of Thames origin, but Cheshire (1983b, c) suggested that only the Lower subunit was of Thames origin. The Upper subunit is thought by Cheshire (1983) to be solely outwash and a possible equivalent of the Hoddesdon (Cocks Lane) Member (Lea Valley, note 1): if this is correct, it is also a member of the Lowestoft Formation (East Anglia).

(18) Lowestoft Formation (Central East Anglia, note 12).

(19) Watton Road Member. Stratotype: laminated silts up to 6 m at Watton Road Quarry, Ware [TL 341149] It overlies the Winter Hill Member (Westmill Lower subunit) near Ware. It is a lake deposit formed by the damming of the Thames by Lowestoft ice.

(20) Moor Mill Member. Stratotype: at Moor Mill [TL 143025]. It overlies the Winter Hill (Westmill) Member south of St.Albans. Lake deposits formed by damming of the Thames by Lowestoft ice and thus classified as part of the Lowestoft Formation and Middle Thames Formation.

(21) Ware Member. Stratotype: at Watton Road, Ware [TL 342162]. Till up to 2 m thick that overlies the Winter Hill Member (Westmill lower subunit) in the east and locally ice-dammed lake deposits of the Watton Road Member. Gibbard (1977). It is restricted to the eastern Vale of St. Albans (Gibbard 1977), but Cheshire (1983) and Allen et al. (1990) considered it extended south west as far as Watford where it includes the Eastend Green Member (note 22).

(22) Eastend Green Member. Stratotype: Waterhall Farm [TL 297106]. Till typical of the Lowestoft Formation up to 10 m thick. It overlies the Winter Hill (Westmill) Member in the central and western Vale of St. Albans, and locally ice-dammed lake deposits (Moor Mill Member, note 20). It was correlated by Gibbard (1979) with the Finchley Member in north London (Mole–Wey valley note 7).

(23) Smug Oak Member. Stratotype: at Moor Mill [TL 114026]. It overlies the Eastend Green Member (note 22) in the central and western Vale of St. Albans; and is confluent with the Black Park Member of the Thames at Uxbridge (note 25). It is overlain locally by the Hatfield Member and ascribed to the late Anglian (note 26).

(24) Maidenhead Formation. This is characterized by gravels dominated by flint and minor local lithologies including Greensand Chert and vein quartz. Its quartz content declines progressively from oldest to youngest members (Gibbard 1985,1989). It includes all the units from the Black Park Member to the Staines Member.

(25) Black Park Member. Stratotype: up to 4 m of gravel and sand at Black Park [TQ 006832] (Gibbard 1985, 1989). It was first recognized morphologically by Hare (1947). It is the first lithostratigraphical unit of the Thames that lies along the modern valley course through London (Hare 1947; Gibbard 1979). It also floors the Caversham Channel between Reading and Henley where it contains abundant Palaeolithic artefacts (Wymer 1968), but may be partially reworked here by later streams (Gibbard 1985).

(26) Hatfield Member. Stratotype: University of Hertfordshire [TL 212075]; parastratotype: at Stanborough [TL 183031]. A discontinuous lenticular unit of organic and silts and clays, pond or shallow lake sediments with fossil assemblages biostratigraphically correlated with the late Anglian to Hoxnian (oxygen isotope stages 12 to 11?). This correlation has also been made by aminostratigraphy and correlation with oxygen isotope stage 9 (Bowen et al. 1989). It is overlain by colluvial sediment.

(27) Slade Oak Lane Member. Stratotype: at Slade Oak as a doline infilling of sediment [TL 018897]. Palaeobotany of an organic unit indicates correlation with the second half of the Hoxnian (Gibbard et al. 1986a).

(28) Boyn Hill Member. Stratotype: up to 6 m of gravel and sand at Boyn Hill, Maidenhead [SU 878809]; parastratotype: at SU873813 (Gibbard 1985, 1989). First recognized at Boyn Hill, Maidenhead by Dewey & Bromehead (1915).

(29) Lynch Hill Member. Stratotype: upto 6 m of gravel and sand at Lynch Hill, Slough [SU 950822] (Gibbard 1985, 1989). First recognized morphologically by Hare (1947). It contains abundant Palaeolithic artefact assemblages (Wymer 1968) and has yielded vertebrate fossils.

(30) Taplow Member. Stratotype: up to 6 m of gravel and sand at Taplow Station [SU 919816] (Gibbard 1985, 1989). It was first recognized by Dewey and Bromehead (1915) and contains Palaeolithic artefacts (Wymer 1968) and rare vertebrate fossils.

(31) Spring Gardens Member. Stratotype: up to 2 m of gravel and sand at Canada House Trafalgar Square [TQ 30008037-29958037] where it underlies the Trafalgar Square Member (Gibbard 1985).

(32) Trafalgar Square Member. Stratotype: at Canada House, Trafalgar Square [TQ 30008037–29958037]. Up to 12 m of gravel, sand, silt and detritus mud resting either on Tertiary or pre-existing Pleistocene deposits. No definitive report has yet been published on the adjacent Uganda House site and its important palaeontology (Franks 1960; Gibbard 1985, 1994). It occurs as discontinuous spreads. These sediments are correlated biostratigraphically with the Ipswichian (oxygen isotope sub-stage 5e) (Gibbard 1985). This correlation is also made by aminostratigraphy (D-aIle/L-Ile ratios of 0.11 ± 0.005 ($n = 5$) for *Bithynia*; 0.113 ± 0.005 ($n = 3$) for *Trichia* and 0.094 ± 0.004 ($n = 3$) for *Cepaea* (Bowen et al. 1989).

(33) Reading Town Member. Stratotype: gravel and sand at Reading [SU 733737] (Gibbard 1985, 1989). First recognized as the 'lower Taplow' Terrace by Sealy & Sealy (1956). It contains Palaeolithic artefacts (Wymer 1968) and has yielded vertebrate fossils, including reworked *Hippopotamus*. Bridgland (1994) included this in the Taplow Member (note 30).

(34) Kempton Park Member. Stratotype: up to 7 m of gravel and sand at Kempton Park [TQ 118703] (Gibbard *et al.* 1982; Gibbard 1985, 1989). It was first recognized as the 'Upper Floodplain Terrace' by Dewey & Bromehead (1921). It includes the discontinuous channel fills that have yielded both faunal and floral fossil assemblages of both cold and temperate aspects. Radiocarbon ages range from 43 to 35 000 BP. Bridgland (1994) included this unit, the Trafalgar Square Member, and Spring Gardens Member in his Kempton Park Formation.

(35) Langley Member. Stratotype: predominantly fine sediment; clayey silt, silt, to clay, commonly massive but locally stratified and associated with periglacial structures ('brickearth') at Langley [TQ 002800]. It is probably colluvium but may be primary loess in places. It covers fluvial aggradations, particularly units 29–34 inclusive, and may be polycyclic in origin. TL dates suggest the main mass was deposited about 17 000 BP (Gibbard *et al.* 1987), but older ages have also been obtained. It has yielded vertebrate remains and Palaeolithic artefacts (Wymer 1968; Gibbard 1985). It may include a palaeosol at Iver (Lacaille 1936).

(36) Shepperton Member. Stratotype: up to 12 m of gravel and sand at Shepperton [TQ 070669] (Gibbard 1985, 1989). It was first recognized as the 'Lower Floodplain' Terrace by Dewey & Bromehead (1921), and underlies the modern floodplain. It has yielded vertebrate fossils and is known to include fossiliferous channel fills. Radiocarbon ages from channel fills range from 15 to 10 000 B.P (Colne Valley note 11; Upper Thames note 14). Bridgland (1994) included this and the Staines Member in his Shepperton Formation. Tributary equivalents include the Pang Valley Member, Wye Valley Member and Brent Valley Member (Gibbard 1995) (for other units see the Kennett Valley).

(37) Staines Member. Stratotype: at Staines [TQ 042685]. An alluvial complex of predominantly fine-grained deposits of silt, clay, mud, peat, marl, tufa, with sand and gravel that immediately underlie the modern floodplain surface throughout main river and tributary valleys. It was defined by Gibbard (1985) for sediments overlying the Shepperton Member and tributary valley equivalents. It is the lateral equivalent of the Tilbury Member (Lower Thames note 25). The sediments are rich in archaeological and fossil material.

Lower Thames Valley

P. L. Gibbard

(1) Epping Forest Formation. Type area: Epping Forest. This includes high-level, pre-Thames gravels of the Epping Forest area. They are 1–2 m thick and comprise flint with subordinate quartz and Greensand chert pebbles. This assemblage typifies that of streams draining the Weald, south of the present Thames (Gibbard 1979, 1982, 1985; Bridgland 1988*a*). The gravels are poorer in Greensand chert than those of the Mole-Wey stream to the west (Gibbard 1994).

(2) High Beach Member. Stratotype: gravels (2 m) at High Beach [TQ 408978]. Possible upstream equivalent of the Shooter's Hill Member (Gibbard 1994).

(3) Debden Green Member. Stratotype: gravels (2 m) at Debden Green [TQ 429981]. Possibly equivalent to Wandle Formation Norwood Member (Gibbard 1994).

(4) Buckhurst Hill Member. Stratotype: gravels at Buckhurst Hill [TQ 408941]. A restricted petrographic assemblage, possibly equivalent to the Effra Member of the Wandle Formation (note, 4) (Dines & Edmunds 1925; Gibbard 1994).

(5) Woodford Green Member. Stratotype: gravels at Woodford Green [TQ 395911]. Possible equivalent to the Effra Member of the Wandle Formation (note, 4) (Gibbard 1994).

(6) Pebble Gravel Formation (Middle Thames, note 2).

(7) Warley Member. Gravels at Warley [TQ 513915] (Dines & Edmunds 1925). Of fluvial origin, up to 2 m thick and of Kentish Weald origin. Its elevation suggests considerable age. It may represent an early course of the Darent–Cray (Wooldridge 1927; Gibbard 1994).

(8) Lowestoft Formation (Central East Anglia, note 12).

(9) Hornchurch Member. Formerly named the Hornchurch Till. It was discovered by Holmes (1892, 1894) in the Hornchurch railway cutting, where the till is 4.5 m thick and rests on London Clay at *c*.32 m O.D. and is overlain by the Orsett Heath Member (note 14) [TQ 54708737] (Bridgland 1994; Gibbard 1994). It is correlated by Whiteman (1987) with the Newney Green Member (Eastern Essex, note 10).

(10) Robin Hood's Pool Member. Stratotype: gravel (2 m) on bedrock at Robin Hood's Pool [TQ 415968]. It contains a diverse pebble assemblage including exotic lithologies, notably *Rhaxella* chert, probably of glacial origin. It is, therefore, included in the Lowestoft Formation. It may represent a kame terrace formed marginal to an ice lobe in the pre-diversion Wandle valley (Gibbard 1994).

(11) Lower Thames Formation. Type area: Lower Thames Valley. Characterized by gravels dominated by flint and minor local lithologies (Gibbard 1994; Gibbard & Allen 1995). It includes all those units between the Dartford Heath Member to Tilbury Member (units 12–25).

(12) Dartford Heath Member. Stratotype: gravel and sands 4.25 m thick on bedrock at Dartford Heath [TQ 514737]. Mapped as Boyn Hill Terrace by Dewey *et al.* (1925) and Dines & Edmunds (1925). Gibbard (1979, 1985, 1989) followed Zeuner (1959) in separating this as an earlier unit predating the local Boyn Hill Terrace deposits. He correlated it with the late Anglian Black Park Member upstream. Bridgland (1994) grouped the Dartford Heath, Swanscombe and Orsett Heath Members into an Orsett Heath Formation. 'Loam-filled channels' ('Wansant Loam') locally overlie and abut the Dartford Heath Member (Wymer 1968), and may be related to sediments in the neighbouring Bowman's Lodge pit [TQ 518738]. The site has yielded an important assemblage of Palaeolithic artefacts. The sediments post-date the Dartford Heath Member and are related to a local drainage system (Gibbard 1994).

(13) Swanscombe Member. Stratotype: at Swanscombe [TQ 595745] (Wymer 1968; Conway 1969, 1970*a*,*b*, 1971, 1972, 1985; Conway & Waechter 1977). Neighbouring sites include Ingress Vale [TQ 595748], Rickson's [TQ 611743], and Crayland's Lane [TQ 604746]. The lithostratigraphy is based particularly on Bridgland *et al.* (1985), Bridgland (1994) and Gibbard (1994). Sediments of fluvial and non-fluvial origin have yielded Palaeolithic artefacts and faunal remains, including a human skull. Fossil assemblages (particularly Mollusca) indicate that the sequence spans the Hoxnian. D-aIle/L-Ile ratios of 0.3 ± 0.017 ($n = 34$) have been used to correlate the Swanscome Member with oxygen isotope stage 11 and not oxygen isotope stage 9 that is represented by D-aIle-L-Ile ratios of 0.24 at Hoxne (Bowen & Sykes 1994; Bowen *et al.* 1989).

(14) Orsett Heath Member. Stratotype: gravels up to 6 m thick overlying bedrock at Orsett Heath [(TQ 628810). This was originally proposed by Bridgland (1983*a*, 1988*a*) and replaces the Fairlop Gravel (Gibbard 1985) for a cold climate aggradation, younger than that at Swanscombe, but abutting the sediments at that site (11) (Gibbard 1994). Gravels of this member also overlie the till at Hornchurch (Hornchurch Member), indicating that they are of post-Hoxnian (Wolstonian) age according to Gibbard (1985, 1994), but correlated with oxygen isotope stage 12 (Anglian), in part, and oxygen isotope stage 10 by Bridgland (1994). It is the downstream equivalent of the Boyn Hill Member of the Middle Thames.

(15) Corbets Tey Member. Stratotype: 3.5 m of gravels and sands on bedrock at Corbets Tey [TQ 570844]. The Geological Survey included this member in either the Boyn Hill or Taplow Terraces. It was originally identified as the Barvills Gravel by Bridgland (1983), but later defined by Gibbard (1985, 1994) and Gibbard *et al.* (1988) as the Corbets Tey Member. It is the downstream equivalent of the Lynch Hill Member of the Middle Thames. A possible Roding valley-equivalent of these deposits has also been recognized (Dines & Edmunds 1925). Division into upper and lower subunits was proposed by Bridgland (1994) who identified intercalated interglacial sediments: e.g. at Purfleet (16), a relationship disputed by Gibbard (1994).

(16) Purfleet Member. Stratotype: up tp 5 m of gravel, sand, intertidal silts and associated deposits at Purfleet [TQ 568785] (Hollin 1977). It was recognized as an independent unit by Bridgland (1994) and correlated with oxygen isotope stage 9, as indicated by D-aIle/L-Ile ratios (Bowen unpublished). Gibbard (1994), however, places it in the Aveley Member.

(17) Mucking Member. Stratotype: up to of 5 m of stratified gravel and sand on bedrock at Mucking [TQ 689815]. It was first proposed by Bridgland (1983) . This unit has subsequently been correlated with the Taplow Member of the Middle Thames by Gibbard (1985, 1994), Gibbard *et al.* (1988), and by Bridgland (1988, 1994).

(18) Spring Gardens Bed. (Middle Thames, note 31).

(19) Aveley Member. Stratotype: at Sandy Lane Quarry, Aveley (now infilled) [TQ 552807]. It comprises gravel, sand, silt detritus mud and associated sediments resting either on bedrock or pre-existing Pleistocene sediments. No definitive report has been published on the site and its important palaeontology (Hollin 1977; Gibbard 1994; Bridgland 1994). It occurs as discontinuous spreads that Bridgland (1994) correlated, mainly on the basis of D-aIle/L-Ile ratios (0.148 ± 0.016 (7)), with those at West Thurrock, Crayford (0.17 ± 0.02 (12)) (Bowen *et al.* 1989), and Ilford (Uphall), and with oxygen isotope stage 7. On the basis of pollen biostratigraphy Gibbard (1994) correlated them with the Ipswichian (oxygen isotope sub-stage 5e).

(20) Trafalgar Square Member. (Middle Thames, note 32) It includes deposits at Harder's Road [TQ 34647649] (Gibbard 1994).

(21) West Thurrock Member. Stratotype: Lion Tramway Cutting, West Thurrock [TQ 59777792]. This fluvial gravel and sand deposit abuts and post-dates the sand and 'brick-earth' of the Aveley Member sequence exposed farther north in the cutting (Hollin, 1977). The gravels and sands are 9 m thick and rest on bedrock at −4 m O.D. (Gibbard 1994).

(22) East Tilbury Marshes Member. Stratotype: at East Tilbury Marshes [TQ 688784]. It was first recognized by Bridgland (1983, 1988) and correlated with the Kempton Park Member of the Middle Thames (Gibbard *et al.* 1988; Gibbard 1994; Bridgland 1994) (Middle Thames, note 34). The gravel and sands are up to 5 m thick and rest on Thanet Sand. In the east they mainly underlie the Tilbury Member (note 25). A Roding valley equivalent the South Woodford Member is also found (stratotype: TQ 413884).

(23) Langley Member. (Middle Thames, note 35) It varies from a sandy silt to remobilized Tertiary clay, sometimes termed 'brickearth'. It is now generally accepted that the most abundant type, clayey silts, were formed as a combined loess and waterlain or colluvial deposit (Gibbard 1994). It was TL dated to: 115-153 ka (Parks & Rendel 1992*b*). It does not include the laminated or massive fossiliferous 'brickearths' of the area (Hollin 1977). The main mass overlies the Corbets Tey and Mucking Members, although a veneer is also present on the East Tilbury Marshes and the Aveley Members.

(24) Shepperton Member (Middle Thames note 36) This is not exposed but underlies modern, predominantly fine floodplain sediments. The term was proposed by Gibbard (1985). Equivalent aggradations occur in tributary valleys, including the Fleet Valley Member (stratotype: TQ 314909) and the Roding Valley Member (stratotype: TQ 436839) (also separate notes for other valleys).

(25) Tilbury Member. Type-area: around Tilbury. It comprises fine-grained deposits of silt, clay, mud, peat, marl, tufa, sand and gravel that underlie the marsh and water meadow land fringing the rivers east of central London. In the Lower Thames valley, Devoy (1979) recognized five discrete biogenic beds (numbered Tilbury T I-V), separated by inorganic beds (Thames I-V) based on the World's End, Tilbury stratotype (TQ 64667540). The term Tilbury Member was defined by Gibbard (1994) for the sediments overlying the Shepperton Member and tributary valley equivalents The Tilbury deposits pass laterally into the Staines Member in the Middle Thames area (Gibbard 1985, 1994).

Kennett and Pang Valleys

P. Collins

(1) Kennett Valley Formation. This is characterized by gravels dominated by flint, subordinate quartzite and traces of chalk and vein quartz. It includes several members (notes 2 to 10 below). Terrace surfaces are developed on these units (Thomas 1961; Walder 1967; Chartres 1980; Cheetham 1980).

(2) Cold Ash Member. Stratotype: 3 m of sandy gravel on bedrock at Cold Ash [SU 507715].

(3) Bucklebury Member. Stratotype: 5 m of sandy gravels on bedrock at Furze Hill [SU 426687] (White 1902).

(4) Silchester Member. Stratotype: 5 m of sandy gravel on bedrock at Silchester [SU 625620]. It is confluent with the Black Park Member of the Maidenhead Formation (Middle Thames) near Henley (White 1902; Walder 1967; Thomas 1961; Gibbard 1982) (Middle Thames, note 25) and Blackwater-Loddon Callow Hill/Heckfield Heath Member at Shinfield, Reading (Blackwater/Loddon valley, note 7) (Gibbard 1982). It is Anglian in age on the basis of lithostratigraphical correlation downstream.

(5) Hamstead Marshall Member. Stratotype: up to 3 m of sandy gravels on bedrock at Hamstead Marshall [SU 415665]

Table 13. *Correlations between the Kennett, Pang, Blackwater, Loddon, Mole, Wey and Wandle Valleys and oxygen isotope stratigraphy*

δ¹⁸O	1973	KENNET & PANG VALLEYS	BLACKWATER-LODDON VALLEYS	COLNE VALLEY	MOLE-WEY VALLEYS	WANDLE VALLEY
1	Flandrian	**KENNET VALLEY FORMATION** (1)	**BLACKWATER-LODDON FORMATION** (3)	**COLNE FORMATION** (4)	**MOLE-WEY FORMATION** 4	**WANDLE FORMATION** (1)
		Midgham Member (10)	Staines Member (13)	Staines Member (12)	Staines Member (13)	Staines Member (9)
2	Devensian	Heale's Lock Member (9)	Whistley Mill Member (12)	Colney Street Member (11) / Langley Member (10) / Kempton Park member (9)	Mole Valley Member (12)	Wandle Valley Member (8)
3		Brimpton Member (8)	Woodley Member (11)	Horton Close Member (8)	Byfleet Member (11) / Wreccelsham Member (10)	Mitcham Member (7)
4						
5			Farnham Members (10)			
5e	Ipswichian					
6	Wolstonian	Thatcham Member (7) / Boxford Member (6) / Hamstead Marshall Member (5)	Twyford Member (9) / Beech Lane Member (8)	Denham Village Member (7) / Goulds Green Member (6) / Broom Warren Member (5) / Rose Green Bed 3 / (Hatfield Member 2)	Farnham members (9)	Halling Park/Wrythe Member (6) / Fairfield Member (5)
to						
?10						
9	Hoxnian					
to						
11						
12?	Anglian	Silchester Member (4)	Callow Hill & Heckfield Heath members (7) / Burleigh & Warren Heath members (6) / Chobham Common & Fox Hills (5) & Easthamstead (4) members	**LOWESTOFT FORMATION** / Smug Oak Member (1)	Oxshott Heath (8) / Finchley Member (7) / Coldfall Wood Member (6) / St George's Hill Member (5)	Effra Member (4)
pre-12		Bucklebury Member (3) / Cold Ash Member (2)	**CAESAR'S CAMP FORMATION** (2) / **RED CRAG FORMATION** / Netley Heath Member (1)		**PEBBLE GRAVEL FORMATION** (1) / Northaw Member (3) / Stanmore Member (2)	Norwood Member (3) / Shooter's Hill Member (2)

(Chartres *et al.* 1976; Bridgland 1994).

(6) Boxford Member. Stratotype: at Boxford [SU 415717]. It is limited to the Lambourn Valley and consists of up to 4 m of periglacially disturbed sandy gravel that includes large diameter (> 1.5 m) sarsens and flint clasts.

(7) Thatcham Member. Stratotype: up to 4 m of sandy gravel on bedrock at Thatcham [SU 499673] (Chartres 1980; Cheetham 1980).

(8) Brimpton Member. Stratotype: up to 8 m of sandy gravels in a depression on London Clay at Brimpton [SU 568651]. It is overlain by up to 2 m of silty gravel that, elsewhere, overlies Chalk and Tertiary rocks (Bryant *et al.* 1983; Worsley & Collins 1995).

(9) Heale's Lock Member. Stratotype: sandy gravel on bedrock at Heale's Lock [SU 565664]. It is normally up to 4 m, but locally up to 12 m in thickness (Worsley & Collins 1995; Collins *et al.* 1996). It is correlated with the Kennet floodplain gravel of Gibbard (1985) and with the Shepperton Member (Middle Thames, note 36).

(10) Midgham Member. Stratotype: fossiliferous silt, peat/tufa, sand and gravel at Midgham [SU 564663]. It is laterally heterogeneous and up to 3 m in thickness. It overlies the Heales Lock Member (Holyoak 1983; Worsley & Collins 1995), and is correlated with the Staines Member (Middle Thames, note 37).

Blackwater – Loddon Valleys

P. L. Gibbard

(1) Netley Heath Member (Red Crag Formation, South and East Suffolk, note 1). Stratotype: gravel and sand with marine fossils between 152 and 204 m O.D. at Netley Heath [TQ 080495] (Dines & Edmunds 1929).

(2) Caesar's Camp Formation. Comprises high-level gravels in the area west of Aldershot. It is 6 m thick and predominantly comprises flint with subordinate quartz and Greensand chert pebbles (Dines & Edmunds 1929; Clarke & Dixon 1981; Clarke & Fisher 1983).

(3) Blackwater–Loddon Formation. This is characterized by gravels dominated by flint and with subordinate quartz and Greensand chert (Gibbard 1994; Gibbard & Allen 1995). Terrace surfaces are developed on its members (Clarke & Dixon 1981).

(4) Easthampstead Member. Stratotype: gravel and sand on bedrock at Easthampstead [SU 858655] (Gibbard 1982).

(5) Chobham Common Member & Fox Hills Member. Stratotypes: at Chobham Common [SU 949650] and Fox Hills [SU 915550]. Both consist of gravel and sand on bedrock (Gibbard 1982).

(6) Burleigh Member & Warren Heath Members. Stratotypes: at Burleigh [SU 909698] and Warren Heath [SU 775598]. Both consist of gravel and sand on bedrock (Gibbard 1982).

(7) Callow Hill Member & Heckfield Heath Member. Stratotypes: at Callow Hill [SU 996690] and Heckfield Heath [SU 717627]. Both consist of gravel and sand resting on bedrock (Gibbard 1982). They are correlated with the Silchester Member of the Kennett Valley (Kennett & Pang Valleys, note 4) and the Mole–Wey Oxshott Heath Member (Mole–Wey Valleys, note 8). They are possibly equivalent to the Dippenhall Member of the Wey valley (Mole–Wey Valleys, note 9).

(8) Beech Lane Member. Stratotype: gravel and sand at Beech Lane [SU 747707]. It is the equivalent of the Boyn Hill Member of the Thames (Middle Thames, note 28) (Gibbard 1985).

(9) Twyford Member. Stratotype: gravel and sand at Twyford [SU 790772]. It is the equivalent of the Lynch Hill Member of the Thames (Middle Thames, note 29).

(10) Farnham Members (Mole–Wey Valleys, note 9).

(11) Woodley Member. Stratotype: gravel and sand at Woodley [SU 775733]. It is the equivalent of the Reading Town Member of the Middle Thames (Middle Thames, note 33).

(12) Whistley Mill Member. Stratotype: gravel and sand at Whistley Mill [SU 788745]. It is the equivalent of the Shepperton Member of the Middle Thames (Middle Thames, note 36). It includes channel fills of fossiliferous fine-grained sediments that have yielded evidence for cold, full- and late-glacial flora (e.g. at Mychett: Gibbard unpublished).

(13) Staines Member (Middle Thames, note 37).

Colne Valley

(see also Vale of St. Albans)

P. L. Gibbard

(1) Smug Oak Member (Lowestoft Formation, Middle Thames, notes 18 & 23). Possibly regarded as earliest evidence of the River Colne, but it consists of up to 6 m of glacial outwash (Gibbard 1985). It is confluent with Black Park Member (Maidenhead Formation) of the Thames at Uxbridge (Middle Thames, note 25).

(2) Hatfield Member (Middle Thames, note 26).

(3) Rose Green Bed. Stratotype: colluvial and lacustrine deposits in hollows at Rose Green [TL 212075] (Gibbard 1974). Strata H and I of Sparks *et al.* (1969).

(4) Colne Formation. This is characterized by gravels dominated by angular and with subordinate rounded flint, quartz and minor exotic lithologies, and associated sediments.

(5) Broom Warren Member. Stratotype: gravel and sand at Broom Warren [TQ 024845]. It is the equivalent of the Boyn Hill Member of the Thames (Middle Thames, note 28).

(6) Gould's Green Member. Stratotype: gravel and sand at Gould's Green [TQ 082808]. It is the equivalent of the Lynch Hill Member of the Thames (Middle Thames, note 29). Overlain at type locality by the Langley Member.

(7) Denham Village Member. Stratotype: gravel and sand at Denham [TQ 041863]. It is the equivalent of the Taplow Member of the Thames (Middle Thames, note 30).

(8) Horton Close Member. Stratotype: gravel, sand and silt at Horton Close [TQ 070802]. It contains a fossil assemblage that indicates correlation with the first half of the Ipswichian (Gibbard & Boreham unpublished).

(9) Kempton Park Member. (Middle Thames, note 34).

(10) Langley Member. (Middle Thames, note 35).

(11) Colney Street Member. Stratotype: gravel and sand at Colney Street [TL 151014]. It is the equivalent of the Shepperton Member of the Thames (Middle Thames, note 36). It includes channel fills of fossiliferous fine-grained sediments throughout the valley – evidence for cold, full- and late-glacial flora and fauna. Radiocarbon dates span the period 14.3 to 11.2 ka inclusively (Godwin 1964; Coope 1982; Gibbard & Hall 1982; Gibbard 1985).

(12) Staines Member. (Middle Thames, note 37).

Mole and Wey Valleys

P. L. Gibbard

(1) Pebble Gravel Formation. (Middle Thames, note 2).

(2) Stanmore Member. Stratotype: Harrow Weald Common [TQ 147929]. Previously termed '500 foot' or 'Higher' Pebble Gravel (Wooldridge 1960; Green & McGregor 1978a). In part of Mole-Wey origin (Bridgland 1994) (Middle Thames, note 6).

(3) Northaw Member. Stratotype: Northaw Great Wood [TQ 281040]. Previously termed '400 foot' or 'Lower' Pebble Gravel (Wooldridge 1960; Avery & Catt 1983). In part of Mole-Wey origin (Bridgland 1994).

(4) Mole–Wey Formation. This is characterized by gravels dominated by flint and with subordinate quartz and Greensand chert. It includes deposits of the previous Mole–Wey drainage that crossed the present Thames Valley (Wooldridge & Linton 1955 [first published 1939]). These consist of the St. George's Hill (5) and Finchley (7) members. Because the St. George's Hill Member is equivalent to the Winter Hill Member of the Middle Thames it is also part of the Middle Thames Formation (Middle Thames & Vale of St. Albans, note 16). Similarly, the Finchley Member and the Coldfall Wood Member is part of the Lowestoft Formation (Central East Anglia, note 12).

(5) St. George's Hill Member. Stratotype: at St. George's Hill [TQ 085624]. It is the equivalent of the Blackwater-Loddon Burleigh Member (Blackwater–Loddon note 6) and the Winter Hill Member (Middle Thames, notes 16) at Dollis Hill in north London [TQ 235862] (Gibbard 1977, 1979, 1983).

(6) Coldfall Wood Member. Stratotype: Coldfall Wood [TQ 276901]. It consists of lacustrine laminated silt and clay deposited when the Anglian ice-sheet blocked the former Mole-Wey drainage (Gibbard 1979).

(7) Finchley Member. Stratotype: at Finchley [TQ 255901]. It consists of till in the Finchley–Cockfosters–Hendon area that is correlated with the Eastend Green Member in the Vale of St. Albans (Gibbard 1979, 1983) (Middle Thames note 22).

(8) Oxshott Heath Member. Stratotype at Oxshott Heath [TQ 141614]. It is the equivalent of the Callow Hill Member (Blackwater-Loddon Valleys, note 7) (Gibbard 1979, 1982). It is possibly equivalent to the Dippenhall Member (Farnham members – below) (Oakley 1939).

(9) Farnham members (not subdivided). These are identified morphologically as Terraces A, B and C in descending order and consist of sand and gravel up to 2.5 m and include the Dippenhall Member (Gibbard 1979). They have yielded Palaeolithic artefacts (Oakley 1939).

(10) Wrecclesham Member. Stratotype: at Wrecclesham [SU 820446]. This was originally identified as Farnham Terrace D (note 9), gravel and sand with a fossiliferous channel fill (Bryant *et al.* 1983; Gibbard *et al.* 1987). Mousterian artefacts occur. Radiocarbon ages from channel samples: 36 to 27 ka; TL ages: 106 and 107 ka (Gibbard *et al.* 1987).

(11) Byfleet Member. Stratotype at Byfleet (stratotype: SU 836466). Correlated with the Kempton Park Member (Middle Thames, note 34) (Gibbard 1985). It may be equivalent to Farnham Terrace E deposits (Dines & Edmonds 1929; Oakley 1939), and the Bramley Wey First Terrace (Thurrell *et al.* 1968).

(12) Mole Valley Member. Correlated with the Shepperton Member (Middle Thames, note 36) (Gibbard 1985). It may be equivalent to the Mickleham Bed (stratotype: TQ 169514) that consists of chalky fan gravels (Docherty 1969).

(13) Staines Member. (Middle Thames, note 37).

Wandle Valley

P. L. Gibbard

(1) Wandle Formation. Gravels dominated by flint, with subordinate quartz and Greensand chert. It is subdivided into members associated with the development of the Wandle Valley. High level members are correlated with the Epping Forest Formation (Lower Thames, note 1). Lower members are confluent with the Maidenhead Formation (Middle Thames, note 24). These gravels are poorer in Greensand chert than those of the Mole–Wey Valley (Gibbard 1994).

(2) Shooter's Hill Member. Stratotype: at Shooter's Hill [TQ 436765]. This is the upstream equivalent of the High Beach Member (Lower Thames, note 2) (Gibbard 1994).

(3) Norwood Member. Stratotype: gravel and sands at Norwood [TQ 333700] (Peake 1971, 1982). Also called the Crystal Palace Gravels (Macklin 1981). It is the possible equivalent to the Debden Green Member (Lower Thames, note 3) (Gibbard 1994).

(4) Effra Member. Stratotype: gravels and sands at Effra [TQ 327655] (Peake 1971, 1982). It is the possible equivalent to the Buckhurst Hill or Woodford Members (Lower Thames, notes 4 & 5) (Gibbard 1995).

(5) Fairfield Member. Stratotype: gravel and sand at Fairfield [TQ 327655]; parastratotype at [TQ 291739]. Correlated with the Lynch Hill Member (Middle Thames, note 29).

(6) Halling Park/Wrythe Member. Stratotype: gravel and sand at Halling Park [TQ 280700]; parastratotype at [TQ 275656] (Peake 1971, 1982). The possible equivalent of the Taplow Member (Middle Thames, note 30).

(7) Mitcham Member. Stratotype: gravel and sand at Mitcham [TQ 280682] (Peake 1971, 1982). The possible equivalent of the Kempton Park Member (Middle Thames, note 34) (Gibbard 1985).

(8) Wandle Valley Member. Stratotype: gravel and sand beneath modern floodplain alluvium in the Wandle Valley at [TQ 294653]. Originally named the Floodplain Terrace (Peake 1971, 1982). Correlated with the Shepperton Member (Middle Thames, note 36) (Gibbard 1985). Silt lenses in the gravels (ascribed to the Mitcham Terrace) contain cold climate Coleoptera (Peake 1971) radiocarbon dated to $10\,130 \pm 120$ BP.

(9) Staines Member. (Middle Thames, note 37). Organic material beneath the floodplain surface near Mitcham [TQ 279683] (Peake 1971).

Lea Valley

P. L. Gibbard

(1) Hoddesdon Member (Lowestoft Formation, Central East Anglia, note 12).

(2) Lea Formation. Consists of gravel, sand and associated sediments aligned along present valley of the River Lea. The material is predominantly flint with minor exotic constituents.

(3) Stamford Hill Member. Stratotype: 8 m of gravels and sands at Stamford Hill [TQ 340877]. These contain Palaeolithic artefacts (Wymer 1968; Gibbard 1994). Correlated with the

Table 14. *Correlations between the Lea, Darent, Cray and Medway Valleys and Southeast Essex (Dengie Peninsula and Southend Area & the Tendring Plateau) and oxygen isotope stratigraphy*

stage	δ¹⁸O	LEA VALLEY	DARENT & CRAY VALLEYS	MEDWAY VALLEY	DENGIE PENINSULA & SOUTHEND	TENDRING PLATEAU
Flandrian	1	**LEA FORMATION** (2) Tilbury Member (11)	**DARENT FORMATION** (3) Tilbury Member (8)	**MEDWAY VALLEY FORMATION** (1) Tilbury Member (13)	**LOWER THAMES FORMATION** (7) Tilbury Member (14) Essex Coast Member (13)	**LOWER THAMES FORMATION** (8) Tilbury Member (14) Essex Coast Member (13)
Devensian	2			Aylesford Member (12)		
	3	Lea Valley Member (10) Spring Wood Member (9) Leyton Member (8) Hackney Downs Member (7)	Darent Valley Member (7) Hawley Member (6)	Holling member (11) Binney Member (10)	Shepperton Member (12)	Shepperton Member (12)
	4					
	5					
Ipswichian	5e	Highbury Member (6) Waterhall Farm Member (5)			Barling Member (11)	Barling Member (11)
Wolstonian	6	Leytonstone Member (4) Stamford Hill Member (3)		Stoke Member (9) Newhall Member (8) Shakespeare Farm Member (7)	Asheldham Member (part) (8)	Mersea Island Member (10)
	to					
	10					
Hoxnian	9 to 11				Tillingham Member (10) Shoeburyness Member (9)	Clacton Member (9)
Anglian	12?	**LOWESTOFT FORMATION** Hoddesdon Member (1)	Dartford Heath Member (5) Darenth Wood Member (4)	Dagenham Farm Member (6)	Asheldham Member (8) Caidge Member (7) St. Lawrence Member (6)	**LOWESTOFT FORMATION** (7) Holland member (6) Wivenhoe Member (5)
pre-Anglian	pre-12		**PEBBLE GRAVEL FORMATION** (1) Warley Member (2)	Holland Member () Clinch Street Member (5) High Halstow Member (4) Lodge Hill Member (3) Cobham Park Member (2)	**KESGRAVE FORMATION** (1) Mayland Member (5) Ashingdon Member (4) Oakwood Member (3) Daws Heath Member (2)	**KESGRAVE FORMATION** (1) Little Oakley (4) Ardleigh Member (3) Waldringfield Member (2)

Corbets Tey Member (Lower Thames, note 15).

(4) Leytonstone Member. Stratotype: 8 m of gravels and sands at Leytonstone [TQ 373898]. Correlated with the Mucking Member (Lower Thames, note 17) (Gibbard 1994).

(5) Waterhall Farm Member. Stratotype: sands, silt and marl at Waterhall Farm [TL 299099] that have yielded mammalian and other vertebrate material beneath the low terrace. Probably Ipswichian (Gibbard 1974, 1977).

(6) Highbury Member. Stratotype: at Highbury [TQ 340857]. A sequence of yellow to grey sand, silt and organic sediments overlying Leytonstone Member gravel and sand and overlain by slope deposits ('brickearth') in the Hackney Downs, Shacklewell and Highbury areas. Correlated with the Ipswichian (Gibbard 1994).

(7) Hackney Downs Member. Stratotype: gravel and sand at Hackney Downs [TQ 34578613]. It rests locally on the Highbury or Leytonstone Members or bedrock (Gibbard 1994).

(8) Leyton Member. Stratotype: gravels and sands at Leyton [TQ 848613]. Maximum thickness 5m (Gibbard 1994). Correlated with the East Tilbury Marshes Member (Lower Thames, note 22).

(9) Spring Wood Bed. Stratotype: silt at Spring Wood [TL 297102].

(10) Lea Valley Member. Stratotype: gravel and sand in the Lea Valley at [TQ 3595]; parastratotype at [TQ 387828]. It underlies the modern floodplain and a 'Low Terrace'. It may include two separate units: an older one, including fossiliferous channel sediments (the 'Lea Valley Arctic Bed'); and a younger infill of gravel and sand (Wymer 1985; Gibbard 1994). The older one represents the 'Ponder's End Stage' of Warren (1916). The organic beds contained cold climate plant assemblages with radiocarbon ages of 28 000 to 21 530 BP. The Lea Valley Member extends upstream at least as far as the Hertford area and is correlated (possibly only the younger subunit) with the Shepperton Member (Lower Thames, note 24) (Gibbard 1994).

(11) Tilbury Member (Lower Thames, note 25).

Darent–Cray Valleys

P. L. Gibbard

(1) Pebble Gravel (Middle Thames & Vale of St. Albans, note 2).

(2) Warley Member (Middle Thames & Vale of St. Albans, note 7).

(3) Darent Formation. This consists of Darent Valley deposits.

(4) Darenth Wood Member. Stratotype: 20 cm of gravel and sand of Weald origin at Darenth Wood [TQ 572718]. Probably deposited by the Darent (Gibbard 1994).

(5) Dartford Heath Member. (Lower Thames, note 12).

(6) Hawley Member. About 6 m of gravel and sand at Hawley [TQ 553718] (Gibbard 1994).

(7) Darent Valley Member. Stratotype: 3 m of gravel and sand at [TQ 555714]. It is overlain by the Tilbury Member (Lower Thames, note 25). The gravel consists almost totally of flint, with less than 2% of small quartz pebbles and Greensand chert. Possible equivalent of the Shepperton Member (Lower Thames, note 24) (Gibbard 1994). It contains a subarctic mammalian fauna and archaeological implements (Carreck unpublished).

(8) Tilbury Member (Lower Thames, note 25).

Medway Valley

D. R. Bridgland

(1) Medway Valley Formation. This consists of the gravel and sand units of River Medway origin. It was previously called the Hoo Gravel Formation (Bridgland & Harding 1985). It is best preserved on the Hoo Peninsula, between the estuaries of the Thames and Medway. All its members that are separated on an altitudinal basis contain a characteristic assemblage of flint, Greensand (mostly chert) and rare Hastings Beds rocks. These are correlated with gravel units in the Southend area, the post- diversion Thames sequence Low-level East Essex Formation and pre-Thames diversion units of the High-level East Essex Formation.

(2) Cobham Park Member. Stratotype: gravel and sand at Cobham Park [TQ 700684] mapped by the Geological Survey as '? Pliocene' (1951, New Series, Sheet 272, Chatham). But an Early Pleistocene age is considered more likely by comparison with Middle Thames sequences and on the basis of its altitude. It has no known equivalents (Bridgland 1983a, 1989; Bridgland & Harding 1985).

(3) Lodge Hill Member. Stratotype: gravel and sand at Lodge Hill [TQ 757739] resting on bedrock (Bridgland 1983a, 1989; Bridgland & Harding 1985).

(4) High Halstow Member. Stratotype: gravel and sand at High Halstow [TQ 782753] on bedrock. It is the possible upstream equivalent of one of the high-level members in Easterm Essex (Eastern Essex, note 1) (Bridgland 1983a, 1989; Bridgland & Harding 1985).

(5) Clinch Street Member. Stratotype: gravel and sand at Clinch Street [TQ 790761]. It is preserved only on the Hoo Peninsula, although downstream equivalents may occur in Essex (Bridgland 1983a, 1989; Bridgland & Harding 1985).

(6) Dagenham Farm Member. Stratotype: gravel and sand at Dagenham Farm [TQ 828777]. Correlation with other units is problematical (Bridgland 1983a, 1989; Bridgland & Harding 1985).

(7) Shakespeare Farm Member. Stratotype: About 3 m of gravel and sand at Shakespeare Farm Member [TQ 814774] at 30 m O.D. Locally, a deeper channel-fill extends down to below 20 m O.D. Palaeolithic artefacts are found in this unit (Bridgland 1983a, 1989; Bridgland & Harding 1985).

(8) Newhall Member. Stratotype: gravel and sand at Newhall [TQ 830768]. Palaeolithic artefacts may come from this unit (Bridgland 1983a, 1989; Bridgland & Harding 1985).

(9) Stoke Member. Stratotype: gravel and sand at Stoke [TQ 822748] (Bridgland 1983a, 1989; Bridgland & Harding 1985).

(10) Binney Member. Stratotype: gravel and sand at Binney [TQ 848774] (Bridgland 1983a, 1989; Bridgland & Harding 1985).

(11) Halling Member. Stratotype: gravel and sand at Halling [TQ 705605] (Cook & Killick 1924). The name Halling was linked to the 'Lower Floodplain Terrace' of the Thames-Medway system by King and Oakley (1936). It underlies the Tilbury Member (Medway Valley, note 13) and may be the same as the lowest submerged aggradation offshore from the Thames estuary (Bridgland & D'Olier 1995; Bridgland & Harding 1985; Bridgland 1989) It contains a subarctic mammalian fauna and archaeological implements (Carreck, unpublished).

(12) Aylesford Member. The 'second terrace' of the River Medway [TQ 728595] which may represent an Early Devensian aggradation. It contains a temperate fauna and archaeological implements (Carreck 1964) as well as *Mammuthus*.

(13) Tilbury (Lower Thames, note 25).

The Tendring Plateau, Dengie Peninsula and the Southend area

P. L. Gibbard

Dengie Peninsula and Southend area

(1) Kesgrave Formation (South & East Suffolk. note 11). It comprises Thames gravels and sands including a high frequency of quartz and quartzite pebbles of Midlands origin. It was first defined by Rose *et al.* (1976) and Rose and Allen (1977), and was divided into a Sudbury Formation (higher) and a Colchester Formation (lower). Later the term Kesgrave Group was proposed by Whiteman and Rose (1992). The Kesgrave Formation is correlated with the Middle Thames Formation (Middle Thames, note 8). In this region it consists of gravel, sand and associated sediments of pre-Anglian age deposited by the Medway and is dominated by Weald lithologies, particularly Lower Greensand chert and 'Tertiary' flint.

(2) Daws Heath Member. Stratotype: sand and gravel at Daws Heath [TQ 806888]. This includes the Claydons Gravel of Bridgland (1994). It may be the correlative of the Bures Member of the Thames (Bridgland 1988, 1994) (Eastern England, Eastern Essex, note 4).

(3) Oakwood Member. Stratotype: gravel and sand at Oakwood [TQ 823883]. Possible upstream equivalent of the Moreton Member of the Thames (Bridgland 1988, 1994) (Eastern England, Eastern Essex, note 5).

(4) Ashingdon Member. Stratotype: gravel and sand at Ashingdon [TQ 854933]. Possible upstream equivalent of the Waldringfield Member of the Thames (Bridgland 1988, 1994). (Tendring Plateau, note 6).

(5) Mayland Member. Stratotype: gravel and sand at Mayland [TQ 833764]. Possible upstream equivalent of the Little Oakley Member of the Thames (Bridgland 1988, 1994). It includes the 'Belfairs Gravel' of Bridgland (1994).

(6) St. Lawrence Member. Stratotype: gravel and sand at St. Lawrence [TQ 897468]. Possible upstream equivalent of the Wivenhoe Member of the Thames (Bridgland 1988, 1994). It includes the 'Canewdon Gravel' of Bridgland (1994).

(7) Caidge Member. Stratotype: gravel and sand at Caidge [TQ 657636]. Possible upstream equivalent of Thames' Holland Member (Bridgland 1988, 1994). It includes the 'Chalkwell Gravel' of Bridgland (1994).

(8) Asheldham Member. Stratotype: gravel and sand at Asheldham [TL 973017]; parastratotype at [TL 993057]. The oldest Thames–Medway unit consists of fluvial and lacustrine deposits (Bridgland 1988, 1994; Gibbard 1994). Bridgland (1988, 1994) considers that his 'Southchurch/Asheldham Formation' also includes a substantial channel fill of gravel overlying interglacial estuarine sediments ('Southend Channel interglacial deposits'). But Gibbard (1994) and Gibbard *et al.* (1995*a*, *b*) suggest that the channel fill sediments post-date the Southchurch/Asheldham aggradation and that the member is the downstream equivalent of Dartford Heath Member (Lower Thames, note 12) and is, therefore, late Anglian. It includes the 'Southchurch Gravel' of Bridgland (1994).

(9) Shoeburyness. Stratotype: at Shoeburyness [TQ 855934]. Freshwater-estuarine silt, sand, organic sediment, and basal

gravel and sand, filling a large channel. It is believed to be the equivalent of the Tillingham Member and is, therefore, Hoxnian (Tendring Plateau, note 10) (Roe 1994).

(10) Tillingham Member: Stratotype: East Hyde [TQ 980041]. It comprises silt, sand, organic sediment and basal gravel and sand filling substantial channels at sites such as East Mersea and Tillingham. It is freshwater and estuarine in origin and is correlated with the Hoxnian (Roe 1994, 1995).

(11) Barling Member. Stratotype: gravel and sand at Barling [TQ 931901] (Gruhn *et al.* 1974). Bridgland *et al.* (1993) correlate this with the Corbets Tey Member (Lower Thames, note 15).

(12) Shepperton Member (Middle Thames note 36). This underlies the Tilbury Member and is submerged offshore (Bridgland *et al.* 1993).

(13) Tilbury Member. Comprises fine-grained deposits of silt, clay, mud, peat, marl, tufa, sand and gravel that underlie the marsh and water meadow land fringing the rivers (Lower Thames note 25).

(14) Essex Coast Member. Stratotype: coastal marsh and associated sediments at Ridgemarsh [TQ 029940] shown by radiocarbon ages to span the last 7000 years (Greensmith & Tucker 1980).

Tendring Plateau

(1) Kesgrave Formation

(2) Waldringfield Member (East Anglia, South & East Suffolk, note 16).

(3) Ardleigh Member. Stratotype: gravel and sand at Ardleigh [TM 053283] (Bridgland 1994). This was deposited upstream of the Thames confluence with Medway and is correlated with the the Little Oakley Member downstream (Bridgland *et al.* 1990; Bridgland 1994; Whiteman & Rose 1992). It contains fossiliferous organic sediments at Ardleigh and at Broomfield where palaeobotanical assemblages of early Middle Pleistocene 'Cromerian Complex' age have been discovered (Bridgland 1994; Gibbard *et al.* 1996).

(4) Little Oakley Member. Stratotype: fossiliferous silts, sands and associated sediments of 'Cromerian' (*s.l.*) age at Little Oakley [TM 223294] (Bridgland *et al.* 1990). D-aIle/L-Ile ratios from *Valvata piscinalis* are: 0.324 ± 0.004 (2) and 0.336 ± 0.027 (4) (Bridgland 1994).

(5) Wivenhoe Member. Stratotype: gravel and sand at Wivenhoe [TM 048232]. This was deposited upstream of the Thames confluence with the Medway. It is the 'Kesgrave Thames' equivalent to the 'Kesgrave Thames-Medway' 'Cooks Green Member' of Bridgland (1988, 1994). It is overlain by the fossiliferous 'Wivenhoe Bed' organic sediments that contain palaeobotanical assemblages of possible early Middle Pleistocene 'Cromerian Complex' age (Bridgland 1994).

(6) Holland Member. Stratotype: gravel and sand at Holland on Sea [TM 211166]. It was deposited downstream of the Thames confluence with the Medway and is equivalent to the 'Kesgrave Thames' 'St. Osyth Member' of Bridgland *et al.* (1988) and Bridgland (1994) upstream at [TM 120174]. The upper part of both consists of outwash (Lowestoft Formation – Central East Anglia, note 12) and Medway fluvial sediment. It is Anglian in age (Bridgland 1988, 1994).

(7) Lowestoft Formation (Central East Anglia, note 12).

(8) Lower Thames Formation (Thames Valley, Lower Thames, note 11). It comprises gravel, sand and associated sediments of Thames-Medway origin in this area. It also includes some members of the Medway Valley Formation.

(9) Clacton Member. Stratotype: at Clacton [TM 144127]. Silt, sand, organic sediment and basal gravel and sand filling channels. First recognized by Warren (1923). Fossil assemblages indicate that the sediments are Hoxnian. D-aIle/L-Ile ratios of 0.3 ± 0.001 (2) (*Trichia*) and 0.3 ± 0.002 (3) (*Cepaea*) correlate the Clacton member with the Swanscombe Member (Bowen *et al.* 1989). They have yielded an important Palaeolithic assemblage.

(10) Mersea Island Member. Stratotype: gravel and sand at Mersea Island [TM 014137]. Bridgland (1988, 1994) considers this to be of Thames origin but it may represent the River Blackwater. It overlies Hoxnian sediments unconformably at Cudmore Grove, East Mersea (Roe 1994).

(11) Barling Member (Dengie Peninsula & Southend, note 11)

(12) Shepperton Member (Dengie Peninsula & Southend, note 12)

(13) Tilbury Member (Lower Thames, note 25).

(14) Essex Coast Member (Dengie Peninsula & Southend, note 13)

Chapter 5

South and Southeast England

P. L. GIBBARD & R. C. PREECE

With contributions from M. R. Bates, D. H. Keen, M. Waller & A. Long

South and Southeast England consists of the counties south of the Thames catchment, and east of the Dorset–Devon border. Spreads of Pleistocene gravels and sands occur extensively at a wide range of altitudes, where they cap interfluves and plateaux, underlie terraces, occur beneath the modern rivers or underlie now submerged terraces beneath the Solent, Southampton Water and nearshore shelf. Colluvial and aeolian sediments are abundant throughout the region, while marine littoral accumulations occur close to the coast. Dry valley fills and doline infillings occur locally in areas underlain by Chalk bedrock.

The Hampshire Basin was drained by a major trunk stream of comparable size and antiquity to the Thames. This 'Solent River' previously flowed eastwards across southeast Dorset and south Hampshire as an extension of the modern River Frome and therefore formed the major axial stream of the Hampshire Basin (Everard 1954; Allen & Gibbard 1994). Much of what may have been its lower course was drowned by eustatic sea-level rise during the Holocene and a large area of the southern catchment has been lost to marine coastal erosion. Extensive deposits of this river and its tributaries occur in southeast Dorset, south-west Hampshire and the Isle of Wight. Tributary streams, particularly those draining Hampshire, Dorset and Wiltshire, such as the Hampshire Avon, Stour and Test also have significant aggradations. Palaeolithic artefacts are associated with some of the lower gravels, but most are devoid of archaeology and are unfossiliferous.

A complicating factor is long-term tectonic uplift that is reflected in the stairway-like distribution of coastal sediment accumulations in the Hampshire–West Sussex area and potentially (Preece et al. 1990); while uplift of the Weald–Artois axis has also occurred (Smith 1985a, b, 1989).

The major problem with the study of the plateau gravels of fluvial, coastal or colluvial origin is the lack of chronology both as geochronology and for correlation. Although the sequences probably represent a considerable part of the Pleistocene, the ages of the gravels themselves can rarely be determined directly, and the absence of associated datable material generally renders the age of the sequences uncertain. Pre-Holocene organic deposits within fluvial aggradations are known at low-level, such as those at Stone Point (West & Sparks 1960; Brown et al. 1975), in the Avon Valley at Ibsley (Barber & Brown 1987), in the Newtown River estuary on the Isle of Wight (Munt & Burke 1987) and at Pennington Marshes (Allen et al. 1995) in fluvial aggradations. Similarly, coastal sediments at low level include fossiliferous sequences at Selsey (West & Sparks, 1960), Bembridge (Preece et al. 1990)

and Black Rock (White 1924; Hodgson 1964). High-level fossiliferous accumulations are rare but are known from Bembridge School, on the Isle of Wight (Holyoak & Preece 1983; Preece et al. 1990) and at Boxgrove, near Chichester (Roberts 1986; Roberts et al. 1994; Bates et al. 1997; Roberts & Parfitt in press).

The general lack of pre-Holocene biostratigraphical and geochronological control, coupled with the fact that area has remained beyond the maximum glacial limit throughout the Pleistocene, give rise to currently intractable stratigraphical problems. The extra-glacial location means that no exotic clast input, that could offer potential markers by which the sequences might be related to those farther north, has apparently occurred in the river valleys. This is in contrast to the Thames Valley and the coastal aggradations.

Kent

With contributions from M. P. Waller & A. J. Long

(1) Kentish Stour Formation. Type-area: Stour Valley, Kent. This includes fluvial and associated deposits of the River Stour that occur as a series of terrace gravels of gravel along its length. Sand containing Palaeolithic implements occurs at Fordwich. It underlies a high terrace with its base at up to 40 m O.D. Its age is unknown (Dewey et al. 1925; Holmes 1971; Roe 1977). A lower or Sturry Terrace gravel and sand, also containing Palaeolithic implements, occurs 18–24 m O.D. (Dewey et al. 1925; Holmes 1971; Roe 1977).

(2) Chislet Member. Stratotype: Wear Farm, Chislet [TR 224650]. Mollusca including *Corbicula fluminalis* and *Pisidium clessini* have been obtained from sands of the Second Terrace of the River Stour near Preston [TR 244608]. *C. fluminalis* and 'Paladilhia radigueli' are also reported from Second Terrace deposits at Wear Farm [TR 223652] and Grove Ferry, near Chislet (Dewey et al. 1925; Holmes 1971).

(3) Folkestone Battery Bed. Stratotype: at Folkestone Battery [TR 231359]. Fluvial deposits about 1 m thick with temperate molluscs and *Hippopotamus*. D-aIle/L-Ile ratios from *Trichia hispida* of 0.124 ± 0.12 (13), together with other faunal evidence suggest correlation with the Ipswichian, oxygen isotope sub-stage 5e (Bridgland et al. 1995).

(4) Kennington Member. Stratotype: valley floor gravels and sands of the River Stour at Kennington [TR 030447]. It includes fossiliferous channel fills with a cold stage biota. Radiocarbon ages range between 28 and 40 000 BP.

(5) Brook Formation. Stratotype: Brook [TR 066445]; para-

Table 15. *Correlations between Kent, Sussex, Isle of Wight, Hampshire and Dorset and oxygen isotope stratigraphy*

δ18O	1973	KENT	SUSSEX	ISLE OF WIGHT	HAMPSHIRE	DORSET
1	Fn	Wateringbury Tufa (17) ROMNEY MARSH FORMATION (11) Cheyne (15) Dungeness (16) Rye (13) Dowels (14) & Robertsbridge (12) members BROOK FORMATION (5) Holywell Coombe Beds (8) Holborough Bed (7) Upper Halling Bed (6) PEGWELL FORMATION (9) Halling Quarry Bed (10)	SUSSEX VALLEYS FORMATION (17) Cuckmere Member (20) Arun Member (19) Lower Ouse Member (18) Beachy Head Bed (16) PEGWELL FORMATION (15)	Gore Cliff Bed (19) Totland Bay Tufa Bed (18) SOLENT FORMATION (1) Yarmouth Member (17) Gatcombe Bed (16) Hannover Member (15) Watcombe Bottom Bed (14)	NEW FOREST FORMATION (2) Fawley Bed (25) Cranes Moor Bed (24) Lower Avon Member (23)	Chesil Beach (17) Blashenwell Tufa Bed (16) Rimsmoor Bed (15) FROME-PIDDLE FORMATION (2) Poole Harbour Member (14) Hyde Member (13)
2	Dev					
3			WEST SUSSEX COAST FORMATION (1)	Brook Bay Member (13) Howgate Bed (12)	Holbury Member (22) Christchurch Bay Member (21) Holdenhurst Member (20) North End Copse Member (19)	Stoborough Member (12) Fisherton Bed (11)
5-4		KENTISH STOUR FORMATION (1) Kennington Member (4)				
5e	Ip	(Folkestone Battery Bed -3)	Pagham Member (14)	Lane End Member (11) Newtown Bay Bed (10) Bembridge Foreland Member (9)	Ibsley Member (18) Pennington Member (17)	
6 to	Wo	Chislet Member (2)	Supermarket Member (13) Chichester Member (12) Nyton Member (11) West Wittering Member (10) Black Rock Member (9) Life Boat Station Member (8) Norton Member (7) Cams Bridge Member (6) Ham Farm Member (5) Aldingbourne Member (4)	Priory Bay Member (8) Headon Warren Bed (7)	Stone Point Bed (16) Lepe Member (15) Milford-on-Sea Member (14) Stanswood Bay Member (13) Taddisford Farm Member (12) Tom's Down Member (11) Old Milton Member (10) Mount Pleasant Member (9) Setley Plain Member (8) Beaulieu Heath Member (7)	East Holme Member (10) Worgret Member (9) West Knighton Member (8) Stokeford Heath Member (7)
10						Higher Hyde Heath Member (6)
10 9 to 13	Ho		Eartham Member (3) Slindon Member (2)	Steyne Wood Member (6) Baring Road Member (5) Lynn Farm Member (4) Black Down Member (3) St George's Down Member (2)	Tiptoe Member (6) Sway Member (5) Holmsley Ridge Member (4) Whitefield Hill Member (3) RINGWOOD FORMATION (1)	Tonerspuddle Heath Member (5) Black Hill Member (4) Green Hill Member (3)
pre-13						Dewlish Bone Bed (1)

stratotype: the Devil's Kneadingtrough [TR 076452]. Late-glacial and Holocene slope and valley sediments flooring dry valleys and extending as lobes beyond them (Kerney *et al.* 1964; Smart *et al.* 1966; Preece 1994).

(6) Upper Halling Bed. Stratotype: at Upper Halling [TQ 692635]. Late-glacial slope deposits with Allerød soil (Kerney 1963). Radiocarbon ages range between $11\,240 \pm 110$ BP (lower half) and $10\,900 \pm 120$ BP (upper half) of the Allerød soil (Preece 1994). D-aIle-L-Ile ratios from 'layer G', corresponding to the Younger Dryas (Kerney 1963), on *Trichia hispida* are: 0.036 ± 0.001 (3) (Bowen *et al.* 1989).

(7) Holborough Bed. Late-glacial slope deposits with 'Allerød soil' at Holborough [TQ 702626] (Kerney 1963).

(8) Holywell Coombe Beds. Fossiliferous late-glacial deposits at Holywell Coombe [TR 220379] including those of colluvial, paludal and pedogenic origin, overlain by early to mid-Holocene tufa and later hillwash deposits (with artefacts). Many supporting radiocarbon dates (Kerney *et al.* 1980; Preece 1992; Preece & Bridgland 1998*a,b*).

(9) Pegwell Formation. Stratotype: Pegwell Bay [TR 353644]. Loessic deposits up to 3 m thick with cold stage molluscan fauna at some sites (Preece 1990); also termed 'head brickearth'. It includes deposits at: Faversham [TQ 993617], Bobbing [TQ 893653], Reculver [TR 204693] and Spotlane Quarry [TQ 794541] (Pitcher *et al.* 1954; Kerney, 1965). TL dates range from between 10 and 50 ka (Wintle 1981; Parks & Rendell 1992*a*).

(10) Halling Quarry Bed. Stratotype: at Halling [TQ 728595]. A periglacial deposit of loessic character with land snails, believed to be Middle Devensian in age, occurs below a full late-glacial sequence of slope deposits (Kerney 1971).

(11) Romney Marsh Formation. Type-area: Romney Marsh. Comprises fossiliferous silts, clays and peats of Holocene age that underlie the modern land surface. It attains its greatest extent and thickness along the south coast within the depositional complex of Romney Marsh. It includes the beach deposits of Dungeness foreland, the deposits of the former wetlands of Walland, Romney and Denge Marshes, and the alluvial fills of a series of valleys which run from the Weald into the western side of Walland Marsh (most notably the Rother and Brede).

(MW & AL)

(12) Robertsbridge Member. Stratotype: at Robertsbridge [TQ 743240]. Inorganic fills in the upper courses of the river valleys, commonly composed of coarse silts and up to 10 m and more in thickness. Pollen analysis suggests a mid-Holocene age (Scaife, in Burrin 1988). Over the middle courses of the valleys it interdigitates and grades into the Dowels Member (Burrin 1988; Waller *et al.* 1988).

(MW & AL)

(13) Rye Member. Stratotype: near Rye [TQ 915206]. Clays, silts and sands underlying the Dowels Member in lower valleys and across Walland Marsh. Maximum thicknesses occur near Rye (*c.*30 m) where deposition began before 6940 ± 160 (Long *et al.* 1996). Foraminifera and diatoms indicate intertidal and sub-tidal environments (Waller *et al.* 1988; Long *et al.* 1996). Interdigitates with the Dowels Member (Waller *et al.* 1988; Long & Innes 1995*a*) at a number of locations (Tooley & Switsur 1988).

(MW & AL)

(13) Dowels Member. Stratotype: at Dowells [TQ 984310]. Woody detrital moss peat that accumulated throughout the Holocene at Pannel Bridge 9960 ± 110 to 3160 ± 160 BP (Waller 1993, 1994; Long & Innes 1995*a,b*; Tooley & Switsur

1988; Long *et al.* 1996). In lower valleys and on the marshes it is underlain by the Rye Member

(MW & AL)

(15) Cheyne Member. Stratotype: at Cheyne [TQ 989219]. Formerly named the Young alluvium by Green (1968), comprising clays, silts and sands. It overlies the Dowels Member in the lower valleys (Waller *et al.* 1988; Long & Innes 1995*a*) and its maximum thickness is *c.*5 m. Palaeontology indicates intertidal and sub-tidal deposition (Waller *et al.* 1988; Long *et al.* 1996). The Cheyne Member overlies and interdigitates with the Dungeness Member (Plater 1992; Long & Hughes 1995; Plater & Long 1995).

(MW & AL)

(16) Dungeness Member. Stratotype: at Dungeness [TQ 095170]. Comprises gravels and pebbly sands that outcrop at Dungeness foreland-Denge Beach and other locations (Hey 1967*b*; Greensmith & Gutmanis 1990; Long & Hughes 1995). West of Dungeness minimum ages for gravel deposition are: 3410 ± 160 (Tooley & Switsur 1988) and 2040 ± 200 BP (Long & Hughes 1995).

(MW & AL)

(17) Wateringbury Tufa Bed. 4 m of fossiliferous Holocene tufa at Wateringbury [TQ 687535] (Kerney *et al.* 1980).

Sussex

With contributions by M. R. Bates

(1) West Sussex Coast Formation. Type area: West Sussex. Raised beaches and associated coastal or littoral sediments (Hodgson 1964).

(2) Slindon Member. Stratotype: Boxgrove [SU 920085]. Consists of up to 7 m of erratic-free flint beach gravels (the 'Slindon Gravels', often referred to as the 'Goodwood-Slindon Raised Beach') resting on a platform cut across Chalk with an upper limit at about 42 m O.D. It is replaced laterally and vertically by sands ('Slindon Sands') and overlain by silts ('Slindon Silts'). It is traced 2.5 km east (at Eman's Pit) and west (at Waterbeach). The silts contain an abundant vertebrate and molluscan fauna associated with hominid remains and artefacts (Roberts 1986; Roberts *et al.* 1994). Palaeontological evidence suggests correlation with a temperate episode at the end of the Cromerian Complex, possibly the equivalent of oxygen isotope stage 13 (Roberts *et al.* 1994; Roberts & Parfitt unpublished). D-aIle/L-Ile ratios of 0.29 ± 0.025 (27), however, suggest correlation with Swanscombe in the Lower Thames and with oxygen isotope stage 11 (Bowen & Sykes 1988, 1994).

(3) Eartham Member. Stratotype: Boxgrove [SU 920085]. Consists of up to 12 m of coarse flint solifluction gravels interstratified with silts that overlie unconformably the Slindon Member. Minimum age TL dates on the intercalated silts: 175–229 ka (Parks & Rendell 1992*a*).

(4) Aldingbourne Member. Stratotype: Aldingbourne Park Pit [SU 931071]. Consists of 6 m of marine sands (Aldingbourne Sands) and gravels (Aldingbourne Gravels) with a significant erratic content. It lies between 17 m and 25 m O.D. in a narrow strip between Chichester and Arundel along the line of the A27 road. It contains archaeological artefacts (Fowler 1932; Calkin 1934), but its age is uncertain.

(5) Ham Farm Member. Stratotype: Earnley [SZ 825947]. Consists of 1.5 m of intertidal sediments filling a channel cut into bedrock on the foreshore. Pollen of *Abies* and 'Type x' in moderate quantities suggest an interglacial of Middle Pleistocene age (West *et al.* 1984). A single D-aIle/L-Ile ratio of 0.33 was obtained from *Macoma balthica* (Preece *et al.* 1990).

(6) Cams Bridge Member. Stratotype: Cams Bridge [SU 601061]. Consists of 3 m of marine gravels and sands between 15 m and 18 m O.D. intermediate in height between the Aldingbourne and Norton Members (Palmer & Cook 1923; ApSimon *et al.* 1977). It may be the lateral equivalent of either the sediments at Ratham Mill and Sparrows Rough, east of Chichester (Shephard-Thorn *et al.* 1982), which occur at similar heights, or those of the higher Aldingbourne Member.

(7) Norton Member. Stratotype: Norton Farm [SU 925063]. Consists of 4 m of marine sands ('Norton Sands') between 5.5 m and 9.5 m O.D. and which contain abundant shells of *Macoma balthica* and microfossils. The sands are overlain by silts ('Norton Silts') that contain a non-marine molluscan assemblage and remains of horse and northern vole. It is traced to Westhampnett, 3.5 km to the west, and similar sediments have been described 4.5 km to the east at Walberton (Lovell & Nancarrow 1983). D-aIle/L-Ile ratios of 0.31 ± 0.003 (3) on *Macoma balthica* have been correlated with oxygen isotope stage 9 (Bowen & Sykes 1988); but vertebrate evidence suggests correlation with oxygen isotope stage 7. It may be the lateral equivalent of the Black Rock Member (Bates *et al.* unpublished).

(8) Life Boat Station Member. Stratotype: at [SZ 863923]. Consists of 2.8 m of freshwater and estuarine sediments between −3.8 m and −1.0 m O.D. filling channels on the foreshore. Probably overlain unconformably by the Pagham Member. It contains temperate elements including *Corbicula fluminalis* and *Palaeoloxodon antiquus* (West & Sparks 1960) together with archaeological artefacts. D-aIle/L-Ile ratios from *Corbicula fluminalis* and *Bithynia tentaculata* suggest an oxygen isotope stage 7 age (Bowen *et al.* 1989). A previous record of *Hippopotamus* has been retracted because of misidentification (Sutcliffe 1995).

(9) Black Rock Member. Stratotype: Black Rock, Brighton [TQ 334033]. Consists of 3.9 m of gravel comprising the raised beach at 8–11.9 m O.D. resting against a fossil cliffline (White 1924; Hodgson 1964). It may be the equivalent of the Norton Member.

(10) West Wittering Member. Stratotype: at West Wittering [SZ 775975]. Consists of a basal erratic-rich gravel (1.5 m thick) overlain by freshwater and estuarine deposits filling a channel cut into bedrock (Reid 1892). The lower fluvial sediments include *Corbicula fluminalis* and *Belgrandia marginata* and contain pollen rich in *Corylus*, *Quercus*, *Pinus* and *Betula* (Preece *et al.* 1990). D-aIle/L-Ile ratios from *Corbicula fluminalis* and *Bithynia tentaculata* suggest correlation with oxygen isotope stage 7 (Bowen *et al.* 1989).

(11) Nyton Member. Stratotype: Norton Farm [SU 92560638]. Consists of 4 m of coarse chalk-rich flint gravels that overlie unconformably the Norton Member, and is correlated with oxygen isotope stage 6 and, or, oxygen isotope stages 2 to 4.

(12) Chichester Member. Stratotype: Westhampnett East [SU 887057]. Consists of sub-rounded, variably decalcified flint gravels (4 m thick) unconformably overlying the Norton Member at Westhampnett East. It forms a fan from the Lavant Valley (Shephard-Thorn *et al.* 1982) and post-dates deposits correlated with oxygen isotope stage 9 or 7. Locally sedimentation may have continued into the Holocene.

(13) Supermarket Member. Stratotype: at Black Rock, Brighton [TQ 334033]. Consists of 16 m of colluvial sediments overlying a raised beach with a cold fauna. Two slope deposit units are separated by a possible fossil soil (White 1924; Hodgson 1964; Keen 1995).

(14) Pagham Member. Stratotype: Selsey Coast Guard Station [SZ 844930]. Marine gravels (1.5 m thick) that outcrop extensively between −2.0 m and +4.0 m O.D. around Chichester and Pagham Harbours and around Selsey Bill (Berry & Shephard-Thorn 1982). It probably overlies the channel deposits of the Earnley, Life Boat Station and West Wittering Members (Reid 1892; West & Sparks 1960; West *et al.* 1984).

(15) Pegwell Formation (Kent note 9). Parastratotype: at Pegwell Bay [TR 353644]. Loessic deposits (head-brickearth) up to 3 m thick with cold stage molluscan fauna (Preece 1990). TL dated at: Sussex Pad [TQ 200060] at 73–88 ka; Hope Gap [TV 510973] at 109 ka; Church Street [TQ 716044; TQ 716115] at 51–61 ka; Goring by Sea [TQ 115181] at 16 ka; Ferring [TQ 095027] at about 11 ka; and Selsey [TQ 846925] at *c.*14 ka (Parks & Rendell 1992*a,b*).

(16) Beachy Head Bed. Late-glacial slope deposits at Cow Gap [TV 595957] with an 'Allerød soil' (Kerney 1963).

(17) Sussex Valleys Formation. Type area; gravels, sands and associated organic sediments of the Lower Ouse, Arun and Cuckmere rivers.

(18) Lower Ouse Member. Fluvial and associated deposits including Holocene alluvium of the Sussex Ouse. The **Brooks Member** (stratotype: around [TQ4109]) consists of Holocene peats and clays (Thorley 1981).

(19) Arun Member. Includes fluvial and associated deposits of the River Arun: fluvial deposits of the First to Sixth Terraces and Holocene floodplain alluvium of the Arun Valley (Burrin & Scaife 1984).

(20) Cuckmere Member. Includes fluvial and associated deposits, including Holocene (Flandrian) floodplain alluvium, of the River Cuckmere. Holocene peat occurs at the base of the buried channel at Arlington [TQ 538074] (Welin *et al.* 1971).

Isle of Wight

(1) Solent Formation. Gravel and sand of south-bank tributaries of the former Solent River (Everard 1954; Allen & Gibbard 1994) known formerly as Plateau Gravels.

(2) St. George's Down Member. Stratotype: at St. George's Down [(SZ 521866)]. At least 7.5 m of gravel and sand at 108 m O.D; the highest Pleistocene fluvial gravel on the island. Palaeocurrent measurements indicate flow was towards the north. It includes chert predominantly of Greensand origin (Allen & Gibbard 1994).

(3) Black Down Member. Stratotype: Black Down [(SZ 511815)]: 4.7 m of gravel (predominantly of flint and Greensand chert) and sand caps the interfluve at 82 m O.D. between the Medina and Eastern Yar (Allen & Gibbard 1994).

(4) Lynn Farm Member. Stratotype: at Lynn Farm [SZ 537894]. At least 1 m of gravel and sand at 75 m O.D. exposed east of Newport across Knight's Cross, Lynn Farm and Twenty Acre Plantation. Locally overlain by 1.2 m of massive matrix-supported diamict of sand and silt with some pebbles (Allen & Gibbard 1994).

(5) Baring Road Member. Stratotype: at Barling Road, Cowes [SZ 482960]. At least 1 m of gravel occurs at about 45 m O.D. on each side of the Medina Valley, Cowes (Allen & Gibbard 1994).

(6) Steyne Wood Member. Stratotype: Bembridge School [SZ 641866]. Fossiliferous estuarine clay (2 m thick) between 38–

40 m O.D. It has normal palaeomagnetism and probably correlates with the latter part of the 'Cromerian Complex' (Holyoak & Preece 1983; Preece et al. 1990).

(7) Headon Warren Bed. Stratotype: an isolated remnant of angular flint gravel (over 4 m thick) at 109 m O.D. at Headon Warren [SZ 312860]. It contains Palaeolithic artefacts (Warren 1900).

(8) Priory Bay Member. Stratotype: Priory Bay [SZ 635899]. Gravel rich in Palaeolithic implements between 29-33 m O.D. Origin uncertain although mapped as 'marine gravel' by the Geological Survey (Preece et al. 1990).

(9) Bembridge Foreland Member. Stratotype: Bembridge Foreland [SZ 652872]. Marine gravel, between 5–18 m O.D. It comprises three beds, orange clast-supported gravel, interbedded sands and clays and an organic silty clay. Pollen includes *Carpinus*. TL dates of c.115 ka on sand lenses suggest correlation with the Ipswichian (Preece et al. 1990).

(10) Newtown Bay Bed. Stratotype: Newton [SZ 422922]. Bone bed (unknown thickness) on the foreshore with mixed fauna of temperate and cold climatic elements. *Hippopotamus amphibius*, *Palaeoloxodon antiquus* and *Bison priscus* suggest an Ipswichian age (Munt & Burke 1987).

(11) Lane End Member. Stratotype: Lane End [SZ 656880]. About 3 m of matrix-supported gravels and sands. Probably fluvial in origin and possibly Devensian in age (Preece et al. 1990). A sedge-peat within the gravels is biostratigraphically undiagnostic (Preece et al. 1990).

(12) Howgate Bed. Stratotype: silt at Howgate [SZ 657874]. It mantles beach gravels at Bembridge and at Howgate [SZ 643864] up to 10 m thick (White 1921; Preece et al. 1990). TL ages: 19–24 ka (Parks & Rendell 1992a,b). Similar deposit at Freshwater Bay (Parks & Rendell 1992a,b).

(13) Brook Bay Member. Stratotype: Brook Bay [SZ 386834]. Fluvial gravels and sands, associated with the formerly more extensive Western Yar, and mapped along the south coast of the island from Shippards Chine to Grange Chine. Gravels include abundant non-durable ferruginous pebbles and chert almost entirely from the Greensand (Allen & Gibbard 1994). Teeth of *Mammuthus primigenius* have been found in gravel at Brook Chine, Grange Chine and Freshwater (Colenutt 1896). It is probably of Devensian age.

(14) Watcombe Bottom Bed. Stratotype: Watcombe Bottom, Ventnor [SZ 544773]. Late-glacial slope deposits with palaeosol in dry valley. Date of 11 690 ± 120 BP from base of palaeosol (Preece et al. 1995).

(15) Hannover Member. Stratotype: near Hanover Point [SZ 382837]. Gravel and sand of the Western Yar (Allen & Gibbard 1994). Includes plant macrofossils especially abundant hazelnuts (*Corylus avellana*), Mesolithic artefacts and bones of *Bos primigenius*. Together with pollen evidence, they have been described as typical of the mid-Holocene (Clifford 1936; Scaife 1987).

(16) Gatcombe Bed. Stratotype: Gatcombe [SZ 502858]. About 3 m of peat and associated deposits containing plant micro- and macrofossils. The sequence extends from the terminal late-glacial and has a full Holocene sequence (Scaife 1987).

(17) Yarmouth Member. Stratotype: Yarmouth [SZ 350896]. A sequence of Holocene estuarine clays and silts interbedded with biogenic sediments, up to 13 m thick (Devoy 1987).

(18) Totland Bay Tufa Bed. Stratotype: Totland Bay [SZ 321867]. Tufa (1 m) with a rich mid Holocene molluscan fauna (Preece 1979).

(19) Gore Cliff Bed. Stratotype: Gore Cliff, Blackgang [SZ 493760]. Slope deposit 3 m thick with land snails. A Bronze age

broach was found at its base (Preece 1980a).

Hampshire

(1) Ringwood Formation. Type area: north of Lyndhurst and east of Ringwood and Fordingbridge. Previously known as the 'Older River Gravel Formation'. It represents the highest gravel and sand deposits of fluvial origin in the Hampshire Basin and consists of large amounts of rounded flints with some Upper Greensand material. Five altitudinally discrete lithostratigraphical units are recognized (Kubala 1980; Clarke 1981; Bristow et al. 1991). These were predominantly deposited by a south-southeast flowing Avon river, although remnants of a Solent River equivalent aggradation are also present at each stage. The height and degraded nature of these deposits imply that they are of considerable age (Allen & Gibbard 1994).

(2) New Forest Formation. It includes all subsequent fluvial members of the Solent system except the Pegwell Bay Formation. In contrast to those of the Ringwood Formation (note 1) quartz, quartzite and other Palaeozoic rocks are fairly common (Bury 1923; Allen & Gibbard 1994). It has also been classified using a numerical scheme (Bristow et al. 1991).

(3) Whitefield Hill Member. Stratotype: Whitefield Hill [SU 187005]. Up to 3 m of gravel and sand of the Solent River.

(4) Holmsey Ridge Member. Stratotype: Holmsey Ridge [SU 214010]. Includes cherts mainly of Upper Greensand and occasionally of Jurassic origin, that demonstrate a link with the western Hampshire Basin that suggests the Solent River system included the River Frome.

(5) Sway Member. Stratotype: Sway [SZ 273991]. Earliest evidence for a north-bank tributary aggradation of the River Stour. Members in the Stour valley are included in the Dorset Stour Formation.

(6) Tiptoe Member. Stratotype: Tiptoe [SZ 258972]. It consists of gravel and sand up to 4.6 m thick. Patches of this unit east of the Avon valley probably represent the downstream equivalents of the Avon and Stour aggradations (for tributary formation units see notes 4,16).

(7) Beaulieu Heath Member. Stratotype: Beaulieu Heath [SU 414055]. Gravels up to 5 m in thickness.

(8) Setley Plain Member. Stratotype: Setley Plain [SZ 305994]. Gravels that probably include the equivalent tributary aggradations of the Stour and Test.

(9) Mount Pleasant Member. Stratotype: Mount Pleasant [SZ 296981]. Gravel up to 6 m in thickness. The lithological composition shows a progressive decrease in the frequency of Upper Greensand chert downstream.

(10) Old Milton Member. Stratotype: Old Milton [SZ 242929]. Up to 4.5 m of gravel and sand.

(11) Tom's Down Member. Stratotype: Tom's Down (SU 450016). Gravel with a maximum thickness of 3.4 m.

(12) Taddisford Farm Member. Gravel (4.7 m thick) at Taddisford Farm [SZ 259924] and includes intraformational periglacial structures. It includes a chert component predominantly of Jurassic origin in the upstream area and of Upper Greensand east of the River Avon. The altitudinally equivalent **High Cliff Member** (stratotype: SZ 212932) was deposited in the lower Avon Valley. This also includes periglacial structures. The Stour valley-equivalent is the **Ensbury Park Member** (stratotype: SZ 082950).

(13) Stanswood Bay Member. Stratotype: Stanswood Bay [SU 473003]. It exceeds 5.4 m in thickness. An equivalent **West**

Southbourne Member (stratotype: SZ 140917) occurs in the lower Stour valley.

(14) Milford-on-Sea Member. Stratotype: Milton-on-Sea [SZ 281914]. Up to 8.2 m thick. The Avon-equivalent **Bransgore Member** (stratotype: SZ 196950) contains markedly less quartz (0.5%) than the Milford-on-Sea Member in which the quartz content is greater (2.0–3.5%). Likewise, the **Knighton Lodge Member** is recognised in the Stour Valley (stratotype: SZ 041973). The chert component in this unit consists predominantly of Upper Greensand (2–5%) and this, together with the low frequency of quartz, distinguishes it from the Milford-on-Sea and Bransgore members.

(15) Lepe Member. Stratotype: Lepe [SZ 458986]. It comprises gravel and sand up to 3.6 m thick. At Stone Point, an organic deposit 2.2 m thick (**Stone Point Bed** – note 16) divides the two lithologically indistinguishable gravel sub-units (Brown et al. 1975; Allen 1991). The fossiliferous organic sediments at Lepe (Reid 1893; West & Sparks 1960; Green & Keen 1987), now thought to belong to oxygen isotope stage-7 age, were previously correlated with the Ipswichian (Allen et al. 1996). Thus, the Lepe lower sub-unit must pre-date the Ipswichian (Allen & Gibbard 1994; Allen et al. 1996).

(16) Stone Point Bed (note 15).

(17) Pennington Member. Stratotype: Pennington Marshes [SZ 324923]. Gravel and sand that includes 90 cm of silty clay and peat at −5 m O.D. Palaeontology indicates that the fine sediments (**Pennington Bed**) are Ipswichian (sub-stage 5e). This allows tentative ascription of the underlying basal gravel (1.8 m) and the overlying upper gravel (3.5 m) to oxygen isotope stage 6 ('Wolstonian' of Allen et al. 1996) and the Devensian respectively. The Burton Rough Member [SZ 189952] and the Southbourne Member [SZ 160908] of the Stour valley represent equivalent north-bank tributary aggradations of the Pennington Member (Allen & Gibbard 1994).

(18) Ibsley Member. Stratotype: Ibsley [SU 147098]. Interglacial deposits beneath fluvial gravels and sands underlying the 4th Terrace (Devensian) have been correlated tentatively with the Ipswichian (Barber & Brown 1987).

(19) North End Copse Member. Stratotype: North End Copse [SU 141001]. Represents the last major phase of gravel and sand deposition in the Avon valley, forming a continuous spread underlying the modern floodplain. It is probably Late Devensian.

(20) Holdenhurst Member. Stratotype: Holdenhurst [SZ 128951]. Represents the last major phase of gravel and sand deposition in the Stour valley, forming a continuous spread underlying the modern floodplain. It is probably Late Devensian.

(21) Christchurch Bay Member. Stratotype: Christchurch Bay [SU 2290]. The Solent River equivalent of 19 and 20 that fills the buried valley in the offshore area (Dyer 1972, 1975).

(22) Holbury Member. Stratotype: Holbury [SU 430042]. Reynolds (1987a, b; Reynolds et al. 1996) identified two superimposed layers of colluvial and or aeolian deposits ('brickearth') overlying the Lepe Member at Stone Point, the lower of which contains palaeoargillic features that imply interglacial pedogenesis. The TL age for the bed is: 98 ka (Parks & Rendell, 1992a,b). Also part of the Pegwell Formation (Kent, note 9).

(23) Lower Avon Member. Stratotype as North End Copse Member (note 19). It comprises fine-grained alluvial sediments up to 6 m thick. The Stour Valley-equivalent is the Lower Stour Member. These deposits immediately underlie the modern floodplain surface and are therefore Holocene.

(24) Cranes Moor Bed. Stratotype: Cranes Moor [SU 193028]. Post-glacial mire complex (Barber & Clarke 1987).

(25) Fawley Beds. Stratotype: near Fawley [SU 477026]. Holocene estuarine deposits consisting of interbedded peats and clays up to 21 m in thickness (Hodson & West 1972).

Dorset

(1) Dewlish Bone Bed. Stratotype: Dewlish [SY 775983]. A bone bed with a temperate vertebrate fauna including *Mammuthus meridionalis* that suggests a 'Cromerian' age (Reid 1890; Carreck 1955)

(2) Frome-Piddle Formation. The type-area comprises the former alluvial deposits of the Rivers Frome and Piddle in the Wareham-Dorchester area (Allen & Gibbard 1994). The major pebble lithologies of this unit are flint, quartz and Mesozoic chert.

(3) Green Hill Member Stratotype: gravels and sands at Green Hill [SY 741933]. This is the highest unit identified. It reaches a maximum thickness of 80 cm and was deposited by the River Frome.

(4) Black Hill Member. Stratotype: Black Hill [SY 838942]. River Frome gravel and sand over 3.4 m thick.

(5) Tonerspuddle Heath Member. Stratotype: Tonerspuddle Heath [SY 832910]. Gravel and sand with a higher quartz component than higher units.

(6) Higher Hyde Heath Member. Stratotype: Higher Hyde Heath [SY 851900]. Gravel (2.2 m) that provides evidence for a northbank tributary equivalent of the River Piddle.

(7) Stokeford Heath Member. Stratotype: Stokeford Heath [SY 872886]. Gravel and sand about 4 m thick of the Rivers Frome and Piddle.

(8) West Knighton Member. Stratotype: West Knighton [SY 742886]; parastratotype: at [SY 745887]. Gravel and sand (2.6 m thick) of both the Rivers Frome and Piddle.

(9) Worgret Member. Stratotype: Worgret [SY 913869]. It represents the highest of three aggradations aligned along the present River Frome course. Equivalent deposits in the Piddle valley and small tributary valleys streams that flowed into both the Frome and Piddle. The Piddle valley **Ford Heath Member** [SY 877887] is distinguished lithologically from Frome valley correlatives by lower quartz frequencies and almost exclusively flint composition.

(10) East Holme Member. Stratotype: East Holme [SY 912855]. 3.2 m of gravel and sand. Correlated with the **Buddens Farm Member** [SY 868892] in the Piddle valley.

(11) Fisherton Bed. Stratotype: Fisherton [SU 134304]. Fine-grained inorganic sediments with a cold climate vertebrate fauna (Reid 1903: Green et al. 1984).

(12) Stoborough Member. Stratotype: Stoborough [SY 906863]. Correlated with the Hyde Member [SY 866908]. Both form a continuous spread of gravel and sand that underlies the modern floodplains of the Frome and Piddle valleys respectively.

(13) Hyde Member. Stratotype: Hyde [SY 866908]. Comprises discontinuous fine-grained alluvial sediments and peat underlying the modern floodplains of both streams and tributaries and overlying the Hyde Farm and Buddens Farm members. Palaeobotanical analyses indicate that the alluvial deposits accumulated during the Late Devensian–Holocene (Allen 1991).

(14) Poole Harbour Member. Stratotype: Poole Harbour [SZ 010904]. Fine-grained estuarine organic and associated sediments (Nicholls 1987; Bristow *et al.* 1991)).

(15) Rimsmoor Bed. Stratotype: Rimsmoor [SY 814922]. Holocene peat doline infill some 20 m in thickness (Waton & Barber 1987).

(16) Blashenwell Tufa Bed. Stratotype: Blashenwell Farm near Corfe [SY 952805]. Holocene tufa (3 m) with Mesolithic artefacts (Preece 1980b).

(17) Chesil Beach Bed. The well-known Holocene barrier beach betweeen the Isle of Portland and Abbotsburry (Carr & Blackley 1973).

Chapter 6

Southwest England

S. CAMPBELL, C. O. HUNT, J. D. SCOURSE, D. H. KEEN & D. G. CROOT

The sequence and nature of Quaternary events have been determined principally from evidence in coastal sections, cave sequences and extensive spreads of unconsolidated sediments in the Somerset and Avon lowlands. Correlation is hampered by their isolated nature and scarcity of samples for dating.

It is generally agreed that Southwest England was not overrun by Pleistocene ice sheets. Fragmentary evidence for the encroachment of an ice sheet along the present north coast, from the Isles of Scilly to north Devon, is, however, widely recorded. It takes the form of giant erratics on shore platforms (e.g. Saunton), possible glacigenic gravels (Isles of Scilly, Trebetherick and Lundy Island) and glacial deposits (Fremington) (Stephens 1973). This has led to the notion that the most extensive of the Pleistocene ice sheets reached its southernmost limit at or near the north Devon and Cornish coasts. Traditionally, this glacial event has been regarded as 'Wolstonian' in age (Mitchell 1960, 1972; Stephens 1966a, b, 1970; Mitchell & Orme 1967; Kidson 1977). The glaciation of the northern Isles of Scilly has since been correlated with the Late Devensian (Scourse 1985, 1987, 1991); evidence has been refuted for glacial deposits at Trebetherick (Kidson 1977; Scourse 1996); and the Fremington Clay (Till) of north Devon has been interpreted as a Late Devensian glacio-marine deposit (Eyles & McCabe 1989a). Recent OSL ages from the Fremington Clay suggest at least an Anglian age (Gilbert 1996). Evidence for an earlier glacial event comes from the Bristol district. Overlying the glacigenic sediments here are deposits thought to be freshwater (Gilbertson & Hawkins 1978a) or 'marginal-marine' (Hunt 1981), that have D-aIle/L-Ile ratios on shells (Andrews et al. 1984) ascribed to oxygen isotope stage 15 (Bowen 1994b). A correlation of that glaciation with oxygen isotope stage 16 or earlier may also be appropriate for some of the large erratics such as the Giant's Rock at Porthleven (Bowen 1994b).

Despite continuing controversy about the extent and timing of glaciation, it is widely agreed that most sedimentary evidence is referrable to the cold, often periglacial, climates of the Pleistocene. Periglacial denudation through some 50 ice-age cycles since c. 2.4 Ma is likely to have been the main agent of geomorphological development (Bowen 1994b). Complex, multiple-facies sequences of periglacial scree, solifluction and slope-wash deposits are ubiquitous, both inland and on the coast. They are commonly cryoturbated and exhibit ice-wedge casts: together with altiplanation terraces on some of the uplands (Guilcher 1950; Te Punga 1957; Waters 1964; Gerrard 1983), extensive blockfields (clitter) on Dartmoor and Bodmin Moor and widespread loess (Keen 1978; Wintle 1981; Scourse 1985, 1987; Roberts 1985). Correlation and subdivision of the head sequences has been based on estimates of the age of raised beach deposits beneath or interbedded with them in the coastal sequences. Proponents of Hoxnian raised beach deposits have divided overlying periglacial sequences into 'lower' or 'main' (Saalian) and 'upper' (Devensian) heads on

that basis (Mitchell 1960, 1972; Stephens 1966a, b, 1970, 1973), whereas supporters of an Ipswichian raised beach have proposed that all the head facies are Devensian (e.g. Bowen 1969a, 1973a; Kidson 1977).

The raised beach units provide marker horizons in the Quaternary sequences of southwest England. In coastal exposures from Dorset (south and southeast England) to the Avon coastlands, raised beach sediments occur resting on a marine platform, overlain by dune sand and various facies of head, loess and slope-wash deposits. The application of TL, U-series and D-aIle/L-Ile dating methods shows that at least three separate high sea-level stands are represented by the sediments (Bowen et al. 1985). Originally these were provisonally ascribed to oxygen isotope stage 7 and sub-stage 5e and the 'unnamed' sea-level event of Bowen et al. (1985). Subsequently the oldest was ascribed to oxygen isotope stage 7 and the two youngest to oxygen isotope sub-stage 5e (Bowen 1994b). At sites where periglacial deposits overlie the beaches correlated with oxygen isotope stage 7 (e.g. Portland West, Godrevy and Pendower), it follows that they may be oxygen isotope stage 6 or younger in age. Most raised beach deposits in the southwest remain undated.

Channel Islands

(1) Vale Formation. Type-area: northern Guernsey. It comprises marine deposits (gravel and sand) which outcrop at elevations greater than 20 m O.D. (Keen 1978). It may be correlated with similar high-level gravels in Jersey and in the Isles of Scilly and Cornwall.

(2) Les Vardes Member. Stratotype: Les Vardes, St Sampson, Guernsey [WV 317825]. Its base lies between 26 and 28 m O.D. It is up to 1.2 m thick and comprises marine gravels and sands. It has not been seen in superposition and its age is indeterminate. On altitudinal grounds it may be older than the comparable deposits of the Pleinhaume Member and is likely to be at least as old as oxygen isotope stage 9 (Keen 1978, 1993).

(3) Pleinheaume Member. Stratotype: Pleinheaume, St Sampson, Guernsey [WV 318818]. The base is at c. 15 m O.D. It occupies hill-top locations in the parishes of St Sampson and The Vale, and consists of marine gravels up to c. 1.2 m thick. The deposit is not seen in superposition and its age is indeterminate. It is likely to be at least as old as oxygen isotope stage 9 (Keen 1978, 1993).

(4) Guernsey Formation. Type-area: Guernsey. It comprises marine (raised beach) and periglacial (head and loess) deposits that are widely exposed in coastal sections (Keen 1978, 1993). It shares broad lithostratigraphic characteristics with the Jersey Formation.

(5) Longis Bay Member. Stratotype: Longis Bay, Alderney [WA 596079]. Its base lies at c. 3.0 m O.D. and it is up to 1 m

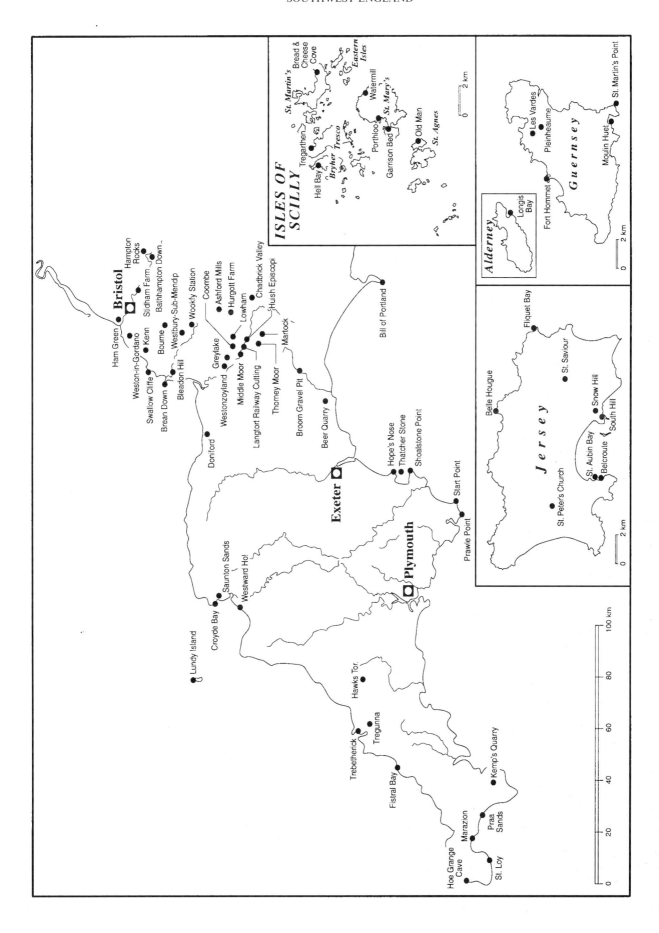

Fig. 7. Localities in Southwest England and Channel Islands.

Table 16. *Correlations between the Channel Islands, Portland Bill, Isles of Scilly and the Axe Valley, Dorset and oxygen isotope stratigraphy*

$\delta^{18}O$	CHANNEL ISLANDS	PORTLAND BILL	AXE VALLEY	ISLES OF SCILLY
1	ST. OUEN FORMATION (13); BRAYE DU VALLE FORMATION (12)			NORTH DEVON FORMATION (7)
2	JERSEY FORMATION (4): St Saviour Beds (11); GUERNSEY FORMATION (4): St Martin's Point Bed (10)			ST. MARTIN'S FORMATION (1): Bread & Cheese (6) Hell Bay (5) Old Man (4) Tregarthen (3) & Scilly Member (2); ST. MARY'S FORMATION (2): Porthloo Member (4)
3	St Aubin Member (10); St Martin's Beds (9)		AXE VALLEY FORMATION (1): Chard Junction Member (6) Kilmington Member (5)	Watermill Member (3)
4	Fliquet Arctic Bed (9); Moulin Huet Beds (8)			
5	St Peter's Member (8); Jerbourg Member (7)		Railway Pit Bed (4)	
5e	Belle Hougue Member (7); Fort Hommet Member (6)	BILL OF PORTLAND FORMATION (1): Portland East Member (4)		
6	Portelet Member (6); Longis Bay Member (5)	Portland Bed (3)	Pratt's Pit Member (3) Broom Member (2)	
7	Belcroute Member (5)	Portland West Member (2)		
8	ST HELIER FORMATION (1): Railway Terminus Member (3) South Hill Member (2)			
9	VALE FORMATION (1): Pleinheaume Member (3) Les Vardes Member (2)			Garrison Bed (1)

thick. It comprises periglacial breccias overlain by gravel of the Fort Hommet Member. An age no younger than oxygen isotope sub-stage 5e is thought likely (Keen 1978).

(6) Fort Hommet Member. Stratotype: Fort Hommet, Câtel [WV 283804]. Its base lies at *c.* 4.0 m O.D. and rests on a marine-abraded platform cut in granite (Keen 1978). It consists of 2.0 m of raised beach sand and gravel. Exposures, now destroyed, at Chouet, Vale [WV 333841] showed deposits of the Fort Hommet Member overlain by the Moulin Huet Beds suggesting an age no younger than oxygen isotope stage 4.

(7) Jerbourg Member. Type-area: southern Guernsey, central Sark and western Alderney. A widespread series of terrestrial, mostly periglacial, deposits comprising: breccia, sand and silt (Moulin Huet Beds), and loess (St Martin's Beds & St Martin's Point Bed).

(8) Moulin Huet Beds. Stratotype: Moulin Huet, St Martin, Guernsey [WV 329752]. Its base lies at *c.* 6.0 m O.D. and it consists of up to 20 m of breccia, sand and silt (head) overlying raised beach gravel of the Fort Hommet Member. Probable oxygen isotope stages 4–2 in age (Keen 1978).

(9) St Martin's Beds. Stratotype: St Martin, Guernsey [WV 324765]. Its base lies at *c.* 100 m O.D; it is up to 5 m thick and it consists predominantly of silt (loess). Similar materials can be traced over the southern plateau of Guernsey, central Sark and western Alderney (Keen 1978). North of St Martin's Point [WV 342755] it overlies the Moulin Huet Beds (*note 8*); at Hommet Paradis, Vale [WV 364828], it was formerly seen to overlie raised beach gravel of the Fort Hommet Member. Such stratigraphical relationships suggest correlation with either oxygen isotope stage 4 or stage 2. It may be the equivalent of the Lizard Formation in Cornwall.

(10) St Martin's Point Bed. Stratotype: St Martin's Point, St Martin, Guernsey [WV 344748]. Its base lies at *about* 10.0 m O.D. where it is up to 8 m thick, and consists of loess which contains, in its upper 1–2 m, a molluscan fauna indicative of Arctic conditions (Keen 1978; Rousseau & Keen 1989). Its age is indeterminate but the fauna is consistent with conditions late in oxygen isotope stage 2.

(1) St Helier Formation. Type-area: St Helier, Jersey. It comprises gravel and sand of presumed marine origin that outcrop at elevations > 18 m O.D. (Keen 1978). It comprises two members of unknown, but at least oxygen isotope stage 9, age. Correlation is made with the Vale Formation, the Garrison Bed of the Isles of Scilly, and deposits of the Cornish Penlee Formation.

(2) South Hill Member. Stratotype: South Hill, St Helier [WV 651477]. Its base lies between 31 and 37 m O.D. It consists of marine gravel and sand up to 5 m thick (Keen 1978). At St Clement's [WV 686473] it is overlain by the St Saviour Member (loess) that provides a minimum age of oxygen isotope stage 5 for the high-level marine deposits. On altitudinal grounds, however, an ascription to at least oxygen isotope stage 9 is likely (Keen 1978, 1993).

(3) Railway Terminus Member. Stratotype: Snow Hill, St Helier [WV 654484]. Its base lies at *about* 18 m O.D. and it occurs in fissures of granite. Local stratigraphical relations are unclear. At La Cotte à la Chévre, St Ouen [WV 554566], it is overlain by a cave earth containing Mousterian artefacts. Thus an age no younger than oxygen isotope stage 7 has been suggested (Callow & Cornford 1986). On altitudinal grounds, an ascription to at least oxygen isotope stage 9 seems likely (Keen 1993).

(4) Jersey Formation. Type-area: Jersey. It comprises marine,

aeolian and head deposits that are widespread around the coast of Jersey (Keen 1978). The Belle Hougue Member is widespread and has been dated by D-aIle/L-Ile ratios and Uranium-series dating to oxygen isotope sub-stage 5e: it forms an important marker horizon in the coastal sections (Keen *et al.* 1981).

(5) Belcroute Member. Stratotype: Belcroute, St Aubin [WV 607482]. Its base lies at *c.* 7.0 m O.D. and it consists of sand in fissures in the shore platform. It underlies the Portelet Member that has been correlated with oxygen isotope stage 6. It was formed during high relative sea levels in oxygen isotope stage 7 at the latest (Keen *et al.* 1993).

(6) Portelet Member. Stratotype: Belcroute, St Aubin [WV 607482]. Its base lies at *c.* 7.5 m O.D. and it consists of a coarse breccia (slate fragments) up to 2 m thick underlying gravels of the Belle Hougue Member. Keen *et al.* (1993) interpret it as a periglacial solifluction deposit (head) and correlated it with oxygen isotope stage 6.

(7) Belle Hougue Member. Stratotype: Belle Hougue, Trinity [WV 656565]. Its base lies at *c.* 4.0 m O.D. It comprises sand and gravel (raised beach deposits) up to *c.* 4 m thick and is widespread around the coast of Jersey. At the type-site, shells of *Patella vulgata* have D-aIle/L-Ile ratios of 0.123 ± 0.024 ($n = 6$). Travertine from the beach deposits has a Uranium-series age of 121 000 + 14 000/ −12 000 BP. Thus it formed during oxygen isotope sub-stage 5e (Keen *et al.* 1981).

(8) St Peter's Member. Stratotype: St Peter's Church, St Peter [WV 595516]. Its base lies at *c.* 85 m O.D. It is a well-sorted, heavily iron-cemented aeolian sand up to 3 m thick, blown some 1–2 km from a probable shoreline to the west. Its relationship to deposits of the St Saviour Beds suggests an age no younger than oxygen isotope stage 4 (Keen 1978).

(9) Fliquet Arctic Bed. Stratotype: Fliquet Bay, St Martin [WV 714534]. Its base lies at 5.8 m O.D. It outcrops on the foreshore at Fliquet Bay and forms the lowest bed of the St Aubin Member at this locality. It comprises a peat, up to 0.6 m thick, which contains fossil insects and pollen of plants of boreal and Arctic types. A radiocarbon date of > 25 000 BP was obtained from wood in the base of the peat, but an age early in oxygen isotope stage 4 is suggested (Coope *et al.* 1980).

(10) St Aubin Member. Stratotype: St Aubin Bay [WV 606478]. The base lies at *c.* 2–3 m O.D. It consists of sand, gravel, scree with a silty (loess) matrix up to 20 m thick (Keen 1978). Its widespread occurrence above raised beach deposits of the Belle Hougue Member indicates an age younger than oxygen isotope sub-stage 5e.

(11) St Saviour Beds. Stratotype: St Saviour [WV 674515]. The base lies at *c.* 80 m O.D. It comprises loess up to 5 m thick. It is widespread on the plateau surface of Jersey (Keen 1978), and although its age has not been determined, it must be younger than oxygen isotope sub-stage 5e because it overlies raised beach gravel of this age on the shore platform at La Motte [WV 674459] (Keen 1993).

(12) Braye du Valle Formation. Type-area: marine silts and sands associated with the Holocene transgression in the west, north and east of Guernsey, south and east Jersey, and eastern Alderney. Pollen and radiocarbon ages indicate a middle Holocene age (Keen 1981; Jones *et al.* 1990).

(13) St. Ouen Formation. Type-area: blown sand associated with the Holocene transgression in the north and west of Guernsey, west, south and east of Jersey and eastern Alderney. A basal radiocarbon age of 3984 ± 50 BP at St. Ouen indicates commencement of sedimentation (Keen 1981; Jones *et al.* 1990).

Portland Bill

(1) Bill of Portland Formation. Type-area: Isle of Portland [SY 675685–SY 689695]. Comprises marine (raised beach) and terrestrial (periglacial head and loam) deposits that extend for over 2 km on the southeast Isle of Portland.

(DHK)

(2) Portland West Member. Stratotype: Bill of Portland [SY 675686]. Base is at 14.1–14.5 m O.D. on a marine platform. Up to 3 m of well sorted sandy gravel arranged in up to seven fining-up units, from pebbles to coarse-grained sand (Davies & Keen 1985). It can be traced for *c.* 200 m south of the stratotype, and also in a disused quarry [SY 680688]. The deposits are planar-bedded, cemented by calcium carbonate and constituent clasts comprise a variety of lithologies but mostly flint (up to 90%). Interpreted as raised beach, it contains marine molluscs, principally fragments of rocky-shore gastropods (Prestwich 1875; Baden-Powell 1930; Davies & Keen 1985) which have provided D-aIle/L-Ile ratios (Davies 1983; Davies & Keen 1985; Bowen *et al.* 1985) indicate an oxygen isotope stage-7 age.

(DHK)

(3) Portland Bed. Stratotype: Bill of Portland [SY 675686]. Base at *c.* 17 m O.D. and it consists of up to 2.7 m of localized massively bedded silt, devoid of coarser material except for a few pebbles derived from the underlying raised beach deposits (Prestwich 1875; Keen 1985). It is interpreted asa slope deposit and is overlain abruptly by head. Its stratigraphical relations suggest that it may be oxygen isotope stage 6 in age, and it may have undergone subsequent weathering during oxygen isotope stage 5 (Davies & Keen 1985; Keen 1985). Bowen *et al.* (1989), however, report D-aIle-L-Ile ratios from the overlying head which would place the bed in stage 7.

(DHK)

(4) Portland East Member. Type-area: between the Bill of Portland [SY 677681] and Longstone Ope Quarries [SY 688691]. It consists of marine (raised beach) and overlying head deposits overlying a marine platform at 6.95–10.67 m O.D. The beach is well exposed a the bill of Portland Lighthouse [SY 678682] where it is up to 0.6 m thick made up of subangular clasts of Portland and Purbeck limestone with a few pebbles of chert and shell debrise in a sandy matrix. It thins to the north-east and is overlain by head. It is uncemented and richly fossiliferous with marine molluscs (Prestwich 1875; Baden-Powell 1930). It is correlated, using D-aIle/L-Ile ratios, with oxygen isotope sub-stage 5e (Davies & Keen 1985; Keen 1985; Bowen *et al.* 1985). It is possible that it is a mixed fauna with elements from oxygen isotope sub-stage 5e (0.1 ± 0.01 (23) and oxygen isotope sub-stage 5a (0.076 ± 0.006 (4) (Bowen *et al.* 1985). the base of the overlying head, modified by periglacial structures (Pugh & Sherman 1967), is at *c.* 14.0–17.7 m O.D. and it is up to 4.6 m thick, comprising a poorly-sorted deposit of angular limestone clasts in a silty matrix. In places it is crudely bedded and, locally, it contains abundant land snails indicative of open-ground conditions (Keen 1985).

(DHK)

Isles of Scilly

(1) Garrison Bed – the Garrison Boulder Bed Member of Scourse (1991). Stratotype: The Garrison, St Mary's [SV 901107]. Its base is at 23 m O.D. and it consists of up to 1 m of clast-supported rounded granite boulders with interstitial sand. Scourse (1991) interpreted it as a raised beach deposit which, on altitudinal grounds, is likely to date from at least oxygen isotope stage 9 (Scourse unpublished). It is not recorded elsewhere, but may have similarities with the Penlee Formation in Cornwall and other 'high-level' gravels in the Channel Islands.

(2) St. Mary's Formation. Formerly the Watermill Formation of Scourse (1991). Type-area: Isles of Scilly. It comprises marine deposits (raised beach) and head. The head contains interbedded organic deposits that have radiocarbon ages. It is present throughout the Isles of Scilly (Scourse 1985, 1987, 1991). The Porthloo Member consists entirely of locally-derived granitic materials and is devoid of foreign material thought to have been introduced during the Late Devensian glaciation (Scourse 1991). The Watermill Member, however, locally contains erratics (Scourse 1991).

(3) Watermill Member – the Watermill Sands and Gravel Member of Scourse (1991). Stratotype: Watermill Cove, St Mary's [SV 925123–924123]. Its base is 4.25 m O.D. It is up to 1 m thick and comprises a clast-supported deposit of granite cobbles and boulders overlain by structureless medium-grained sand. Scourse (1991) interpreted it as a raised beach and noted its widespread occurrence where its altitudinal range varies between 4.25–7.27 m O.D. It contains in places a range of erratics. Its contact with the overlying Porthloo Member is commonly gradational (Scourse 1991). The Watermill Member includes the Chad Girt raised beach of Mitchell and Orme (1967; see also Barrow 1906), which is thus no longer afforded separate stratigraphical status (Scourse 1991).

(4) Porthloo Member – the Porthloo Breccia Member of Scourse (1991). Stratotype: Porthloo, St Mary's [SV 908115]. Its base lies at 5.0 m O.D. and it is up to 5 m in thickness. It is a variable deposit of angular granite clasts (up to boulder grade) set in a matrix of granules, sand and silt. It is poorly sorted, exhibits a preferred downslope orientation of its clasts, and is interpreted as a periglacial solifluction deposit (Scourse 1987). It is the most widespread Pleistocene deposit in the Isles of Scilly. It includes the Porth Seal raised beach of Mitchell and Orme (1967), which is now reinterpreted as soliflucted raised beach sediments derived from the Watermill Member.

(1) St. Martin's Formation. Formerly the Bread and Cheese Formation of Scourse (1991). Type-area: Isles of Scilly. Comprises materials derived from the pre-existing glacial deposits, considered to be Late Devensian by Scourse (1991). It is restricted to the northern Isles of Scilly with the exception of the Old Man Member that occurs in the southern islands (Scourse 1991).

(2) Scilly Member – the Scilly Till Member of Scourse (1991). Stratotype: Bread and Cheese Cove, St Martin's [SV 940158]. Its base lies at *c.* 3.0 m O.D. It is up to 2.0 m in thickness and comprises a poorly-sorted, pale-brown diamict containing a wide range of clast lithologies. Scourse (1985, 1991) interpreted it as a glacigenic deposit of Late Devensian age, possibly a lodgement till. Mitchell and Orme (1967) regarded it as a 'Wolstonian' glacial deposit. It also occurs at other sites including Pernagie and White Island bars (northern Isles of Scilly), at altitudes no higher than 7.0 m O.D. and shows little variation in lithofacies (Scourse 1991). At the stratotype it is overlain by the Tregarthen Member and the Bread and Cheese Member.

(3) Tregarthen Member - the Tregarthen Gravel Member of Scourse (1991). Stratotype: Battery, Tresco [SV 887166]. Its base is at 8 m O.D. and it is up to 4 m in thickness. It comprises a well-sorted sandy gravel with a distinctive and varied clast lithological assemblage. Scourse (1991) interpreted it as proximal outwash derived from a Late Devensian ice sheet. It is also recorded at Bread and Cheese Cove. At the type-site it is interbedded with the Bread and Cheese Member.

(4) Old Man Member – the Old Man Sandloess Member of Scourse (1991). Stratotype: Old Man, Gugh, St Agnes [SV 893085]. Its base is at 6.5 m O.D. and it is up to 1 m thick. It comprises a highly variable deposit of sandy silt with some granite clasts and granules. Scourse (1991) interpreted the deposit as a periglacial aeolian deposit derived from local Late Devensian glacigenic deposits (the Scilly and Tregarthen Members). It is widespread throughout the southern Isles of Scilly where it occurs as a discrete unit interbedded within the Porthloo Member, which must, therefore, have accumulated on at least two separate occasions (Scourse 1991).

(5) Hell Bay Member – the Hell Bay Gravel Member of Scourse (1991). Stratotype: Great Bottom, Bryher [SV 877161]. Its base lies at 5 m O.D. It is up to 1.8 m thick and comprises a moderately well sorted deposit of pebbles in a matrix of sandy silt. Constituent clasts show a marked preferred downslope orientation and lithological characteristics suggest derivation from the Scilly, Tregarthen and Old Man members. Scourse (1991) interpreted the material as periglacial solifluction and mudflow deposits derived from Late Devensian glacigenic materials. It is widespread in the northern Isles of Scilly and is the dominant unit of the St. Martin's Formation. At other locations, the deposit ranges in height from 5–25 m O.D. and shows little lithofacies variation. At most sites the Hell Bay Member is overlain by the Bread and Cheese Member, that contains a mixture of granitic and foreign materials.

(6) Bread and Cheese Member – the Bread and Cheese Breccia Member of Scourse (1991). Stratotype: Bread and Cheese Cove, St Martin's [SV 940158]. Its base lies at 7.8 m O.D. It is up to 3 m thick and comprises large angular granite clasts with some erratics supported by a matrix of poorly-sorted granules, sand and silt. Clasts show a marked preferred downslope orientation. Scourse (1991) interpreted the material as periglacial solifluction deposits derived from local weathered granite and the Scilly, Tregarthen and Hell Bay members. The deposit is widespread in the northern Isles of Scilly, forming the upper part of many coastal sections, and shows considerable lithofacies variation (Scourse 1991).

(7) North Devon Formation (North Devon, note, 12)

Axe Valley

(1) Axe Valley Formation. Type-area: between Winsham, Somerset, and Seaton, Devon [ST 375070 to SY 250900]. An extensive formation of terrace gravels bordering the River Axe and its tributaries including the Blackwater and Yarty (Stephens, 1973). It is composed mostly of flint and chert, but quartz and other pebbles derived from Palaeozoic rocks also occur. It is the richest source of palaeoliths in southwest England (more than 1 800) of Acheulian-type and a 'Hoxnian to Saalian' age has been suggested (Green 1974, 1988; Shakesby & Stephens 1984).

(2) Broom Member. Stratotype: the Railway (Ballast) Pit, Broom, Devon [ST 326020]. Its base is at *c.* 45 m O.D. it is > 16 m thick, and comprises a lower 'flint' gravel overlain by *c.* 0.5 m of iron-stained clay, silt and sand containing pollen (equivalent to the Railway Pit Bed: *unit 3*), in turn overlain by 13–15 m of 'chert' gravels. These are cryoturbated and are capped by a discontinuous stony silt ('Brickearth'). It was deposited at the confluence of the proto-Axe and its Black-

water tributary (Shakesby & Stephens 1984; Green 1988) during a cold climate. The clay, silt and sand represent a more temperate climate.

(3) Pratt's Pit Member. Stratotype: Pratt's Old Pit, Broom, Dorset [ST 328024]. Its base is at about 45 m O.D. and it consists of about 16 m of gravels separated by up to 2 m of clay, sandy clay and loam, the upper gravel, middle beds and lower gravel of Green (1988). Over 900 hand-axes of Acheulian-type were collected by Charles Bean, probably mostly from the middle beds (Green 1988), and correlation with the Broom Member is likely.

(4) Railway Pit Bed. Stratotype: the Railway (Ballast) Pit, Broom, Devon [ST 326020]. Its base is at *c.* 46 m O.D. it is up to 0.5 m thick, and comprises iron-stained clay, silt and sand. It lies between cherty (upper) and flinty (lower) gravels (unit 2). It contains pollen indicative of boreal forest, dominated by *Pnus*, *Picea*, *Betula*, and *Abies*, and extensive open ground. A depositional environment at the end of a Middle Pleistocene (possibly oxygen isotope stage 7) interglacial is suggested, although it may be interstadial (Scourse 1984). Acheulian artefacts are common (Green 1988), thus an age considerably than oxygen isotope stage 7 is possible.

(5) Kilmington Member. Stratotype: Kilmington 'New' Pit, Devon [ST 277976]. Its base is at *c.* 47 m O.D. it comprises at least 3 m of poorly sorted and crudely bedded terrace gravels with discontinuous lenses of silt and sand. The gravels comprise angular to rounded clasts mostly of chert and greensand with varying amounts of flint and a small percentage of farther-travelled material (Shakesby & Stephens 1984); the uppermost 2 m of the gravel is cryoturbated.

(6) Chard Junction Member. Stratotype: Chard Junction, Somerset [ST 342044]. Its base is at *c.* 58 m O.D. It is up to 12 m in thickness, and it comprises over 11 m of terrace gravels containing mostly clasts of flint and chert, overlain by up to 2 m of loamy silt ('brickearth'). The top 1.5 to 2.0 m of gravel is cryoturbated. Mitchell (1960) and Stephens (1970, 1973) interpreted it as having been deposited by 'Wolstonian' meltwater overspilling through the Chard Gap from a postulated Lake Maw. It is now regarded as part of a major cold-stage aggradation, possibly formed during oxygen isotope stage 6.

Cornwall

(1) Penlee Formation. Type area: Land's End Peninsula, west Cornwall. It comprises presumed marine deposits which outcrop discontinuously at elevations > 20 m O.D. (Scourse 1996). It includes a raised beach of clast-supported granite cobbles at *c.* 20 m O.D. in Penlee Quarry, Newlyn (Reid & Flett 1907); a raised beach deposit (29 m O.D.) at Morrab Place, Penzance (Henwood 1843); and similar 'boulder beds', including those at Nanjizal (SW 358236), elsewhere around the Penwith Peninsula. These deposits are analogous to the high-level raised beaches of the Channel Islands (Keen 1978) and the Garrison Bed of the Isles of Scilly (Scourse 1991). Their age is unknown but on altitudinal grounds an oxygen isotope stage 9 age, or older, is likely.

(2) Penwith Formation. Type-area: Land's End Peninsula, west Cornwall. It comprises marine (raised beach) and fluvial and head deposits (the latter with interbedded organic deposits that are radiocarbon-dated). It is present widely in the coastal sections of north and west Cornwall (Scourse 1985, 1996). Its Godrevy Member is a widespread unit (raised beach deposits) of varied ages: at Marazion it is underlain by alluvial gravel,

Table 17. *Correlations between Cornwall, South Devon and North Devon and oxygen isotope stratigraphy*

$\delta^{18}O$	CORNWALL (mainland)		SOUTH DEVON	NORTH DEVON	
1		BRAUNTON	BURROWS	FORMATION (12)	
2	**PENWITH FORMATION** (2) St Loy Member (10)	Hawks Tor Beds (6) **CAMEL FORMATION** (3) Tregunna Member (5) Trebetherick Member (4) **LIZARD FORMATION** (1) Goonhilly Member (2)	**TORBAY FORMATION** (1) Start Point Member (5)	**BARNSTAPLE BAY FORMATION** (1) Lundy Member (5) Fremington Quay Beds (4) Brannam`s Beds (3) Fremington Member (2)	**CROYDE BAY FORMATION** (1) Croyde Member (4)
3	St Loy Bed (11)				
4					
5	Praa Sands Member (9)				
5e	Fistral South Bed (8) Marazion Bed (7)		Thatcher Stone Member (4)		Westward Ho! Bed (3)
6					
7	Pendower Bed (6) Fistral North Bed (5) Porth Nanven Bed (4) Godrevy Member (3)		Shoalstone Member (3) Hope`s Nose Member (2)		Saunton Member (2)
8					
9	**PENLEE FORMATION** (1)				

sand, silt and clay of the Marazion Bed (Taylor & Beer 1981). In most coastal sections, raised beach deposits and dune sand of the Godrevy Member are overlain by head deposits, mostly of soliflucted origin (St. Loy). At Sydney Cove, the Godrevy Member is separated from the St. Loy Member by the Prah Sands Member, a stony clay with evidence of pedogenesis. At St Loy, a breccia of the St. Loy Member contains organic deposits (Scourse 1985, 1996).

(3) Godrevy Member. Formerly the Godrevy Formation Scourse (1985, 1996). Stratotype: Godrevy [SW 582423–SW 581430]. The base lies at 4 m O.D. It is up to 11.5 m thick and comprises a lower bed of clast-supported pebbles and boulders interstratified with sand and shingle, overlain by cross-bedded sands. It overlies a marine platform which varies in height between 4 and 10 m O.D. (Scourse 1985). It is overlain by the St. Loy Member. Its lower part is interpreted as a raised beach deposit, the upper as aeolian sand. At other sites, these components vary in height between 4–11.5 m O.D. and 6.9–16 m O.D. respectively (Scourse 1985, 1996). The raised beach deposits have been correlated with the Hoxnian (Stephens, 1973) or to the Ipswichian (Bowen 1973*a*). D-aIle/L-Ile ratios from *Patella vulgata* suggest a correlation with oxygen isotope stage 7 (Bowen *et al.* 1985). At other sites, similar material has been dated by D-aIle/L-Ile and TL to oxygen isotope sub-stage 5e (Bowen *et al.* 1985; Scourse 1985) indicating that not all

deposits of the Godrevy Member are oxygen isotope stage 7 in age.

(4) Porth Nanven Bed. Stratotype: Porth Nanven, Cape Cornwall [SW 356308]. It lies on a marine platform at *c.* 8.5 m O.D. and is up to 8 m in thickness. It comprises a clast-supported deposit of well-rounded granite clasts which reach boulder size in the uppermost 2 m of the deposit (Scourse 1985; Campbell *et al.* 1998). It is overlain by the St Loy Member and is interpreted as a storm beach. An oxygen isotope stage 7 age is possible (Campbell *et al.* 1998).

(5) Fistral North Bed. Stratotype: Fistral Bay [SW 799625–SW 801623]. Its base lies at *c.* 6.0 m O.D. and it is up to 7 m thick on a marine platform. It is divided into a lower clast-supported deposit of pebbles and cobbles (raised beach) 2 m thick, and an upper deposit of cross-bedded, partially-cemented sand up to 5 m thick (dune sand). It is overlain by up to 2 m of the St. Loy Member and Holocene dune sand. Bowen *et al.* (1985) reported D-aIle-L-Ile ratios of 0.186 ± 0.008 (n = 3) on *Patella vulgata* that they correlated with oxygen isotope stage 7 (Bowen *et al.* 1985; Scourse 1996).

(6) Pendower Bed. Stratotype: Pendower, Gerrans Bay [SW 902382]. Its base lies at *c.* 4 m O.D. It is up to 5.5 m thick and rests on a marine platform between *c.* 4-5 m O.D. (Scourse 1985, 1996). It comprises a strongly cemented pebbly conglomerate up to 3 m thick (raised beach) overlain by cross-bedded sand (dune sand) up to 2.5 m thick (Scourse 1985, 1996). It is overlain by up to 12 m of the St. Loy Member and 0.5 m of the Lizard Formation. The dune sand of the Godrevy Member here has been dated by TL to between 165 and 252 ka (Southgate 1984). Provisional correlation with oxygen isotope stage 7 is suggested (Bowen *et al.* 1985; Scourse 1985, 1996; Campbell *et al.* 1998).

(7) Marazion Bed. Stratotype: Marazion, Penzance [SW 510319]. Its base is at *c.* 6 m O.D. It is up to 5.25 m thick and comprises: (1) a raised beach deposit of sand with some bands of pebbles; and (2) a more poorly-sorted fluvial deposit of sand, sandy clay, gravel and pebbles (up to 3.75 m thick) which occupies a channel cut in slate bedrock. It is overlain by head (up to 1.2 m) and is correlated with the Ipswichian (oxygen isotope sub-stage 5e) (Taylor & Beer 1981; Scourse 1996).

(8) Fistral South Bed. Stratotype: Fistral Bay [SW 798617–SW 795616]. Its base lies at *c.* 6 m O.D. It is over 7 m thick and comprises a lower clast-supported deposit of pebbles and cobbles (raised beach) and an upper, cross-bedded, partially-cemented sand (dune sand). The dune sand is TL dated to 116 ± 8 ka (Southgate 1985) suggesting correlation with oxygen isotope sub-stage 5e. The Fistral North Bed (*note 5*) has D-aIle/L-Ile ratios correlated with oxygen isotope stage 7. Thus, two separate raised beach/dune deposits occur in Fistral Bay.

(9) Praa Sands Member – the Praa Sands Clay Member of Scourse (1985, 1996). Stratotype: Sydney Cove [SW 573280–SW 585212]. Its base is at *c.* 3.45 m O.D. It is up to 3 m thick and comprises a mottled, sandy, silty clay with vein quartz clasts. It lies beneath the St. Loy Member and above the Godrevy Member. It shows ferruginous rhizome casts, evidence of pedogenesis and blackened charcoal-rich horizons (Scourse 1996). It is interpreted as a solifluction deposit derived specifically from a local weathered felsite elvan and subjected to pedogenesis (Scourse 1985, 1996) and it corresponds with the 'Palaeolithic floor' of Reid & Reid (1904) and Reid & Flett (1907). It also occurs at Rosemullion but its age is unknown.

(10) St. Loy Member. Formerly the Penwith Formation of Scourse (1985, 1996). Stratotype: at St Loy [SW 422230]. It is up to 4.25 m thick and comprises a poorly-sorted breccia of angular granite clasts interbedded with sandy silt and granular humic silt. The locally derived clasts range from granule to boulder size and show a marked preferred downslope orientation (Scourse 1985, 1996). It is interpreted as a periglacial solifluction deposit. The granular humic silt has been radiocarbon dated and suggests deposition during the Late Devensian. In adjacent coastal sections, the St. Loy Member overlies the Godrevy Member (Scourse 1985). Locally, the St. Loy Member exceeds 12 m in thickness. Where it overlies a dated raised beach deposit its age can be constrained, but at the type-site the age of its lower unit is indeterminate; its upper unit is probably of Middle to Late Devensian age (Scourse 1985, in press).

(11) St Loy Bed. Stratotype: St Loy [SW 422230]. Its base lies at *c.* 6 m O.D. It is up to 0.5 m thick and comprises a granular humic silt which divides the St. Loy Member (Scourse 1985, 1996). The bed has yielded pollen indicative of tundra vegetation and an Arctic climate, and a radiocarbon date of 29 120 + 1 690/–1 400 BP (Scourse 1985, 1996). Thus a Middle to Late Devensian age (oxygen isotope stages 3 & 2) is indicated for most of the St. Loy Member at this site.

(1) Lizard Formation. Formerly the Lizard Loess Member of Scourse (1996). Type-area: Lizard Peninsula, Cornwall. It comprises thin loessic deposits that are widespread, capping Pleistocene sequences and bedrock in the Lizard and elsewhere in south Cornwall (Coombe *et al.* 1956; Catt & Staines 1982; Roberts 1985). Two principal lithofacies occur: a massive loess and a thin head-loess. The loess is believed to have been derived from glacigenic sediments in the Irish Sea basin (Catt & Staines 1982; Scourse 1985, 1996). Wintle (1981) reports three TL ages from Cornwall including one of 15 900 ± 20% BP from the Lizard Peninsula. Roberts (1985) proposed formational status for the 'Lizard Loess' and defined a stratotype at Kemp's Quarry.

(2) Goonhilly Member. Stratotype: Kemp's Quarry, Goonhilly Downs [SW 721219]. Its base lies at *about* 107 m O.D. It is up to 0.75 m thick and comprises a massively-bedded silt overlying thin clay and serpentine. It is interpreted as Late Devensian loess derived from offshore glacigenic sediments (Wintle 1981; Catt & Staines 1983; Roberts 1985).

(3) Camel Formation. Type-area: Camel Estuary, north Cornwall. It comprises periglacial materials divided into two members: the Trebetherick and the Tregunna Member (Scourse 1985, 1996). These overlie the Godrevy and St. Loy members of the Penwith Formation. The Camel Formation is confined to the Camel Estuary.

(4) Trebetherick Member. the 'boulder gravel' of Arkell (1943) and the Trebetherick Boulder Gravel Member of Scourse (1985, 1996). Stratotype: Trebetherick, Camel Estuary [SW 926770]. Its base lies at 12.2 m O.D. and it is up to 2 m thick. It comprises a structureless deposit which contains a wide range of clast sizes and lithologies set in a poorly sorted matrix. At the stratotype, it rests on the St. Loy Member which is some 3 m thick, which in turn overlies >5 m of the Godrevy Member. The sequence rests on a marine platform at *c.* 6.91 m O.D. The Trebetherick Member is the same as Ussher's (1879) 'Gravel D' and the 'boulder gravel' of Arkell (1943) who interpreted it as a raised beach deposit of Micoquian (= Ipswichian) age. The material has since been interpreted as soliflucted 'Wolstonian' outwash (Stephens 1966a), 'Wolstonian' till *in situ* (Clarke 1969, 1973; Mitchell & Orme 1967) and soliflucted river gravels (Kidson 1977). It was used to delimit the extent of a 'Wolstonian' Irish Sea ice sheet by West (1977). Scourse (1996) demonstrates that the lithological content of the 'boulder gravel' is derived entirely from within the catchment of the River Camel and proposes river ice as a mechanism for its transport. Its stratigraphical relations with the Penwith Formation suggests a Late Devensian age. It is also recorded at Tregunna, Little Petherick and Lellizzick: Scourse divides it into a soliflucted and an *in situ* lithofacies on the basis of clast fabric, sedimentology and geomorphic position (Scourse 1996).

(5) Tregunna Member. Formerly the Tregunna Formation of Scourse (1985, 1996). Stratotype: Tregunna, Camel Estuary [SW 960740]. Its base lies at *c.* 6.5 m O.D. and it is up to 2 m thick. It comprises a breccia of angular (local) slate clasts mixed with some non-local clasts. It is a poorly sorted deposit that exhibits a variety of periglacial structures including fossil ice-wedge casts and festoons. It is interpreted as a solifluction deposit derived from slate bedrock and from deposits of the underlying Trebetherick Member (Scourse 1996). At the stratotype, it overlies the Trebetherick and St. Loy members which rest on a marine platform at *about* 3–4 m O.D. The Tregunna Member differs from the St. Loy Member in containing non-local clasts: it is recorded elsewhere in the Camel Estuary at Little Petherick and Lellizzick (Clarke 1973;

Scourse 1985, 1996).

(6) Hawks Tor Beds. Stratotype: Hawks Tor, Bodmin Moor [SX 150749]. It lies at *c.* 220 m O.D. and is up to 1 m thick. It is a highly variable sequence of silt, sand, gravel, organic mud and peat (Conolly *et al.* 1950; Brown 1977, 1980) and corresponds to units 1–4 of Campbell *et al.* 1998). It is underlain by kaolinized granite (grus) and overlain by humified raised bog peat (unit 5) and non-humified *Sphagnum* peat (unit 6) (Campbell *et al.* 1998). Organic sediments in the stratotype (units 1–4) contain pollen and plant macrofossils that have radiocarbon ages between $13\,088 \pm 300$ BP and 9654 ± 190 BP (Brown 1977, 1980), and the most complete record of Devensian late-glacial conditions in South-West England. The stratotype shows the climatic improvement of the Allerød–Bølling and the return to tundra vegetation and periglacial conditions in the Younger Dryas (Conolly *et al.* 1950; Stephens 1973; Brown 1977, 1980).

South Devon

(1) Torbay Formation. Type-area: between Hope's Nose, Torquay [SX 949637] and Prawle Point [SX 773350]. It comprises marine (raised beach), aeolian (dune sand) and head deposits, extensively exposed in coastal sections (Mottershead 1977*a, b*; Mottershead *et al.* 1987). D-aIle/L-Ile ratios (Davies 1983; Mottershead *et al.* 1987; Bowen *et al.* 1985) and U-series ages (Proctor & Smart 1991) show that the Hope's Nose, Shoalstone and Thatcher Stone members belong to at least two separate sea-level events: oxygen isotope stage 7 and oxygen isotope sub-stage 5e. Reinterpretation of the D-aIle/L-Ile ratios suggested that the Torbay Formation contains a mixed fauna from three high sea-level events: the earliest from oxygen isotope stage 7 and the two later ones from oxygen isotope sub-stage 5e (Bowen 1994*b*). The raised beach deposits are overlain by head, best developed between Start Point and Prawle Point.

(2) Hope's Nose Member. Stratotype: Hope's Nose, Torquay [SX 949637]. Its base lies between 9.1 and 12.1 m O.D. it is to 3 m thick, and comprises raised beach boulders and coarse sand. It is overlain by 1.5 m of dune-bedded sand of the Thatcher Stone Member. It overlies a marine platform and is overlain by head (4 m). It fines-upwards and is well cemented by calcium carbonate. Fossil marine molluscs are common, especially valves of *Ostrea edulis* (Mottershead *et al.* 1987; Keen *unpublished*). D-aIle/L-Ile ratios indicate correlation with oxygen isotope stage 7 (Davies 1983). Revised D-aIle/L-Ile ratios are 0.17 ± 0.012 (12) for stage 7 and from the overlying dune sand, correlated with oxygen isotope sub-stage 5e (Thatcher Stone Member): 0.115 ± 0.01 (4) (Bowen *et al.* 1985).

(3) Shoalstone Member. Stratotype: Shoalstone Point, Torbay [SX 939568]. Its base lies at *c.* 8.5 m O.D. it is up to 1.3 m thick, and consists of beach cobbles and coarse sand, with angular limestone cobbles and boulders at its base on a marine platform. It is by overlain head. It is exposed for over 300 m between Shoalstone Point and Berry Head. It contains an abundant fauna of shells, principally of *Ostrea* but also of *Cerastoderma edule* and gastropods. D-aIle/L-Ile ratios are correlated with oxygen isotope stage 7 and oxygen isotope sub-stage 5e (Davies 1983; Bowen *et al.* 1985). Proctor & Smart (1991) suggest oxygen isotope stage 7 and sub-stage 5e sea-levels based on U-series ages from coastal caves. But reinterpretation of the D-aIle/L-Ile data suggested that a mixed fauna was present in the raised beaches and that there

are elements from three high sea-level events in the Shoalstone beaches (Bowen 1994*b*).

(4) Thatcher Stone Member. Stratotype: Thatcher (Rock) Stone, Torbay [SX 944629]. Its base lies between 7.8 and 10.3 m O.D. it is up to 1.5 m thick, and consists of rounded beach pebbles and cobbles overlain by reddened and cemented sand. It lies on a marine platform and is overlain by up to 5 m of head. It is richly fossiliferous especially in marine gastropods, foraminifera, barnacle plates, fish vertebrae and crab and echinoid debris are also recorded (Mottershead *et al.* 1987). D-aIle/L-Ile ratios correlate it with oxygen isotope sub-stage 5e (Davies 1983; Bowen *et al.* 1985).

(5) Start Point Member. Stratotype: between Start Point [SX 830370] and Prawle Point [SX 773350]. Its base lies at *c.* 3.0 m O.D. it is up to 33 m thick, and comprises head of various lithofacies lying on a marine platform (Mottershead 1971, 1977*a,b*). It is poorly sorted and coarsest close to bedrock. It may contain reworked and/or *in situ* raised beach deposits at its base. Its age probably ranges between oxygen isotope stage 6 through to the beginning of the Holocene.

North Devon

(1) Barnstaple Bay Formation. Type-area: Barnstaple Bay and Lundy Island. This includes a range of glacigenic deposits of controversial origin.

(2) Fremington Member. Type-area: between Yelland [SS 495319] and Lake [SS 555315] and between Penhill Point [SS 517345] and Brynsworthy [SS 529312]. It outcrops in an oval area some 5.6 km long by 2.6 km wide. Its base lies at between 14 and 18 m O.D; and its surface height of outcrop varies between *c.* 15–46 m O.D. It reaches *c.* 30 m in maximum thickness and comprises a sequence of gravel, sand, silt and clay widely referred to as the Fremington Till or Fremington Clay. Most of it (*c.* 60–70% by volume) is a stiff clay. It has traditionally been regarded as deposited by ice (Maw 1864; Zeuner 1959), of Irish Sea origin and Saalian, Gipping or Wolstonian in age (Mitchell 1960, 1972; Stephens 1966*a,b,* 1970, 1973). Some have argued for a glacio-marine origin of Late Devensian age (Eyles & McCabe 1989).

(3) Brannam's Beds. Stratotype: Higher Gorse, Brannam's Clay Pit, Fremington [SS 530316]. Its base lies at 18 m O.D. and it comprises a sequence of: (1) subangular gravel (0.5–1.5 m); (2) dark brown, stone-free homogenous clay with sand pockets (6 m); (3) red-brown clay with frequent clasts (2 m); and (4) mottled stony clay (up to 4 m). Stephens (1966*a,b,* 1970, 1973) grouped the stony and stoneless clays as a till of Irish Sea origin and Saalian age, because it overlies raised beach gravels deemed to be Hoxnian (Mitchell 1960, 1972). Kidson (1977) and Kidson & Wood (1974) interpreted bed 1 as fluvioglacial. Edmonds (1972) interpreted the 'Fremington Clay' as a lacustrine deposit formed in a Saalian proglacial environment. Eyles & McCabe (1989) and Campbell & Bowen (1989) raise the possibility that the material was deposited as a Late Devensian glacio-marine mud.

(4) Fremington Quay Beds. Stratotype: Fremington Quay [SS 511331]. Its base lies at *c.* O.D. It comprises up to 4 m of: (1) poorly-sorted gravel, sand and silt overlain by; (2) pebbly sandy clay with striated stones and erratics (Dewey 1913; Stephens 1973). Bed 1 has been regarded as a raised beach deposit of Hoxnian (Mitchell 1960; Stephens 1966*a,* 1970, 1973) or Ipswichian (Zeuner 1959; Bowen 1969, 1973*a;* Kidson & Wood 1974; Kidson 1977) age. Bed 2 has been interpreted as a glacial deposit of Saalian age (Stephens 1973). Edmonds (1972), however, argued that the 'pebbly drift' at Fremington Quay is a mixture of soliflucted and fluvially-sorted Saalian till. Kidson & Wood (1974) regarded it as Devensian head.

(5) Lundy Member. Stratotype: Lundy Island, Bristol Channel [SS 133475]. It rests on bedrock at *c.* 85–107 m O.D. on the northern side of the Island (Mitchell 1968). It comprises a thin gravel which contains erratics. Mitchell (1968) interpreted the material as outwash deposited by a Saalian Irish Sea glacier. Other views are that it is Late Devensian (oxgen isotope stage 2) (Eyles & McCabe 1989; Scourse 1991; Scourse *et al.* 1991), or older (oxygen isotope stage 16? – Bowen 1994*a,b*).

(1) Croyde Bay Formation. Stratotype: between Morte Bay and Westward Ho! [SS 450410 to SS 420291]. It comprises marine (raised beach), aeolian (dune sand), head, and slope-wash in coastal exposures deposits around Barnstaple Bay (Stephens 1966*a,b*, 1970, 1973; Kidson 1977). Preliminary OSL ages suggest an Ipswichian (oxygen isotope sub-stage 5e) age for the marine units and early Devensian age (oxygen isotope stage 4) for the dune sands (Gilbert 1996).

(2) Saunton Member. Stratotype: Saunton Sands [SS 437379]. Its base lies at *c.* 5 m O.D. and it comprises 0.5–1 m of gravel and sand (raised beach deposits) overlain by *c.* 2–3 m of marine sand and *c.* 10 m of aeolian sands (Gilbert 1996) on marine platforms. It is overlain by up to 21 m of head and slope-wash deposits (Croyde Member). It is marine in origin towards its base, but aeolian in its upper layers; it is unevenly cemented as 'sandrock' with calcium carbonate (Greenwood 1972). It outcrops discontinuously for over 2.5 km and reaches thicknesses greater than 30 m. Locally, it overlies large erratic boulders ('giant erratics') on the shore platform (Stephens 1970, 1973). Radiocarbon ages from *Balanus balanoides* on the marine platform are : > 40 800 BP; and from shells in the raised beach conglomerate and sand: 32 000 + 2800/−1800 BP (Kidson 1974; Kidson & Heyworth 1977). D-aIle/L-Ile ratios from marine shells (Bowen *et al.* 1985) indicate a mixed fauna of oxygen isotope stage 7 and oxygen isotope sub-stage 5e (Bowen 1994*b*).

(3) Westward Ho! Bed. Stratotype: Westward Ho! [SS 421291]. Its base lies at *c.* 8–9 m O.D. and it comprises an uncemented deposit (up to 4.5 m thick) of rounded Carboniferous cobbles; no erratics are present (Stephens 1970; Kidson & Heyworth 1977). In places a thin head unit separates it from the underlying platform. It is overlain by up to 3 m of head (Stephens 1970). It is unfossiliferous and is regarded as Ispwichian (oxygen isotope sub-stage 5e) (Stephens 1970, 1973; Kidson 1977; Kidson & Heyworth 1977).

(4) Croyde Member. Stratotype: Middleborough House, Croyde Bay [SS 430398]. Its base lies at *c.* 5 m O.D. and it comprises *c.* 6 m of locally derived head, sand and slope-wash deposits, overlying marine platforms (Stephens 1966*a, b*, 1970). Elsewhere it ranges up to 21 m in thickness and forms a prominent terrace between Middleborough House and Pencil Rock. It commonly overlies the Saunton Member. It is interpreted as a mixture of head and slope-wash deposits. Stephens (1966*a,b*, 1970, 1973) divided it into a Main Head (Saalian) and Upper Head (Devensian) and inferred weathering (Ipswichian) between them. Bowen (1969) and Kidson (1977) suggested it was undifferentiated and accumulated during the Devensian.

(12) Braunton Burrows Formation. Type area: southwest England. It includes all the aeolian sand deposits of southwest England (Kidson *et al.* 1989; Chisholm 1996).

Somerset and South Gloucestershire

(1) Kenn Formation. Type-area: Avon and north Somerset. It consists of glacigenic deposits interpreted as till, glacio-marine, and outwash at Kenn, Court Hill, Nightingale Valley, Failland Ridge, Bathampton Down and Bleadon Hill (Hawkins & Kellaway 1971; Colbourne *et al.* 1974; Gilbertson & Hawkins 1978*a,b*; Andrews *et al.* 1984). It is subdivided into the Bleadon, Bathampton Down, Nightingale, Kennpier and Kenn Court members. It underlies 'Cromerian' (correlated with oxygen isotope stage 15) deposits at Kenn, hence must be at least as old as oxygen isotope stage 16.

(2) Bleadon Member. Stratotype: Bleadon Hill [ST 350573]. Comprises up to 6 m of cobbly gravel and sands lying at *c.* 82 m O.D. on the south slopes of Bleadon Hill, contains a derived Lower Jurassic microfauna, and is interpreted as glacial outwash (Findlay *et al.* 1972).

(3) Bathampton Down Member. Stratotype: Bathampton Down [ST 774650]. It comprises unconsolidated, erratic-rich silty and clayey gravels found in fissures and cavities in Jurassic limestone. It is interpreted as reworked remanié tills (Conybeare & Phillips 1822; Weston 1850; Hawkins & Kellaway 1971).

(4) Nightingale Member. Stratotype: Kenn [ST 4269]. It comprises erratic-rich gravels and sandy gravels, interpreted as outwash, underlying and interdigitating with silt- and clay-rich diamicts of the Kennpier Member in the Kenn lowlands, where they are over 6 m thick, and at Court Hill [ST 473723], where they are 7.6 m thick, and Nightingale Valley [ST 450752] (Trimmer 1853; Greenly 1921; Hawkins & Kellaway 1971; Gilbertson & Hawkins 1978*a,b*; Hunt unpublished).

(5) Kennpier Member. Stratotype: Kenn [ST 4269]. It comprises diamict, containing erratic boulders and smaller clasts, interpreted as till. Up to 2 m of stony (some clasts in excess of 1 tonne) silty diamict overlies and interdigitates with gravel and sand of the Nightingale Member at Kenn. Around 2 m of silty diamict interdigitates with the Nightingale Member at Court Hill. It is also present on the Failland Ridge (Hawkins & Kellaway 1971; Gilbertson & Hawkins 1978*a,b*; Colbourne *et al.* 1974), and may occur beneath deposits of the Burtle Formation at Greylake No. 2 Quarry (Hunt unpublished).

(6) Kenn Court Member. Stratotype: Kenn Court [ST 414688]. It comprises up to 0.8 m of shelly, till-like material and sands containing a cold-water, brackish fauna of foraminifera (Gilbertson & Hawkins 1978*a*) interpreted by Andrews *et al.* (1984) as glacio-marine.

(7) Yew Tree Formation. Stratotype: Yew Tree Farm [ST 42256927]. It comprises 2–3 m of estuarine and freshwater silty sands infilling depressions in the surface of the Kenn Formation at Yew Tree Farm and Kennpier Footbridge [ST 427698]. It contains abundant molluscs, pollen and dyno-flagellate cysts indicative of a temperate but fairly continental climate, and a regional vegetation of mixed-oak forest (Gilbertson & Hawkins 1978*a*; Hunt 1981). D-aIle/L-Ile ratios of 0.385 ± 0.007 (2), 0.405 ± 0.05 (2) and 0.38 ± 0.08 (2) on *Corbicula fluminalis* are interpreted as indicating an age of between 400 and 600 ka by Andrews *et al.* (1984), but other similar ones of 0.38 ± 0.1 (5) are correlated more precisely with Waverley Wood, Warwickshire and oxygen isotope stage 15, between 478 and 524 ka (Bowen *et al.* 1989; Shotton *et al.* 1993) .

(8) Middle Hope Formation. Stratotype: Swallow Cliff, Middle Hope [ST 325661]. Comprises raised beach, other interglacial, and interbedded slope and aeolian sediments.

Table 18. *Correlations between Somerset and South Gloucestershire and oxygen isotope stratigraphy.*

SOMERSET & SOUTH GLOUCESTERSHIRE

δ¹⁸O	SOMERSET	SOMERSET & SOUTH LEVELS	SOUTH GLOUCESTERSHIRE
1		FORMATION (12)	
2	**MIDDLE HOPE FORMATION** (8)		**DONIFORD FORMATION** (6) / **PARRETT FORMATION** (1)
			Ashford Member (11)
			Huish Member (10)
3	Brean Member (13)		Middle Moor Member (9)
			Combe Member (8)
			Low Ham Member (7)
4			*Whatley Palaeosol* (6)
5			Portfield Member (5)
5e	Swallow Cliff Member (12)		
6	Woodspring Member (11)		
7	*Middle Hope Palaeosol* (10)		Chadbrick Member (4)
			Whatley Member (3)
			Hurcott Member (2)
8	Weston Member (9)		
9			
10		**WOOKEY FORMATION** (1)	**BURTLE FORMATION** (2)
11	**AVON FORMATION** (1)	Wookey Station Member (4)	Middlezoy Member (5)
12	*Bathampton Palaeosol* (5)	*Burrington Palaeosol* (3)	Greylake Member (4)
13	Bathampton Member (4)	Burrington Member (2)	Kenn Church Member (3)
	Stidham Member (3)		
	Ham Green Member (2)		
15	**YEW TREE FORMATION** (7)		**WESTBURY-SUB-MENDIP FORMATION** (1)
16 >	**KENN FORMATION** (1)		
	Kenn Court Member (6)		
	Kennpier Member (5)		
	Nightingale Member (4)		
	Bathampton Down Member (3)		
	Bleadon Member (2)		

(9) Weston Member Stratotype: Weston-in-Gordano [ST 450749]. It comprises a 5 m thick sequence consisting of two marine gravel units, separated by terrestrial sediments and overlain by freshwater silts (containing *Corbicula*) and slope deposits. The sequence is undated but a correlation with oxygen isotope stages 7–9 is possible (ApSimon & Donovan 1956; Hunt unpublished).

(10) Middle Hope Palaeosol. Stratotype: Swallow Cliff, Middle Hope [ST 325661]. Comprises up to 0.5 m of stony silty clay exhibiting pedogenic features consistent with interglacial weathering. It is overlain by the Woodspring and Swallow Cliff members.

(11) Woodspring Member. Stratotype: Swallow Cliff, Middle Hope [ST 325661]. It comprises up to 0.5 m of sandy silt with some stones and a sparse terrestrial mollusc assemblage. It is overlain by the Swallow Cliff Member (Briggs *et al.* 1991) that is correlated with oxygen isotope sub-stage 5e.

(12) Swallow Cliff Member. Stratotype: Swallow Cliff, Middle Hope [ST 325661]. It consists of up to 1 m of cemented cobbly gravel with an abundant fauna of shoreline molluscs. It is interpreted as a raised beach deposit (Sanders 1841; Ravis 1869; Briggs *et al.* 1991). D-aIle/L-Ile ratios suggested correlation with oxygen isotope stage 7 (Davies 1983), although both previous (Andrews *et al.* 1979) and subsequent D-aIle/L-Ile ratios (Bowen & Sykes 1988) indicate correlation with oxygen isotope sub-stage 5e.

(13) Brean Member. Stratotype: Brean Down [ST 295588]. It comprises up to 18 m of slope deposits and aeolian sand overlying the 'reindeer stratum', a 2 m thick deposit containing interstadial mammal and mollusc remains, which in turn overlies a further 8 m of slope and aeolian deposits (Palmer 1931; ApSimon *et al.* 1961; Hunt unpublished; Currant & Jacobi unpublished). Although these deposits are not dated, correlation with oxygen isotope sub-stage 5d to oxygen isotope stage 2 seems likely. Similar slope deposits and aeolian sediments are widespread in north Somerset and Avon: comparable but less complex sequences occur at Holly Lane, Clevedon [ST 417726]; Clapton Nurseries [ST 450729]; Wynhol Valley [ST 449728]; Clevedon Court [ST 426714]; and Avonmouth [ST 523774] (Gilbertson & Hawkins 1974, 1983). Thin coversands, also attributed to this Member, occur widely across north Somerset and Avon, for example, at Kenn [ST 4269] (Gilbertson & Hawkins 1978a).

(1) Avon Formation. Type-area: Avon Valley between Bathampton and the mouth of the Avon [ST 7866 to ST 5079]. It comprises fluvial gravels and related sediments of the River Avon, conventionally grouped into a series of terraces, now re-classified as: the Ham Green Member, the Stidham Member and the Bathampton Member.

(2) Ham Green Member. Stratotype: Ham Green [ST 539768]. It comprises gravels of the Avon with a surface at *c.* 30 m above present river level (Davies & Fry 1929). It is 3–4 m thick, contains erratic clasts and shows imbrication consistent with deposition from the early Avon (Hunt unpublished). A basal lag of the remains of large mammals was reported in the last century from the base of the Member at Victoria Pit, Twerton (Winwood 1889; Davies & Fry 1929), and a basal sand with interglacial or interstadial molluscs was described from beneath this unit in the railway cutting at Twerton by Winwood (1875). The age of these deposits is unclear.

(3) Stidham Member. Stratotype: Stidham Farm, Saltford [ST 674684]. It comprises up to 2 m of trough cross-bedded gravels with a coarse basal lag which contains remains of 'mammoth' (Moore 1870; Woodward 1876; Davies & Fry 1929). Its

surface lies at *c.* 12 m above the present Avon. Stratigraphical relations suggest a possible correlation with oxygen isotope stage 8.

(4) Bathampton Member. Stratotype: Hampton Rocks Railway Cutting [ST 778667]. It consists of up to 3 m of trough cross-bedded gravels (Weston 1850; Woodward 1876) which contain a 'cold-stage' mollusc assemblage. The deposits are overlain by an interglacial soil profile and coversands. The surface of the sequence lies at *c.* 3-5 m above the modern Avon (Hunt 1990b). The interglacial nature of the palaeosol suggests that the gravels of the Bathampton Member can be no younger than oxygen isotope stage 6.

(5) Bathampton Palaeosol. Stratotype: Hampton Rocks Railway Cutting [ST 778667]. It comprises a cryoturbated, rubified, clay-rich soil profile which contains calcrete developed on gravels of the Bathampton Member. It is correlated, provisionally, with the Burrington Palaeosol and interglacial conditions in oxygen isotope sub-stage 5e (Hunt 1990b).

(1) Wookey Formation. Stratotype: Wookey Station Railway Cutting [ST 53154630]. Comprises gravels, silts and palaeosols of the Mendip alluvial fans (Woodward 1876; Green & Welch 1965; Macklin & Hunt 1988).

(2) Burrington Member. Stratotype: Bourne [ST 483598]. Comprises over 1.0 m of cobbly fan gravels found in north Mendip, corresponding to the Hayvat and Ashford units of Pounder & Macklin (1985) which pre-date the interglacial Burrington Palaeosol (Findlay 1977; Pounder & Macklin 1985): these gravels are correlated with oxygen isotope stage 6.

(3) Burrington Palaeosol. Stratotype: Bourne [ST 483598]. It comprises an interglacial palaeosol developed on the Hayvat unit of Burrington Member gravels in north Mendip (Findlay 1977; Pounder & Macklin 1985). It may be oxygen isotope sub-stage 5e in age.

(4) Wookey Station Member. Stratotype: Wookey Station Railway Cutting [ST 53154630]. It comprises over 3 m of coarse cobbly gravels with some silty channel fills correlated with oxygen isotope stage 2 (Macklin & Hunt 1988) and probably equivalent to Pounder and Macklin's (1985) Ashley and Link Lane units in north Mendip.

(1) Westbury-sub-Mendip Formation. Stratotype: Westbury-sub-Mendip [ST 507504]. It comprises cave deposits with an abundant fauna of mammal bones and rare archaeological artefacts. It includes a basal unit with interglacial fossil mammals indicative of a mixed-oak forest biotype, followed by a unit with taxa indicative of a cold continental climate and boreal vegetation, a third unit also with taxa indicative of a mixed-oak forest and finally a unit with taxa indicative of severe Arctic conditions. Recycled early Pleistocene faunal elements are present throughout the sequence. The fauna of both temperate phases compares fairly closely with the Boxgrove fauna and can be placed, on biostratigraphical grounds, between the type-Cromerian and the Hoxnian (Bishop, 1974 1982; Currant *pers. comm.* 1995). Similar deposits occur at Batscombe Quarry, Cheddar (Hawkins & Tratman 1977).

(2) Burtle Formation. Stratotype: Greylake No. 2 Quarry [ST 385336]. It comprises marine sands and gravels with a few interbedded palaeosols and lenses of freshwater sand (Buckland & Conybeare 1824; Bulleid & Jackson 1937, 1941; Kidson *et al.* 1978). A *Corbicula* shell from 'Old Sea Bank' (probably somewhere in the Greylake quarries: Gilbertson 1979) yielded a D-aIle/L-Ile ratio of 0.26 (Hunt *et al.* 1984) which suggests that part of the Burtle Formation may be as old as oxygen isotope stage 9, or that some of its fauna may have been reworked from pre-existing deposits (see also note 4).

(3) Kenn Church Member. Stratotype: Kenn Church [ST 412686]. It comprises up to 1.7 m of marine sands in the Kenn area (Welch 1955; Gilbertson & Hawkins 1978*a*). D-aIle/L-Ile ratios (*c.* 0.2) indicate a correlation with oxygen isotope stage 7 (Andrews *et al*. 1984).

(4) Greylake Member. Stratotype: Greylake No. 2 Quarry [ST 385336]. It comprises the lower marine sand at Greylake as reported by Bulleid & Jackson (1937), up to 2 m thick and recently verified by Hunt (unpublished). It contains a rich shelly marine fauna (Bullied & Jackson 1937) and channel fills with a freshwater fauna (Gilbertson 1979), separated by cemented palaeosol and erosion from the Middlezoy Member. A *Corbicula* shell from the freshwater fauna originally yielded a D-aIle/L-Ile ratio of 0.18 (Hunt *et al*. 1984; Hunt 1990*b*), but a re-run of the sample, however, has yielded a ratio of 0.203 confirming an oxygen isotope stage 7 age, but with the possibility that it is slightly older (Bowen unpublished).

(5) Middlezoy Member. Stratotype: Greylake No. 2 Quarry [ST 385336]. It comprises the upper marine deposits at Greylake as reported by Bulleid & Jackson (1937) and described in detail by Kidson *et al*. (1978). These deposits fill what is probably a channel scoured through deposits of the Greylake Member. The deposits consist of up to 2.5 m of intertidal silts which pass upwards into 3.5 m of marine sands and gravels with a rich marine shelly fauna (Bulleid & Jackson 1937; Kidson *et al*. 1978). D-aIle/L-Ile ratios of around 0.14 (Andrews *et al*. 1979) indicate correlation with oxygen isotope sub-stage 5e.

(6) Doniford Formation. Type-area: Doniford to Watchet [ST 091432–ST 077435]. It comprises up to 6 m of trough cross-bedded and massively-bedded fluvial and 'head gravels' laid down in cold-climatic conditions, probably during oxygen isotope stage 2 (Gilbertson & Mottershead 1975).

(1) Parrett Formation. Type-area: the Parrett Valley and its tributaries between Martock [ST 4420] and Westonzoyland [ST 3636]. Comprises fluvial gravels, sands, silts and organic deposits of the valleys of southern Somerset.

(2) Hurcott Member. Stratotype: Hurcott Farm [ST 512296]. It comprises up to 1 m of coarse, cobbly fluvial gravels with a sparse mollusc fauna, older than the Chadbrick Member (Hunt 1987).

(3) Whatley Member. Stratotype: Langport Railway Cutting [ST 426272]. It comprises *c.* 2 m of trough cross-bedded gravels with a sparse cold-climate mollusc fauna, calcreted and overlain by a cryoturbated rubified palaeosol (note 6). It pre-dates the Portfield Member (Woodward 1905; Hunt 1987).

(4) Chadbrick Member. Stratotype: Chadbrick Valley, Somerton [ST 51252955]. It comprises 0.5 m of cemented gravels containing fossil molluscs (Hunt *et al*. 1984) and pollen (Hunt 1990*a*) both consistent with a temperate climate and a mixed-oak forest biotype. A single D-aIle/L-Ile ratio on *Corbicula* of

0.18 (Hunt *et al*. 1984; Hunt 1990*a*), and re-run at 0.225 by Bowen (unpublished), indicate correlation with oxygen isotope stage 7 age or older.

(5) Portfield Member. Stratotype: Portfield [ST 40632657]. It comprises over 1 m of freshwater silty clays with interglacial molluscs and plant macrofossils (Hunt 1987). D-aIle/L-Ile ratios averaging 0.145 on *Bithynia tentaculata* and 0.157 on *Lymnaea peregra*, are correlated with oxygen isotope stage 7 (Bowen unpublished). It is overlain up to 3 m of fluvial sands, sandy gravels and silts with a sparse cold-climate mollusc fauna [ST 40592658] that is correlated with oxygen isotope stage 6 (Hunt 1987).

(6) Whatley Palaeosol. Stratotype: Langport Railway Cutting [ST 426272]. It comprises a cryoturbated, rubified, clay-enriched horizon overlying a 'plugged' calcrete developed on gravels of the Whatley Member (Hunt 1987).

(7) Low Ham Member. Stratotype: Low Ham Valley [ST 43902900]. Up to 3 m of sediment with pollen, molluscs, ostracods and plant macrofossils and a dominantly grassy interstadial biotype, that indicate a relatively high sea level (Hunt 1987). D-aIle/L-Ile ratios averaging 0.43 on *Succinea* and *Trichia*, 0.073 on *Succinea*, 0.133 on *Pisidium*, 0.61 on *Valvata* and 0.81 on *Pisidium* suggest an age late in oxygen isotope stage 5 (Hunt, Bowen & Whatley unpublished).

(8) Combe Member. Stratotype: Combe [ST 41132848]. Plane and trough cross-bedded sands with a sparse cold-climate mollusc fauna. It post-dates the Low Ham Member and thus may be oxygen isotope stage 4 in age (Hunt 1987).

(9) Middle Moor Member. Stratotype: Middle Moor [ST 406282]. It comprises over 3.5 m of coarse trough cross-bedded and massive unfossiliferous gravels ascribed to oxygen isotope stage 4 on morphostratigraphical grounds (Hunt 1987).

(10) Huish Member. Stratotype: Huish Episcopi [ST 42902645]. Comprises 1–3 m of coarse trough cross-bedded gravels overlain by a channel fill with 'interstadial' fauna (Hunt 1987). It is believed to have been deposited during the Late Devensian (oxygen isotope stage 2) and the channel fill may be Allerød–Bølling (Windermere Interstadial) in age. It contains clasts of of sand and silt within the Huish Member at Thorney Moor [ST 427237] that contain sparse pollen, mostly *Alnus*, molluscs and ostracods that may indicate a previous inter-stadial event.

(11) Ashford Member. Stratotype: Ashford Mills [ST 35951870]. It consists of 1–4 m of unfossiliferous generally-massively bedded coarse gravel. A Younger Dryas age is suspected on lithostratigraphical grounds (Hunt 1987).

(12) Somerset Levels Formation. Type-area: Somerset Levels. Holocene marine and estuarine alluvium, fluvial alluvium and associated peat beds of the Somerset Levels (Kidson & Heyworth 1976).

Chapter 7

Wales

D. Q. BOWEN

With contributions from S. Aldhouse-Green & G. S. P. Thomas

The style of Quaternary deposits in Wales is influenced by its Palaeozoic rocks and surrounding offshore, partly onshore, basins of Mesozoic and Cenozoic ones. Its dissected plateaux and mountains were the source areas for ice that spread on to the lowlands that were also, in part, glaciated by contemporaneous ice from the Irish Sea Basin.

The stratigraphical record in Wales consists mainly of glacial deposits with the source areas of the ice indicated by erratics in the Meirion, Elenid, Eryri (Snowdonia), Brecknockshire (of Breconshire), Rhondda and St Asaph Formations. Within the Late Devensian glaciated areas any record of earlier events is sparse, with notable exceptions at Pontnewydd Cave and Pen-y-bryn near Caernarfon. Outside Late Devensian glaciation an incomplete record extends to the Ipswichian (oxygen isotope sub-stage 5e). Pre-Ipswichian deposits are fragmentary and mostly preserved on, or within, caves of Carboniferous limestone.

Earlier base-lines for correlation and dating (Bowen 1974) that included late-glacial biostratigraphy and ^{14}C ages, 'Ipswichian' raised beaches and ^{14}C ages for 'Middle Devensian' deposits in adjacent parts of England, are less useful now that 'Middle Devensian' ^{14}C ages are probably minimum age estimates only. This has been offset, however, by the application of aminostratigraphy (D-aIle/L-Ile), uranium-series, TL and ESR dating that has enabled finer subdivision and more effective correlation and dating of earlier Devensian and pre-Devensian stratigraphic units.

Lithostratigraphical continuity and comparability of depositional style in similar geomorphic settings is the primary means of correlation of the major formations. Geochronologically the Late Devensian glaciation is constrained by a 22.8 ± 2 ka ^{36}Cl rock exposure age in Gower (Bowen 1994b) with deglaciation at Glanllynnau in Gwynedd, north-west Wales, over by about 17.3 ka calendar years. The Younger Dryas glaciation in Snowdonia is constrained by ^{36}Cl ages to between $12\,900 \pm 2000$ and about $11\,600 \pm 1300$, which corresponds to the calendar ages for the Younger Dryas in the Greenland ice-cores (Bowen et al. 1994; Phillips et al. 1994).

Earlier Devensian rocks are correlated by U-series ages from caves in Gower, Pembrokeshire and Clwyd. The marine members of the Pennard Formation are correlated by aminostratigraphy, uranium-series and TL age estimates. These major stratigraphical markers in Wales are readily correlated with similar ones in Southwest England.

Remaining problems include: (1) the subdivision and correlation of pre-sub-stage 5e deposits; (2) the apparent absence of Early and Middle Devensian deposits: that is, other than the record from caves; (3) the nature of the coalescence and subsequent decoupling of the Welsh and 'Irish Sea' ice-sheets over time. An important aspect of this is the debate over the marine (glaciomarine) or terrestrial origin of some 'Irish Sea' deposits.

The regional order in which this report is presented is from Gower, the best known region with a long sequence, thence southwest Wales where a similarly long sequence is known, to regions where Devensian rocks dominate the record: that is northwest, northeast Wales and finally southeast Wales.

South and West Gower

(1) **Llanddewi Formation**. Stratotype: Hills Farm Borehole [SS 452861] on the crest of the Paviland Moraine. This showed 21.5 m of glacial gravels, sand and gravel and sand overlying 1.5 m of red clay, possibly till, on Namurian shales at 78 m O.D. It is composed of quartz sand and Coal Measure sandstone and shale fragments, and minor quantities of coal, flint, basalt and rhyolite. The Llanddewi Formation (Bowen 1969b) is extensive and relatively little dissected in west Gower. This may be because it overlies Carboniferous limestone. It is the product of glaciation by Welsh ice from the north numerous Namurian (Millstone Grit) quartzite boulders of differenet sizes lie on its surface. It also contains erratics of 'Irish Sea' provenance (George 1933) that were probably derived from an earlier larger glaciation (Bowen 1970). Its age is uncertain, but its field relationships show that it antedates oxygen isotope stage 7 and possibly stage 9 (Bowen et al. 1985). It has been suggested that it may have occurred during oxygen isotope stage 12 time (Bowen 1989).

(2) **Pennard Formation**. Stratotype: Hunts Bay [SS 5686] (Bowen 1970, 1971a). This formation is coextensive with periglacial and underying marine deposits that form the coastal drift terraces of south and southwest Wales. What unifies these deposits of different origin is that they are predominantly composed of local rock consitituents.

(3) **Minchin Hole Member**. Stratotype: Minchin Hole Cave [SS 562868]. It consists of marine sand overlying bedrock at 9.9 m O.D. overlain by the High Tor Member at 11.8 m O.D. (Sutcliffe & Bowen 1973; Bowen 1973c). D-aIle/Ile ratios indicate an oxygen isotope stage 7 age (Bowen et al. 1985). TL ages are: 164.4, 183.2 and 226.0 ka (Southgate 1985).

(4) **High Tor Member**. Stratotype: Minchin Hole Cave [SS 562868]. It consists of head deposits of the 'inner talus' and head remnants of an 'outer talus' up to 20 m (Sutcliffe & Bowen 1973; Sutcliffe et al. 1987). A basal tongue, with a large form of *Microtus oeconomus*, indicative of severe cold conditions, separates the Minchin Hole Member from the Hunts Bay Member. The Hunts Bay Member lies unconformably across the Minchin Hole and High Tor Members that form a low cliff against which the younger member was deposited (Bowen 1973c). Its age ranges between oxygen

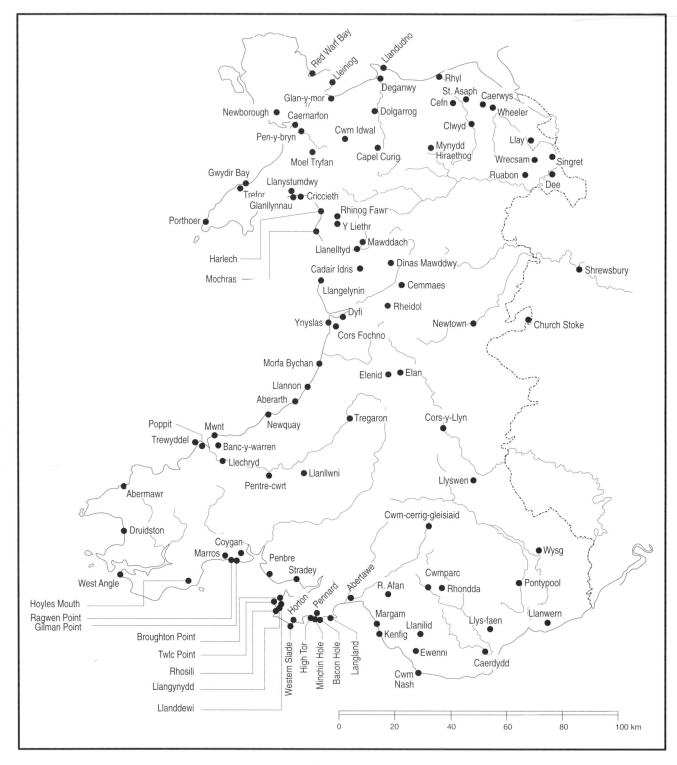

Fig. 8. Localities in Wales.

isotope stages 6 and 1.

(5) Hunts Bay Member. Stratotype: Hunts Bay between [SS 562868] and [SS 566865]). A cemented beach gravel overlying a shore platform that slopes from below mean sea-level to about 10 m O.D. (George 1932; Bowen 1970, 1971a). It consists predominatly of Carboniferous limestone pebbles but also some foreign to Gower. D-aIle/L-Ile are correlated with the

calibrated site of Bacon Hole, thence with sub-stage 5e. Older D-aIle/LIle ratios from the outcrop on the east of Hunts Bay [SS 566866] represent a reworked fauna correlated with stage 9 (Bowen et al. 1985).

At Bacon Hole [SS 559 868] it is represented by the 'sandy breccio conglomerate', 'sandy cave earth' and 'shelly sand' of Stringer et al. (1986). They also contain a mammalian fauna

Table 19. *Correlations between Gower and South West Wales and oxygen isotope stratigraphy*

δ18O	GOWER SOUTH & WEST	GOWER NORTH	GOWER EAST	SOUTH WEST WALES – CARMARTHEN BAY	CARMARTHENSHIRE	PEMBROKESHIRE
1	GWYNLLWG (22)	& KENFIG (23)	FORMATIONS		TREGARON (22) & KENFIG (24)	GWYNLLWG (23) & TYWI (25) FORMATIONS
2	Horton Member (9) — PENNARD FORMATION (2) — Rhosili Member (8)	ELENID FORMATION (13) Llangynydd Member (15); Llanmadoc Member (14)	Horton Member (21) BRECKNOCKSHIRE FORMATION (19); Langland Member (20)	PENNARD FORMATION (1); Marros Member (5)	ELENID FORMATION (6) Stradey Member (10); Llyn-y-Fan Member (9); Pentrecwrt Member (8)	ST. ASAPH FORMATION (17) Horton Member (21); Trefgarn Member (20); Trewyddel Member (19); Abermawr member (18)
3	High Tor Member (4)	PENNARD FORMATION (10); Broughton Member (12)	PENNARD FORMATION (16); Rotherslade Member (18)	Gilman Member (4)		PENNARD FORMATION (13); Pendeudraeth Member (16)
4	Slade Member (7)					
5	Bacon Hole Member (6)					Hoyles Member (15)
5e	Hunts Bay Member (5)	Hunts Bay Member (11)	Hunts Bay Member (17)	Hunts Bay Member (3)	Hunts Bay Member (7)	Hunts Bay Member (14)
6	High Tor Member (4)			Coygan Member (2)		
7	Minchin Hole Member (3)					
8						
9						
10						
11						
12	LLANDDEWI FORMATION (1)					
16						PENFRO FORMATION (11); West Angle Member (12)

indicative of a warm temperate climate (Currant *et al.* 1984). Lying within and upon the 'shelly sand' are stalagmite fragments with U-series ages of: 129 ± 16, 125 ± 26, 129 ± 30, 116 ± 18 and 122 ± 11 ka (mean age 124.2 ± 5.4) (Currant *et al.* 1984; Stringer *et al.* 1986; Sutcliffe *et al.* 1987). This is the basis for calibrating D-aIle/L-Ile ratios in the 'sandy breccio conglomerate', 'sandy cave earth' and 'shelly sand' and their correlation with oxygen isotope sub-stage 5e (Bowen *et al.* 1985). Any possibility that the 'sandy breccio conglomerate', 'sandy cave earth' and 'shelly sand' Bacon Hole may be correlated with oxygen isotope sub-stage 5a (80 ka), because they could represent an older stalagmite incorporated into a younger (5a) deposit, may be discounted because stalagmite in the overlying deposits of the Bacon Hole Member (note 6) has a U-series age of 81 ± 18 ka (Currant *et al.* 1984).

At Horton [SS 484854] the Hunts Bay Member is represented by a fossiliferous beach gravel with a larger proportion of erratics than usual on a platform at 10 m O.D. (George 1932; Bowen 1970; Mitchell 1972) The D-aIle/L-Ile ratios indicate a mixed fossil gastropod population with some of stage 7 but others of sub-stage 5e age (Bowen 1994*b,c*).

At Minchin Hole Cave, the Hunts Bay Member includes the *Patella* beach and '*Neritoides* Beach' of George (1932) and Sutcliffe *et al.* (1987) with characteristic D-aIle/L-Ile ratios of the Hunts Bay Member (Bowen *et al.* 1985).

(6) Bacon Hole Member. Stratotype: Bacon Hole Cave [SS 559 868]. It consists of two contiguous units: (a) stratified head deposits, with stalagmite layers, that dip into Bacon Hole Cave; and (b) slope deposits outside the cave. The latter are subdivided into lithological units by Currant *et al.* (1984); Stringer *et al.* (1986) and Sutcliffe *et al.* (1987): their 'upper cave earth' has been correlated with a similar unit exposed in an excavation inside the cave that has a mammalian fauna indicative of a warm temperate climate. A stalagmite that overlies this unit inside the cave has a U-series of 81 ± 18 ka. Stalagmite overlying the sequence has U-series ages of 13 ± 3 and 12.8 ± 8 ka (Currant *et al.* 1984).

(7) Slade Member. Stratotype: Western Slade Bay [SS 483 856]; parastratotype: Eastern Slade Bay [SS 487857]. It consists of basal red silty and sandy clay, limestone head but predominantly of matrix supported gravel composed of glacial erratics. Geomorphologically it is part of the coastal drift terrace but differs in its geometry as a fan-shaped unit emanating coastwards from the fault-guided valley of Western and Eastern Slade. East and west of the two bays it is replaced by limestone head of the Pennard Formation. Its base passes below beach level, its western margin appears to merge with limestone head, but on the east side of Eastern Slade the limestone head contact overlies the margin of the Slade Member. Its upper surface is mantled by the Horton Member.

It was originally interpreted as glacial material *in situ* (George 1933; Wirtz 1953; Mitchell 1960; Zeuner 1959). But later intrepreted as redeposited glacial drift derived from the Llanddewi Formation along the Western and Eastern Slade Valleys by colluvial, alluvial and solifluction processes (Bowen 1970, 1971*a*, 1973*a*). Elsewhere, lenses of the Slade Member occur within head of the Pennard Formation Member or as a channel infill on its upper surface, as in the centre of Hunts Bay.

(8) Rhosili Member. Stratotype: Rhosili Bay [SS 415 880] to [SS 414900]. Head derived from the Devonian rocks of Rhosili Down. A lower head unit (about 2 m) is separated from an upper one (about15 m) by the Llangynydd Member (North Gower note 15) that thins from north to south. Its base passes

below beach level.

(9) Horton Member. Stratotype: Horton [SS 482855]. Loess (62% silt) with up to six horizons based on colour differences that may indicate pedogenesis (Case 1983, 1984). It occurs throughout Gower in coastal exposures and on interfluves, as at Hunts Farm [SS 563873].

North Gower

(10) Pennard Formation.

(11) Hunts Bay Member. Broughton Bay [SS 417931]. Raised beach gravel. D-aIle/L-Ile ratios indicate correlation with oxygen isotope sub-stage 5e (Campbell *et al.* 1982; Bowen *et al.* 1985).

(12) Broughton Member. Stratotype: Twlc Point, Broughton Bay [SS 417931]. It consists of limestone head that overlies the Hunts Bay Member. It is overlain by the Llanmadoc Member. It also includes 'soliflucted till' (Slade Member) and limestone head (Campbell & Shakesby 1985).

(13) Elenid Formation (Mid-Wales note 9). It consists of glacial deposits that mantle Gower north of the Devensian ice limit. Its minimum age is indicated by ^{36}Cl age of 22.8 ± 2 ka from Arthur's Stone, an erratic boulder that stands close to the reconstructed ice-limit on Cefn Bryn (Bowen 1994*a,b*; Phillips *et al* 1994).

(14) Llanmadoc Member. Stratotype: Broughton Bay [SS 4293]. Parastratotype of the **Elenid Formation** that shows it overlying the Pennard Formation including the Hunts Bay Member of oxygen isotope sub-stage 5e age. It consists of glacial deposits: 'lower shelly diamicts' and 'upper stony diamict' both of which show tectonic structures. The former contains marine shells (D-aIle/L-Ile ratios: *Littorina littoralis* 0.073, 0.082 & 0.098; *Arctica islandica* 0.2, 0.14, 0.25, and *Turritella communis* 0.21 & 0.18) (Campbell *et al.* 1982); and derived wood fragments with ^{14}C ages of 42 ka and $68 + 13 - 5$ ka (Campbell & Shakesby 1985, 1986*a,b*, 1994). D-aIle/L-Ile ratios on *Macoma balthica* of: 0.07 and 0.11, suggest Late-Devensian and Early to Middle Devensian ages respectively (Bowen *et al.* 1986; Campbell & Shakesby 1986, 1994).

(15) Llangynydd Member. Type-area: between Llangynydd (Llangennith) and Rhosili (Prestwich 1892; George 1933; Bowen 1970). A wedge of fluvioglacial sand and gravel that thins southwards beyond a Late Devensian ice-margin located at the north end of Rhosili Bay. Prestwich (1892) collected mollusc shells from this unit (George 1933).

East Gower

(16) Pennard Formation (South & West Gower note 2).

(17) Hunts Bay Member. East side of Langland Bay [SS 613871] where it consists of aeolian sand (D-aIle/L-Ile: *Cepaea nemoralis* 0.014 ± 0.13 (3) and *Helicella sp* 0.12 ± 0.006 (4) (Bowen unpublished), overlying raised beach with D-aIle/L-Ile ratios correlated with sub-stage 5e (Bowen *et al.* 1985).

(18) Rotherslade Member. Stratotype: east of Langland Bay [SS 613871]. Head overlying the Hunts Bay Member and underlying the Langland Member.

(19) Brecknockshire Formation (South East Wales note 1). Parastratotype: Langland Member (below).

(20) Langland Member. Parastratotype of the Brecknockshire Formation exposed on the east side of Langland Bay [SS 613871]. It consists of a crudely stratified gravelly unit interpreted as a glacial deposit with characteristic Upper Palaeozoic clasts especially the characteristic Devonian, but no Lower Palaeozoic material. It overlies both the Rotherslade Member and the Hunts Bay Member (oxygen isotope sub-stage 5e) of the Pennard Formation. Because it is laterally co-extensive with the Elenid Formation farther west in Gower the ^{36}Cl rock exposure age from Cefn Bryn of 22.8 ± 2 ka (Bowen 1994a, b; Phillips et al. 1994) places a constraint on the maximum extent of the ice responsible for deposition of the Langland Member.

(21) Horton Member. Drainage cutting through the Langland Formation, east of Langland Bay [SS 612872]. It consists of colluvium that includes re-worked Langland Formation glacial clasts as well as an admixture of the Horton Member. In part, it is the 'upper loam' of George (1932, 1933) and 'slope wash' of Bowen (1970).

(22) Gwynllwg Formation. (South East Wales note 11). Holocene marine and estuarine alluvium in the Llwchr and Burry Estuary.

(23) Kenfig Formation (South East Wales note 12). Holocene blown sands at Llangennith, Whitford Burrows, Horton, Oxwich and Three Cliffs Bay.

South West Wales

(Carmarthenshire & Pembrokeshire)

(1) Pennard Formation. (South & West Gower note 2). This formation occurs in Carmarthen Bay (Bowen 1970a), the south Pembrokeshire coast (Leach 1933), inside Milford Haven (Dixon 1921).

(2) Coygan Member. Stratotype: Coygan Cave [SN 285094]. It consists of stalagmites, cave earths, sand and clay with ^{14}C and U-series ages showing that it ranges in age between oxygen isotope stage 6 and the Holocene. It was subdivided by Aldhouse-Green & Scott (in press).

(SA-G)

(3) Hunts Bay Member. (i) at Broadhaven, South Pembrokeshire [SS 978942]. Cemented beach gravel on raised platform (Dixon 1921; John 1970). D-aIle/L-Ile ratios indicate correlation with oxygen isotope sub-stage 5e (Bowen et al. 1985). (ii) beach gravels at Ragwen Point [SN 220071] (Strahan et al. 1909; Bowen 1970) and at Marros Sands [SN 213073] where they consists of rounded and sub-rounded local clasts on a raised shore-platform overlain by a sandy silty mud containing seeds and fruits, moss stems, beetle fragments and pollen indicative of a treeless environment (Bowen 1970). Cemented sands, probably related to marine regression, pass below modern beach level at Pendine.

(4) Gilman Member. Stratotype: Gilman Point [SM 228073]. Typical head cyclothem developed on limestone limestone that fines upwards from a basal cemented blocky head (Bowen 1977a).

(5) Marros Member. Stratotype: Marros Sands [SN 214073]. About 1 m of shale head overlain by up to 3 m of angular sandstone head (Bowen 1970). It overlies the Ragwen Member.

(6) Elenid Formation (Mid-Wales note 9). Previously named the Central Wales Drift in South Wales (Bowen 1970). It is distinguished from the Brecknockshire Formation by the addition of Lower Palaeozoic clasts. It consists of glacial deposits, till, sands and gravels (Strahan 1907a, b; Strahan et al. 1909) described in detail in the Gwili Valley (Campbell

1984). Pingo basins containing Holocene sediments lie on its surface around Llanpumpsaint [SN 419291], Pont-ar-sais [SN 442 283], Llansadwrn [SN 695315], Farmers and Ffald-y-Brenin [SN 6444] and Garth Lwyd [SN 6343] (Bowen 1974). It includes overlying late-glacial deposits.

(7) Hunts Bay Member at Craig Lon [SN 420022] where fossiliferous sand proved in mine-shaft (Strahan 1907) was interpreted as raised beach because it is overlain by 15.5 m of diamict that is probably Elenid Formation (Bowen 1980).

(8) Pentrecwrt Member. Stratotype: Pentrecwrt [SN 394 395]. Up to 2 m of compact yellow-grey clay with Lower Palaeozoic erratics interpreted as till (Bowen 1974). Upstream this crops out on the south bank of the Teifi at Llandysul. It occurs on the floor of the Teifi Valley and infills abandoned meanders: for example, at Craig Gwrtheyrn (Price 1976). Pingo basins with Holocene deposits lie on its surface (Price 1976).

(9) Llyn-y-Fan Member. Type-area: base of the Devonian scarp of Bannau Sir Gaer to Fan Hir of Mynydd Du [SN 803216] to [SN 836197]. It includes all of the morainic deposits and moraine ridges of seven cirques of probable Younger Dryas age between Llyn-y-Fan Fach and Fan Hir (Ellis-Gruffydd 1977).

(10) Stradey Member. Type-area: west of Llanelli [SS 491014]. It consists of head mantling the dip slopes of the Pennant Measures, and the alluvial gravels emanating from Cwm Bach and Cwm Mawr (Bowen 1980).

(11) Penfro Formation. Stratotype: Llandre Gravel Quarry [SN 093203]. 5 m of glacial gravels with local clasts and erratics from north Pembrokeshire. It is widespread in south Pembrokeshire overlying bedrock south of Mynydd Preseli and the Trefgarn-Roch ridge. Throughout Pembrokeshire and western Carmarthenshire it is highly dissected and, on the basis of a comparison with the relatively undissected Llanddewi Formation of Gower, it is probably older than oxygen isotope stage 12 (Bowen 1970). It was deposited by an extensive 'Irish Sea' ice-sheet and, on the basis of the age of glacial deposits in the Bristol region, it has been ascribed to oxygen isotope stage 16 (Bowen 1994b; Campbell & Bowen 1989).

(12) West Angle Member. Stratotype: West Angle Bay [SM 853031]. Stiff purplish clay containing containing scratched, including igneous, clasts, interpreted as till by Dixon (1921), Leach (1933) and Bowen (1974).

(13) Pennard Formation (Gower note 2). This occurs throughout the area. Lithofacies variability is controlled by local Palaeozoic bedrock.

(14) Hunts Bay Member (i) at West Angle Bay [SM 853031] where it consists of cemented beach gravels and sands, silts, loams and peat (Dixon 1921). The uncemented deposits contain organic remains and wood fragments. Although pollen analysis suggested a Hoxnian age (Stevenson & Moore 1982) it was correlated with the Ipswichian (oxygen isotope sub-stage 5e) by Bowen (1974). (ii) cemented beach gravel correlated at Druidston Haven [SM 862173] (John 1970).

(15) Hoyles Member. Stratotype: Hoyles Mouth Cave [SS 110002]. It consists of stalagmite, breccia and silt units. ^{14}C, TL and U-series ages show that it ranges in age between oxygen isotope sub-stage 5e and the Holocene.

(SA-G)

(16) Pendeudraeth Member. Stratotype: Abermawr [SM 883346]. Head derived from local bedrock (Jehu 1904; John 1970; Bowen 1973a, 1974, 1977a). Lithofacies variability indicates changing conditions of deposition: some Bed are water-lain and there is evidence of some intraformational weathering. The head contains some rounded erratic pebbles probably derived from pre-existing glacial deposits. Formerly known as the 'upper rubble drift' of Jehu (1904) and 'upper head' of John (1970).

(17) St. Asaph Formation (North East Wales note 3).

(18) Abermawr Member. Stratotype: Abermawr [SM 883346]. Up to 2.5 m of 'Irish Sea Till', interpreted as lodgement till by John (1970), but as a glaciomarine mud by Eyles and McCabe (1989*a*). It contains some erratics from northern sources (Jehu 1904), wood fragments and marine shells. Radiocarbon ages on the wood fragments gave infinite ages (John 1970). D-aIle/ L-Ile ratios on *Macoma* indicate a Late Devensian age. It is overlain by about 4 m of sand and gravel, interpreted as either outwash (John 1970; Bowen 1974) or marine beach deposits (Eyles & McCabe 1989*a*). This is extensive inland and occurs on the valley floors of the upper Western Cleddau, around Casmorys, and its former course north-west to Abermawr, where it carries kettle holes.

(19) Trewyddel Member. Type-area: the high ground between the estuaries of the Teifi and Nefern. An extensive outcrop of sand and gravel up to about 195 m O.D.(Bowen 1971*b*, 1982*b*)

(20) Trefgarn Member. Terraces of outwash sand and gravel well developed in the type area [SM 955215] (Bowen 1974).

(21) Horton Member. At Maenorbyr [SR 055977] and Musselwick [SM 820063] the loess is cryoturbated and infills small ice-wedges in the underlying Pennard Formation (Case 1983).

(22) Tregaron Formation (Mid-Wales note 17). Peat occurs throughout the area and its biostratigraphy (pollen) has been investigated at Llanllwch west of Carmarthen (Thomas 1965).

(23) Gwynllwg Formation. (Southeast Wales note 11). Holocene marine and estuarine alluvium in the Burry Estuary and Carmarthen Bay.

(24) Kenfig Formation. (Southeast Wales note 12). Holocene dune sands at Penbre, Cefn Sidan, Pendine, Freshwater West and Whitesands Bay.

(25) Tywi Formation. Type-area: upstream and downstream from Carmarthen. Alluvium of Holocene age.

Mid-Wales

(1) St. Asaph Formation (North East Wales note 3). Consists of blue to dark grey 'Irish Sea till' that outcrops along the coast of Cardigan Bay from Llanrhystud southwards. Exposures have been described at Aberaeron, Newquay, Mwnt (Williams 1927), Gwbert and Trwyn-carreg-ddu (Jones 1965) where it has been interpreted as till. Eyles & McCabe (1989*a*), however, believe it is a glacio-marine mud.

(2) Hunts Bay Member Member. Stratotype: [SN 145491]. Stratified beach gravels and sand overlying a rock platform (Jones 1965); the 'Poppit raised beach' of John (1970). The unit occurs for about 1 km at about 2 m above high water mark and is overlain by the Poppit Member and unknown thickness of the Newquay Member.

(3) Aberarth Member. Stratotype: Aberarth [479640]. Head including 'soliflucted Irish Sea' glacial material, overlain by slope gravels (Watson 1976). Elsewhere in Cardigan Bay it consists of head and gravels and includes the Newquay Member [413598], Aberaeron Member [451626] and about 5 m of 'brown head'at Morfa Bychan. At Poppit Sands [SM 145490]. it consists of head overlying the Hunts Bay Member overlain in turn by the Newquay Member (John 1970).

(4) Newquay Member. Stratotype: Newquay [SN 415606]. Exposures of mud ('Irish Sea Till') are exposed in cliffs for about 1 km. It corresponds with the 'lower boulder clay' of

Williams (1927), 'Ballycroneen Till' of Mitchell (1960) and 'Fremington Till' of Mitchell (1962), but it is interpreted as a glacio-marine mud by Eyles & McCabe (1989*a*).

(5) Mwnt Member. Stratotype: Traeth-y-Mwnt [SN 193519]. Structurally deformed muds and gravelly diamict interpreted as glacio-marine in origin (Eyles & McCabe 1989*a*).

(6) Banc-y-Warren Member. Stratotype: Banc-y-Warren [SN 204475]. Shelly sand and gravel (Jehu 1904; Williams 1927; Jones 1965; Bowen 1973*a*; Helm & Roberts 1975; Allen 1982; Bowen & Lear 1982; Eyles & McCabe 1989*a*). It contains marine shells with D-aIle-L-Ile ratios from *Macoma balthica* that indicate a Devensian age (Bowen & Henry 1984).

(7) Llannon Member. Stratotype: Llansanffaid [510675]. Alluvial gravel of the Afon Peris and Afon Clydan alluvial fans. It extends south from the mouth of the Peris to Morfa [500660] and is characterized by intraformational large cryoturbation structures (Watson 1976, 1977). Immediately north of the mouth of the Peris it overlies till (Elenid Formation) of the Llannon Moraine. Mitchell (1960) identified the 'Llanstffraid soil' on the surface of the Elenid Member that he correlated with the Ipswichian but it failed to reveal any signs of pedogenesis (Bowen 1974).

(8) Horton Member. (Gower note 9). Loess at Morfa Bychan (Watson & Watson 1967).

(9) Elenid Formation. Type-area: the 'High Plateau' of Central Wales. (Elenid is the name used in the *Mabinogion* for the high ground about Pumlumon), At its parastatotype the **Llanmadoc Member** (Gower note 14) overlies the Broughton and Hunts Bay Member (sub-stage 5e) at Broughton Bay, north-west Gower [SS 4293] which is the only locality where its stratigraphical relationships are seen. The **Elenid Formation** is the new name for those deposits described as 'glacial' but partly re-arranged by periglacial slope processes by Wood (1959), Potts (1971) and Bowen (1973*a*, 1974). It is mapped by the British Geological Survey as:'Till, including mass movement deposits on slopes' on the Davies *et al*. (1997) 1 : 50 000 Sheets that cover a large area of mid-Wales (Davies *et al*. 1997). The **Elenid Formation** also consists of the 'boulder clay' and 'morainic drift' of the Aberystwyth and Machynlleth 1 : 50 000 Sheet (Cave & Hains 1986). It also includes deposits on which pingos formed, e.g. at Cwrtnewydd and Talgarreg (Watson 1976); as well as the deposits of Cwm Tinwen [SN 832748] and Cwm Du [SN 811740] in Cwm Ystwyth (Watson 1966). Seismic stratigraphy shows that the **Elenid Formation** extends offshore for up to 8 km in the central part of Cardigan Bay (Garrard & Dobson 1974). At its extremities in Gower and the Welsh borderlands stratigraphical relationships suggest that it is Late Devensian. It also includes a variety of post-deglaciation but pre-Holocene deposits, including late-glacial organic and inorganic deposits, on its surface.

(10) Morfa Bychan Member. Stratotype: Morfa Bychan [563770]. It lies below high ground, up to about 200 m O.D. composed of Aberystwyth Grits. It was subdivided by Watson & Watson (1976) into (i) yellow head; (ii) blue head; (iii) gravels; (iv) brown head, who interpreted the entire succession as periglacial slope deposits. Wood (1959) and Bowen (1973*a, b*, 1974), however, argued that it consisted largely of redeposited glacial deposits and it is mapped as such on the British Geological Survey 1 : 50 000 Llanilar Sheet (Davies *et al*. 1997). It extends offshore for about 8 km (Garrard & Dobson 1974).

(11) Trefaldwyn Member. Type-area: the Severn Valley between Newtown and Shrewsbury and the country north-

Table 20. *Correlations between Mid-Wales and Northwest Wales and oxygen isotope stratigraphy*

δ¹⁸O	MID-WALES			N W WALES		
1		TWYI FORMATION (19) GWYNLLWG FORMATION (18) TREGARON FORMATION (17) YSTOG FORMATION (16)		KENFIG (38) TYWI (37) GWYNLLWG (36) & TREGARON FORMATIONS (35)		ST.ASAPH FORMATION (28) Trefor Member (34) Caernarfon Member (33) Afon Hen Member (32) Môn Member (31) Moel Tryfan Member (30)
2	ST.ASAPH FORMATION (1) Horton Member (8) Llannon Member (7) Banc-y-Warren Member (6) Mwnt Member (5) Newquay Member (4)	ELENID FORMATION (9) Rheidol Member (15) Llyswen Member (14) Llechryd Member (13) Llanllwni Member (12) Trefaldwyn Member (11) Morfa Bychan Member (10)	ERYRI FORMATION (1) Cwm Idwal Member (14) Clynnog Member (13) Lleiniog Member (12) Capel Curig Member (11) Dolgarrog Member (10) Glan-y-mor Member (9) Aber Ogwen Member (8) Penrhos Member (7)	MEIRION FORMATION (17) Mawddach Member (27) Cadair Idris Member (26) Tal-y-llyn Member (25) Y Llethr Member (24) Dinas Mawddwy Member (23) Llangelynin Member (22) Llanystumdwy Member (21) Afon Wen Member (20) Criccieth Member (19) Rhinog Member (18)		
3			Porth Oer Member (6)			
4	Aberarth Member (3)					
5			Pen-y-Bryn Member (5) Seiont Member (4)			
5e	Hunts Bay Member (2)		Dyffryn Member (3)			Hunts Bay Member (29)
6			Mochras Member (2)			

east of Clun Forest (Brown 1971; British Geological Survey Montgomery Sheet 1994). It consists of till, morainic drift, sand, gravel and glaciolacustrine deposits. It is in contact with, and in part overlies, the Stockport Formation along the Welsh Borderland (Cheshire-Shropshire and Staffordshire Lowlands note 10).

(12) Llanllwni Member. Stratotype: gravel pit [SN 465406]. It consists of 6 m of glacial gravel overlying the Pentrecwrt Member. It occurs on the floor and lower slopes of the Teifi Valley between Tregaron and (including the Dulas Valley, above Lampeter) and Cardigan, and in tributary valleys: e.g. Afon Grannell above Llanwnen, where it is overlain by the Llechryd Member. In places: e.g. around Maesycrugiau, it has been terraced. The Member includes the delta gravels at Lampeter (Watson 1965), Llanybydder and Rhyddlan (Parry unpublished), Pencarreg and Llanwnen (Charlesworth 1929).

(13) Llechryd Member (Llechryd Clay of Bowen & Lear 1982). Stratotype: Llechryd gravel pit [SN 211436]. Laminated silt and clay overlie the Llanllwni Member (Jones 1965; Bowen & Lear 1982; Lear 1985). It is a mappable unit on the floor of the Teifi Valley as far upstream as Pentrecwrt, and discontinuously thereafter.

(14) Llyswen Member. Type-area: the Wye Valley between Doldowdod and Hay-on-Wye. It consists of sand and gravel in well-defined terraces (Pocock 1940). Similar terraced gravel infills occur in many Mid-Wales valleys: e.g. the Lower Teifi (Jones 1965).

(15) Rheidol Member. Type-area: Rheidol Valley. Terraced fluvial gravels (Cave & Hains 1986).

(16) Ystog Formation. Type-area: Church Stoke [2593]. Holocene lacustrine deposits (British Geological Survey 1:50 000 Montgomery Sheet, 1995).

(17) Tregaron Formation. Stratotype: Cors Garon [SN 680630]. Raised peat bog deposits of Holocene age (Godwin & Mitchell 1938; Turner 1964; Hibbert & Switsur 1976). Cors Caron is one of the largest raised bogs in Britain. It consists mostly of Holocene deposits with some basal late-glacial deposits. The base of the formation is defined at the base of Pollen Zone 3 of Hibbert & Switsur (1976) where *Corylus* is first represented continuously in the profile and is ^{14}C dated as 9750 ± 220 (11 600 cal) BP. Correlatives of the Tregaron Formation sometimes overlie a longer late-glacial sequence. In mid-Wales it is described at Gors Lwyd [SN 857756], a bog at about 380 m O.D. with a pollen record that spans the late-glacial and Holocene (Moore & Chater 1969); and at Cors Fochno (Borth Bog) (Godwin & Newton 1938; Moore 1968). It occurs at Cors y Llyn (SO 016552) where Holocene basin peats are underlain by late-glacial clay and silt (Moore 1978).

(18) Gwynllwg Formation (South East Wales note 11). Marine and estuarine alluvium of the Dyfi that includes 'submerged forest' at Ynys Las (Haynes & Dobson 1969; Wilks 1979).

(19) Tywi Member (South West Wales note 25). Holocene valley alluvium in the Dyfi, Teifi, Ystwyth, Rheidol, Upper Severn, Wye, and Usk Valleys.

Northwest Wales

(1) Eryri Formation. Type area: Snowdonia where it includes all the glacial and associated fluvioglacial deposits that originated from valley glaciers in Snowdonia, including the Nant Ffrancon and Llanberis Pass glaciers (Howells *et al.* 1985). Some of these were admixed with material distributed by the more powerful Meirionydd ice-cap. It is correlated with: the Meirion Formation with which it merges in the south and

in the Conwy Valley; and with the St. Asaph Formation in the west, north and east. It also includes late glacial organic, morainic and periglacial deposits. Notable among the late-glacial deposits are: Cwm Dywthwch [SH 570580] (Seddon 1957); Clogwynygarreg [SH 560538] (Ince 1983); Cors Geuallt [SH 734596] (Crabtree 1972); and Nant Ffrancon [SH 632633] (Seddon 1962). Its age is indeterminate: some deglaciation and rock-exposure may have occurred at 32.9 ± 2 ka ([36]C calendar years) on the plateau above Cwm Idwal (Phillips *et al.* 1994). Deglaciation is indicated by 14.5 ka (17.2 cal.) at Glanllynnau.

(2) Mochras Member. Stratotype: Mochras Farm Bore-hole [SH 553259]. Till with local grit boulders overlying Tertiary deposits at a depth of 77.47 m. 'Brown stony boulder clay' at Mochras [SH 558272] is correlated with the upper local grit rich till of the Mochras Borehole (Whittow & Ball 1970) that overlies the Dyffryn Member (Allen & Jackson 1985).

(3) Dyffryn Member. Stratotype: Mochras Farm Bore-hole [SH 553259]. 8 m of finely banded silts with moss partings with a moss fauna, leaves and 'hystrichospheres' (Herbert-Smith unpublished). Its age is unknown (Allen & Jackson 1985). It is tentatively correlated with sub-stage 5e.

(4) Seiont Member. Stratotype: Pen-y-bryn brickworks, Caernarfon [SH 490615] (Addison & Edge 1992). Fluviatile gravel of local origin overlying bedrock and overlain by the Pen-y-bryn Member (Addison & Edge 1992).

(5) Pen-y-bryn Member. Stratotype: Pen-y-bryn brickworks, Caernarfon [SH 490615]. Biogenic sediments (Addison & Edge 1992) consisting of 'peats, peaty muds and litter horizons intercalated with muds, sands and fine gravel' (Chambers *et al.* 1995). It overlies the Seiont Member and is overlain by the glacial deposits of the Penrhos Member. Pollen analysis suggest several 'interstadials'. Radiocarbon ages range from about 31 to about 60 ka; U-series from about 100 to 200 ka (Addison & Edge 1992; Chambers *et al.* 1995; Heijnis & Plicht 1992). It is is provisionally correlated with oxygen isotope substages 5a and 5c (Addison & Edge 1992; Chambers *et al.* 1995).

(6) Porth Oer Member. Stratotype: Porth Oer [SH 167301]. Diamict mostly of sand and gravel, in part cemented. Recently interpreted as Late Devensian or younger in age (Gibbons & McCarroll 1993), although previously considered to be a raised beach overlain by cemented sand (Jehu 1909; Synge 1964; Saunders 1968a).

(7) Penrhos Member. Stratotype: Pen-y-bryn brickworks, Caernarfon [SH 490615]. It consists of Grey Till, 'dominated by slates, mudstones and the distinctive Padarn Tuff' (Addison & Edge 1992), and gravels called the 'fluvioglacial Snowdonian gravels and sands' by Whittow & Ball (1970) and the 'Intermediate Gravels' by Addison & Edge (1992). It is overlain by the Caernarfon Member (31).

(8) Aber Ogwen Member. Stratotype: Aber Ogwen [SH 612723]. 'Grey-brown massive Welsh till' (Whittow & Ball 1970).

(9) Glan-y-mor Member. Stratotype: Glan-y-mor [SH 618274]. Its base is not seen, but it is overlain by silts, sand and gravel correlated with the Penrhos Member (note 7). It is overlain by the St.Asaph Formation (28).

(10) Dolgarrog Member. Type-area: west of Dolgarrog, Trefriw and Llanrwst to grid line 70 (Howells *et al.* 1981). 'Boulder clay' that consists of greyish brown clay with abundant clasts of local rocks.

(11) Capel-Curig Member. Type-area: the country around Capel Curig, Betws-y-coed, Dolwyddelan and Penmachno (Howells *et al.* 1978). Local Welsh till and less extensive associated fluvioglacial sand and gravel.

Table 21. *Correlations between Northeast Wales and Southeast Wales and oxygen isotope stratigraphy*

$\delta^{18}O$	NORTHEAST WALES	SOUTH EAST WALES
1	CAERWYS FORMATION (18) TYWI FORMATION (17) KENFIG FORMATION (16) GWYNLLWG FORMATION (15) TREGARON FORMATION (14)	CWM NASH FORMATION (14) TYWI FORMATION (13) KENFIG FORMATION (12) GWYNLLWG FORMATION (11) TREGARON FORMATION (10)
		GLAMORGAN FORMATION (7) Cwm Parc Member (9) Ewenni Member (8) Pontypool Member (3)
2	MEIRION FORMATION (7) Ruabon Member (8) Hiraethog Member (6)	BRECKNOCKSHIRE FORMATION (1) Craig-cerrig-gleisiaid Member (6) Margam Member (5) Wysg Member (4) Pontypool Member (3) Llanwern Member (2)
	STOCKPORT FORMATION (9) Llai Member (13) Wheeler Member (12) Singret Member (11) Dee Member (10) Ruabon Member (8)	
3		
4	ST. ASAPH FORMATION (3) Hiraethog Member (6)	
5		
5e	Deganwy Member (5)	
6	Llandudno Member (4)	
7	CEFN FORMATION (2)	
8	PONTNEWYDD FORMATION (1)	

(12) Lleiniog Member. Stratotype: Lleiniog [SH 619787]. The 'Lleiniog Gravels' of Greenly (1919) are exposed in a section up to 0.5 km in length and consist of erratic clasts from northern Britain as well as the Conwy basin (Helm & Roberts 1984). It was subdivided by Greenly (1919) and Helm & Roberts (1984). Hart (1990) suggested that it consists of outwash from both Welsh and Irish Sea ice.

(13) Clynnog Member. Stratotype: Gwydir Bay [SN 38 47]. The 'Clynnog Till' of Simkins (1968) and part of the 'upper boulder clay' of Jehu (1909). A 'stony grey till' (Saunders 1968a,b).

(14) Cwm Idwal Member. Stratotype: Cwm Idwal [SH 645596]. It consists of the moraines within the cirque. ^{36}Cl ages for boulders on the Cwm Idwal moraines are: outer moraine $12\,900 \pm 2000$, and intermediate moraine $11\,600 \pm 1300$ that correspond to the calendar ages for the Younger Dryas indicated by the GRIP Greenland ice-core (Bowen et al. 1994; Phillips et al. 1994).

(17) Meirion Formation. Type-area: northwest Wales, south of Snowdonia. Glacial deposits of the Meirionydd ice-cap. The type area consists of an extensive area lying west and east of a line reconstructed by Foster (1968) and Rowlands (1970) that corresponded to the axis of the 'Meirionethshire ice-cap' (Foster 1968). It lies west of Arenig Fach and Arenig Fawr and east of Rhinog Fawr. The thickest ice was centred on the Vale of Trawsfynydd (Greenly 1919). It is the most extensive glacial unit in North Wales and corresponds with the 'Arenig Drift' of McKenny-Hughes (1887) in Clwyd. In the east it is coextensive with the Stockport Formation of Late Devensian age (Cheshire–Shropshire–Staffordshire note 10). It also includes a variety late-glacial deposits such as head, stratified scree and alluvial deposits.

(18) Rhinog Member. Type-area: around Rhinog Fawr. Grey to olive coloured till that is influenced by changes in local bedrock: e.g. between Llandanwg and Moelfre [SH 626246] the member is redder and more gravelly (Allen & Jackson 1985) and was probably deposited by the Dwyryd-Glaslyn glacier, as was the Llanstumdwy Member (note 21). At higher levels blocky tills occur (Allen & Jackson 1985).

(19) Criccieth Member. Stratotype: Criccieth [SH 507380]. The 'Criccieth Till' of Simkins (1968) and part of Jehu's (1909) 'lower boulder clay'. A 'grey shaly till of Snowdonian origin' (Whittow & Ball 1970). It may be Early as opposed to Late Devensian.

(20) Afon Wen Member. Stratotype: Glanllynnau [SH 456373]. It consists of laminated clay, silt, sand and gravel. The 'Afon Wen suite' of Simkins (1968) and part of the 'Intermediate Sands and Gravels' of Jehu (1909).

(21) Llanystumdwy Member. Stratotype: Glanllynnau [SH 456372]. The 'Llanystumdwy Till' of Simpkins (1968) and part of the 'upper boulder clay' of Jehu (1909) that consists of 'brown stony Welsh till' (Whittow & Ball 1970). Its origin is controversial: Boulton (1977) believed it was deposited by the same ice-sheet as the underlying Criccieth Member (20), whereas others (Bowen 1973a; Campbell & Bowen 1989) believe it was deposited later during a readvance of ice from the Glaslyn and Dwyryd Valleys. At Glanllynnau organic deposits at the base of a kettle hole gave a radiocarbon age of 14 469 (Coope & Brophy 1972) which when calibrated is 17.3 ka calendar years and about the timing of Heinrich Event I (Bowen in press).

(22) Llangelynin Member. Type-area: between Llwyngwril and Tonfannau. Till with erratics from Cadair Idris, Aran Fawddwy, Mesozoic rocks from offshore, as well as red clay

from the Oligocene Bed of Tremadoc Bay. It overlies head of the Pennard Formation and redeposited till (Bowen 1974).

(23) Dinas Mawddwy Member. Type-area: between Dinas Mawddwy and Cemmaes (between [SH 860149] and [SH 840060]). It consists of extensive valley bottom till as inferred from seismic stratigraphy (Thomas & Summers 1982) and glacio-fluvial, glacio-marginal and glaciolacustrine sediments (Thomas & Summers 1983).

(24) Y Lethr Member. Type-area: Rhinog Fawr [SH 655290] & Rhinog Fach (SH 665270). Head deposits on steep slopes that are extensive south of Y Lethr (Allen & Jackson 1985). The Lethr Member is representative of all the 'upper head' deposits in North West Wales, many of which are seen in coastal sections in Llyn.

(25) Taly-y-llyn Member. Stratotype: Tal-y-llyn Valley [SN 753 134]. This is a distinctive lithofacies derived from shales or mudstones (stratified scree), up to 18 m thick between two Bed of unsorted 'platy' head (Watson 1976). It is also widespread in Mid-Wales.

(26) Cadair Idris Member. Cirque moraine deposits at for example: Llyn Cau [SH 718123] and protalus ramparts along the northern face of Cadair Idris [SH 714133]. These are all believed to be Younger Dryas in age (Campbell & Bowen 1989).

(27) Mawddach Member. Type-area: Mawddach Valley around the Tyn-y-groes Hotel [SH 729232]. It consists of fluvioglacial sand and gravels but in the immediate type area may have been reworked by fluvial action to form terraces (Allen & Jackson 1985).

(28) St Asaph Formation (North East Wales note 3).

(29) Hunts Bay Member. Stratotype: Red Wharf Bay [SH 532816]. It consists of fossiliferous marine gravel composed of limestone pebbles and is overlain by head (Whittow & Ball 1970). It is correlated with the Llanddona raised beach (Campbell et al. 1995).

(30) Moel Tryfan Member. Stratotype: Moel Tryfan [SH 520560]. Sands with marine shells (Trimmer 1831; Campbell & Thompson 1991). A 'bulk' radiocarbon age on shells gave 33.7 ka (Foster 1968, 1970a). D-aIle/L-Ile ratios on the shells indicate a Late Devensian age.

(31) Môn Member. Inland, it consists mainly of grey-brown till with clasts predominantly derived locally (Greenly 1919; Smithson 1953; Whittow & Ball 1970). Greenly (1919) proposed a tripartite subdivision of: lower boulder clay, middle sands and gravels, upper boulder clay. This was sustained at 14 sites and although Whittow & Ball (1970) proposed different 'phases' of glaciation, all of the glacial deposits of the island are proposed as a single member. In places it acquires a characteristic red colour, as at Red Wharf Bay (Whittow & Ball 1970).

(32) Afon Hen Member. Stratotype: Gwydir Bay [SH 3747]. The 'Aberafon Formation' of Simkins (1968) and part of the 'Intermediate Sands and Gravels' of Jehu (1909).

(33) Caernarfon Member. Stratotype: Pen-y-bryn brickworks , Caernarfon [SH 490615]. Up to 7 m of 'Upper (Irish Sea) Till' (Addison & Edge 1992; Chambers et al. 1995).

(34) Trefor Member. Type-area: coastal exposures between Nefyn [SH 276415] and Trefor [SH 389479]. The 'Trevor Till' of Simkins (1968) and part of the 'lower boulder clay' of Jehu (1909). It outcrops at various places in Llŷn: e.g. at Dinas Dinlle [SH 435563] where it is repeated by thrust faulting (Reade 1893; Jehu 1909; Whittow & Ball 1970; Harris et al. 1996); Porth Nefyn [300407]; and Porth Neigwl [290256]. It was called an 'Irish Sea Till' with shell fragments by Campbell

& Bowen (1989), but glacio-marine mud by Eyles & McCabe (1989).

(35) Tregaron Formation. (Mid-Wales note 17) Regionally this includes many Holocene sites where late-glacial and Holocene deposits occur, notably at Cors Geuallt [SH 734596] northeast of Capel Curig (Crabtree 1972), Clogwynygarred [SH 560538], west of Snowdon (Ince 1981) and Cwm Dwythwch [SH 570580] the most northerly cirque in Snowdonia (Seddon 1957).

(36) Gwynllwg Formation. Type-area: Morfa Dyffryn [SH 560250]. Holocene marine and estuarine alluvium together with beach shingle gravel of Morfa Dyffryn, Morfa Harlech, the Dwyrhyd estuary and Ro Wen (Allen & Jackson 1985).

(37) Tywi Formation. Type-area: around the confluence of the Mawddach and Wnion Rivers [SH 710190]. It consists of late-glacial fluvial gravels and Holocene alluvium.

(38) Kenfig Formation. Type-area: Newborough Warren, Mon [SH 4263]. Dune sands of Holocene age.

Northeast Wales

(1) Pontnewydd Formation. Stratotype: Pontnewydd Cave [SH 014710]. It consists of stalagmites, sands, clays and breccia and includes hominid fossils. Radiocarbon, TL and U-series ages indicate that it spans the time from oxygen isotope 8 to the Holocene (Green 1981; Green et al. 1981; 1984; 1989). The 'upper and lower sands and gravels' contain clasts of volcanic rocks and flint that indicate an 'Irish Sea' glaciation during stage 8 or earlier.

(S. A-G)

(2) Cefn Formation. Stratotype: Cefn Cave west entrance [SH 023704]. It consists of laminateds silts and clays and stalagmite. U-series ages indicate that it spans the time from oxygen isotope 8 to the Holocene. A mammalian fauna includes *Hippopotamus* (Green 1986; Green & Walker 1991).

(S. A-G)

(3) St Asaph Formation. Type-area: The coastal area of north-west Clwyd and the lower parts of the Vale of Clwyd and the lower Conwy Valley. It also includes the glacial deposits on Halkyn Mountain as well as those farther south on Gloppa Hill, west of Oswestry. Its characteristics have long been known (Strahan 1890) and it is named after the St Asaph Drift of McKenny Hughes (1887). It consists of Northern or 'Irish Sea' glacial and fluvioglacial deposits. It lies mostly below 60 m O.D. but rises from about 160 m south of Colwyn Bay to about 183 m east of the Vale of Clwyd. The till consists of red or red brown clay with a relatively low stone content. The clasts are local but also include Criffel Granite and Eskdale Granite. It also contains over 20 species of marine shells (Warren et al. 1984). Whereas the boundary between the St Asaph and Meirion Formations is well known, Warren et al. (1984) concluded that in the Vale of Clwyd 'there was considerable overriding of one sheet by the other' leading to 'mixed and interbedded tills'. Along the coastal plain, however, the St Asaph Formation overlies the Meirion Formation (Reade 1885; Strahan 1886; McKenny Hughes 1887; Whittow & Ball 1970; Warren et al. 1984). Boreholes near Llandudno, Deganwy, Llandudno Junction, Rhos-on-Sea and Llysfaen also show this (Warren et al. 1984). In part, the St Asaph Formation appears to post-date the 18 ka ^{14}C age (21.4 ka cal.) from a mammoth bone originally collected from one of the Tremeirchion caves in the Vale of Clwyd [SJ 308370] (Rowlands 1971).

(4) Llandudno Member. Stratotype: Oval borehole [SH 775 819]. Up to 4 m of possible boulder clay at a depth of between about 25 and 29 m (Warren et al. 1984).

(5) Deganwy Member. Stratotype: Oval borehole [SH 754 190]. Up to 6 m of 'Older Marine and Estuarine Deposits' at a depth of between about 19 to 25 m: 'Clay, reddish brown, silty, thinly laminated; scattered pebbles and boulders; pollen; *Protoperidinium* cf. leonis, *Spiriferites spp.* (indet.), *S.* cf *pachydermus*, *S.* cf. *ramosus*' (Warren et al. 1984). Other borehole records across Morfa Conwy and along the Conwy estuary show 'sands, silts and laminated clays up to 20 m thick' lying between two boulder clays (Warren et al. 1984).

(6) Hiraethog Member. Up to 1 m of head beneath the Meirion and St Asaph Formations (Warren et al. 1984).

(7) Meirion Formation (Northwest Wales note 17). It consists of grey to dark-grey till with pebbles and boulders deposited by a north-easterly moving ice-sheet (Strahan 1885). The clasts are mostly of local rocks but some are from Snowdon and the Harlech Dome. The boundary between the Meirion Formation and the St Asaph Formation is clear in some areas, but in others the red colouring of the former probably indicates the result of what Warren et al. (1984) believed to be the overriding of the two ice-sheets. The surface of the Formation is drumlinized in the Conwy Valley, on Mynydd Hiraethog and in the southern part of the Vale of Clwyd and its left bank tributary valleys (Warren et al. 1984). The Ruabon Member is also included in the Stockport Formation because that it includes both Welsh and 'Irish Sea' glacial deposits (Thomas 1985a).

(8) Ruabon Member. Type-area: [SJ 305436]. A grey or brown sandy and stony till with local Silurian and Carboniferous clasts with far-travelled Welsh erratics. It overlies bedrock west of the River Alyn and underlies the Dee Member to the east. The Ruabon Member is part of both the Meirion and Stockport Formations.

(9) Stockport Formation (Midlands: Cheshire, Staffordshire, Shropshire note 10). Type-area: Wrexham [SJ 335500]. A complex glacigenic sequence occupying the Welsh borderland between Mold and Wrexham (Thomas 1985a) that records the coalescence and subsequent uncoupling of Late Devensian Welsh and Irish Sea ice sheets. It is correlated with the Stockport Formation of Cheshire–Shropshire–Staffordshire.

(GSPT)

(10) Dee Member. Type-area: the Dee Valley [SJ 364531]. It floors most of the valley and is correlated with the 'Lower Boulder Clay' of the tripartite sequence of Wedd et al. (1928).

(GSPT)

(11) Singret Member. Type-area: around Singret [SJ 344556]. Deposits of an ice-front alluvial fan, sandar and proglacial and ice-contact lacustrine sediment deposited during uncoupling of the two ice-sheets in the area of the Wrexham 'delta terrace' (Thomas 1985a).

(GSPT)

(12) Wheeler Member. Type-area: the Wheeler Valley between Bodfari [SJ 094700] and Rhydymwyn [SJ 206668]. Sand and gravel deposits forming sub-glacial eskers, ice-front alluvial fans, sandar and deltas occupying the floor of the Wheeler and upper Alyn Valleys (Brown & Cooke 1977; Thomas 1984a; 1985a).

(GSPT)

(13) Llai Member. Type-area: around Marford [SJ 358560]. Thin and discontinuous sheets of diamict that thin westwards and intercalate with the Singret and Wheeler Members. It is equivalent of the 'Upper Boulder Clay' of Wedd et al. (1928)

and is interpreted as a resedimented debris flow from a stagnating Irish Sea ice sheet margin (Thomas 1985a).

(GSPT)

(14) Tregaron Formation. Holocene peat found on the high ground of Mynydd Hiraethog.

(15) Gwynllwg Formation. Type-area: between Rhyl and Abergele on the coastal plain below 6 m O.D. It consists of marine and estuarine alluvium and associated peat Bed, with submerged forest (Strahan 1886; Tooley 1974; Warren *et al.* 1984).

(16) Kenfig Formation. Dune sand along the coastal margin of north east Wales between Llandudno and the Point of Ayre.

(17) Tywi Formation. Alluvium, river terrace samds amd gravels and alluvial fans throughout the region. In the Vale of Clwyd it is up to 8 m thick (Warren *et al.* 1984).

(18) Caerwys Formation. Stratotype: south of Caerwys [SJ 312 371]. The most extensive tufa outcrop in Britain that covers about 200 acres (Preece 1978).

Southeast Wales

(1) Brecknockshire Formation. The Brecknockshire Drift of David (1883) and Bowen (1970). Stratotype: east side of Langland Bay where its stratigraphical relationships with earlier deposits are exposed (Gower note 19). The source area for the glaciers that deposited the formation consists of the dip slopes of Fforest Fawr, the Cynon, Nedd and Tawe Valleys. It is characterized by Upper Palaeozoic, notably Devonian, but no Lower Palaeozoic erratics (Bowen 1970). The major characteristic of the formation is the presence of Old Red Sandstone erratics but no Lower Palaeozoic ones. Its thickness is variable and it is widespread in the Tawe, Cynnon and Usk Valleys and is the product of ice from the Brecon Beacons and the long dip-slopes of Fforest Fawr. Its upper part includes late-glacial organic deposits at Traeth Mawr, Breconshire (Walker 1984) as well as cirque morainic drifts in the Brecon Beacons (Lewis 1970).

(2) Llanwern Member (Pennard Formation – Gower note 5). Type-area: Gwent Levels [ST 3787]. Fossiliferous marine gravels correlated with oxygen isotpe sub-stage 5e by D-aIle/L-Ile ratios (Andrews *et al.* 1984) and additional measurements on *Littorina sp* 0.087 ± 0.067 (3); *Nucella sp* 0.095 ± 0.009 (8); *Macoma sp* 0.15 ± 0.009 (6) (Allen in press).

(3) Pontypool Member (Pennard Formation – Gower note 2). Type-areas: west of Pontypool and north of Risca outside the extent of the Late Devensian glaciation (Bowen 1970). It consists of head deposits that in its type-areas probably represent all of Devensian time. Its upper layers are widespread in Southeast Wales on hill slopes overlying Late Devensian glacial deposits: for example in the country around Maesteg and Pontypridd (Woodland & Evans 1968). It occurs in coastal locations: e.g. Cwm Marcross [SS 915684] and also forms terraces of partly reworked glacial materials in the uplands.

(4) Wysg Member. Type area: the Usk Valley between its source and Cemais Comawndwr 5 km downstream of Abergavenny (Williams 1968b). It consists predominantly of

Devonian material but contains Silurian erratics from the Wye Basin (Lewis 1970).

(5) Margam Member. Type area: east of Swansea Bay, between Margam [SS 8086], Kenfig [SS 790820] and Porthcawl [SS 808782] (Charlesworth 1929; Wilson *et al.* 1990). A piedmont end-moraine (Bowen 1970) of Late Devensian age as is shown by its stratigraphical relationships on the west side of Swansea Bay (Gower note 19).

(6) Craig-cerrig-gleisiaid Member. Stratotype: Craig-cerrig-gleisiaid [SN 964220]. Glacial deposits of a cirque glacier. The innermost morainic or protalus ridge is, on the basis of pollen analysis, correlated with the Younger Dryas (Walker 1980). The outer morainic accumulations antedate the Younger Dryas and could correspond to the time of the Heinrich I Event (Bowen in press).

(7) Glamorgan Formation. Type area: Rhondda Fawr Valley [ST 020] to [SN 9201]. Glacial deposits of till, sand and gravel and gravelly drift up to 30 m thick (Woodland & Evans 1968). Named the Glamorgan Drift by David (1883) and followed by Bowen 1970). In the coalfield valleys it is distinguished by erratics derived exclusively from the Coal Measures. Beyond the coalfield other Devonian and Triassic erratics occur.

(8) Ewenni Member (St Asaph Formation – Northeast Wales note 3). Type area: Ewenni [SS 9077]. Dark brown and purplish red clays, silts and sands, with gravel lenses with small pebbles that may be dropstones occur at Glanwenny (Wilson *et al.* 1990). It is correlated with the 'glacial silts and clays' in the British Geological Survey borehole at the Pencoed Brick Pit (Wilson *et al.* 1990), where Storrie (Strahan & Cantrill 1904) discovered shells of *Cyprina islandica* in what Strahan & Cantrill (1904) described as an 'Irish Sea till' overlain by a Welsh till. Its age is uncertain. But it could be pre-Ipswichan (oxygen isotope sub-stage 5e) (Bowen 1970); or Late Devensian and of glacio-marine origin (Eyles & McCabe 1989).

(9) Cwm Parc Member. Type-locality: the head of Cwm Parc at Graig fawr [SS 925 961] and Graig fach [SS 932 953]. Cirque morainic deposits with a Younger Dryas end-moraine in Graig fawr (Bowen 1970).

(10) Tregaron Formation (Mid-Wales, note 17).

(11) Gwynllwg Formation. Type-area: the coastal plain between Cardiff and Newport on the Gwynllwg (Wentlooge) Level [ST 239778]. It consists of Holocene marine and estuarine alluvium. Allen (1987) subdivided these deposits into four formations (Wentlooge, Rumney, Awre and Northwick). Farther west in Swansea Bay it consists of marine alluvium that was subdivided by the pollen analysis of its intercalated peat Bed (Godwin 1940) and ^{14}C dated by Godwin & Willis (1961, 1964).

(12) Kenfig Formation. Type-area: Kenfig Burrows [SS 790810]. Holocene sand dunes (Higgins 1933).

(13) Tywi Formation (South West Wales note 25). Floodplain alluvium, river terrace and alluvial fan deposits throughout the region.

(14) Cwm Nash Formation. Stratotype: Cwm Nash [SS 905700]. Tufa deposits of Holocene age that contains soil horizons and land snail faunas (Bowen 1970; Evans *et al.* 1978).

Chapter 8

Northern England

G. S. P. THOMAS

With contributions from J. Boardman & D. Huddart

The character of Quaternary deposits in Northern England is largely determined by its Palaeozoic rocks and by surrounding Mesozoic sedimentary basins in the Irish and North Seas. The region was strongly affected by ice from Scottish sources that crossed the offshore Mesozoic basins, passing onshore along the coasts of Lancashire, Cumbria, Northumbria and East Yorkshire and coalescing with local ice radiating outwards from the uplands of the Pennines, the Lake District and Northumbria.

The stratigraphical record in Northern England comprises glacial deposits overlain by extensive marine, estuarine and inter-tidal sediments along the low coastal margins of Lancashire, Morecambe Bay, the Solway Lowlands and adjacent parts of the Irish Sea basin, and by lake sediments, lowland moss basins and blanket upland peats. The glacial deposits reflect either offshore or local ice sources but other than in the Isle of Man the chronostratigraphic relationship between them, and the nature of ice sheet coalescence and subsequent uncoupling during various glacial stages, is unclear.

The marine deposits record successive transgression during glacio-eustatic and glacio-isostatic sea level record since the Late Devensian (oxygen isotope stage 2) and are well constrained by radiocarbon ages, especially along the Lancashire coast. The climatic fluctuations of the Devensian late-glacial are well recorded in numerous kettle basin infills throughout the region and are constrained by radiocarbon ages and biostratigraphy.

With the exception of parts of south Derbyshire and Yorkshire the region lies wholly within the limits of the Late Devensian (oxygen isotope stage 2) glaciation. Thus most of the exposed formations are of that age and are correlated by lithostratigraphic continuity, depositional style and geomorphology. Geochronologically they are constrained by minimum radiocarbon ages (about 14.5 ka) and by late-glacial biostratigraphy, but no maximum age has been established. With the exception of speleotherms and fossiliferous cave, lake and river terrace sediments in Derbyshire and Yorkshire and the offshore deposits of the Luce Bay Formation in Cumbria, Early and Middle Devensian deposits (oxygen isotope stages 4 and 3) appear unrepresented.

No well defined, geochronologicaly constrained unit is known for the Ipswichian (oxygen isotope sub-stage 5e) in the region, although mammalian sequences in limestone fissures in Lancashire, organic muds and palaeosols in the Lake District, cave deposits, river terrace deposits and estuarine sediments in Derbyshire and Yorkshire, and inter-till peats in Northumbria have been ascribed to oxygen isotope stage 5. In the Isle of Man, a distinctive buried marine cliff with sea-stacks and caves, underlying Late Devensian glacial deposits at Ballure has been ascribed to oxygen isotope stage 5

(Thomas 1985b).

Deposits older than those of oxygen isotope stage 5 are poorly known and geochronologically unconstrained but glacial sediments underlying supposed oxygen isotope stage 5 deposits in the Isle of Man, Cumbria and Northumbria, or occurring outside the maximum limits of the Late Devensian glaciation (oxygen isotope stage 2) in Derbyshire and Yorkshire, have been ascribed to oxygen isotope stages 6 or 8. At Skippersea Bay in Northumbria high-level temperate marine faunas have been correlated with oxygen isotope stage 7 by means of aminostratigraphy. They may be the same age as water eroded notches and sea stacks on the north shore of Morecambe Bay (Tooley 1985). Marine silts in deep boreholes in the northern Isle of Man may represent oxygen isotope stages 7 or 9, and the underlying glacigenic sediments of the Ayre Formation may be correlated with oxygen isotope stages 8, 10 or older.

Outstanding stratigraphical problems in the region include the poor stratigraphical framework for deposits older than oxygen isotope stage 5; the lack of well constrained oxygen isotope sub-stage 5e sequences; the paucity of Middle and Early Devensian deposits (oxygen isotope stages 2 & 3); the precise stratigraphic relationship between local and offshore sources of glacial sediment in oxygen isotope stage 2; the status of the supposed Scottish Readvance episode in the Late Devensian (oxygen isotope stage 2 glaciation) of the Lake District (Huddart 1991; Thomas 1985b); and the debate concerning the glaciomarine or terrestrial origin of Late Devensian deglaciation sequences of deposits around the coastal margins (Eyles & McCabe 1989a).

Isle of Man

(1) Isle of Man Formation. Stratotype: Borehole VI, Point of Ayre [NX 440035]. Known only from boreholes (Lamplugh 1903; Smith 1930). It underlies the Ayre Formation and comprises about 70 m of sands, gravels and diamicts of northern origin overlying bedrock at a maximum depth of -146 m. The age of the formation is indeterminate but on the basis of the overlying succession may be correlated with oxygen isotope stage 8; it could, however, be older.

(2) Ayre Formation. Recorded in Borehole IV, Point of Ayre [NX 465050]. It consists of up to 8 m of shelly silts and sands known only from boreholes at depths between −65 and −73 m. The bed was described by Lamplugh (1903) as marine. Its age is unknown but is provisionally correlated with oxygen isotope stage 7 or 9 (Thomas 1977, 1985b).

(3) Kiondroughad Formation. Stratotype: Borehole 16, Kiondroughad [NX 395015]. It is only known from boreholes (Lamplugh 1903; Smith 1930) and comprises c. 60 m of sands, gravels and diamicts of northern origin. It rests partly on a

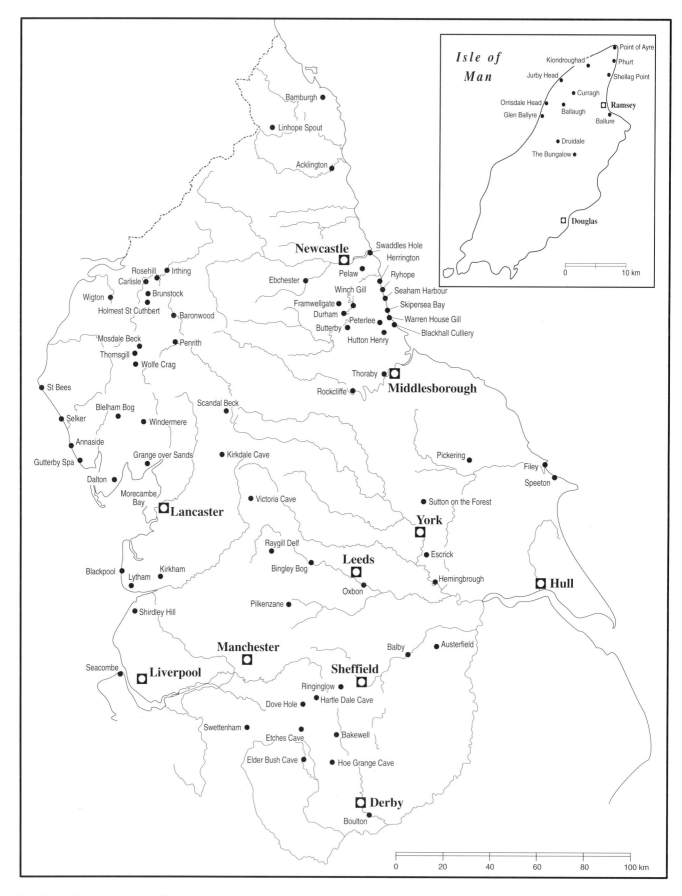

Fig. 9. Localities in the North of England.

Table 22. *Correlations between Northwest England and oxygen isotope stratigraphy*

δ¹⁸O	ISLE OF MAN	LANCASHIRE	CUMBRIA	YORKSHIRE & DERBYSHIRE	NORTHUMBRIA
1	**POINT OF AYRE FORMATION (13)** Ayre, Cranstal & Ballaquark Farm Members; **BUNGALOW FORMATION (12)**	**LYTHAM FORMATION (7)**; **SWETTENHAM FORMATION (6)**	**SOLWAY FORMATION (19)**; **GRANGE FORMATION (18)**; **BLELHAM FORMATION (17)**	**RINGINGSLOW FORMATION (19)**	**THORABY FORMATION (14)**
2	**CURRAGH FORMATION (11)**; **BALLAUGH FORMATION (10)** Ballacregga, Ballyre, Ballaleigh, Sulby, Ballaugh, Crawyn & Ramsey members; **SNAEFELL FORMATION (9)** Druidale, Ballure, Mooar members; **JURBY FORMATION (6)** Glen Ballyre Bed (8), Jurby Head Bed (7), Ballateare, Ballaquark, Cranstal, Nappin, Phurt & Trunk members; **ORRISDALE FORMATION (5)** Orrisdale Head, Bishop's Court, Ballavarkish, Ballacottier, Kionlough & Dog Mills members; **SHELLAG FORMATION (4)** Bride, Crosby, Cronk Ny Laa, Wyllin & Kirk Michael members	**SEACOMBE FORMATION (5)**; **SHIRDLEY HILL FORMATION (4)**; **KIRKHAM FORMATION (3)**	**WINDERMERE FORMATION (16)** St. Bees Head Bed (15); **WOLF CRAGS FORMATION (14)**; **MORECAMBE BAY FORMATION (13)**; **THRELKELD FORMATION (12)** Threfkeld, Lobbs & Mosedale members; **BLACK COMBE FORMATION (11)** Annaside, Gutterby & St Bees members; **CARLISLE FORMATION (10)** Rose Hill, Holme St. Cuthbert & Brunstock members; **PENRITH FORMATION (9)** Baronwood & Eden members; **IRTHING FORMATION (8)** Lanerstock, Brampton & Great Easby members; **SELKER FORMATION (7)**	**SUTTON FORMATION (18)**; **BINGLEY BOG FORMATION (17)**; **ESCRICK FORMATION (16)**; **FILEY FORMATION (15)**; **PICKERING FORMATION (14)**; **HEMINGBROUGH FORMATION 13**	**BAMBUGH FORMATION (13)**; **BRADFORD KAINS FORMATION (12)**; **EBCHESTER FORMATION (11)**; **LINHOPE SPOUT FORMATION (10)**; **ACKLINGTON FORMATION (9)**; **SUNDERLAND FORMATION (8)** Pelaw, Swaddles Hole, Ryhope, Herrington & Seaham Harbour Members; **WEAR FORMATION (7)** Framwellgate, Butterby, Durham & Winch Gill Members; **EAST DURHAM FORMATION (6)** Horden, Peterlee & Blackhall Members; **ROCKCLIFFE FORMATION (5)**
3				Hartle Dale Bed (12)	
4				Oxbow Bed (11)	
5			**LUCE BAY FORMATION (6)** Scandel Beck Bed (5)	Stump Cross Bed (10)	
5e		**RAYGILL DELF FORMATION (2)**	**WIGTON FORMATION (3)** Lindal Cote Bed (4); Troutbeck Palaeosol (2)	**ALVASTON FORMATION (5)** Elder Bush (9) Austerfield (8) & Kirkdale (7) & Victoria Beds (6); **RAINCLIFF FORMATION (4)**	Hutton Henry Bed (4)
6/8	**KIONDROUGHAD FORMATION (3)**	**PILKENZANE FORMATION (1)**	**THORNSGILL FORMATION (1)**	**BAKEWELL FORMATION (3)**; **BALBY FORMATION (2)**	**WARREN HOUSE FORMATION (3)**
7/9	**AYRE FORMATION (2)**				**EASINGTON FORMATION (2)**
pre-9	**ISLE OF MAN FORMATION (1)**			**DOVE HOLE FORMATION (1)**	**BLACKHALL COLLIERY FORMATION (1)**

extensive level rock platform between −41 and −53 m O.D. and partly on the Ayre Formation (Thomas 1985b). Its age is unknown but probably corresponds with oxygen isotope stages 6 or 8.

(4) Shellag Formation. Stratotype: Shellag Point [NX 460000]. A stratigraphically complex glacigenic sequence overlain unconformably **by** the Orrisdale Formation. The **Bride Member** [NX 460000] is a well consolidated, fine-grained basal diamict extending as far south as Douglas. It is overlain by the **Crosby Member** [NX 460000], a sequence of channeled sands and gravels, and the **Cronk ny Arrey Laa Member** [NX 46000], a coarse, cryoturbated ice front alluvial fan gravel. The sequence is tectonized into a series of thrust folds at the Bride Moraine (Thomas 1984b) and is believed by Dackombe & Thomas (1991) and Thomas (1976, 1985b) to represent a land-based retreat sequence. Eyles & Eyles (1984) interpret the sequence as subaqueous rainout and fan deposition in front of a grounded ice-shelf. The **Wyllin Member** [SC 309906], correlated with the Bride Member, is a massive, fine-grained diamict, heavily deformed and suceeded by the **Kirk Michael Member** [SC 309906]. This contains assemblages of *Turrittella communis* either reworked into proglacial sands or as erratics consisting of the former sea-floor complete with *in situ* fauna (Lamplugh 1903; Mitchell 1965).

(5) Orrisdale Formation. Stratotype: Orrisdale Head [SC 319930]. A stratigraphically complex glacigenic sequence that overlies the Shellag Formation unconformably. It consists of disconformably, northward off-lapping units formed by minor oscillatory ice-advances. It is overlain by the Jurby Formation (Thomas 1985b). The **Orrisdale Head Member** [SC 319930] is a stratified coarse diamict formed subglacially (Dackombe & Thomas 1991), or by glaciomarine density underflow and pelagic rainout (Eyles & Eyles 1984). The **Bishop's Court Member** [SC 319930] is a 30 m sequence of sands and gravels formed in a series of diachronous marginal sandur on an unstable, ice-cored supraglacial topography (Thomas *et al.* 1985). The **Ballavarkish Member** [NX 462007] and the **Ballacottier Member** [NX 462007] offlap to the north of the Bride Moraine and are similar to the Orrisdale Head and Bishops's Court members. Eyles & McCabe (1991) regard these members as subaqeous. The **Kionlough Member** [SC 455987] comprises debris flow and ice-front alluvial fan sands and gravels and is regarded as a breakdown product of the deformation of the Bride Moraine (Thomas 1984b). The member passes distally into the **Dog Mills Member** [SC 456988], a sequence of massive and laminated sands, silts and clays, with extensive soft-sediment and dewatering structures, containing a rich microfauna indicative of cold, low-salinity estuarine-intertidal environments. The member may be penecontemporaneous with lagoonal sediments occuring beneath Holocene marine sediment in the Vannin Sound offshore (Hughes 1978; Pantin 1978).

(6) Jurby Formation. Stratotype: Jurby Head [SC 343980]. A stratigraphically complex glacigenic sequence that overlies the Orrisdale Formation unconformably and forms northward offlapping units generated by minor oscillatory readvances during retreat (Thomas 1985b). The **Ballateare Member** [SC 343980], the **Ballaquark Member** [NX 465013] and the **Cranstal Member** [NX 468020] are all stratified coarse diamicts deposited subglacially. The **Nappin Member** [SC 343980] and **Ballaquark Farm Member** [NX 465013] represent marginal sandur systems. The **Trunk Member** [SC 317923] shows rapid vertical and lateral facies variation and extensive flow folding and is interpreted as a resedimented debris flow from the front

of a stagnating margin, possibly into a water body (Dackombe & Thomas 1991).

(7) Jurby Head Bed. Stratotype: Jurby Head [SC 343982]. Peats and organic muds in kettle basins in surface of Jurby Formation.

(8) Glen Ballyre Bed. Stratotype: Glen Ballyre [SC 314915]. Peats, organic muds and calcareous marls in kettle basins on the surface of the Orrisdale Formation (Mitchell 1965; Dickson *et al.* 1970; Joachim 1978). Radiocarbon ages range from at least 18 900 BP (Shotton & Williams 1971; 1973) to 10 550 BP.

(9) Snaefell Formation. Stratotype: Druidale [SC 355878]. Extensive head, scree and slope wash deposits covering the upland area and of exclusively local origin (Thomas 1976). The **Druidale Member** [SC 355880] comprises coarse scree overlying bedrock, succeeded by units of solifluctate intercalated with redeposited diamict. Two units of gravel occur in the sequence representing local fluvial reworking. The lower units probably date from the Early Devensian, but the majority are probably Late Devensian periglacialy re-worked local diamict (Evans & Arthurton 1973; Bowen 1973a; Thomas 1985b). The **Ballure** and **Mooar** Members [SC 458934] and [SC 303894] comprise local head and scree and intercalate with Orrisdale Formation glacigenic sediments at low elevations around the island margin (Thomas 1976). The Ballure Member buries a fossil cliff, sea stack and rock platform at Ballure. These marine features are probably oxygen isotope sub-stage 5e in age (Thomas 1976, 1984b).

(10) Ballaugh Formation. Type area: Ballaugh [SC 348935]. Devensian late-glacial gravel dominated mountain-front alluvial fans, commonly cryoturbated and overlying the Orrisdale Formation. The **Ballacregga** and **Ballyre Members** [SC 310908] and [SC 314914] overlie late-glacial organic sediments and are younger than 10 550 BP (Dickson *et al.* 1970; Mitchell 1965). The **Ballaleigh, Sulby** and **Ballacoraige Members** [SC 303894], [SC 388948] and [SC 340950] began accumulating earlier and the Ballaleigh fan has open-system pingos on its surface (Watson 1970). The **Crawyn Member** [SC 340950] is an extensive, sandy distal alluvial fan deposit displaying extensive cryoturbation. The **Ramsey Member** [SC 458934] interdigitates with members of the Orrisdale Formation glacigenic sequence (Thomas 1976).

(11) Curragh Formation. Type area: Curragh [SC 365950]. Mud and pebbly sand, passing up into amorphous peat, in a large interior wetland basin. Radiocarbon ages range from the Allerød to recent (Erdtman 1925; Mitchell 1965).

(12) Bungalow Formation. Type area: The Bungalow [SC 395868]. Extensive upland blanket peat that grew after 2850 BP (Kear 1976; Russell 1978). It is locally dissected and overlain by younger alluvial gravels.

(13) Point of Ayre Formation. Type area: Point of Ayre [NX 440035]. Extensive shingle beach ridges, underlain by lagoonal basins, and backed by a degraded raised cliff. The **Ayre Member** (NX 440035) comprises off-lapping gravel ridges with overlying blown sand and dunes. The earliest beach accumulation began at 7825 BP with a sea-level between −0.6 and 2.2 m (Tooley 1978). The **Cranstal Member** [NX 455025] comprises diatomite, fen peat, fresh-water lake muds and brackish-water clays showing a marine connection at 7825 BP, ceasing by 7370 BP (Phillips 1967; Tooley 1978). The **Phurt Member** [NX 467027] comprises laminated silts, peats, palaeosols, and a forest bed of pollen zone V1a age capped by lake muds of the Boreal-Atlantic transition. Its upper part contains Mesolithic and Neolithic artefacts.

Lancashire

(1) Pilkenzane Formation. Stratotype: Pilkenzane [SE 112007]. Weathered local till regarded by Johnson & Walthall (1979) as pre-Ipswichian.

(2) Raygill Delf Formation. Stratotype: Raygill Delf [SD 941452]. Mammalian fauna in clays in limestone fissure (Miall 1880) identified as Ipswichian by Earp *et al.* (1961).

(3) Kirkham Formation. Stratotype: Kirkham [SD 430320]. West-central and southern Lancashire is underlain by the classic tripartite sequence of 'Upper Boulder Clay', 'Middle Sands' and 'Lower Boulder Clay' defined by Hull (1864) and extending into adjacent parts of Cheshire. Its composition is determined by bedrock in the Lake District, Irish Sea or more northerly sources. Coastal sections include Blackpool [SD 307399] and Knott End [SD 346475] near Liverpool. Inland sections are limited but the most comprehensive detail has been provide by Longworth (1985) from borehole and section detail through the Kirkham Moraine of Gresswell (1967). This reveals complex variation, both vertically and laterally between tills, outwash and lacustrine sediment. Thickness extends to about 100 m in the Mersey and the rock floor shows extensive tunnel valley systems (Howell 1973; Grayson 1972). It is correlated with the Stockport Formation of Cheshire (Worsley 1991).

(4) Shirdley Hill Formation. Stratotype: Shirdley Hill [SD 360129]. Extensive, relatively homogeneous fine sand regarded as a coastal blown sand of Holocene age (De Rance 1877; Wray & Cope 1948) or as a Late Devensian outwash deposit (Tooley 1977). Tooley (1985) suggested that they may be a coastal facies of the Seacombe Formation (note 5).

(5) Seacombe Formation. Stratotype: Seacombe [SJ 320905]. At Seacombe shelly sand overlies till (Reade 1894). At Crosby and Blackpool a foraminifera-rich till contains cold-water estuarine and subtidal forms (Reade 1895). These sites may be equivalent to the Late Devensian glacio-marine sediments of the Dog Mills, Isle of Man and the adjacent offshore Irish Sea.

(6) Swettenham Formation. Stratotype: Swettenham [SJ 800675]. Deposits of late-glacial and Holocene river terraces in the major river valleys, including three on the Lune, three on the Ribble (Price *et al.* 1963) five in the Dane tributary of the Mersey (Johnson 1969) and the high terrace of the Mersey. Higher terraces date from the late-glacial to *c.* 7000 BP. The middle and lower terraces date from *c.* 5000 BP to modern (Harvey 1985).

(7) Lytham Formation. Stratotype: Lytham [SD 383280]. This includes all the marine, estuarine and valley floor alluvium of the lower Mersey, Ribble and Lune together with the low coasts between. It includes the *Scrobicularia* and Lower *Cyclas* Clays (De Rance 1877), Formby and Leasowe Marine Bed, Downholland Silt (Wray & Cope 1948), Preesall Shingle (De Rance 1877) and numerous large peat moss basins, both coastal and inland. Many of the inland basins accumulated in former kettle or glacial lake basins and began organic accumulation in the late-glacial; whereas the coastal and estuarine basins began accumulating between pollen zones IV and VIII of the Holocene (Shimwell 1985). It includes the British stratotype for the Holocene at Red Moss [SD 631101] (Hibbert & Switsur 1976). Evidence of 12 phases of marine transgressive overlap and 12 of regressive overlap between 9200 BP and the present were discovered by Tooley (1982, 1985).

Cumbria

(1) Thornsgill Formation. Stratotype: Thornsgill [NY 381243]. A coarse, weathered, tectonically deformed local diamict with basal sands, regarded as pre-Ipswichian, oxygen isotope sub-stage 5e by Boardman (1985, 1991). Its upper surface is deeply weathered as the **Troutbeck Palaeosol** (note 2). It may be the same age as the scattered till units overlying bedrock at Willowford, Glassonby, Gillcambon Beck and Westwood Park (Eastwood *et al.* 1968; Huddart *et al.* 1977; Trotter 1929), Gilsland (Trotter & Hollingworth 1932), and the lower till below organic sediments at Dalton in Furness (note 4), and the sandstone-rich till beneath the Scandal Beck Bed (note 5).

(2) Troutbeck Palaeosol. Stratotype: Thornsgill [NY 381242]. On the surface of the Thornsgill Formation, it is radiocarbon dated > 56 000 BP, and *c.* 90 000 a BP by U-Series (Boardman 1985). These indicate a probable oxygen isotope sub-stage 5 age.

(3) Wigton Formation. Stratotype: Wigton [NY 253487]. A borehole record of clay lenses within till containing *Turrittella communis*, foraminifera and ostracods (Eastwood *et al.* 1968). The fauna may not be *in situ* but was ascribed to the Ipswichian (oxygen isotope sub-stage 5e) by Evans & Arthurton (1973) and Huddart *et al.* (1977).

(4) Lindal Cote Bed. Stratotype: Dalton in Furness [SD 247746]. Organic deposits, containing leaves and fruits, between two tills at Lindal Cotes and Crossgates (Bolton 1862; Hodgson 1862; Kendall 1881). These were tentatively regarded as Ipswichian (oxygen isotope sub-stage 5e) by Huddart *et al.* (1977).

(5) Scandel Beck Bed. Stratotype: Scandel Beck [NY 743024]. Organic muds, sands and peats containing macro fossils occur between an underlying sandstone rich till and an overlying limestone rich till (Carter *et al.* 1978). Radiocarbon ages of 36 300 BP and >42 000 (Shotton & Williams 1973) may suggest an oxygen isotope stage 5 age. The Bed may be equivalent to undated organic sands at Low Hurst (Evans & Arthurton 1973)

(6) Luce Bay Formation. Off-shore boreholes, between Luce Bay and Ramsey Bay, show 6 m of fossiliferous marine silt with molluscs of low boreal affinities indicating water depths of 20–50 m. The silt is underlain by sands gravels and till resting on bedrock, and overlain by 20 m of till. It was thought to be of oxygen isotope stage 4 or 5 age by Tooley (1985).

(7) Selker Formation. Stratotype: Selker Point [SD 077887]. A sandy pebbly till, often deformed, of northern origin, considered by Huddart (1991) to be a basal lodgment product of Late Devensian 'Main Glaciation' by Scottish and northern Irish sea ice impinging on to the western margin of the Lake District. It extends south through Furness and is correlated with the Kirkham Formation (Lancashire) and the Stockport Formation (Cheshire and Shropshire).

(8) Irthing Formation. Stratotype: Irthing Valley [NY 500605]. A complex glacigenic sequence underlying the Carlisle Lowland and referred to the Late Devensian 'Main Glaciation' from Scottish and Pennine sources (Huddart 1991). It formed in ice-marginal and ice-contact environments during retreat. The **Lanerstock Member** [NY 555638] is a subglacial diamict of dominantly local composition; the overlying **Brampton Member** (NY 530612) comprises sand and gravel deposited in delta, fluvial crevasse fills and esker systems; and the **Great Easby Member** [NY 540628] represents penecontemporaneous fine grained lacustrine deposition. For an alternative interpretation see Note 9.

(9) Penrith Formation. Stratotype: Penrith [NY 515300]. Complex glacigenic sequence underlying the Vale of Eden and regarded as Late Devensian 'Main Glaciation' age (Huddart 1991). The **Baronwood Member** [NY 514430] is a variable sequence of sands, gravels, silts and diamicts deposited in esker systems, pro-glacial sandur and ice-walled lakes. The underlying **Eden Member** [NY 436570] is a coarse, red basal lodgement till overlying bedrock.

(10) Carlisle Formation. Stratotype: Carlisle [NY 400555]. A complex glacigenic sequence underlying the Carlisle Lowlands and considered by Huddart (1991) to represent deposits of a terrestrially based Late Devensian ice sheet during the 'Scottish Readvance' phase. An alternative explanation for this formation, and the underlying Irthing Formation is provided by Eyles & McCabe (1989, 1991) who interpreted all the sedimentary sequences and landforms as either tidewater deltas or glaciomarine morainal banks. In Huddart's interpretation the members represent an upward-coarsening succession from the **Rose Hill Member** [NY 434562], an ice-marginal lacustrine deposit, through the **Holme St Cuthbert Member** [NY 125472], a delta sequence into the **Brunstock Member** [NY 413596], a subglacial till carrying Scottish erratics.

(11) Black Combe Formation. Type area: Gutterby Spa [SD 130810]. A stratigraphically complex glacigenic sequence (c. 40 m) deposited at the retreating margin of a terrestrially based Late Devensian Irish Sea ice-sheet during the 'Scottish Readvance' phase (Huddart 1991) in west and south Cumbria. The **Annaside Member** [SD 088862] comprises an upward coarsening succession from silt to fine sand, through medium sand into gravel, deposited in a proglacial sandur and regarded by Huddart (1991) as the signature for terrestrial readvance. The **Gutterby Member** [SD 098243] comprises a tripartite succession of sandy till, sands and gravels and further till, often tectonised, and representing *in situ* decay of the readvancing margin. The **St Bees Member** [NX 965114] consists of laminated silts and clays passing up into sands and gravels in a prograding lacustrine sequence (Huddart 1991). Eyles & McCabe (1989) regarded the formation, particularly at St Bees, to be the result of subaqueous resedimentation of unstable sediment released from the margins of tidewater glaciers.

(12) Threlkeld Formation. Stratotype: Mosedale Beck [NY 369291]. An extensive, often drumlinised, glacigenic sequence in the NE Lake District of Late Devensian age (Boardman 1991) deposited before 14 623 BP (Pennington 1978). The **Threlkeld Member** [NY 369291] is up to 20 m thick and dominantly a basal lodgement facies. It passes upwards locally into melt-out and flow-till facies. The **Lobbs Member** [NY 356239] consists of laminated clays, silts and fine sands associated with kame, kettle and esker complexes formed during ice disintegration. The **Mosedale Member** [NY 355233] is a coarse gravel formed by ice-front alluvial fan sedimentation.

(13) Morecambe Bay Formation. Stratotype: Morecambe Bay [SD 360690]. Fluvioglacial and lacustrine sediments, including sands, silts and clays and laminated and varved clays resting on an extensive floor of till (Knight 1977) probably equivalent to the Selker and Kirkham formations. Known only from off-shore boreholes and representing distal outwash sedimentation from the retreat of Late Devensian Lake District ice.

(14) Wolf Crags Formation. Stratotype: Wolf Crags Corrie [NY 354227]. Cirque glacial deposits of Younger Dryas age (Boardman 1991). It is a coarse-grained local till formed by

basal lodgment and surface frost action, showing fluted, hummocky and ridge forms. It is correlated with similar diamicts in 64 Younger Dryas cirques and valley basins (Sissons 1980). Outwash terraces lie beyond cirque and valley glacier limits. Its age ranges from Late Devensian to the early Holocene (Smith & Boardman 1989).

(15) St. Bees Head Bed. Stratotype: St. Bees Head [NX 965115]. Late-glacial silts, organic clays and peats in kettle basins (Coope & Joachim 1980).

(16) Windermere Formation. Stratotype: Lake Windermere [SD 395985]. Silt, clay and organic infilling Lake Windermere. A 'lower laminated unit' consists of laminated silt and clay overlying gravel and till and marks the retreat of Late Devensian ice from the Windermere basin between about 15 000 BP and 14 500 BP (Coope & Pennington 1977; Pennington 1977, 1978). Seasonal melt from active ice ceased at about 14 500 BP. Penecontemporaneous aeolian action during retreat deposited loess across limestone surfaces in Morecambe Bay and thick loess sequences in Kirkham Cave (Vincent & Lee 1981; Vincent 1982; Gale & Hunt 1985). A 'middle silt' unit consists of organic silts showing a record of climatic amelioration into the Windermere interstadial. An 'upper laminated unit' represents re-establishment of cirque glaciers during the Younger Dryas. These sediments are associated with extensive talus formation, gelifluction and development of rock glaciers in surrounding areas (Sissons 1980; Vincent & Lee 1982)

(17) Blelham Formation. Stratotype: Blelham Bog [NY 264005]. Fine-grained inorganic and organic sediment in numerous lake basins and bogs in the region. Vegetational and climatic history has been established between 14 330 BP and the Neolithic (Gale & Hunt 1985; Pennington & Bonney 1970). It includes the coastal mosslands of Duddon and Leven estuaries (Shimwell 1985), and the mosses of the Solway Lowlands (Barber *et al.* 1994) that are mostly younger than 5000 BP.

(18) Grange Formation. Type-area: Grange-over-Sands [SD 410780]. Holocene estuarine and alluvial deposits in the Cumbrian part of Morecombe Bay. At least five marine transgressions have been recognised between 9270 BP to 1545 BP (Huddart *et al.* 1977; Tooley 1974, 1978, 1982). It is correlated with the Solway Formation and the Lytham Formation of Lancashire.

(19) Solway Formation. Type area: Solway Lowlands [NY 200600]. Holocene estuarine and alluvial infill in the Solway Lowlands and adjacent parts of the west Cumbrian coast. It includes older beach gravels and laminated silts and clays (Dixon *et al.* 1926; Eastwood *et al.* 1968), together with successive marine transgressions during glacio-isostatic and eustatic sea level reco since the Late Devensian (Haggart 1989: Huddart *et al.* 1977; Jardine 1975, 1982; Tooley 1974, 1978, 1982). It is correlated with the Grange Formation.

North, West and South Yorkshire and Derbyshire

(Note that Holderness is treated in Chapter 2 on Eastern England)

(1) Dove Hole Formation. Stratotype: Victoria Quarry Cave [SK 079769]. Yellow-red clay containing irregularly distributed bone and teeth of *Crocuta*, *Palaeoloxodon* and *Equus*. It was ascribed to the Lower Pleistocene (Villafranchian) by Spencer

& Melville (1974) and as not later than Brammertonian by Stuart (1982).

(2) Balby Formation. Stratotype: Balby [SE 562004]. Decalcified till containing local rock types and Lake District erratics found outside the Late Devensian glacial limit (oxygen isotope stage 2) between 100 and 300 m O.D. east of the Pennine foot slope around Leeds, Wakefield and Sheffield (Catt 1991). At Balby it includes units of laminated clay, suggestive of an existing Lake Humber, and gravels. Similar deposits at Brayton Barff (Catt 1977b).

(3) Bakewell Formation. Stratotype: Shining Bank Quarry [SK 230652]. Thick (> 15 m) basal tills and interbedded lacustrine clays and sands with Lake District and Scottish erratics overlying striated bedrock (Burek 1991).

(4) Raincliff Formation. Formerly referred to as the 'Speeton Shell Bed' or 'Speeton Formation'. Names discontinued because 'Speeton' is a standard subdivision of the Cretaceous. Stratotype: Speeton [TA 147758]. Fossiliferous sands and silts (3 m) of cool temperate estuarine origin. Regarded as Hoxnian by Catt & Penny (1966) and Catt (1991), by comparison with Kirmington interglacial deposits in Lincolnshire, but as Ipswichian Zone II(f) by West (1969) on palynology. D-alle/L-Ile ratios indicate an oxygen isotope stage 5 age (Knudsen & Serjup 1988; Bowen & Sykes 1991).

(5) Alvaston Formation. Stratotype: Boulton Moor [SK 385315]. Gravels of the Beeston Terrace of the River Derwent. Mammalian fauna correlated with the Ipswichian (oxygen isotope sub-stage 5e) (Jones & Stanley 1974).

(6) Victoria Bed. Stratotype: Victoria Cave [SD 837651]. Lower cave earth containing a mammalian fauna correlated with the Ipswichian (oxygen isotope sub-stage 5e) (Boylan 1972, 1977a).

(7) Kirkdale Bed. Stratotype: Kirkdale Cave [SD 678856]. Cave earths with a mammalian fauna correlated with the Ipswichian (oxygen isotope sub-stage 5e) (Boylan 1972, 1977a)

(8) Austerfield Bed. Stratotype: Austerfield [SK 673974]. Plant and insect remains in fluviatile deposits identified as Ipswichian Zone Ip.III by Gaunt et al. (1972). Probably equivalent deposits at Allenton [SK 370320] (Godwin 1975), and at Leeds [SE 285335] that include *Hippopotamus* (Edwards et al.1950).

(9) Elder Bush Bed. Stratotype: Elder Bush Cave [SK 098549]. Travertine layer containing leaf impressions and fauna including *Panthera*, *Crocuta*, *Vuples*, *Bison* and *Hippopatamus* (Bramwell 1964), thus Ipswichian (oxygen isotope sub-stage 5e) in age. Similar cave sites of probable oxygen isotope stage 5 age occurs at Hoe Grange Cave [SK 223560] (Bemrose & Newton 1905, Ford 1976) and Etches Cave [SK 076676].

(10) Stump Cross Bed. Stratotype: Stump Cross Cave [SE 088635]. Flow stone encasing wolverine fauna dated by U-series to 83 000 BP (Sutcliffe et al. 1984, 1985). Similar ages of 61 000 BP occur in Gavel Pot, NW Yorkshire (Gascoyne et al. 1983) and 45 000–90 000 BP in caves in the Craven District (Atkinson et al. 1978)

(11) Oxbow Bed. Stratotype: Oxbow [SE 361300]. Silts within fluviatile sand and gravel with flora and insect fauna radiocarbon dated at 38 600 BP (Gaunt et al. 1970); this may be a minimum age estimate.

(12) Hartle Dale Bed. Stratotype: Hartle Dale Cave [SK 163803]. Contain a Middle Devensian (oxygen isotope stage 3) fauna of *Dicerorhinus*, *Bos* and *Mammuthus* (Pennington 1875). Similar deposits including *Microtus*, *Bison*, *Rangifer* and *Ursus* were found at Windy Knoll [SK 126830] (Dawkins 1877; Pennington 1875). At Elder Bush Cave (note 9) oxygen isotope stage 5 deposits are succeeded by a Middle Devensian

fauna of *Crocuta*, *Panthera*, *Ursus*, *Bison* and *Dicerorhinus* (Coles et al..1985). It is likely that this fauna is of oxygen isotope stage 5 age.

(13) Hemingbrough Formation. Type Site: Hemingbrough [SE 675316]. Unfossiliferous laminated clays and sands, with dropstones, deposited in an extensive Lake Humber with shorelines at 52 m, 30 m and 8 m (Catt 1991; Gaunt 1976, 1981). Bone from the highest lake stage was radiocarbon dated to 27 000 BP (Gaunt 1974). A palaeosol on laminated clay at West Moor, Doncaster was radiocarbon dated to 11 100 BP (Gaunt et al. 1971), providing a minimum age for disappearance of the lake.

(14) Pickering Formation. Type Area: Pickering [SE 800840]. Lacustrine clays and silts of glacial lakes Pickering, Eskdale and Glaisdale (Kendall 1902).

(15) Filey Formation. Type Area: Filey Bay [TA 130780]. A glacigenic sequence of tills, gravels, sands and laminated clays exposed in bays between Saltburn and Filey (Bisat 1939; Edwards 1981). It overlies the Speeton Formation. The tills are the equivalent to the Late Devensian part of the Holderness Formation (Eastern England: Holderness & Lincs, note 12).

(16) Escrick Formation. Type Area: Escrick [SE 630430]. Complex glacigenic assemblage of red or grey tills with Carboniferous Limestone, Triassic Sandstone and Lake District volcanic erratics, sands and gravels and laminated silts and clays (Gaunt 1970).

(17) Bingley Bog Formation. Type Site: Bingley Bog [SE 115428]. Late Glacial (Allerød-Windermere Interstadial and Younger Dryas) lake and kettle basin organic infills including Bingley Bog, inside the limits of the Aire Glacier (Keen et al. 1988); at Seamer Carrs, an inter-drumlin depression in the Vale of York (Jones 1976); at Seamer Carrs and Flixton, Vale of Pickering (Schadla-Hall 1987); at Willow Garth in the Yorkshire Wolds (Bush & Ellis 1987; Bush & Flenley 1987); in a hollow in the Escrick Moraine at Tadcaster (Bartley 1962); in the Ure valley (Walker 1955); at Malham Cove (Pigott & Pigott 1963) and in levee deposits at Cawood, near Selby (Gaunt 1981; Jones & Gaunt 1976). It also includes equivalent cave deposits at Victoria Cave, Settle (Campbell 1977; Wymer 1981), Dead Man's Cave, (Campbell 1977; Jenkinson 1984) and Mother Grundy's Parlour and Pin Hole Cave at Creswell Crags (Campbell 1977; Jenkinson 1984; Jenkinson et al. 1985; Mellars 1969, 1974; Rowe & Atkinson 1985). The oldest radiocarbon age is from a kettle-hole basin at Kildale Hall, Vale of York, at 6713 BP (Jones 1977a).

(18) Sutton Formation. Type Site: Sutton on the Forest [SE 608640]. Widespread blown sand in Vale of York with interbedded organic layers radiocarbon dated as: 10 700 and 9950 BP at Sutton on the Forest (Gaunt et al. 1971, Mathews 1970). Similar deposits dated 10 280 and 10 550 BP at Messingham [SE 911040] (Catt 1977).

(19) Ringingslow Formation. Type Site: Ringingslow Bog [SK 266833]. Holocene valley fill alluvium, lake and kettle basin organic sediment younger than Zone II and upland peat at numerous sites throughout the region. It includes blanket peats of: Pennines (Conway 1947, 1954; Hicks 1971, Tallis 1964; Tallis & Switzer 1983); raised peats of the Vale of York (Jones 1976; Smith 1958); organic infill in the North York Moors (Jones 1977b, 1978; Simmons et al. 1982; Simmons & Cundill 1974); in the Leven valley (Jones 1976); the Vale of Pickering (Cloutman 1988); at Sedgefield (Bartley et al. 1976); at Tadcaster (Bartley 1962); and at Malham (Pigott & Pigott 1963); the alluvium of the Aire and Calder valleys (Bartley 1964; Keen et al. 1988); cave earths at Mother Grundy's

Parlour, Creswell Crags (Campbell 1977); and the Burton Salmon Shell Marl (Norris *et al.* 1971).

Northumbria

(1) Blackhall Colliery Formation. Stratotype: Blackhall Colliery [NZ 460395]. Fissure fillings in Triassic rocks containing clay with pyritised plant fragments and seeds. The flora is possibly Lower Pleistocene (Trenchman 1920; Reid 1920) or Upper Tertiary (Pennington 1969) in age. These deposits are overlain by clay containing molluscs, insects, peat, rodent teeth and vertebra of *Elephus* of unknown interglacial age (Reid 1920; Lesne 1920, 1926).

(2) Easington Formation. Stratotype: Skippersea Bay [NZ 443453]. Cemented fine gravel and sand with a temperate molluscan fauna radiocarbon dated $> 38\,000$ BP overlying a rock platform at 32 m O.D. (Smith & Francis 1967). D-alle-L-Ile ratios are correlated with oxgen isotope stage 7, with a reworked fauna from oxygen isotope stage 9 (Bowen *et al.* 1991).

(3) Warren House Formation. Stratotype: Warren House Gill [NZ 447423]. Grey sandy till along the coast of Northumberland and Durham containing Scandinavian erratics, shells, and North Sea Tertiary erratics. It is believed to be at least as old as oxygen isotope stage 6 (Francis 1970). It is overlain locally by loess (Trenchman 1920).

(4) Hutton Henry Bed. Stratotype: Hutton Henry [NZ 432366]. A raft of peat incorporated in till, and regarded as Ipswichian in age (oxygen isotope sub-stage 5e) (Beaumont *et al.* 1969).

(5) Rockcliffe Formation. Stratotype: Rockcliffe [NZ 313085]. A series of four till sheets, the lowest three of which contain shell fragments and which are separated from the upper till by units of laminated clay (Francis 1970).

(6) East Durham Formation. Type Area: Durham coast [NZ 445430]. It consists of extensive outcrops along Durham coast. The **Blackhall Member** [NZ 473385] is a thick (>15 m) grey-brown stony basal till on bedrock and contains Permian and Carboniferous erratics. The **Peterlee Member** [NZ 420405] comprises extensive fine sand, silts and clays passing up into gravels. It was interpreted as ice marginal and glaciolacustrine sediment by Francis (1970). It underlies and interdigitates with the **Horden Member** [NZ 464422], a brown sandy till passing downwards into red silty sand at base and westwards into laminated clays of the Durham Member of the Wear Formation (Francis 1970).

(7) Wear Formation. Type area: Central and southwest Durham [NZ 274422]. A complex assemblage of tills, sands and gravels and extensive laminated clay. The **Winch Gill Member** [NX 307457] is a stiff grey basal till, resting on bedrock, that contains lavas, tuffs and granite from the Lake District, granite from Scotland and local limestone and red Triassic and Devonian sandstone (Francis 1970). It is succeeded by the **Durham Member** [NZ 274422], a thick (>80 m) and extensive sequence of glaciofluvial sands and gravels and glaciolacustrine silts and laminated clays, fining southwards (Smith & Francis 1967). This member is overlain in the Wear valley by a complex of thin, patchy and discontinuous tills of variable composition and considered by Francis (1970) to represent ice-marginal flow tills. These are represented by the **Butterby Member** [NZ 283382] and the **Framwellgate Member** [NZ 269451] (Francis 1970). The three members are correlated with the 'Lower Boulder Clay' (Durham Member?), 'Middle Sands and Gravels' (Butterby

Member?) and 'Upper Stoney Clay' (Framwellgate Member?) of Smith & Francis (1967).

(8) Sunderland Formation. Type Area: Sunderland [NZ 393568]. Complex assemblage of tills, gravels, sands and clays in coastal areas north and south of Sunderland (Smith 1981). The **Seaham Harbour Member** [NZ 432495] is a dark brown or grey stony till overlying bedrock containing local Coal Measures and Magnesian limestones as well as far-travelled erratics from Southern Scotland, the Pennines and the Eden valley. It is subdivided into a number of discrete units of basal and supraglacial origin (Smith 1981). The **Herrington Member** [NZ 338535], equivalent to the 'Tyne and Wear Complex' of Smith (1981) comprises laminated and bedded clays and silts with interbedded sands and stony clays. Includes trace-fossils of freshwater crustacea (Woolacott 1905) and regarded as deposits of an ice-dammed Lake Wear (Beaumont 1968; Smith 1981). The **Ryhope Member** [NZ 416522] comprises strongly cryoturbated sand and gravel deposited in channels in the surface of the Seaham Harbour Member and regarded by Smith (1981) as of deltaic and proglacial fluviatile origin. The **Swaddles Hole Member** [NZ 369690], equivalent to the 'Durham Upper Boulder Clay' of Smith (1981) is a stiff stony brown basal till containing local clasts and Cheviot granites (Smith 1981). The **Pelaw Member** [NZ 310625] is a blocky brown pebbly and silty clay up to 9 m thick underlying much of the surface of Sunderland and adjacent districts. Regarded as a flow till by Francis (1970) and as a solifluction deposit by Smith (1981).

(9) Acklington Formation. Stratotype: Acklington [NU 229020]. It consists of till that has been drumlinised along the coast north of the Tyne. It consists of glaciotectonised and rafted bedrock overlain by cross-cutting lodgement till units within and between which occur subglacially channeled gravels, sands and silts deposited in a single phase of subglacial deposition (Eyles & Sladen 1981; Eyles *et al.* 1982).

(10) Linhope Spout Formation. Stratotype:: Linhope Spout [NU 958171]. Locally derived basal tills overlain by thick solifluction deposits characteristic of the Cheviot Hills region (Douglas 1991).

(11) Ebchester Formation. Type Area: Broom Hill [NZ 095564]. Dark grey-brown sandy till, correlated with the Wear Formation. It is overlain by an extensive sequence of ice-contact, proglacial and lacustrine delta sediments associated with sub-glacial channel systems, ice-contact slopes and delta terraces (Allen & Rose 1986).

(12) Bradford Kains Formation. Type area: Bambugh [NU 166295]. It consists of sands and gravels that originated as subglacial esker systems and proglacial sandur (Parsons 1966). Similar deposits occur in the valleys of the Coquet, Warnbeck, Blyth and Tyne (Smith *et al.* 1973)

(13) Bambugh Formation. Stratotype: Embleton's Bog [NU 166295]. Kettle-hole and glaciolacustrine basin fills ranging in age from the late-glacial to Holocene pollen zone VII (Bartley 1966). Other sites of the same age include Neasham, near Darlington, where an Allerød mud revealed a skeleton of *Alces alces* radiocarbon dated to 10 850 BP (Blackburn 1952), and Thorpe Bulmer, near Hartlepool.

(14) Thoraby Formation. Type Area: Teesside [NZ 465165]. It includes all the marine, estuarine and valley floor alluvium of the lower Tyne, Wear and Tees and adjacent coastal areas. It includes evidence for at least three marine transgressions, corresponding to -10.6 m by 9,680 BP; to -2.4 m by 6, 050 BP; and to -0.3 m by 5,240 BP (Tooley 1978, 1982).

Chapter 9

Scotland

D. G. SUTHERLAND

The northerly location of Scotland in the British Isles, its mountainous terrain largely on its western side, openness to the northeast Atlantic and consequent high precipitation, ensured that it was a major centre of ice throughout the Pleistocene. Powerful ice-streams left glacial deposits on the continental shelf (Chapter 11), glaciated Ulster, northeast England, the Irish Sea Basin, notably as far south as Pembrokeshire in Wales, County Waterford in Ireland and the Wolverhampton district in Staffordshire.

The main centres of ice accumulation were in the north and west of Scotland, with other centres located in the Southern Uplands and in Skye. The 'pre-glacial' watershed, that lay to the west of Scotland, ensured that the most spectacular glacial erosion occurred in the north and west. Deep and extensive glacial erosion effectively removed most of the deposits of pre-Late Devensian over wide areas. Such deposits are only poorly preserved in the 'rain-shadow' areas of northeast Scotland and in the Inverness region, along with other fortuitous preservation elsewhere as, for example, in Ayrshire, but even there the record only extends back to the Middle Devensian.

The stratigraphical record is mostly established from the lowland areas remote from the highlands of deep glacial erosion. Thus the lithostratigraphical imprint of highland ice is defined in these areas and up-glacier correlation is with the extensive but undefined glacial deposits.

In the 1973 report pre-Devensian glacial deposits were only reported from northeast Scotland ('shelly indigo till') (Mitchell *et al.* 1973). Since then that situation has only been marginally improved. Important sequences of Quaternary rocks occur at and around Kirkhill and Tiendland in north-east Scotland, and around Inverness. Correlation of these, however, while possible locally, is hampered by appropriate tools. Thus limited data from OSL and D-aIle/L-Ile methods enables some wider correlation to be attempted. At Tiendland and Kirkhill the reality is that events between the 'Hoxnian' and 'Ipswichian' are inferred, and estimated correlations are made using the palaeosols that subdivide the sequences.

During deglaciation of the Devensian ice sheet marine transgression occurred in coastal areas across the isostatically depressed crust. The Younger Dryas (Loch Lomond) glaciation involved a large ice-cap in the southwest Highlands with lesser ice-caps and corrie (cirque) glaciers elsewhere. Pollen analytical work combined with radiocarbon dating has provided a detailed picture of late-glacial and Holocene vegetational change.

The account of stratigraphical units starts in northeast Scotland, where the known succession appears to be relatively the most complete then, progressively, to other areas where correlation is most secure.

Northeast Scotland

(1) Kirkhill Formation. This is the longest sequence in Scotland. Stratotype: the old Quarry Kirkhill [NK 010525] and its surroundings; parastratotype: Leys gravel pit [NK 006525]. The old Quarry at Kirkhill is now infilled but boreholes to its south and southeast have revealed the succession. It may be taken as representative of the 'Inland "Series"' of glacial deposits in northeast Scotland (see: Fig. 8.1 in Gordon 1993).

(2) Leys Member. Stratotype: Leys gravel pit [NK 006525]. Referred to as the Leys Till (thickness: 2 m) by Hall & Jarvis (1993a). It underlies the Denend Member and is interpreted by Hall & Jarvis (1993b) as having been deposited by a glacier moving from the west.

(3) Kirkton Member. Stratotype: old Kirkhill quarry and surrounds [NK 010525]. An angular, clast-supported local gravel, resting on bedrock and interfingering with the Pitscow Member. It was referred to as the Kirkhill Gelifluctate Complex 1 by Connell & Hall (1984) and Hall & Jarvis (1993b), is 2 m thick and is interpreted as a periglacial slope deposit.

(4) Denend Member. Stratotype: Leys gravel pit [NK 006525]. A 3 m thick bouldery gravel with sand matrix. It is extensively disturbed with localised collapse and slumping features, large-scale folding and wedge structures. Hall & Jarvis (1993a) suggest that it either rests on or is a facies of the Pitscow Formation. Hall & Connell (1986) interpret it as a meltwater deposit.

(5) Pitscow Member. Stratotype: old Kirkhill quarry and surrounds [NK 010525]. Less than 2 m of mainly horizontal light olive-brown coarse sands with thin beds of gravel possibly deposited by meltwater (Connell & Hall 1984) in a periglacial environment (Hall & Jarvis 1993a). They either rest on or are lateral equivalents of the Leys Member

(6) Kirkhill Palaeosol. Stratotype: old Kirkhill quarry and surrounds [NK 010525]. Developed on a marked unconformity truncating the Pitscow Member. It has been been interpreted either as a podsol deposited under humid temperate conditions (Connell *et al.* 1982; Hall & Jarvis 1993a), or a cold-water gley (Connell & Romans 1984). It is about 0.5 m thick and was called the 'Kirkhill lower buried soil' by Hall & Connell (1991) and Hall & Jarvis (1993a).

(7) Swineden Member. Type area: around the old Kirkhill quarry. It is draped on the Kirkhill Palaeosol and consists of less than 1 m of lower, thin, black to brown, laminated organic mud and an upper, weakly organic, poorly stratified sand. The organic material is interpreted (Connell & Hall 1984; Hall & Jarvis 1993a) as reworked from slopes and is probably derived

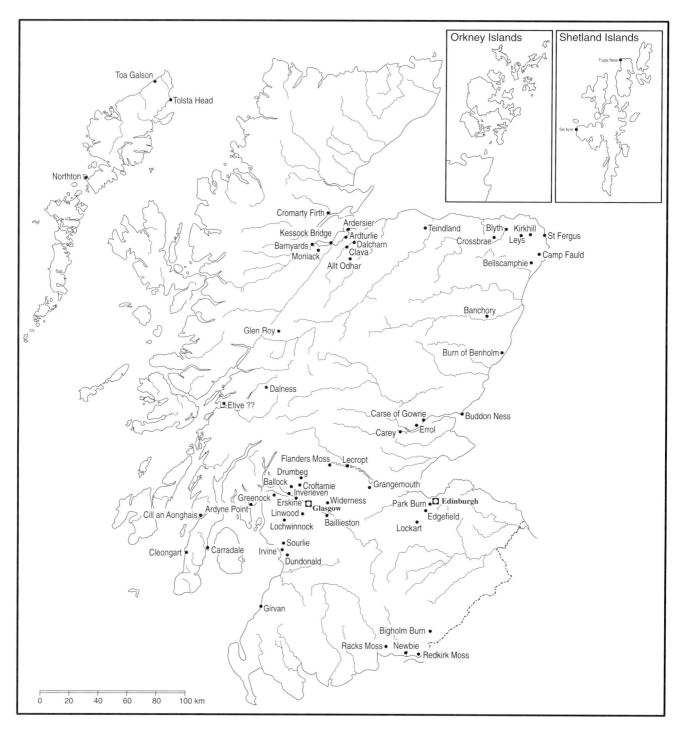

Fig. 10. Localities in Scotland.

from the upper layers of the underlying Kirkhill Palaeosol. Radiocarbon age: >47 360 BP.

(8) Corse Member. Stratotype: old Kirkhill quarry and surrounds [NK 010525]. A variable sequence of sandy gravels and gravelly sands less than 1 m in thickness, overlying the Swineden Member, that formed in a periglacial environment (Connell & Hall (1984). Referred to as the Kirkhill Gelifluctate Complex 2 by Hall & Connell (1991) and the Kirkhill Gelifluctate Complex 3 by Hall & Jarvis (1993a).

(9) Rottenhill Member. Stratotype: old Kirkhill quarry and surrounds [NK 010525] A 2.5 m thick yellowish-brown compact matrix-supported diamict. Weathered during the development of the overlying Backfolds Palaeosol (Connell & Hall 1984; Hall & Jarvis 1993a). Referred to as the Kirkhill lower till by Hall & Connell (1991) and Hall & Jarvis (1993a).

(10) Backfolds Palaeosol. Stratotype: old Kirkhill quarry and surrounds [NK 010525]. Developed in the top 0.2 m of the Rottenhill Formation (Connell & Romans 1984; Hall & Jarvis 1993a). Its upper layers are truncated. Referred to as the Kirkhill upper palaeosol by Hall & Connell (1991) and Hall &

Table 23. *Correlations between Northeast Scotland and oxygen isotope stratigraphy*

$\delta^{18}O$	NORTHEAST SCOTLAND			
1	Alluvium	Marine Alluviuem	&	Blowen Sand
2	**KIRKHILL FORMATION** (1) Todholes Member (20) Thinfords Member (19) St Fergus Member (18) Auchmedden Member (17) Blyth Member (16)	**TEINDLAND FORMATION** (1) Altonside Member (8)	**BELLSCAMPHIE FORMATION** (1) Kippet Hills Member (5) Hatton Member (4)	
3	Crossbrae Member (15) Howe Member (14)	Woodside Member (7)		
4	Hythie Member (13) East Leys Member (12) Corsend Member (11)	Castleton Formation (9)	Pitlurg Member (3)	
5		Badentinian Member (6)		
5e	Backfolds Palaeosol (10)	Tiendland Palaeosol (5)		
6				**CAMP FAULD FORMATION** (1)
7				Berryley Member (4) Hardslacks Member (3)
8	Rottenhill Member (9)	Orbliston Member (4) Deanshillock Member (3) Red Burn Member (2)	Elton Member (2)	Corse of Balloch Member (2)
9	Corse Member (8)			
10				
11	Swineden Member (7) Kirkhill Palaeosol (6)			
12	Pitscow Member (5) Denend Member (4) Kirkton Member (3) Leys Member (2)			

Jarvis (1993a). It resembles a gleyed brown-earth profile and is probably interglacial.

(11) Corsend Member. Stratotype: old Kirkhill quarry and surrounds [NK 010525]. A 0.3 m thick brownish-yellow diamict with a predominance of angular clasts; probably a periglacial slope deposit (Connell & Hall 1984). It rests on the truncated surface of the Rottenhill Member (9) and is referred to as the Kirkhill Gelifluctate Complex 3 by Hall & Connell (1991), and the Kirkhill Gelifluctate Complex 4 by Hall & Jarvis (1993a).

(12) East Leys Member. Stratotype: Leys gravel pit [NK 006525]. Up to 2 m of reddish-brown diamict with shell fragments (Hall & Connell 1986; Hall & Jarvis 1993a). It is referred to as the East Leys Till by Hall & Jarvis (1993a) deposited by ice moving from the west.

(13) Hythie Member. Stratotype: old Kirkhill quarry and surrounds [NK 010525]. Up to 2 m brown matrix-supported diamict, the lateral equivalent of the East Leys Member (Connell et al. 1982; Connell & Hall 1984; Hall & Jarvis 1993a). Referred to as the Kirkhill Upper till by Hall & Jarvis (1993a) deposited by a glacier moving from the west.

(14) Howe Member. Stratotype: Howe of Blyth quarry [NJ

842575]. Coarse, crudely bedded gravels interbedded with debris flows. Interpreted by Hall et al. (1995) as ice proximal glaciofluvial fan deposits. TL ages on a sand lens gave: 45.5 ± 3.8 and 36.8 ± 3.6 ka.

(15) Crossbrae Member. Stratotype: Crossbrae farm [NJ 752513]. Sandy peat (Hall 1984; Hall & Connell 1991; Whittington 1994) that palynology suggests is interstadial and possibly earlier than radiocarbon dates of: $26\,400 \pm 170$ BP and $22\,380 \pm 250$ BP (Whittington 1994).

(16) Blyth Member. Stratotype: Howe of Blyth quarry [NJ 842575]. Brown, compact, matrix-supported sandy diamict named the Blyth Till by Hall et al. (1995).

(17) Auchmedden Member. Stratotype: Howe of Blyth quarry [NJ 842575]. Crudely parallel bedded cobble gravel with rare cross-bedded sand lenses, probably an outwash fan (Hall et al. 1995).

(18) St Fergus Member. Stratotype: St Fergus [NK 1052]. Dark grey to dark greyish brown compact calcareous silts with local sand laminae and with scattered clasts interpreted as glaciomarine. Concentrations of marine shell fragments occur (Hall & Jarvis 1989) with a radiocarbon age of $13\,200 \pm 200$ BP.

(19) Thinfords Member. Stratotype: Howe of Blyth quarry [NJ

842575]. Gravel and sand with interbedded peat ([14]C 11 320 BP). TL ages, probably maxima, from a sand lens, of 13.6 ± 1.4 ka and 13.9 ± 3.5 ka). Referred to as the 'Blyth Peat' by Hall et al. (1995).

(20) Todholes Member. Stratotype: old Kirkhill quarry and surrounds [NK 010525]. A cryoturbated quartzite cobble and pebble gravel (Hall et al. 1995) overlying the Thinfords Member.

(1) Tiendland Formation. Stratotype: Teindland gravel pit [NJ 297570]. This serves as a standard for the Pleistocene deposits of the area around Tiendland in lower Strathspey, but is also representative of the 'Blue Grey "Series"' that outcrops along the southern shore of the Moray Firth (see: Fig 8.1 in Gordon & Sutherland 1993). It has been referred to as a key locality for interpreting the Quaternary history of Scotland (Gordon & Sutherland 1993) and contains a palaeosol with pollen of both 'interglacial' and ' interstadial' aspect.

(2) Red Burn Member. Stratotype: Teindland gravel pit [NJ 2957]. A stiff, reddish-brown, compact, matrix-supported diamict (Hall et al. 1995) referred to as the Red Burn Till by Hall et al. (1995). It rests on bedrock and is overlain by the Deanshillock Member and is probably lodgement till.

(3) Deanshillock Member. Stratotype: Teindland gravel pit [NJ 2957]. A loose, clast supported, coarse gravel with sand lenses probably glaciofluvial. Referred to by Hall et al. (1995) as the Teindland Gravel. Base unseen but overlain by and partly interdigitated with the Orbliston Member.

(4) Orbliston Member. Stratotype: Teindland gravel pit [NJ 2957]. 0.6 m of pale brown sand and silty sand with thin, undulating parallel laminae and small lenses of structureless pebble gravel (Hall et al. 1995). It rests on and interdigitates with the Deanshillock Member and is overlain by the Teindland Palaeosol. It is considered to be an ice-marginal glaciofluvial sediment.

(5) Teindland Palaeosol. Stratotype: Teindland gravel pit [NJ 2957] (Fitzpatrick 1965; Edwards et al. 1976; Romans 1977; Hall et al. 1995). Referred to as the Teindland Buried Soil by Hall et al. (1995). It is developed in the sand of the Orbliston Member and is overlain by the Badentinian Member. It is podsolic and palynology indicates that it formed towards the end of an interglacial.

(6) Badentinian Member. Stratotype: Teindland gravel pit [NJ 2957]. 0.3 m of sands resting on the Teindland Palaeosol. The Tiendland Formation is penetrated by high-angle shears and faults extending from the overlying Woodside Member (Hall et al. 1995). Referred to as the Teindland Upper Sand by Hall et al. (1995) and probably deposited in a pond from the erosion of the palaeosol and then increasing amounts of glacigenic material. Luminescence ages: 79 ± 6 ka and 67 ± 5 ka.

(7) Woodside Member. Stratotype: Teindland gravel pit [NJ 2957]. A complex sequence of loose, brown interbedded diamicts, sands and silty sand with organic material. Termed the Teindland Till by Hall et al. (1995), it overlies the Badentinian Member. It has been interpreted as a till (Fitzpatrick 1965; Edwards et al. 1976), solifluction deposit (Romans 1977), or debris flow and pond sediment in a sub-glacial cavity (Hall et al. 1995).

(8) Altonside Member. Stratotype: Teindland gravel pit [NJ 2957]. Dark grey to grey brown compact diamict with a silty sand matrix. Referred to as the Altonside Till by Hall et al. (1995). Its stratigraphical relations are unknown but Hall et al. correlate it with the lower of two tills recorded in the Elgin area by Peacock et al. (1968) and Aitken et al. (1979)

(9) Castleton Formation. Stratotype: near Castle of King

Edward [NJ 723562]. A dark grey supported diamict with a silty clay matrix. It contains frequent marine shell remains (Miller et al. 1987). Described by Jamieson (1906) as overlying a marine shell bed in situ. Radiocarbon age: >44 200 BP, but D-aIle/L-Ile ratios on Arctica islandica fragments of 0.078 ± 0.010 suggest a Late Devensian age.

(1) Bellscamphie Formation. Stratotype: Bellscamphie [NK 019338]. This is based on the section described by Jamieson (1906) at Bellscamphie. It consists of three tills, two of which may pre-date the Devensian. These belong to the 'Red "Series" Formation' that extends along the northeast coast of Aberdeenshire (see: Fig. 8.1 in Gordon & Sutherland 1993).

(2) Elton Member. Stratotype: Bellscamphie [NK 019338]. 2 m of brown overconsolidated matrix-supported diamict with a sandy silt matrix (Hall & Jarvis 1995). Referred to as the Bellscamphie Lower Till by Hall & Jarvis (1993b). It rests on bedrock, is overlain by the Pitlurg Member and is interpreted as lodgement till.

(3) Pitlurg Member. Stratotype: Bellscamphie [NK 019338]. Up to 2.5 m of dark grey overconsolidated slightly calcareous diamict with a platy structure and a clayey silt matrix. It contains sparse marine faunal remains (Hall & Jarvis 1995). It is the equivalent of the 'indigo boulder clay' of Jamieson (1906) and was referred to as the Bellscamphie Middle Till by Hall & Jarvis (1993b). Lower and upper contacts with the Elton and Hatton members are sharp. Interpreted as a lodgement till. D-aIle/L-Ile ratios on Arctica islandica have a minimum value of 0.101 that indicate a Devensian age.

(4) Hatton Member. Stratotype: Bellscamphie [NK 019338]. 3 m of red calcareous diamict with sparse pebbles and cobbles supported by a clay-silt matrix. Locally it shows a crude layering (Hall & Jarvis 1995). It contains abraded marine shell fragments. Forms part of the Red Series (Synge 1956; Sissons 1967; Sutherland 1984; Hall 1984) and was called the Bellscamphie Upper Till by Hall & Jarvis (1993b). It is interstratified with the Kippet Hills Formation and is interpreted as flow till.

(5) Kippet Hills Member. Stratotype: Bellscamphie [NK 019338]. Up to 5 m of pinkish-grey, clast supported, poorly sorted gravel in a sandy matrix with crude sub-horizontal bedding and locally rich in marine shell fragments. Elsewhere it thicknes to between 15 and 20 m. It forms part of the 'Red Series' (Synge 1956; Sissons 1967; Sutherland 1984; Hall 1984) and the Bellscamphie Gravels and Sands (Hall & Jarvis 1993b). It is interstratified with the Hatton Member and is interpreted as glaciofluvial ice-contact and proglacial sediment. D-aIle/L-Ile ratios greater than 0.5 from derived Arctica islandica shells may be Cromerian in age (Bowen unpublished).

(1) Camp Fauld Formation. Stratotype: Camp Fauld [NK 049410].

(2) Corse of Balloch Member. Stratotype: Camp Fauld [NK 049410]. Dark grey silty diamict (Whittington et al. 1993) interpreted as lodgement till.

(3) Hardslacks Member. Stratotype: Camp Fauld [NK 049410]. A humified terrestrial peat with a minerogenic component dominated by silt ('peat A' of Whittington et al. (1993). It is palynologically dissimilar to the Berryley Member (note 4) (Whittington at al. 1993) but both may have formed in different parts of the same interstadial event. Radiocarbon ages are infinite. TL ages on sands above the member are: 160 ± 16 ka and 137 ± 18 ka (Duller et al. 1995).

(4) Berryley Member. Stratotype: Camp Fauld [NK 049410]. Humified terrestrial peat with beds of weakly organic sands ('peat B' of Whittington et al. 1993). Radiocarbon ages are infinite. TL ages on sands from below the Berryley Member are: 251 ± 24 ka (Duller *et al.* 1995).

Inverness Area

(1) Clava Formation. Stratotype: Clava [NY 7674]. The formation is based on the succession at a disused claypit at Clava at about 150 m O.D. some 9 km east of Inverness and sections along the lower Cassie Burn and the lower Finglack Burn, tributaries of the River Nairn.

(2) Cassie Member. Stratotype: Clava [NY 7674]. 6.5 m of dark yellowish-brown compact diamict with a sandy clay matrix. First described by Horne *et al.* (1894) and interpreted by Merritt (1992) as a basal till (Cassie Till).

(3) Drummore Member. Stratotype: Clava [NH 7674]. About 4 m of crudely stratified, poorly sorted clayey bouldery gravel described by Horne *et al.* (1894) and interpreted by Merritt (1992) as glaciofluvial.

(4) Culdoich Member. Stratotype: Clava [NH 7674]. 2 m of olive-grey compact diamict with a matrix of silty fine-sandy clay which contains sparse shell material, with ^{14}C on *Mya truncata* of > 46 ka, and referred to as the Clava Shelly Till Member by Merritt (1992).

(5) Clava Lodge Member. Stratotype: Clava [NH 7674]. Up to 5 m of dark grey silty clay, clayey silt or silty fine-grained sand beds passing down into sheared soft silty clay with marine micro- and macrofauna most common in the upper beds. Named the Clava Shelly Clay Member by Merritt (1992), it corresponds to the original Clava shell bed described by Horne *et al.* (1894). Horne *et al.* (1894) and Sutherland (1981) considered that the deposits were marine and *in situ*, but Merritt (1992) argued that they were ice transported. His view is supported by D-aIle/L-Ile ratios for *Littorina littorea* of 0.054 ± 0.003 (8) which indicate a Devensian age and ratios of 0.06 ± 0.006 (2) on *Macoma calcarea* which point to a Late Devensian age. Radiocarbon ages are: $> 43\,000$ and $43\,800 \pm 3300$ BP.

(6) Dalroy Member. Stratotype: Clava [NH 7674]. It overlies the Clava Lodge Member conformably and consists of up to 4 m of yellowish-brown, compact, silty fine- to medium-grained sand. Termed the Clava Sand Member by Merritt (1992).

(7) Finglack Member. Stratotype: Clava [NH 7674]. 8 m of compact stony diamict the matrix of which is clay to fine-grained sand thought to be lodgement till (Merritt 1992)

(8) Baddock Member. Stratotype: Jamieson's Pit [NH 79395616]; parastratotype: Clava [NH 7674]. Up to 10 m of compact stony clay diamict with variably developed stratification, probably a subaerial flow till (Merritt *et al.* 1995).

(9) Ardsier Member. Stratotype: Jamieson's Pit [NH 79395616]; parastratotype: Kirkton Pit [NH 7895647]. About a metre of bedded silts, clays and sands showing deformation and disruption of the bedding. Locally it displays rhythmic lamination. The marine microfauna and macrofauna reported by Jamieson (1874), Wallace (1883) and Horne (1923) may not be *in situ* (Merritt *et al.* 1995).

(10) Kirkton Member. Stratotype: Jamieson's Pit [NH 79395616]; parastratotype: Kirkton Pit [NH 7895647]. 1.2 m of unfossiliferous laminated clay, silty clay and silty sand, interpreted as a proximal glaciomarine deposit (Merritt *et al.* 1995).

(11) Bothyhill Member. Stratotype: Bothyhill pit [NH 715491]; stratotype: [NH 78615227]. Well-rounded gravels and pebbly sands with subordinate lenses of planar-laminated, pale yellowish-grey, micaceous, fine- to medium-grained sand fining upwards into silt, overlain unconformably with thinly laminated medium-grained sands contained in channels. Interpreted by Merritt *et al.* (1995) as proximal glaciomarine to glaciofluvial sediments.

(12) Braicklaich Member. Stratotype: Bothyhill pit [NH 715491]; stratotype: [NH 78615227]. Well-rounded gravels and pebbly sands interpreted by Merritt *et al.* (1995) as proximal glaciomarine to glaciofluvial sediments.

(13) Kessock Bridge Member. Stratotype: boreholes under the site of Kessock Bridge [NH 6647]. Soft silt and fine-grained sand with scattered pebbles. Locally it contains marine microfauna and macrofauna. Deposited in a marine environment (Merritt *et al.* 1995). Radiocarbon age (top of member): $10\,945 \pm 85$ BP.

(14) Longman Member. Stratotype: boreholes under the site of Kessock Bridge [NH 6647]. It consists of cobbles, boulders and sands with marine shell fragments. Previously termed the Low Level Gravel of Inverness by Sissons (1981), it overlies the Kessock Bridge Member.

(15) Newton Burn Member. Stratotype: head of the Beauly Firth, [NH 5645]. It consists of sand, gravel and cobbles with some silt and clay, interpreted as a lag gravel produced by marine littoral marine erosion (Sissons 1981; Firth & Haggart 1989). It overlies, with marked unconformity, on the Finglack and Kessock Bridge Members, and is overlain by the Barnyards and Beauly Members.

(16) Culbokie Member. Stratotype: boreholes in the Cromarty Firth [NH 5961]. It is a variably sandy, clayey silt which is weakly laminated in places, contains scattered clasts and a marine microfauna and macrofauna. It overlies glacial deposits and is interpreted as marine sediment deposited during interstadial conditions. A radiocarbon age from the middle of the Culbokie Member gave: $12\,455 \pm 135$ BP. Called the Lower Findhorn Beds by Peacock *et al.* (1980).

(17) Balmeanach Member. Stratotype: boreholes in the Cromarty Firth [NH 5961]. It is a poorly sorted, clayey to sandy silt with scattered clasts and some grit lenses with rare marine microfauna and macrofauna. It is interpreted as a marine sediment deposited during conditions colder than at present. It is overlain conformably by the Ardullie Member. Called the Upper Findon Beds by Peacock *et al.* (1980).

(1) Dalcharn Formation. Stratotype: Dalcharn [NH 815452]–[NH 816454]. This is based on a thick sequence of tills beneath which biogenic sediments occur. The principal exposure is in a river cliff of the Allt Dearg at Dalcharn about 6 km southwest of Cawdor.

(2) Dearg Member. Stratotype: (Dalcharn [NH 815452–NH 816454]). A metre of yellowish-brown stiff matrix-supported diamict overlain unconformably by the Craig an Daimh Member. Interpreted by Merritt & Auton (1990) as lodgement till.

(3) Craig an Daimh Member. Stratotype: Dalcharn [NH 815452]–[NH 816454]. Up to 3 m of compact diamict with weathered clasts. It becomes progressively bleached towards the top where it passes into the Rehiran Member. Interpreted as fluvial or glaciofluvial (Merritt & Auton 1990).

(4) Rehiran Member. Stratotype: Dalcharn [NH 815452]–[NH 816454]. Up to 1 m of light-grey to white compact diamict with small fragments of organic material disseminated throughout. It has a chaotic fabric and a gradational basal contact with the Craig an Daimh Member. Geochronology: ^{14}C $>41\,300$ BP; Luminescence: 68.3 ± 6.0 ka and 50.3 ± 7.8 ka from the base of the member (Duller *et al.* 1995). The Dalcharn Cryoturbate

Table 24. *Correlations between Inverness, the Outer Hebrides and Shetland and oxygen isotope stratigraphy*

δ¹⁸O	INVERNESS	OUTER HEBRIDES	SHETLAND
1	**CROMARTY FORMATION (1)** Barnyards Member (6), Lemlair Member (3)	**NORTHTON FORMATION (13)**	**SHETLAND FORMATION (1)**
2	Moniack Member (5), Ardullie Member (2); Beauly Member (7), Foulis Member (4); **ALLT ODHAR FORMATION (1)** Cam Monadh Member (8), Beinn an Uain Member (7), Bein Bhreac Member (6), Kincraig Member (5); **DALCHARN FORMATION (1)** Ruallan Member (8), Cantray Member (7); **CLAVA FORMATION (1)** Culbokie (16) Balmeanach (17), Longman (14) Newton Burn (15), Kessock Bridge (13), Bothyhill (11) Braicklaich (12), Ardsier (9) Kirkton (10), Finglack (7) & Baddock (8) Members	**LEWIS FORMATION (1)** Mullach Sgar Member (12), Village Bay Member (11), Port Beag Member (10)	Burrier Wick Member (8)
3	Dalroy Member (6)	Ruaival Member (9), Abhainn Member (8), Tolsta Head Member (7)	Sandness Member (7)
4	Athais Member (6); Clava Lodge Member (5), Culdoich Member (4), Drummore Member (3), Cassie Member (2)	Dun Member (6)	Deepdale Member (7)
5	Odhar Member (4), Allt Member (3); Drummournie Member (5), Rehiran Member (4)	Galson Member (5)	Sel Ayre Member (6)
5e			Dale Member (5)
6		Thorabroc Member (4), Sgarbh Sgeir Member (3)	
7			Uyea Member (4)
8	Suidheig Member (2)	Toa Galson Bed (2)	
9	Craig an Daimh Member (3), Dearg Member (2)		
11			Fugla Ness Member (3)
12			South Wick Member (2)

Member of Walker *et al.* (1992).

(5) Drummournie Member. Stratotype: Dalcharn [NH 815452]–[NH 816454]. About 0.5 m of olive-grey compact crudely laminated silt with wisps of pebbly sand and fine peaty material overlying compact resedimented carbonaceous gravelly sandy-silt/clayey-sand diamict containing lenses of white fine- to coarse-grained sand and compressed finely stratified sandy peat. Peaty material is also disseminated throughout the diamict. It passes gradationally into the underlying Rehiran Member. Named the Dalcharn Biogenic Member by Walker *et al.* (1992). The origin of the Rehiran and Drummournie members is unclear, but Walker *et al.* (1992) consider that they may result from the reworking and partial destruction of palaeosol and peat deposits, perhaps by cryogenic processes during periglacial episodes. Four biostratigraphical zones (D1 to D5) have been established (Walker *et al.* 1992) across both members and the palynology suggests interglacial conditions suitable for plant growth. Palaeomagnetic analysis suggests that they both lie within the Brunhes Polarity Chron.

(6) Athais Member. Stratotype: Dalcharn [NH 815452]–[NH 816454]. 8.5 to 9.5 m of brown to yellowish-brown compact diamict with laterally discontinuous laminae of silty fine-grained sand and contorted lenses of gravel. Walker *et al.* (1992) called it the Dalcharn Lower Till Formation and interpreted it as a melt-out till, although Merritt & Auton (1990) subdivided it into upper lodgement, middle meltout and lower basal meltout/lodgement facies which they called the Upper, Middle and Basal members.

(7) Cantray Member. Stratotype: Dalcharn [NH 815452]–[NH 816454]. 5.5 tp 6.5 m of brown compact diamict, distinguished by differences in clast lithology and fabric from the Ruallan Member. Interpreted as lodgement till by Walker *et al.* (1992). The 'Lower Member' of the Dalcharn Upper Till Formation of Walker *et al.* (1992).

(8) Ruallan Member. Stratotype: Dalcharn [NH 815452]–[NH 816454]. It overlies the Cantray Member unconformably and consists 3 to 3.5 m of compact dark yellowish-brown diamict interpreted as lodgement till (Walker *et al.* 1992). This is the 'Upper Member' (Walker *et al.* 1992) of the Dalcharn Upper Till Formation of Walker *et al.* (1992).

(1) Allt Odhar Formation. Stratotype: Allt Odhar section [NH 798368]. The formation is based on a sequence of glacial deposits that contains peat in a stream section at Allt Odhar.

(2) Suidheig Member. Stratotype: Allt Odhar section [NH 798368]. 1.5 m of light brown to compact yellowish-brown diamict (Walker *et al.* 1992). It underlies, with an erosional contact, the Allt Member and is more weathered than the Beinn an Uain, Beinn Bhreac and Kincraig Members.

(3) Allt Member. Stratotype: Allt Odhar [NH 798368]. Up to 1.5 m of poorly sorted, clast-supported cobble gravel with lenses of better sorted, finer gravel, sandy gravel and cross-stratified sand. It is considered fluvial or glaciofluvial (Walker *et al.* 1992) and underlies the Odhar Member.

(4) Odhar Member. Stratotype: Allt Odhar section [NH 798368]. It comprises up to 0.6 m of pebbly peaty sand, amorphous peat, fibrous peat and interlaminated sand and peat interpreted as a backswamp or river cut-off deposit subject to intermittent flooding. Biostratigraphybased on pollen and coleoptera indicate that the climate was slightly cooler than present. It is probably Early Devensian in age and interstadial in character (^{14}C: 51 100; U-series: 106 + 11/-10 ka (Walker *et al.* 1992); Luminescence: 37.1 ± 3.5 ka (uppermost peaty sand) and 57.9 ± 5.3 ka and 53.8 ± 5.8 ka (lowermost interlaminated sand and peat) (Duller *et al.* 1995)).

(5) Kincraig Member. Stratotype: Allt Odhar section [NH 798368]. 2,2 m of olive-grey to yellowish-brown compact clayey-silt diamict with fine subhorizontal stratification and lenses of silty fine-grained sand, pebbly medium- to coarse-grained sand and dense, clayey, poorly sorted gravel. Referred to as the Paraglacial Member by Walker *et al.* (1992) it is interpreted as Late Devensian lodgement till. Its upper contact with the Beinn Bhreac Member and its lower contact, with the Odhar Member, are gradational. Interpreted by Walker *et al.* (1992) as a sheared till resulting from original periglacial or pro-glacial debris-flow deposition and subsequent shearing by the overriding glacier that was responsible for the deposition of the Beinn Bhreac Member. The shearing also incorporated part of the underlying Odhar Member.

(6) Beinn Bhreac Member. Stratotype: Allt Odhar section [NH 798368]. Up to 6 m of olive-grey to yellowish-brown compact diamict, referred to as the Moy Lower Till Member by Walker *et al.* (1992) and interpreted as lodgement till. It is distinguished by a higher sand content and greater degree of weathering than the Beinn an Uain Member.

(7) Beinn an Uain Member. Stratotype: Allt Odhar section [NH 798368]. 10 m of olive-greycompact diamict which was termed the Moy Upper Till Member by Walker *et al.* (1992).

(8) Carn Monadh Member. Stratotype: Allt Odhar [NH 798368]. Up to 10 m of pale compact olive-grey subhorizontal silty sandy gravel interpreted by Walker *et al.* (1992) as ice-marginal outwash fan gravels deposited during the retreat of the Late Devensian ice sheet.

(1) Cromarty Formation. Includes several members recognised from borehole investigations in the Cromarty Firth (below).

(2) Ardullie Member. Stratotype: boreholes in the Cromarty Firth [NH 5961]. About 20 m of generally well sorted interbedded marine silt and fine-grained sand, in part crudely laminated. It contains some clasts, plant debris and marine faunal remains (Peacock *et al.* 1980). It is overlain, unconformably, by the Lemlair and Foulis Members, and it overlies conformably the Balmeanach Member. Deposited in colder conditions than present (Peacock *et al.* 1980; Peacock & Harkness 1990). A radiocarbon age from the middle of the unit gave: 10 005 ± 110 BP.

(3) Lemlair Member. Stratotype: boreholes in the Cromarty Firth [NH 5961]. The Lower Cromarty Beds of Peacock *et al.* (1980). Up to 14 m of well-sorted, fine-grained micaceous sand with beds of micaceous silt. There are a few lenses of pebbles or shells and plant debris is present throughout. It is interpreted as a marine sediment deposited in conditions similar to the present. Marine shells from its base gave radiocarbon ages of 7750 ± 160 BP and 6920 ± 360 BP.

(4) Foulis Member. Stratotype: boreholes in the Cromarty Firth [NH 5961]. The Upper Cromarty Beds of Peacock *et al.* (1980). About 9 m of well-sorted silt with fine-grained sand. Marine faunal remains and plant debris occurs throughout. Interpreted as a marine sediment deposited in conditions similar to the present.

(5) Moniack Member. Stratotype: Moniack [NH 540440]. Up to 15 m of dark brown to black peat, silty at base and near its gradational contacts with the Beauly Member with which it is interstratified. Gradational contact at base with the overlying Barnyards Member (Haggart 1986, 1987; Firth & Haggart 1989). Its base is radiocarbon dated 9610 ± 130 BP; the contact with the base of the Beauly Member is dated 7100 ± 110 BP.

(6) Barnyards Member. Stratotype: Barnyards [NH 531469]. About 3 m of pink to grey laminated clayey silt (Firth & Haggart 1989). Called the Barnyards Beds by Firth & Haggart

(1989), it rests upon the Newton Burn Member and is overlain, with a gradational contact, by the Moniack Member. Its surface forms broad steps and it is interpreted as estuarine, deposited during a falling sea level.

(7) Beauly Member. Stratotype: Barnyards [NH 531469]; parastratotype: Moniack [NH 540440]. Up to 4 m of estuarine deposits that consist of grey silts and clays with some shell fragments and thin sand beds. Named the Beauly Beds by Firth & Haggart (1989), and more widely referred to as carse (Sissons 1967, 1981). The top of Beauly Member is dated 5510 ± 80 BP; with a date of 4760 ± 90 BP on top of the Beauly Member. It is interstratified with the Moniack Member and its surface is gently stepped.

Outer Hebrides

(1) Lewis Formation. This comprises the Pleistocene deposits of north-west Lewis. Its subdivision is based on coastal exposures.

(2) Toa Galson Bed. Stratotype: cliff section [NB 448600]. 0.2 m of dark brown compacted peat with a thin bed of silt at its base (Sutherland & Walker 1984), resting on bedrock and conformably overlain by the Sgarbh Sgeir Member. Palynology indicates accumulation in a relatively mild interstadial or interglacial. Radiocarbon age: $> 47\,150$ BP.

(3) Sgarbh Sgeir Member. Stratotype: cliff section [NB 448600]. Less than a metre of reddish-brown compact well sorted fine- to medium-grained sand (Sutherland & Walker 1984) resting conformably on the Toa Galson Bed and underlying, with possible erosional contact, the Thorabroc Member. Possibly marine in origin.

(4) Thorabroc Member. Stratotype: cliff section [NB 448600]. 0.4 m of firm brown, matrix-supported diamict with angular to angular clasts in a silty sand matrix, with minor silt lenses with a weak lamination interpreted as a periglacial slope deposit (Sutherland & Walker 1984). It overlies unconformably the Sgarbh Sgeir Member.

(5) Galson Member. Stratotype: cliff section [NB 448600]. Up to 3.5 m of yellowish-brown stratified sand and gravel with primary horizontal bedding. Gravel clasts are well rounded and up to small boulder in size and generally show horizontal imbrication. Near the surface the bedding is disrupted and the clasts are commonly vertically arranged (McCann 1968; Peacock 1984; Sutherland & Walker 1984). It overlies the Thorabroc Member unconformably, and is interpreted as a marine beach, the upper part of which has been periglacially disturbed.

(6) Dun Member. Stratotype: cliff sections [NF 098985]. Greyish-brown compact matrix supported diamict with cobble- to boulder-sized clasts set in a silty sand matrix, interpreted as a till (Sutherland *et al.* 1984). Termed the Ruaival drift by Sutherland *et al.* (1984), rests on bedrock and is unconformably overlain by the Ruaival Member.

(7) Tolsta Head Member. Stratotype: Tolsta Head [NB 55724682]. One metre thick, it comprises two lithofacies: an upper bed of organic detritus with sand lenses and a lens of sand and angular rock fragments; and a lower bed of fine sand with a low organic content and iron staining (Birnie 1983). Plant micro-and macro-fossils are present throughout but are more abundant in the upper bed. The deposit rests on bedrock and has been truncated by the overlying Port Beag Member (von Weymarn & Edwards 1973; von Weymarn 1979; Birnie 1983). Palynology indicates that the deposit is interstadial. The lower sediments are considered to be fluvial and the upper

sediments lacustrine (^{14}C age: $27\,330 \pm 240$ BP).

(8) Abhainn Member. Stratotype: stream section [NF 097984]. Dark brown, compact moderately well sorted, medium-grained sand with isolated angular pebbles and boulders. Organic material occurs throughout the sand and is locally concentrated in wisps and thin lenses. Base not seen but it is unconformably overlain by the Ruaival Member (Sutherland *et al.* 1984). Palynology indicates mild oceanic climate. It is interpreted as redeposited soil material. ^{14}C minimum age is $24\,710 + 1470/-1240$ BP.

(9) Ruaival Member. Stratotype: cliff sections [NF 098985]. A brown, loose, compact, matrix-supported, clast rich diamict with a sandy matrix, with lenses of bedded sand and angular clasts (Sutherland *et al.* 1984). It rests unconformably upon the Abhainn and Dun Members and was referred to as the 'Ruaival head' by Sutherland *et al.* (1984).

(10) Port Beag Member. Stratotype: Tosta Head [NB 55724682]. 2 m of reddish-brown matrix-supported diamict with a notable proportion of clasts of Torridon Sandstone interpreted as lodgement till (von Weymarn & Edwards 1973; von Weymarn 1979). At its base it contains eroded blocks of the underlying Tolsta Head Member.

(11) Village Bay Member. Stratotype: cliff sections [NF 1099]. Two facies have been identified, a lower, hard matrix-supported diamict with a silty sand matrix that locally displays laminae of silt and fine sand towards the top, and a structureless clast-supported bouldery rubble (Sutherland *et al.* 1984). It rests on bedrock and is overlain by the Mullach Sgar Member. Interpreted as till, the lower facies as lodgement till with melt-out features in its upper part, and the upper facies a supraglacial sediment.

(12) Mullach Sgar Formation. Stratotype: cliff section [NF 098988]. Loose, greyish-brown, clast supported diamict which is bouldery at the base interpreted as rock fall forming a protalus rampart. It forms an arcuate ridge and rests on the Village Bay Member and the Ruaival Member (Sutherland *et al.* 1984).

(13) Northton Formation. Stratotype: Northton [NF 9890]. Sand, interstratified with numerous thin palaeosol, lacustrine and archaeological horizons (Burleigh *et al.* 1973; Crawford & Switsur 1977; Ritchie 1979). Its surface is irregular and moundy or flat to gently sloping. An aeolian sediment with ^{14}C ages of: 5700 ± 170 BP and 1235 ± 65 BP.

Shetland

(1) Shetland Formation. This is defined to include all the mappable Quaternary deposits in the islands.

(2) South Wick Member. Stratotype: Ness [HU 312913]. Grey, sandy, pebbly, matrix-supported diamict which close to bedrock becomes bouldery and clast supported. Referred to by Hall *et al.* (1993*a*) as the 'Fugla Ness Lower Till' and interpreted as lodgement till.

(3) Fugla Ness Member. Stratotype: Fugla Ness [HU 312913]. 1.5 m of compact peat, pebbly at its base, with minor lenses and thin beds of granules and laminated organic muds and sands and some pebbles. Locally, it contains a basal bed of laminated brown silt. It is draped on the surface of the South Wick Member (Chapelhowe 1965; Hall *et al.* 1993*a*). It accumulated in a temperate climate and has a ^{14}C age of $> 51\,700$ BP.

(4) Uyea Formation. Stratotype: Fugla Ness [HU 312913]. 3 m of laminated light yellow-brown, granular local pebble breccia. It contains lenses and zones of disseminated organic matter and peat. It is referred to by Hall *et al.* (1993*a*) as the Fugla Ness Breccia. It has an erosional lower contact with the Fugla Ness Member and is unconformably overlain by the Burrier Wick Member. Interpreted as a slope deposit. TL (maximum) ages: 290 ± 25 ka and 147 ± 14 ka (Duller *et al.* 1995).

(5) Dale Member. Stratotype: Sel Ayre [HU 176540]. Clast-supported, partly openwork rubble with angular sandstone blocks in a sandy matrix interpreted as a periglacial slope deposit. Referred to as the Sel Ayre Lower Breccia by Hall *et al.* (1993*b*). It rests on bedrock and is overlain by the Sel Ayre Member.

(6) Sel Ayre Member. Stratotype: Sel Ayre [HU 176540]. Uo to 1 m of clay, sand, peat, organic muds and rubble beds. The peat is highly compressed and humified, the sequence is progressively sandier and coarser upwards, and the upper part is bleached with weathered rinds on clasts. Referred to as the 'Sel Ayre Organic Sands and Gravels' by Hall *et al.* (1993*b*), it corresponds to units 2–7 of Mykura & Phemister (1976). It overlies conformably the Dale Member and has a gradational upper contact with the Deepdale Member. Interpreted by Hall *et al.* (1993*b*) as initial pond sedimentation followed by peat accumulation during a period of mild (interstadial) climate, followed by minerogenic inwash into the basin during a period of climatic decline (see also: Birks & Peglar (1979). Radiocarbon age: > 52 200 BP. TL age (upper part of organic sands): 98 ± 10 ka and 105 ± 7 ka (Duller *et al.* 1995)).

(7) Deepdale Member. Stratotype: Sel Ayre [HU 176540]. Up to 4 m of crudely stratified, mainly matrix-supported sandy and gritty rubble interpreted as a periglacial slope deposit. Referred to as the Sel Ayre Upper Breccia by Hall *et al.* (1993*b*), it corresponds with unit 8 of Mykura & Phemister (1976). It has a gradational basal contact with the Sel Ayre Member, and is overlain unconformably by the Sandness Member.

(8) Sandness Member. Stratotype: Sel Ayre [HU 176540]. 2.7 m of brown, matrix-supported, sandy diamict with prominent boulder lags and lenses of subangular pebbles. Referred to as the Sel Ayre Till by Hall *et al.* (1993*b*), it corresponds with unit 9 of Mykura & Phemister (1976). It overlies the Deepdale Member unconformably and is interpreted as lodgement till.

(9) Burrier Wick Member. Stratotype: Fugla Ness [HU 312913]. 2 m of pinkish-grey, compact, matrix-supported, stony diamict with a silty sandy matrix (Chapelhowe 1965; Hall *et al.* 1993*a*). Referred to by Hall *et al.* (1993*a*) as the Fugla Ness Upper Till. It rests unconformably on the Uyea Member, and is interpreted as lodgement till.

Dumfriesshire

(1) Redkirk Formation. Comprises members of Late Devensian and Holocene age that indicate the transition from glaciomarine to marine, estuarine and brackish water conditions..

(2) Black Burn Member. Stratotype: Bigholm Burn [NY 316812]. 1.7 m of blue-grey or pinkish, horizontally laminated clay and silt with scattered clasts and lenses of sand and gravel (Moar 1969; Bishop & Coope 1977; Gordon 1993). It underlies the local equivalent of the Redkirk Point Member and is probably glaciolacustrine.

(3) Redkirk Point Member. Stratotype: Redkirk Point [NY 301652]. 0.3 m of carbonaceous silt and fine sand overlain by a highly compacted peat (Bishop & Coope 1977). The peat is referred to as Peat 1 by these authors. It rests on till or bedrock and is overlain by the Rigfoot Member. It is interpreted as

fluvial at the base, succeeded by basin peats. Radiocarbon ages on peats from Redkirk Point and neighbouring sites range from $12\,940 \pm 250$ BP to $10\,900 \pm 130$ BP.

(4) Bigholm Burn Member. Stratotype: Bigholm Burn [NY 316812]. 3 m of grey crudely bedded gravel with locally imbricate gravel horizons and cross- and flat-bedded sand lenses. At the top are thin, dark grey, slightly organic, silt lenses and the gravel contains blocks of peat and sand clasts. Coleopteran remains in the silt lenses indicate deposition in a cold climate (Bishop & Coope 1977; Gordon 1993). It rests on the local equivalent of the Redkirk Point Member and is overlain by the Healy Hill Member. Bishop & Coope (1977) interpreted the deposits as the product of solifluction but Gordon (1993) suggested that it is more probably a braided fluvial deposit with overbank silts. Maximum limiting luminescence ages are: 19.9 ± 1.9 ka and 21.3 ± 4.6 ka (Duller *et al.* 1995).

(5) Healy Hill Member. Stratotype: Bigholm Burn [NY 316812]. 2.5 m of brown organic mud with plant macrofossils (Moar 1969; Bishop & Coope 1977). It rests unconformably on the Bigholm Burn Member and is overlain by the Racks Member. It was interpreted by Bishop & Coope (1977) as a fluvial sediment but the high proportion of lacustrine micro- and macrofossils may suggest deposition in a pond or possibly a backswamp. Radiocarbon ages are: 9590 ± 170 BP and 9470 ± 170 BP; and 8650 ± 170 BP from the contact with the Racks Member. The pollen biostratigraphy indicates correlation with regional pollen zone F1, which suggests that the radiocarbon dates may be too young.

(6) Rigfoot Member. Stratotype: Redkirk Point [NY 301652]. Grey, bedded, silt and fine sand (Bishop & Coope 1977). It rests on the Redkirk Point Member, is overlain by the Racks Member and is considered to be estuarine.

(7) Racks Member. Stratotype: Racks Moss [NY 0373]. Loose to compact, dark brown to black peat (Nichols 1967). It rests on the Rigfoot Member and is interstratified with the Newbie Member, a function of marine transgression and regression. Radiocarbon ages are: (i) the earliest age for the lower contact with the Newbie Member: 8140 ± 150 BP; (ii) the latest age for the lower contact with the Newbie Member: 7250 ± 100 BP; (iii) the earliest age for the upper contact with the Newbie Member: 6650 ± 120 BP; and the latest age from the upper contact with the Newbie Member: 4290 ± 100 BP.

(8) Newbie Member. Stratotype: Newbie [NY 165651]. Up to 6 m of grey silt and fine sand with thin beds and lenses of peat. Marine micro- and macrofaunal remains occur sparsely (Jardine 1964, 1971, 1975; Nichols 1967; Bishop & Coope 1977). It has gradational contacts with the interstratified Racks Member and is interpreted as estuarine.

Ayrshire

(1) Sourlie Formation. Stratotype: Sourlie opencast pit [NS 3341].

(2) Littlestone Member. Stratotype: Sourlie opencast pit [NS 3341]. Grey diamict, interpreted as a lodgement till. enclosing sand sheets. Referred to as unit A by Jardine *et al.* (1988). It rests on bedrock and is overlain with sharp contact by the Red Burn Member.

(3) Lawthorn Member. Stratotype: Sourlie opencast pit [NS 3341]. A compact clay-rich gravel that passes laterally into a clayey sand. It overlies the Littlestone Member and is overlain, with sharp irregular contact, by the Armsheugh Member.

Table 25. *Correlations between Dumfriesshire, Ayrshire, the Glasgow region, the South West Highlands and Kintyre and oxygen isotope stratigraphy*

δ18O	DUMFRIESSHIRE	AYRSHIRE	GLASGOW REGION	S W HIGHLANDS & KINTYRE
1	**REDKIRK FORMATION** (1) Newbie Member (8) Racks Member (7) Rigfoot Member (6)	**GIRVAN FORMATION** (10) Enoch (14) Woodside (15) Shewalton (12) Dundonald (13) & Irvine (11) Members	**CLYDE VALLEY FORMATION** (1) Law Member (16) Gourock Member (15) Clippens Member (14) Erskine Member (13) Lochwinnoch Member (12) Linwood Member (11) Paisley Member (10)	**ARGYLE FORMATION** (12) Eas na Broige Member (17) Carradale (15) & Dalness (16) Members Clashgour Member (14) Cill an Aonghais (13) **ROY FORMATION** (11) **ETIVE FORMATION** (10)
2	Healy Hill Member (5) Bigholm Burn Member (4) Redkirk Point Member (3) Black Burn Member (2)	**MOUNT HOUSE FORMATION** (9) **TAYBURN FORMATION** (8) **SOURLIE FORMATION** (1) Auchenwinsey Member (7) Eglinton Member (6)	Bridgeton Member (9) Ross Member (8) Bellshill Member (7) Broomhouse Member (6) Cadder Member (4) Wilderness Member (5)	**ARDYNE FORMATION** (5) Kilmartin Member (9) Ardyne Point Member (8) Toward Member (7) Killellan Member (6) Corputechan Member (4)
3		Red Burn Member (5) Armsheugh Member (4)	Broom Hill Member (3)	
4		Lawthorn Member (3)		
5		Littlestone Member (2)		**CLEONGART FORMATION** (1)
5e			Baillieston Member (2)	
6				
7				Tangy Glen Member (3)
8				Barr Member (2)

Interpreted as an ablation deposit (Jardine *et al.* 1988).

(4) Armsheugh Member. Stratotype: Sourlie opencast pit [NS 3341]. Cross-stratified sand and gravel interpreted as outwash (Jardine *et al.* 1988).

(5) Red Burn Member. Stratotype: Sourlie opencast pit [NS 3341]. Organic-rich clay and silt overlain by laminated sand that contains mammalian remains as well as terrestrial and lacustrine floral remains (Jardine *et al.* 1988). It overlies the Arsmheugh Member and is overlain by the Doura Member. Interpreted as shallow pond sediment deposited during an interstadial. Four radiocarbon ages range from $29\,290 \pm 350$ BP to $33\,270 \pm 370$ BP.

(6) Eglinton Member. Stratotype: Sourlie opencast pit [NS 3341]. Pink-brown diamict containing some shell fragments resting unconformably on the Red Burn Member and interpreted as lodgement till. D-aIle/L-Ile ratios on *Arctica islandica* fragments are: 0.056 ± 0.007, and indicate a Late Devensian age.

(7) Auchenwinsey Member. Stratotype: Sourlie opencast pit [NS 3341]. A grey diamict separated from the Eglinton Member by an erosion surface (Jardine *et al.* 1988). Interpreted as lodgement till.

(8) Tayburn Formation. Stratotype: Tayburn [NS 5143]. Dark brown to red, matrix-supported diamict with numerous pebble-sized clasts and characteristic clay mineralogy (Adb-Alla 1988) interpreted as till. Unconformably overlies the Auchenwisney Member.

(9) Mount House Formation. Stratotype: near Mount House [NS 408369]. A greyish-brown, laminated, silty clay with some sand partings with a marine microfauna (Boyd 1986*a*) that is interpreted as marine to glaciomarine. Its upper part consists of brown marine gravel and sand. It overlies the Auchenwisney Member (Boyd 1986*a*).

(10) Girvan Formation. Comprises the following members.

(11) Irvine Member. Stratotype: Irvine [NS 324372]; stratotype: Dundonald Burn [NS 337372]. Two lithofacies characterise this member, finely horizontally bedded clay grading upwards into organic detritus (Boyd 1988) and compacted grey sand with *Pholas* shells which becomes peaty upwards (Smith 1896; Boyd 1986*b*). The base is not seen but it has a gradational upper contact with the Shewalton Member. It is probably marine and deposited during a period of falling sea level.

(12) Shewalton Member. Stratotype: Shewalton Moss [NS 348354]. Peat, sandy at base and sandy or silty at its contacts with the Irvine and Girvan Members (Jardine 1962; Boyd 1988). It has a gradational lower contact with the Irvine Member and is interstratified with the Dundonald and the Woodside Members, a consequence of sea-level change. Radiocarbon dates are: (i) base of the unit: $10\,510 \pm 120$ BP; (ii) the earliest contact with the Irvine Member: 9780 ± 90 BP; (iii) the earliest contact with the base of the Enoch Member of the Girvan Member and the Woodside Member: 3940 ± 190 BP.

(13) Dundonald Member. Stratotype: Dundonald Burn [NS 337372]. It consists of yellow sand with beds of gravel and locally abundant marine shell fragments (Boyd 1986*b*) overlying unconformably the Shewalton Member and overlain unconformably by the Woodside Member. A littoral marine sediment deposited during a period of sea-level rise and then fall.

(14) Enoch Member. Stratotype: Enoch Farm [NX 204994]. Beds of grey organic-rich silt, silty clay and brown, silty fine-grained sand and sand. Marine micro- and macrofaunal remains are present and plant debris is common (Jardine

1962). It is interstratified with the Shewalton and Dundonald Members, lies unconformably on the Shewalton Member and is unconformably overlain by the Woodside Member. The Enoch Member is interpreted as an estuarine deposit deposited during a period of sea-level rise and then fall.

(15) Woodside Member. Stratotype: Woodside area [NS 3236]. It consists of loose, yellow aeolian sand, generally with a marked hummocky surface topography (Jardine 1980; Boyd 1986*b*). It rests unconformably on the Dundonald Member and is locally interstratified with the Shewalton Member.

The Glasgow Region

(1) Clyde Valley Formation. This consists of all the Quaternary deposits infilling the Clyde Valley around and downstream of Glasgow. Overall it constitutes a mappable unit that is capable of subdivision into a number of members. Its age includes the Holocene, consisting largely of marine, estuarine and lacustrine deposits, to a glaciation of unknown age represented by the Baillieston Member that probably antedates sub-stage 5e. Details of the distribution of the members, that are identified largely from boreholes, their thicknesses and sedimentary characteristics and inferences of origin are to be found in Browne & McMillan (1989).

(2) Baillieston Member. Stratotype: section at the M8 Baillieston Interchange [NS 693641]. Reddish-brown to dark greyish-brown, compact diamict with a matrix of sandy silty clay deposited by ice (Browne & McMillan 1989).

(3) Broomhill Member. Stratotype: Erskine Bridge borehole [NS 46357251]. Consists of reddish-brown, compact, unfossiliferous, thinly bedded silty clay with wisps, laminae and beds of grey or buff silt and sand, with some clasts and lenses of diamict; it displays minor faults (Browne & McMillan 1989). It overlies the Baillieston Member and underlies the Wilderness Member both with unconformable boundaries. It is interpreted as a glaciolacustrine deposit.

(4) Cadder Member. Stratotype: Wilderness area [NS 605720]. A dense framework-supported, bouldery gravel and sand and coarse-to fine-grained, with some pebbly, sand and silt. The gravel is mainly thickly bedded and trough cross-bedded in sets that interfinger with sands. The sands are trough cross-bedded, ripple laminated and horizontally laminated. The deposits are faulted (Browne & McMillan 1989). It is overlain by the Wilderness Member but the presence of possible frost cracks in the surface of the deposit (Rolfe 1966) implies a hiatus between the two. The deposits are fluvial to fluviodeltaic in origin laid down in a periglacial environment (Brown & McMillan 1989). A radiocarbon age of $27\,500 + 1370/-1680$ on woolly rhinoceros bone fragment provides a maximum age for the Cadder Member. Maximum Luminescence ages are: 120 ± 23 ka; 133 ± 15 ka and 126 ± 16 ka.

(5) Wilderness Member. Stratotype: Wilderness area [NS 605720]. A reddish-brown, brownish grey or greenish grey, compact, diamict with boulders, pebbles and gravel in a sandy silty clay matrix, interpreted as till. Normally unfossiliferous, it locally contains derived estuarine to marine micro- and macrofaunal remains (Rose 1981; Browne & McMillan 1989). It overlies the Cadder Member and includes several members.

(6) Broomhouse Member. Stratotype: Broomhouse gravel pits [NS 675625]. Pebbly, coarse to fine-grained sand and silt, and bouldery gravel with sand. Disrupted and deformed bedding is common. The typical surface expression of the Member is as irregular mounds and hummocks. It is interpreted as ice-contact, glaciofluvial sediment (Browne & McMillan 1989) and it overlies the Wilderness Member.

(7) Bellshill Member. Stratotype: Crossford borehole [NS 83754616]. It consists of a brownish-grey, firm to stiff, silty clay with wisps, laminae and beds of silt and sand. Rhythmic bedding (varves) and isolated lenses of diamict occur and there is a scatter of clasts throughout (Brown & McMillan 1989). It is interpreted as glaciolacustrine. It overlies the Wilderness Member.

(8) Ross Member. Stratotype: Ross House borehole [NS 73905504]. Moderate to dense, laminated medium- and fine-grained sand with laminae and thin beds of silt (Brown & McMillan 1989). Considered to be deltaic deposits that interdigitate with the glaciolacustrine sediments of the Bellshill Member. Elsewhere they overlie the Wilderness Member and are overlain, with minor unconformity, by the Paisley Member.

(9) Bridgeton Member. Stratotype: Bridgeton Borehole [NS 61206367]. It comprises two typical lithologies: fine-to medium-grained and fine- to coarse gravel and boulders in a sandy matrix. It is generally compate and is interpreted as subaqueous outwash (Browne & McMillan 1989). It lies between the Ross and Paisley members.

(10) Paisley Member. Stratotype: Linwood borehole [NS 44596588]. Consists of soft to firm, brownish-grey to reddish-brown, bedded clays and silts containing sparse marine micro- and macrofaunal remains. It displays colour laminations, some clasts, and locally is folded or faulted. Probably glaciomarine (Jardine 1986; Browne & McMillan 1989).

(11) Linwood Member. Stratotype: Linwood borehole [NS 44596588]. Grey thickly bedded silts and clays with some marine fossils, and some isolated clasts. Interpreted as estuarine to marine (Browne et al. 1977; Jardine 1986; Browne & McMillan 1989), it is broadly equivalent to the Clyde beds (Peacock 1975; Sutherland 1984). Radiocarbon ages on marine shells range from $13\,100 \pm 265$ to $11\,930 \pm 120$ BP.

(12) Lochwinnoch Member. Stratotype: Lochwinnoch borehole [NS 35185812]. Dark brown, silty clay with silt and sand layers. Relatively rich in organic detritus but towards the base is increasingly minerogenic with thin colour laminations (Browne & McMillan 1989). Interpreted as freshwater lacustrine sediments. A radiocarbon age near the top of the unit is: $11\,210 \pm 190$.

(13) Erskine Member. Stratotype: Erskine Bridge borehole [NS 46357251]. Brownish grey to greyish brown, fossiliferous, estuarine silty clay with sand and silt laminae, with organic debris (Browne & McMillan 1989).

(14) Clippens Member. Stratotype: Linwood borehole [NS 44596588]. Dark brown to black peat interbedded with and gradational contacts with the Erskine Member (Browne & Macmillan 1989) (Jardine 1975, 1986; Boyd 1986). Radiocarbon ages range between: 9540 ± 50 at the base to 3650 ± 60 BP.

(15) Gourock Member. Stratotype: Gourock No2 borehole [NS 244777]. Buff and grey, silty fine-to coarse-grained sand. Marine and brackish water microfauna and macrofauna. Interpreted by Browne & McMillan (1989) as shallow estuarine deposits with strong fluvial influence.

(16) Law Member. Stratotype: Law Borehole [NS 83575247]. Grey, fine- to coarse-grained fluvial sands with silt and traces of fine gravel and dark brownish-grey, sub-angular to rounded fine gravel with sand. Plant remains are present (Browne & McMillan 1989).

Southwest Highlands and Kintyre

(1) Cleongart Formation. Stratotype: Cleongart Glen [NR 668347].

(2) Barr Member. Stratotype: Cleongart Glen [NR 668347]. About 1 m of compact, coarse-grained, unfossiliferous sand and gravel (Horne et al. 1897). It has a sharp upper contact with the Tangy Glen Member and rests on bedrock. Its origin is uncertain but was thought to be till by Jessen (1905).

(3) Tangy Glen Member. Stratotype: Cleongart Glen [NR 668347]. Up to 8 m of dark blue shelly clay, with scattered clasts, some boulder sized (Horne et al. 1897). Commonly referred to as the Tangy Glen High Level Shell Bed (Sutherland 1981, 1993). It overlies the Barr Member and is overlain unconformably by the Corputechan Member. It is marine or glaciomarine (Horne et al. 1987; Jessen 1905; Sutherland 1981) but it has been partly (Munthe 1897), or wholly (Synge & Stephens 1966) considered to be till. Mean D-aIle/L-Ile ratios on *Arctica islandica* are 0.249 that indicate an oxygen isotope stage 8 age for the fauna (Bowen & Sykes 1988).

(4) Corputechan Member. Stratotype: Cleongart Glen [NR 668347]. Up to 22.5 m of reddish-brown compact diamict. It rests unconformably on the Cleongart Member (Horne et al. 1897) and is interpreted as till.

(5) Ardyne Formation. Stratotype: Ardyne Point [NS 007684]. It consists of the following members.

(6) Killellan Member. Stratotype: Ardyne Point [NS 007684]; parastratotype: Killellan farm [NS 107696]. Laminated silty clay, silt and fine-grained sand which also shows marked colour lamination between light brown and reddish-brown, with isolated angular clasts and sparse marine microfauna and macrofauna. It corresponds to Unit 1 of Peacock et al. (1978) and has a gradational upper contact with the Toward Member. It is probably an ice-proximal glaciomarine sediment.

(7) Toward Member. Stratotype: Ardyne Point [NS 007684]. Greyish brown clayey silt to silty sand with gravel lenses and scattered clasts, an abundant marine microfauna, macrofauna, and sparse plant debris (Peacock et al. 1978). It includes Unit 2 and Unit 3 of Peacock et al. (1978) at Ardyne and a major part of the Clyde Beds of Peacock (1975) and Sutherland (1984). It is conformable with both the underlying Killellan Member and the overlying Ardyne Member, and is interpreted as a marine sediment deposited in relatively mild interstadial conditions. Radiocarbon ages range between $13\,615 \pm 135$ BP and $10\,990 \pm 120$ BP. D-aIle/L-Ile D/L ratios on *Arctica islandica* are: 0.055 ± 0.006 (Bowen unpublished).

(8) Ardyne Point Member. Stratotype: Ardyne Point [NS 007684]. Grey to brown, poorly sorted, clayey silt to silty sand with sand lenses and thin beds with scattered clasts locally common. It contains a marine microfauna and macrofauna, and plant debris. Referred to by Peacock et al. 1978 as Unit 4 it forms part of the Clyde Beds of Peacock (1975) and Sutherland (1984). It overlies the Toward Member conformably and is interpreted as marine, but deposited in a much colder climate than the Toward Member. [14]C ages range between $10\,740 \pm 110$ BP and 9915 ± 80 BP (Peacock et al. 1978).

(9) Kilmartin Member. Stratotype: sand pit [NR 833994]. Yellowish-brown, horizontally bedded sand and gravel. Its surface forms terraces (Gray & Sutherland 1977). It overlies the Killellan Member and is probably outwash, deposited and dissected during falling sea level.

(10) Etive Formation. Stratotype: Achnacree–Achnaba area [NM 9336]. Generally weakly horizontally bedded sand and gravel with subsidiary lenses of laminated sand, silt and clay. Surface morphology varies from moundy to flat and it is probably glaciofluvial and ice-marginal (McCann 1966; Gray 1975, 1993).

(11) Roy Formation. Type area: Glen Roy. Comprises two lithofacies Miller (1987): brown to fawn laminated fine sand that cap the formation and silt and grey-blue laminated silts and clays, both glaciolacustrine in origin. The laminations are probably varves and up to 250 ± 10 have been counted at a single locality. The sediments are extensively deformed with faulting, ball-and-pillow structures and slumping evident (Ringrose 1989).

(12) Argyle Formation. Consists of the following Holocene members.

(13) Cill an Aonghais Member. Stratotype: at [NR 776618]. Organic freshwater lacustrine muds (Birks 1993). Radiocarbon ages range between 9690 ± 140 BP at the base, to $2420b \pm 80$ BP.

(14) Clashgour Member. Stratotype: Clashgour [NN 2443]. Dark brown peat with woody detritus locally concentrated in layers (Bridge *et al.* 1990). Commonly referred to as blanket peat, this is of the 'unconfined mire' type of Hulme (1980). Radiocarbon ages range between 9370 ± 70 BP at the base to 3260 ± 60 BP.

(15) Carradale Member. Stratotype: Carradale [NR 7940]. Consists of well-stratified fluvial sands and gravels with lenses of fine sands and silts containing organic detritus. Its surface is commonly stepped (Tipping *et al.* 1994). Radiocarbon ages range between 7580 ± 80 BP and 230 ± 50 BP.

(16) Dalness Member. Stratotype: Dalness [NN 192514]. Loose matrix-supported diamict with a dominantly sandy matrix probably a debris flow deposit. Individual beds are separated by palaeosols (Brazier *et al.* 1988) that are radiocarbon dated between 4480 ± 300 BP and 570 ± 50 BP

(17) Eas na Broige Member. Loose, poorly sorted, unstratified to well-stratified sand and gravel of an alluvial fan (Brazier *et al.* 1988). At least in part, it post-dates 550 ± 50 BP.

The Loch Lomond Area

(1) Clyde Valley Formation (Glasgow, note 1).

(2) Baillieston Member (Glasgow note 2).

(3) Wilderness Member (Glasgow note 5).

(4) Linwood Member (Glasgow note 11).

(5) Killearn Member. Stratotype: Killearn borehole [NS 51008467]. Reddish brown or orange, dense to dense, unfossiliferous, fine to medium-grained sand with silt and clay layers and thin beds of fine gravel or sand with gravel (Browne & McMillan 1989). It overlies the Linwood Member and underlies the Gartocharn and Blane members. Its origin is unclear but is probably fluvial to deltaiabout The lacustrine Gartness Silts of Rose (1981) are part of this member.

(6) Gartocharn Member. Stratotype: Mains of Kilmarnock borehole [NS 44838829]. Up to 5 m of brown to brownish-grey, compact, matrix-supported diamict commonly containing marine shell fragments. The matrix is sandy clay or silty clay and clasts include blocks of marine (shelly) clay derived from the Linwood Member. It overlies the Linwood and Killearn members, interdigitates with the Blane Member and is overlain by the Drumbeg Member. Interpreted as till (Rose 1981, 1989; Browne *et al.* 1983; Rose *et al.* 1988; Browne & McMillan 1989). A maximum radiocarbon age is given by marine shells: $11\,710 \pm 60$ BP and $11\,790 \pm 60$ BP.

(7) Croftamie Member. Stratotype: Pirniehall by Croftamie [NS 47278618]. Consists of up to 0.4 m of organic detritus conformably overlain by the Blane Member. It overlies the Linwood and Killearn members and interdigitates with the Gartocharn and Drumbeg Members. It is glaciolacustrine with a radiocarbon age of $10\,560 \pm 160$ BP.

(8) Blane Member. Stratotype: Killearn borehole [NS 51008467]. Consists of firm to stiff, unfossiliferous, rhythmically bedded (varved) clays and silts with fine sand lenses and thin beds of diamict. Disturbance and faulting of the bedding is common (Rose 1981; Rose *et al.* 1988; Browne & McMillan 1989).

(9) Drumbeg Member. Stratotype: Drumbeg sand and gravel pit [NS 484882]. Reddish brown or orange, fine-to medium-grained sand with silt layers or silt with sand and clay layers. Pebbly beds occur near the top as well as thin diamict lenses. Abundant marine shell fragments occur. It is locally faulted (Rose 1981; Browne & McMillan 1989) and interdigitates with the Gartocharn, Blane and Balloch members. It is interpreted as a glaciofluvial to glaciodeltaic deposit. A maximum radiocarbon age from marine shell fragments is $11\,700 \pm 170$ BP.

(10) Inverleven Member. Stratotype: Inverleven borehole [NS 39757509]. It consists of angular to subrounded boulders, cobbles, gravel and pebbles in a clayey sand matrix with frequent marine shells. There is a marked unconformity at the base where the formation rests on the Paisley and Linwood members. It is overlain by the Clyde Formation (Browne & McMillan 1989) and is considered to be an estuarine lag gravel. A minimum radiocarbon age is $10\,350 \pm 139$ BP (a further age on shell, that may be derived, is $10\,920 \pm 140$ BP).

(11) Balloch Member. Stratotype: Inverleven borehole [NS 39757509]. Three lithofacies have been described, in descending order: grey, clayey silt, silt, clay and sand; grey soft, thinly bedded clayey silt, silt and clay with many fine to medium-grained sand beds and isolated clasts with rare marine shell and plant remains; and grey soft to firm, clay and silt with many silt laminae and thin sandy silt beds, showing colour laminations, scattered clasts and rare marine shells (Browne & McMillan 1989). It rests conformably upon the Inverleven Member, is interstratified with the Drumbeg Member and overlain by the Erskine and Gourock members. Interpreted as pro-deltaic glaciomarine sediments.

(12) Buchanan Member. Stratotype: Mains of Kilmaronock borehole [NS 44838829]. Brown, brownish-grey and reddish-brown colour banded, soft to stiff, thinly bedded silty clay with many laminae of silt and in places sand and scattered isolated clasts. It is tightly folded and faulted and contains a marine microfauna and sparse macrofauna which may possibly be derived (Browne & Macmillan 1989). It overlies the Gartocharn Member and is overlain by the Kilmaronock. It is probably marine, deposited in an almost-landlocked Loch Lomond basin

(13) Kilmaronock Member. Stratotype: Mains of Kilmaronock borehole [NS 44838829]. Brown to brownish-grey, firm to stiff, thinly bedded silt with many clayey silt, silty clay and sand layers. Plant remains and dark organic-rich beds occur. A lacustrine deposit, it rests conformably on the Buchanan Member and is interstratified with the Erskine Member (Dickson *et al.* 1978; Stewart *et al.* 1984; Browne & McMillan 1989). Radiocarbon ages range between 9360 ± 170 BP and 640 ± 50 BP.

(14) Endrick Member. Stratotype: Mains of Kilmaronock borehole [NS 44838829]. Reddish brown, loose, fine- to medium-grained sand with some silt layers. The deposit contains abundant plant remains and some dark organic clay

Table 26. *Correlations between Loch Lomond, the Forth-Teith area, the Tay-Earn area, Aberdeen and East Strathmore and oxygen isotope stratigraphy*

δ¹⁸O	LOCH LOMOND	FORTH - TEITH	TAY - EARN	ABERDEEN-EAST STRATHMORE
1	**CLYDE VALLEY FORMATION** (1) Erskine Member (15) Endrick Member (14) Kilmaronock Member (13) Buchanan Member (12) Balloch Member (11)	**GRANGEMOUTH FORMATION** (12) Skinflats Member (17) Grangemouth Docks (16) Saltgreen Member (15) Claret Member (14) Flanders Moss Member (13)	**TAY FORMATION** (1) Hole of Clein Bed (9) Carey (8) Buddon (7) & Kingston Member (6) Friarton Member (5)	
		FORTH-TEITH FORMATION (1) Letham Member (11) Lecropt Member (10) Bothkennar Member (9)		**MILL OF FOREST FORMATION** (1) Lochton Member (6) Glen Dye Member (5) Banchory Member (4) Drumlithie Member (3) Ury Member (2)
2	Inverleven Member (10) Drumbeg Member (9) Blane Member (8) Croftamie Member (7) Gartochan Member (6) Killearn Member (5) Linwood Member (4) Wilderness Member (3)	Abbotsgrange Member (8) Kinneil Kerse Member (7) Loanhead Member (6) Roslin Member (5) Edgefield Member (4) Lockart Members (3) Park Burn Member (2)	Culfargie Member (4) Powgavie Member (3) Errol Member (2)	
3				
4				
5				
5e	Baillieston Member (2)			
6				
7				

bands. It is usually flat bedded but locally cross-bedding occurs and there is an overall coarsening upwards and is probably fluvial, but may in part be deltaic (Browne & McMillan 1989). It is transitional at its basal contact with the Kilmaronock Member but has a sharp contact where overlain by the Erskine Member.

(15) Erskine Member (Glasgow, note 13).

The Forth-Teith Area

(1) Forth-Teith Formation. Consists of the following members.

(2) Park Burn Member. Stratotype: stream sections by the Park Burn [NT 331668]. It consists of compact dark grey fissile matrix-supported diamict with local lenses of sand, gravelly sand and gravel (Kirby 1968, 1969a,b). A proportion of the clasts have been derived from the west. It rests on bedrock and is overlain by the Lockart and the Loanhead members. Referred to by Kirby (1968, 1969a) as a basal till, it is lodgement till, although glaciofluvial lenses may suggest a partial meltout origin.

(3) Lockart Member. Stratotype: stream sections [NT 240579]. Stiff, red-brown or grey, matrix-supported diamict (Kirby 1968, 1969a). Referred to as the Intermediate Till by Kirby (1968, 1969a), it contains a proportion of clasts derived from the south or south-west. It overlies the Park Burn Member and is overlain, locally with gradational contact, by the Edgefield Member. It is probably lodgement till, although Martin (1981) suggested that it may be meltout till.

(4) Edgefield Member. Stratotype: gravel pit [NT 292661]. Yellowish-brown, stratified sands and gravels with lenses and beds of sandy diamict and rare beds of laminated silty clays. Referred to as the Midlothian Sands and Gravels by McCall & Goodlet (1952) and the Middle Sands and Gravels by Mitchell & Mykura (1962). It overlies the Park Burn and the Lockhart members and is overlain unconformably by the Roslin Member. It consists of glaciofluvial deposits of ice-contact and pro-glacial environments.

(5) Roslin Member. Stratotype: gravel pit [NT 292661]. Reddish-brown, matrix-supported diamict. Referred to by Kirby (1968, 1969a) as Roslin Till; by McCall & Goodlet (1952) as the Roslin Upper Boulder Clay and by Mitchell & Mykura (1962) as the Southern Uplands Readvance Boulder Clay. It overlies the Edgefield Member. Kirby (1968, 1969a) interpreted it as lodgement till deposited by a readvance of ice from the northwest; Mitchell & Mykura considered that the readvance was from the southwest but Martin (1981) described it as a flow till.

(6) Loanhead Member. Stratotype: boreholes in the Grangemouth area. It consists of up to 20 m of brown, slightly micaceous, soft to firm, plastic silty clay with laminae and thin beds of pale and dark reddish brown clay, quartzose silt and fine-grained sand. Scattered angular clasts occur throughout and there is a limited marine micro- and macrofauna. Referred to as the Loanhead Beds by Brown et al. (1984) and interpreted as glaciomarine.

(7) Kinneil Kerse Member. Stratotype: Kinneil Kerse boreholes 2 and 4 [NS 963812]. Up to 13 m of grey, soft to firm, laminated clayey silt with thin bands of brown silty clay. Laminae and thin beds of quartzose silt and fine-grained sand, which may display ripple- and cross-lamination are common. Gravel-sized clasts occur sporadically throughout. Referred to as the Kinneil Kerse Beds by Browne et al. (1984). It rests conformably upon the Loanhead Member but has a greater diversity of marine faunal remains. Considered by Browne et

al. (1984) to be glaciomarine.

(8) Abbotsgrange Member. Stratotype: Grangemouth No. 8 borehole [NS 9582]. Some 35 m of black, grey or brownish-grey, well-bedded, micaceous, loose silts with many laminae and thin beds of fine-grained sand and soft to firm dark grey silty clay. The lower part of the sequence is particularly sandy and contains some clasts, suggesting an unconformity. Marine faunal remains occur throughout. Referred to as the Abbotsgrange Beds by Browne et al. (1984) and interpreted as marine as sea-level fell and climate ameliorated.

(9) Bothkennar Member. Stratotype: Bothkennar No. 3 Borehole [NS 91858465]. Up to 4 m of subangular to rounded, fine to coarse gravel, cobble and boulder-sized clasts in a variable matrix of loose to compact, clayey sandy silt with a sparse marine fauna rests with marked unconformity on earlier deposits (Browne et al. 1984; Paul et al. 1995). It was originally termed the Buried Gravel Layer by Sissons (1969), later interpreted by him (Sissons 1974) as the product of intense marine erosion associated with the 'Main Lateglacial Shore-line'.

(10) Lecropt Member. Stratotype: northern Carse of Stirling, [NS 7797]. A fluvial gravel, sandy gravel and pebbly sand that lies unconformably on the Abbotsgrange Member and is overlain by the Letham Member (Smith et al. 1978; Laxton & Ross 1983).

(11) Letham Member. Stratotype: boreholes near Letham [NS 8588]. It consists of a grey, micaceous silt and sand with a sparse marine fauna (Browne et al. 1984). It overlies the Bothkennar Member and is overlain by the Flanders Moss Member. It is referred to by Browne et al. (1984) as the Letham Beds and is equivalent to the Buried Beach deposits (Sissons 1966, 1969; Kemp 1976) which Sissons subdivided on altitudinal, morphological and stratigraphical criteria into the High Buried Beach, Main Buried Beach and Low Buried Beach. These are estuarine sediments deposited during falling sea level.

(12) Grangemouth Formation. Comprises the following Holocene members.

(13) Flanders Moss Member. Stratotype: East Flanders Moss [NS 6398]. Dark brown to black peat. It overlies the Letham Member and is interstratified with the Claret and Grangemouth Docks members – a consequence of relative sea-level rise and fall (Sissons 1966, 1972, 1983; Sissons & Brooks 1971; Sissons & Smith 1965; Robinson 1993). Radiocarbon ages range from: 9840 ± 70 BP at its base; 8270 ± 160 BP in contact with the Letham Member; and 7850 ± 60 near the base and 4120 ± 105 near the top of the Claret Member.

(14) Claret Member. Stratotype: Bothkennar HW3 Borehole [NS 92068585]. Black to dark grey soft, sulphide-rich, fossiliferous clayey silts and silty clays some of which are laminated (Browne et al. 1984; Paul et al. 1995). It commonly overlies the Flanders Moss Member with which there are gradational contacts. Part of the estuarine Carse deposits of the east coast of Scotland (Sissons 1966; Browne et al. 1984; Robinson 1993; Smith 1993). Radiocarbon ages on shells are range between: 7750 ± 130 BP and 3825 ± 130 BP.

(15) Saltgreen Member. Stratotype: Bothkennar HW3 Borehole [NS 92068585]; parastratotype: Grangemouth Docks Borehole 114 [NS 94668382]. Dark greyish-brown clayey silt probably lagoonal (Browne et al. 1984; Paul et al. 1995).

(16) Grangemouth Docks Member. Stratotype: Grangemouth Docks Borehole 114 [NS 94668382]. Brownish black or grey, soft to soft, micaceous, well laminated silty clays and clayey silts with many laminae and thin bands of fine-grained quartzose sand. It contains variable amounts of decaying vegetable matter as well as marine faunal remains. Interpreted as a tidal channel deposit. Radiocarbon ages on marine shells near its base are: 4025 ± 85 BP and 2945 ± 80 BP.

(17) Skinflats Member. Stratotype: Bothkennar HW3 Borehole [NS 92068585]. Dark grey, crudely bedded, clayey silt with lenses of marine shells probably an intertidal deposit. ^{14}C ages on marine shell near its base: 3045 ± 80 BP.

The Tay-Earn

(1) Tay Formation. Comprises the following members.

(2) Errol Member. Stratotype: Inchcoonans clay pit [NO 242233]; parastratotype: Gallowflats [NO 211202] clay pit. About 6 m of red to blue to yellowish-brown, laminated clays, sandy clays or silts with a sparse marine micro- and macrofauna. Pebbles occur scattered throughout the deposit (Davidson 1932; Peacock 1975; Paterson 1981). Paterson et al. (1981) named it the Errol Beds. It is interpreted as glaciomarine to marine and was deposited in an estuary during a period of falling sea level. Probably deposited during deglaciation of the Late Devensian ice-sheet between about 17 000 and 13 000 years BP (Gordon 1993).

(3) Powgavie Member. Stratotype: Powgavie boreholes [NO 29122532]. Dark brownish-grey, laminated clay with scattered clasts, the laminae consisting of couplets of pale silt or fine sand grading upwards into clay, with sparse marine micro-fauna and macrofauna. It was interpreted as an estuarine sediment by Paterson et al. (1981) who named it the Powgavie Clay. Base unseen but overlain conformably by the Culfargie Member.

(4) Culfargie Member. Stratotype: Culfargie borehole [NO 16751749]. A largely unfossiliferous sand with subordinate silt and gravel named the Culfargie Beds by Paterson et al. (1981). Its lower contact is gradational with the Errol Member and Powgavie Member and it is interpreted as deltaic or pro-deltaic deposited in an estuary during a period of falling sea level.

(5) Friarton Member. Stratotype: Friarton Bridge boreholes [NO 1322]. Sands and gravels occupying channels cut into the Errol and the Culfargie members and overlain by the Carey Member. It incorporates both the Earn Gravel and the Friarton Gravel of Paterson et al. (1981) and Armstrong et al. (1985) and is interpreted as fluvial.

(6) Kingston Member. Stratotype: Kingston borehole [NO 30072696]. Sand, with a sparse marine microfauna and macrofauna, occupying a channel cut into the Errol, Powgavie and Culfargie Members. Paterson et al. (1981) named it the Kingston Sand. It is interpreted as pro-deltaic in origin.

(7) Buddon Member. Stratotype: Buddon Ness area [NO 5432]. A compact, fine-grained sand with abundant shell fragments with pebbles and boulders towards base resting with marked unconformity on the Errol Member (Paterson 1981) and is interpreted as a littoral marine deposit.

(8) Carey Member. Type-area: sections beside River Earn [NO 1717], [NO 1917] and [NO 1818]. Sand and silt with thin beds of clay. Gradational contacts with the overlying Hole of Clein Member. Interpreted as estuarine deposits (Cullingford et al. 1980; Paterson et al. 1981; Armstrong et al. 1985) with a stepped surface morphology indicating intervals of stable sea-level.

(9) Hole of Clein Bed. Stratotype: Glencarse area [NO 2022]. Dark brown to black peat. Gradational lower contact with the Carey Member. It is interstratified, with gradational contacts, with the Carse of Gowrie Member. Partly equivalent to the Sub-Carse Peat of Paterson et al. (1981). The interstratification is a consequence of relative sea-level rise and fall as has been demonstrated by Cullingford et al. (1980), Morrison et al. (1981), Paterson et al. (19081) and Smith et al. (1985). ^{14}C ages range between: 9640 ± 140 BP and 6170 ± 90 BP.

Aberdeen and Eastern Strathmore

(1) Mill of Forest Formation. Stratotype: Carron Water river section [NO 86178545]. Red-brown, sandy diamict with lenses of clay-bound gravel and clasts predominantly of Devonian rocks. Interpreted as till (Synge 1956; Simpson 1948). Overlain conformably by the Ury and Drumlithie Members. A peat bed, known as the 'Burn of Benholm Peat' occurs as an erratic in the formation. Its palynology indicates an interstadial environment (Donner 1960, 1979). ^{14}C age: $> 42 000$ and $> 50 600$ BP.

(2) Ury Member. Stratotype: British Geological Survey borehole [NO 887878]. Red-brown laminated silt and clay with lenses of fine-grained sand interpreted as glaciolacustrine. Overlain by the Drumlithie Member.

(3) Drumlithie Member. Stratotype: Kaim of Clearymuir gravel pit [NO 79838149]. Red-brown sand and gravel, interbedded with sands and clays, with clasts predominantly of Devonian rocks. Interpreted as glaciofluvial (Synge 1956). It overlies conformably the Ury Member.

(5) Banchory Member. Stratotype: Banchory-Strachan area: Burn of Granney section [NO 60729198]. A gravelly and sandy diamict interpreted as till and overlain conformably by the Glen Dye and Lochton members.

(5) Glen Dye Member. Stratotype: sections on the Miller Burn [NO 635859]. Brown to olive grey, laminated silt and clay with fine-grained sand overlying conformably the Banchory Member. It is conformably overlain by the Lochton Member and is interpreted as glaciolacustrine.

(6) Lochton Member. Stratotype: Lochton gravel pit [NO 75419290]. Sand and gravel with subsidiary laminated sandy diamict and laminated silt. It rests conformably on the Banchory Member and is interpreted as a glaciofluvial deltaic sediment (Brown 1994).

Chapter 10

Ireland

A. M. McCABE

With contributions from P. Coxon

The Quaternary rocks of Ireland are dominated by glacial deposits mostly dating from the last glaciation or glacial cycle. The glaciation of Ireland occurred under optimum conditions of precipitation supply from the northeast Atlantic Ocean. The geomorphology of Ireland that consisted of a vast lowland and peripheral mountain blocks resulted in the development of a major ice-sheet over the central Irish lowlands while individual mountain centres nourished their own ice-caps. The lowland ice sheets dominated each glaciation and probably interacted dynamically with the more transient upland ice caps. During the maximum extent of the Pleistocene ice-sheets and with the notable exceptions of the highest Cork-Kerry, Wicklow and Donegal mountains all of Ireland was ice-covered. Glaciation was further enhanced by ice from Scotland and the Irish Sea Basin that crossed the Irish coastline on several occasions.

Interglacial events are known from 11 sites. A late Tertiary or Early Pleistocene lignite is known from Pollnahallia and one pre-Gortian deposit is known from Ballyline. The location of others is inferred in the extensively karstified surface of the central Plain. Gortian deposits represent a Middle Pleistocene temperate climate, as shown by biostratigraphical (pollen) evidence and an estimated (D-alle-L-Ile) age of *c.* 428–198 ka from the Cork Harbour sequence (Scourse *et al.* 1992)

Except for the Screen Hills and Shortalstown, deposits correlated with oxygen isotope sub-state 5e are apparently absent in Ireland. The Fenit site provides evidence for correlation with oxygen isotope sub-stages 5c and 5d (Kilfenora Formation).

Records of pre-Devensian glaciations are fragmentary and based on erratic distributions and diamicts obtained from drill or well cores. Much of Ireland, however, is covered by extensive Devensian. Early and Middle Devensian records are known from six sites. At Aghnadarragh important evidence for multiple Devensian events occurs. It is the only site that records both Early and Late Devensian glaciations separated by shallow water deltaic sequences with pollen indicating a Arctic vegetation. Except for Derryvree (31 ka), all the other sites lie beyond the range of radiocarbon dating.

Late Devensian deposits indicate a wide range of glacigenic environments. Many record deglaciation events. These are constrained by AMS radiocarbon ages between about 22 ka, in the south where ice advanced on to the continental shelf, and about 15 ka in the north. Recently a detailed picture of millennial scale variability has allowed correlation with other amphi-North Atlantic ice-sheets (McCabe 1996; McCabe & Clark 1998).

Younger Dryas cirque glaciation has been radiocarbon dated at one site. Periglacial activity commenced on deglaciation and persisted into the Younger Dryas. During the Holocene extensive peat formation occurred, especially in the Central Lowlands of Ireland. Along the coastline the late-glacial and Holocene marine transgression produced extensive deposits.

Western Irish Sea Basin

(1) Newtown Bed. Stratotype: Newtown, Co. Waterford [X 7006]. About 9 cm of contorted peat with a radiocarbon age of 38 ka BP beneath till (the Ballyvoyle Till of Watts 1959*b*). Pollen analysis indicates open pinewoods and the peat is correlated with part of the Kilbeg Bed (Watts 1959*b*). It overlies a silt bed that rests on a rock platform. It is representative of an interglacial possibly the Gn IIIb/Gn IV boundary Coxon (1993*b*).

(2) Ballykeerogue Bed. Stratotype: Ballykeerogue-More, Co. Wexford [S 742187]. A freshwater mud (base unknown) with pollen showing the *Alnus/Abies/Taxus* zone of the Gortian (Mitchell & Watts 1993), possibly Gortian pollen zones Gn II and IIIa (Coxon 1993*b*). It lies 30 km south of the end-moraines at Borris, and may have been disturbed by ice and is overlain by sand and gravel (*about* 3 m).

(3) Kilbeg Bed. Stratotype: borehole at Kilbeg, Co. Waterford [S 4802]. Organic lacustrine muds, diatomite and detrital peats on bedrock and overlain by till that occurs outside the South Irish End Moraine, the traditional limit of Late Devensian glaciation Watts (1959*b*). It is correlated with other Gortian sites in Ireland (Coxon 1993*b*).

(4) Shortalstown Formation. Stratotype: Shortalstown, Co. Wexford [T 303114]. About 4 m of ice-sheared estuarine sand and gravel within glaciotectonised diamict units. *Ulmus* pollen has been used to distinguish these Bed from the Gortian and they have been correlated with the Ipswichian and 'zone e' (Jessen & Milthers 1928) of the Eemian (Colhoun & Mitchell 1971). They are correlated with oxygen isotope sub-stage 5e.

(5) Meath Formation. Type area: coastal zone of Co. Meath [O 0675]. Its members show the changing ice-flow strengths and deglacial events along the coastal zone of east central Ireland (McCabe 1973). It lies on striated Carboniferous limestone or on Tertiary/Early Pleistocene pipe infills within the limestone. An offshore advance is represented by the **Drogheda Member** which is a basal till exposed above solution pipes in Tullyallen Quarry [O 0776] (Colhoun & McCabe 1973). Onshore ice-movements, from the Irish Sea Basin are represented by the **Ben Head Member** [O 175685]. The **Mell Member** [O 0776] (up to 40 m O.D.) consists largely of distal glaciomarine muds and sheared gravel overlying the Drogheda Member, and was deposited in an isostatically depressed sector (McCabe 1986). *Delectopecten greenlandicus* fossils *in situ* have AMS radiocarbon ages of 41,800 ± 1500 and 45 200 ± 2000 BP. The **Skerries Member** [O 222615] consists of a gravel overlying

Fig. 11. Localities in Ireland.

glaciomarine muds (McCabe *et al.* 1990). The **Boyne Member** [O 048755] consists of hummocky moraines, eskers, linear moraines, deltas and terraces, formed as the ice withdrew inland.

(6) Bannow Formation. Type area: Bannow, Co. Wexford [S 8307]. Coarse-grained diamicts with inland erratics from the

north (Synge 1964), disturbed by possible periglacial structures (Culleton 1978c).

(7) Louth Formation. Type area: margins of Dundalk Bay [J 1605]. It consists of ice-marginal and ice-contact glaciomarine sequences greater than 50 m thick that accumulated along the margins of an ice lobe centred on Dundalk Bay (McCabe *et al.*

Table 27. *Quaternary Correlations in Ireland and oxygen isotope stratigraphy*

δ18O	WESTERN IRISH SEA BASIN	NORTH & NORTHERN CENTRAL IRELAND	IRISH MIDLANDS	SOUTHWEST IRELAND	NORTHWEST & WESTERN IRELAND
1	LECALE FORMATION (23) BELLE LAKE FORMATION (22)	BANN (28) MAGILLIGAN (29) BALLYSCULLION (27) & SLIEVE GALLION (26) FORMATIONS	BOG OF ALLEN (14) LITTLETON (13) & FANE (12) FORMATIONS	SUIR (22) LITTLETON (21) & MILLSTREET (20) FORMATIONS	SHANNON (31) ATTYMON (32) MEANBOG (30) & DRUMSKELLAN (29) FORMATIONS
2	BALLYBETAGH (21) NAHANAGHAN (20) GREYSTONES (19) DUFFCARRICK (18) KILLINEY (17) KILLOUGH (15) KILLARD PT (16) ENNISKERRY (14) SCREEN HILLS (13) KILLAKEE (12) STILLORGAN (10) POYNTZ (11) WICKLOW (8) MOURNE (9) LOUTH (7) & BANNOW (6) FORMATIONS	FRUITFIELD (25) BOHILBREAGA (24) FIVEMILETOWN (23) FOYLE (21) & SPERRIN (22) MURNEE HILLS (20) BALLINDERRY (19) PORTBALLINTRAE (18) BALLYRISK (16) CAREY (17) CASTLEROE (15) ARMOY (13) GLENLOUGH (14) BALLYRUTHER (11) GELVIN (12) MAGUIRESBRIDGE (10) & GLENAVY (9) FORMATIONS	NOBBER (11) ARDEE (10) KENTSTOWN (9) GALTRIM (8) TULLAMORE (7) BALLYLANDERS (6) FEDAMORE (5) & BLESSINGTON (4) FORMATIONS	GALTY (18) COOMRÓOANIG (19) MUSKRY (16) FINGLAS (17) LEE (15) & BANTRY (14) BALLINSKELLIGS (13) BEGINISH (11) BEHY (12) BALLYBUNNION (10) KILCUMMIN (8) KILLUMNEY(9) COURTAPARTEEN (7) GLENTAUNATINAGH (6) BALLYVOYLE (5) SOUTH CORK (4) FORMATIONS	MALIN HEAD (27) GORTALECKA (28) ERRIGAL (26) BELDERG (24) MALIN BEG (25) TULLYWEE (22) BROCKHILL (23) GLENCROW (20) BURNFOOT (21) FALCARRAGH (19) CATHDERAL ROCKS (18) DRUMORE (16) LOUGH FIN (17) ALTAWINNY (14) CLEW BAY (15) MULLINASOLE(12) BUNCRANA (13) ACCORYMORE (10) FANORE (11) KNOCKFOLA (8) ALNAPETISTE (9) KILKEE (6) BARNA (7) & BALLYCASTLE (5) FORMATIONS
3		Hollybrook Bed (8) Derryvree Bed (7)		FEOHANAGH FORMATION (3)	ERRIS FORMATION (4)
4	MEATH FORMATION (5)	SISTRAKEEL FORMATION (6) Hollymount Bed (5) Aghnadarragh Bed (4) FERMANAGH FORMATION (3) BOVEVAGH FORMATION (2)		KILFENORA FORMATION (2)	
5					
5e	SHORTALSTOWN FORMATION (4)	Benburb Bed (1)	Baggotstown Bed (3) Kildromin Bed (2) BALLYLINE FORMATION (1)	CORK HARBOUR FORMATION (1)	
6	Kilbeg Bed (3) Ballykeerogue Bed (2) Newtown Bed (1)				Gort Bed (3) Derrynadivva Bed (2)
7 or 9					
Plio-Pleist					POLLNAHALLIA FORMATION (1)

1987). The **Dunany Member** [O 167915] is an ice-pushed morainal bank with interbeded muddy diamict and gravel (McCabe 1973). The **Rathcor Member** [O 180051] consists of ice-pushed diamict and gravel morainic ridges. The **Bush Member** [O 182071] consists of low angled, cross-bedded deltaic sand and gravel. The **Cooley Point Member** [O 217051] is a glaciomarine mud drape containing a low diversity marine microfauna dominated by *Elphidium clavatum* and *Roundstonia globulifera* overlain by outwash associated with the ice advance to the Rathcor Moraine that marks the limit of the last Drumlin event in eastern Ireland (McCabe & Haynes 1996). Monospecific samples of *Elphidium clavatum* are AMS ^{14}C dated to $15\,420 \pm 110$, $15\,790 \pm 110$ and $15\,820 \pm 140$ (McCabe unpublished). These glaciomarine muds show major deglaciation of the Irish Sea Basin before 16 ka and are overlain by deposits correlated with Heinrich Event 1 (McCabe 1996).

(8) Wicklow Formation. Type area: Wicklow Mountains [O 0714]. Tills, morainic sand and gravel, outwash and laminated facies deposited during local expansions and retrcats of mountain ice-caps. Originally five glacial events were identified by Farrington (1934, 1938, 1942, 1944, 1949, 1957, 1966), later accepted by Synge (1977) and Hoare (1975). Synge (1977) proposed a relationship between mountain and lowland ice-masses and Cohen (1979) outlined complex facies sequences that developed during and after the ice-maximum. Ice limits are poorly constrained and the morphological evidence may record the decay cycle of one major ice-advance (McCabe 1986).

(9) Mourne Formation. Type area: the Mourne Plain basin and slopes [J 3010]. It consists of up to 40 m of interbedded glacigenic and glaciomarine sequences (McCabe 1986). Its base is not exposed. The different lithofacies show the dissolution of confluent ice-masses to the lee of the mountains. The **Dunnaval Member** [J 271109] is a regionally extensive emergent beach facies along the coast of south County Down (McCabe *et al.* 1992). It is separated from underlying glaciomarine facies by a prominent wave-cut surface and is contemporaneous with the ice limit marked by the Cranfield Moraine. The **Ballymartin Member** [J 339160] is a coarse grained, compact to stratified diamict with multiple ice-sheet sources. The **Derryogue Member** [J 303125] occurs within channels eroded into the Ballymartin Member and consists of compact and laminated sand and mud. Monospecific samples of *Elphidium clavatum* from these muds have AMS radiocarbon ages of: $17\,160 \pm 130$, $17\,150 \pm 160$, $16\,005 \pm 140$ and $15\,105 \pm 130$. The **Cranfield Member** [J 273111] consists of ice-contact and subaqeous spreads of sands and gravels related to a major ice advance to the mouth of Carlingford Lough (Stephens *et al.* 1975; Stephens & McCabe 1977).

(10) Stillorgan Formation. Stratotype: Stillorgan, Co. Dublin [O 204275]. Tills related to ice-sheet movements from the Irish Sea Basin and the Irish Midlands (Culleton & Creighton 1979).

(11) Poyntz Pass Formation. Stratotype: Jerrettspass, Co.-Down [J O70340]. Largely conformable facies (18 m thick) exposed in a drumlin and retsing on bedrock. It includes all the facies associations associated with drumlin formation along the Poyntz Pass Tunnel Valley system in SE Ulster (Dardis & McCabe 1983; Dardis 1985*a*). The **Jerrettspass Member** consists of undeformed stratified drift and the **Down Member** consists of overlying diamict.

(12) Killakee Formation. Type area: Killakee, Co. Dublin [O 1222]. An ice-marginal fluvioglacial complex resting on bedrock at 380 m O.D. (Synge 1979*b*).

(13) Screen Hills Formation. Type area: Screen Hills [T 1434]. About 30 m of complex deltaic deposits that developed at the margin of rctreating Irish Sea ice (Thomas & Summers 1983; Eyles & McCabe 1989). Its base lies below present sea-level. The **Knocknasillogue Member** [T 155352] consists of compact and laminated muds with derived with *in situ* marine microfaunas (Huddart 1977; Thomas & Summers 1981, 1983). Haynes *et al.* (1995) argue that some of the microfaunal elements are *in situ* and have contemporary analogues in recently deglaciated Arctic areas (Hald *et al.* 1994). It extends south to Kilmore Quay (Mitchell 1960, 1972; Culleton 1978*a*, *b*). It is overlain by the **Blackwater Member** [T 138316] that consists of sands and gravels with derived marine molluscs (McMillan 1964) and erratics of peat containing *Carpinus* pollen (McCabe & Coxon 1993). The **Ballincash Member** [T 142320] is a stratified to compact coarse-grained diamict. Thomas & Summers (1983) suggested a glaciolacustrine setting but others suggest an ice contact glaciomarine setting (Eyles & McCabe 1989*a*; McCabe & O'Cofaigh, 1996).

(14) Enniskerry Formation. Type area: Enniskerry basin [O 2318]. It consists of ice-marginal and subglacial deposits deposited towards the margin of the Irish Sea glacier where it abutted against the rising ground of the Wicklow Mountains. It rests on bedrock. The **Curtlestown Member** [O 185169] consists largely of large-scale gravely foreset Bed overlain by openwork breccia. The **Old Fassaroe Member** [O 271175] consists of interbedded gravel, sand and diamict within cross-cutting channels and is associated with an efflux into a subglacial lake (McCabe & O'Cofaigh 1994). The **Ballyman Member** [O 217190] is a basal till sheared over the ice-contact proximal lake facies along the northern part of the basin. The facies covers an area of 6–7 km^2 and is up to 40 m thick. Farrington (1944) proposed that the Enniskerry Basin deposits were formed in a proglacial lake, but McCabe & O'Cofaigh (1994) suggested that the lake was part of a north–south subglacial meltwater system marginal to the last Irish Sea glacier.

(15) Killough Formation. Stratotype: Killough, Co. Down [J 5537]. Cryoturbated gravel and thick (4 m) beds of compact to laminated red marine clays up to *c.* 19 m O.D. (Morrison & Stephens 1965; Stephens, 1968). The marine clays form a thin but widespread facies along the coastal fringes of Co. Down and form a distinct drape on drumlin bedforms. At Rough Island in Strangford Lough, monospecific samples of *Elphidium clavatum* from the mud drape have AMS radiocarbon ages of $13\,140 \pm 95$.

(16) Killard Point Formation. Type area: margins of the drumlin fields of Co.Down between Killard Point and Ardglass [J 6043]. Mainly reworked glacigenic deposits within stacked channels deposited by mass-flow interbedded with red marine clay (Stephens 1963). It rests on ice-sculptured bedrock. Monospecific samples of *Elphidium clavatum* from the marine clay have AMS radiocarbon ages of: $14\,355 \pm 105$ and $14\,185 \pm 115$. It is interpreted as an ice-contact glaciomarine apron contemporaneous with drumlinisation inland (Stephens *et al.* 1975; McCabe *et al.* 1984). It is correlated with Heinrich Event 1.

(17) Killiney Formation. Stratotype: Killiney, Co. Dublin [O 2624]. Interbedded, multi-storey channel sequences found along the Killiney-Bray embayment. It consists of diamict, mud, gravel and sand deposited during the backfilling of a tunnel valley system showing evidence of minor ice-pushing (Eyles & McCabe 1989*b*). This has been traced offshore (Whittington 1977) into thick sequences of glaciomarine units within a large tunnel valley system (Eyles & McCabe 1989*b*). An earlier interpretation of this formation recognized eight tills deposited by ice advances and readvances (Hoare 1977).

(18) Duffcarrick Formation. Stratotype: Duffcarrick Rocks [T 211589]. Interbedded laminated glaciomarine mud and muddy diamict on ice-moulded bedrock. It forms a distal drape, from plume deposition and rafting, during rapid ice retreat northwards along the coastal belt (McCabe unpublished).

(19) Greystones Formation. Stratotype: Greystones [T 288144]. A stratigraphically complex morainal bank composed of interbedded muds, muddy diamict, sand, coarse-grained diamict and gravel (26 m) deposited from a major glacial efflux to the lee of Bray Head (McCabe & O'Cofaigh 1995). This glaciomarine apron marks a temporary re-equilibration or advance of the ice-sheet margin during rapid deglaciation of the Irish Sea Basin.

(20) Nahanagan Formation. Stratotype: Lough Nahanagan, Co. Wicklow [T 082992]. It consists of glacial deposits that cirque form moraines at *c.* 500 m O.D. A large composite outer moraine has not yet been dated, but smaller inner moraines contain ice-pushed clays which contain a late-glacial *Juniperus/Empetrum* floral assemblage, and ^{14}C ages of 11 500 and 11 600 BP (Colhoun & Synge 1980)

(21) Ballybetagh Formation. Stratotype: Ballybetagh Bog, Co. Dublin [O 2020]. Consists of a thick (5 m) late-glacial sequence of peats and muds (Jessen & Farrington 1938; Mitchell 1976; Watts 1977). AMS ^{14}C ages show that the *Rumex/Salix* zone (Watts 1977) spanned the period 12 600 to 12 400 BP (Cwynar & Watts 1989). The *Juniperus/Empetrum* zone started at 12 400 BP. The age of 10 600 BP for the start of the *Cruciferae* zone, that is transitional to the *Artemisia* zone, dates the climatic deterioration of the Younger Dryas (see also Craig 1978; Barnosky 1985). The *Juniperus/Empetrum* zone lasted from 12 400 to 11 900 BP and was the warmest phase of the late-glacial (Cwynar & Watts 1989). A shift to grassland at 11 900 BP signalled climatic deterioration. The sequence contains the remains of the Irish Elk (*Megaloceros giganteus*) which became extinct immediately before the Younger Dryas. The taphonomy and herd behaviour of *M. giganteus* is discussed by Barnosky (1985).

(22) Belle Lake Formation. Stratotype: at Belle Lake [S 661048]. Freshwater lake muds, peaty lake muds and wood peats of early Holocene age. It overlies late-glacial deposits with a ^{14}C age of $12\,235 \pm 26$. The upper part of the sequence is ^{14}C dated to 5490 ± 25 (Watts 1985).

(23) Lecale Formation. Type area: Lecale [J 4344]. It includes all Holocene marine deposits within estuaries, complex beach ridge and barrier systems (Singh 1970; Singh & Smith 1973; Carter 1983).

North & North Central Ireland

(1) Benburb Bed. Stratotype: Benburb, Co. Armagh [H 80985202]. Compressed peat and lake mud (1.3 m) overlain by a diamict (Boulter & Mitchell 1977; Gennard 1984). Pollen assemblage zones compare with those recognised from Gortian sites (Coxon 1993*b*). ^{14}C age of 46 ka BP. It overlies clay of unknown origin and age.

(2) Bovevagh Formation. Stratotype: Bovevagh Old Church, Co. Londonderry [C 668140]. About 7 m of light grey calcareous diamict with Chalk, flint, Precambrian, Carboniferous, Triassic rocks and balsalt erratics. It includes marine muds with bivalve shells, crustacea and foraminifera (Colhoun

1971). It is widespread on the sputh side of Lough Foyle up to 60 m O.D. Colhoun (1971) considered it to have been transported by Scottish ice, but the geometry of the units suggests that they are *in situ* (McCabe, unpublished). D-aIle/L-Ile ratios are inconclusive, but may indicate an Early Devensian age. A ^{14}C age of 45 262 [SSR 4781] was obtained from whole valves of *Turritella communis*.

(3) Fermanagh Formation. Stratotype at Derryvree, Co. Fermanagh [H 361390]. Basal till, with erratics from the Tyrone igneous complex that indicate ice flowing southwards from Co.Tyrone across southern Ulster. No ice limits for this glaciation have been identified. It is overlain by the Deryvree Formation at the type-site (Colhoun *et al.* 1972). Till units in similar stratigraphical positions are overlain by freshwater peat at Aghnadarragh (47 350 BP – SSR2948) and Hollymount (41 500 BP – BIRM 309). At Aghnadarragh the lower till passes upwards into mud and laminated sand overlain by diamict formed by mass flow. The diamict contains the molar teeth of mammoth. The mammouth tooth enamel have uranium-series ages of between 65 and 95 ka BP (Lister *et al.* in press). The stratigraphical relationships between the till, muds and overlying debris flow units suggest that the latter accumulated in shallow water immediately after deglaciation. Doughty (*pers. comm.*) has identified a sparse flora of northern aspect from the horizon in which the mammoth teeth were found. Together, the lithostratigraphy, biostratigraphy and geochronology suggest major glaciation during the Early Midlandian (oxygen isotope stage 4 or oxygen isotope sub-stage 5d). The base of the lower till at Derryvree is not exposed and is correlated with the basal till at Aghnadarragh that rests on Oligocene lignite.

(4) Aghnadarragh Bed. Stratotype at Aghnadarragh, Co. Antrim [J 735127]. It consists of compressed sheets of disseminated peaty material and rolled wood within a shallow water deltaic facies between two till units of regional extent. The woody detritus was deposited in a shallow water to deltaic environment along the margin of the Lough Neagh basin. ^{14}C ages on the peat are 48.1 ka BP (SSR-2949) and 47.3 ka BP (SSR-2948). Insect remains, pollen and macroscopic fossils suggest an environment of *Betula-Pinus-Picea* woodland, with adjacent areas of swamp and patchy vegetation. Carabidae fossils that are presently found in south Fennoscandia also occur (McCabe *et al.* 1987). The peaty mats are overlain by stratified deltaic deposits and the Glenavy Formation (8). The base of the Aghnadarragh Bed is visible and lies, conformably, on stratified deglacial deposits of the Fermanagh Formation (3). Sedimnetological evidence suggests that the Fermanagh and Aghnadarragh Formations are largely conformable (McCabe *et al.* 1987). The palaeobotanical and geochronological data, together with regional stratigraphy, suggest that the Aghnadarragh event represents climatic amelioration correlated with oxygen isotope sub-stage 5.

(5) Hollymount Bed. Stratotype: Hollymount, Co. Fermanagh [H 356403]. Consists of freshwater mud underlying drumlinised till. Their base overlies a till facies of the Fermanagh Formation. Organic detritus from the mud have a ^{14}C age of 41.5 ka BP (McCabe *et al.* 1978). The palaeobotany and coleopteran assemblage suggest a local environment that was sparsely occupied by herbs of northern aspect. Detrital mud from a similar stratigraphical position at Aghnadarragh gave a ^{14}C age of 46.2 ka BP (SSR-2500). Redeposited organic muds (^{14}C: 32.4 ka BP–SSR-2065) in a similar stratigraphical position have been described at Greenagho, near Belcoo, Co. Fermanagh (Dardis *et al.* 1985). In all three cases the lower

diamict (Fermanagh Formation) is associated with ice flow
from a major centre in north central Ireland and the upper
diamict (Maguiresbridge Formation) is the main drumlin
forming till in the Erne Basin.

(6) Sistrakeel Formation. Stratotype at Sistrakeel, Co. Londonderry [C 627213]. It consists of glaciomarine Bed
(**Ballykelly Member**) overlain by a basal till (**Thorney Hill
Member**) associated with a SW expansion of ice from western
Scotland into the Lough Foyle lowlands. The **Ballykelly
Member** (5 m thick) consists of stacked Bed of stratified
diamict, amalgamated units of cobble gravel, and a (2 m) mud
unit. The mud contains well-preserved marine molluscs with
[14]C ages of 46 785 BP (SRR-4779a), 55 100 BP (SRR-4779b)
and 51 500BP (SRR-4780). The mud contains a well-preserved
microfauna dominated by *Elphidium exclavatum* (90%) with
no evidence of post-mortem sorting. Ostracod species range
from high boreal to low Arctiabout The microfaunas
correspond with a quiet water glaciomarine biocoenosis. D-
aIle/L-Ile ratios on *Arctica islandica* of 0.09 ± 0.01 (n = 42)
may be Middle Devensian in age (Bowen & McCabe
unpublished).

(7) Derryvree Bed. Stratotype: Deryvree, Co. Fermanagh [H
361390]. It consists of organic silts, with ^{14}C age of
$30\,500 \pm {}^{1170}/_{1030}$ BP (Colhoun *et al.* 1972), that accumulated
in freshwater basins. The Bed overlie till of the Fermanagh
Formation, and are overlain by the Maguiresbridge Formation. The peaty detritus is *in situ* and dominated by mosses and
herbs that, together with the remains of coleoptera, indicates a
cold climate of northern aspect. The underlying till (Fermanagh Formation) also occurs in a similar stratigraphical
position at Hollymount and Aghnadarragh and could be
Early Midlandian/Devensian (McCabe 1982).

(8) Hollybrook Bed. Stratotype: Hollybrook, Co. Fermanagh
[H 3733]. A breccia containing erratics on the lee-side of a
large rock drumlin. The base rests on bedrock and is overlain
by till of the Maguiresbridge Formation that forms drumlins.
It is interpreted as a breccia formed in a subglacial cavity prior
to the drumlinisation by the overlying till sheet (McCabe
1969b). It may, however, pre-date glaciation.

(9) Glenavy Formation. Stratotype: Aghnadarragh, Co. Antrim
[J 735127]. A regional till formation on the eastern side of the
Lough Neagh basin forming flat non-drumlinised areas
(McCabe *et al.* 1987). Its base overlies shallow-water sand
that contains a thin bed of detrital peat of arctic aspect ([14]C:
46 620 – SSR 2500). The ice responsible for this till moved NW
across the Lough Neagh Basin and is associated with widespread deformation of Oligocene lignite Bed along the eastern
margin of the Lough Neagh basin.

(10) Maguiresbridge Formation. Stratotype: Derryvree, Co.
Fermanagh [H 3438]. Subglacial till (10 m) within the drumlins
of south Ulster (McCabe 1969a, 1993; Dardis 1985c). Its base
rests on arctic peats dated to 30.5 ka BP. It also includes a
variety of stratified sequences within drumlins that formed
during drumlinisation (Dardis & McCabe 1977).

(11) Ballyruther Formation. Stratotype: Ballyruther, Co.
Antrim [D 358094]. A till with its base overlying sand and
gravel deposited on the flanks of major landslips in east
Antrim. The gravel contains a derived assemblage of molluscs
(Praeger 1895) and igneous erratics of northern provenance.

(12) Gelvin Formation. Stratotype: Ballycallion, Co. Londonderry [C 749120]. Basalt-rich till in the upper Dungiven basin.
It overlies finer-grained diamict, with marine shell fragments,
that is related to an earlier onshore ice movement (Colhoun
1971).

(13) Armoy Formation. Type area: Ballymoney-Ballycastle, Co.
Antrim [C 9728]. A well-defined ridge system of silt, sand and
gravel from Ballymoney northeastwards to Armoy and
Drumawillin (Charlesworth 1939). Its base is not exposed. It
was originally considered to mark the northern limit of
drumlins in County Antrim (Dwerryhouse 1923; Charlesworth
1939; Hill & Prior 1968; Creighton 1974; Stephens *et al.* 1975)
and to mark the landwards limit of a 'late' incursion by ice
from Scotland (Synge 1978). Shaw & Carter (1980) demonstrated that it represented deposition in ponded water,
followed by extensive glaciotectonic deformation.

(14) Glenlough Formation. Stratotype: Glenlough, Co. Antrim
[D 995254]. Local diamict and stratified Bed forming a
carapace on a rock drumlin. Striations and erosional-forms
show that the till was deposited by northward ice-flow from
the Lough Neagh basin across north County Antrim
(McCabe, unpublished). The base overlies basaltic bedrock.

(15) Castleroe Formation. Stratotype: Castleroe, Co. Londonderry [C 857298]. Shallow-water gravel, sand and mud (10 m
thick) deposited by northward flowing meltwater along the
Bann Valley and deformed into low mounds and sag basins
during melting of buried ice. (McCabe unpublished). The base
of the Formation is not exposed.

(16) Ballyrisk Formation. Stratotype: Ballyrisk, Co. Londonderry [C 712248]. A fining upwards sequence (10 m) of sand
and mud deformed and overlain by a diamict sequence. It
forms the basal unit associated with a late surge of ice from
Scotland into the northern part of the Roe Valley. The
associated ice limit is marked by morainic mounds around
Moys and it created an extensive body of ponded water in the
Dungiven depression recorded by high level deltas farther
south in the Owenbeg and Faughan valleys (McCabe
unpublished).

(17) Carey Formation. Stratotype: Drumadoon, Co. Antrim [D
174398]. A deltaic sequence of large-scale gravel foreset Bed
overlying debris flow units re-sedimented from a glacial efflux
(McCabe & Eyles 1988). Sedimentation was directed northwards, along the Carey Valley, from a major ice efflux along
the valley axis. Delta levels show deposition in ponded water
up to 100 m O.D., that was controlled by a high relative sea-
level. Dwerryhouse (1923) and Charlesworth (1939) considered
that the delta was related to water ponded by a Scottish ice-
sheet. Stephens *et al.* (1975) and Synge (1978) related diamict
facies variation to composite ice advances.

(18) Portballintrae Formation. Stratotype: Portballintrae, Co.
Antrim [C 923423]. Shallow-water, wave-influenced rhythmically bedded sand and mud. Its base truncates and overlies
resedimented diamict. It is overlain by near-shore Holocene
gravels (McCabe *et al.* 1994). The muds and sands contain a
marine microfauna of low diversity that is interpreted as
having accumulated shortly after ice withdrawal from the
coast of north Antrim.

(19) Ballinderry Formation. Type area: Ballinderry Valley, Co.
Tyrone [H 6780]. Interbedded glaciolacustrine and efflux
sequences deposited during easterly ice-wastage towards the
Lough Neagh depression (Dardis 1985a, c). The base overlies
till. The cross-valley 'moraine' complex borders the drumlin
fields west of Lough Neagh and cover an area of 600 km^2
(Dardis 1985b, c). The genesis and environmental significance
of the ridges was discussed by Charlesworth (1924, 1939),
Gregory (1925), Synge & Stephens (1960), Colhoun (1972) and
Dardis (1985a, c).

(20) Murnee Hills Formation. Type area: Murnie Hills, Co.
Londonderry [C 7050]. High level deltaic sand and gravel

deltas of lakes along the northern margins of the Sperrin Mountains and Dungiven depression (McCabe unpublished). Base not exposed.

(21) Foyle Formation. Type area: Foyle Valley, Co. Londonderry [C 4619]. Deposits forming a succession of morainic ridges and fluvioglacial terraces bordering the Foyle Valley associated with ice-retreat southwards (Colhoun 1970). The base overlies bedrock and drumlin tills.

(22) Sperrin Formation. Type area: Sperrin Mountains [H 4985]. Fluvioglacial deposits associated with ice-wastage in the valleys of the main Sperrin Mountains (Colhoun 1970, 1972). The base generally overlies till.

(23) Fivemiletown Formation. Type area: Clogher Valley, Co. Tyrone [H 4648]. Sand and gravel of a well-defined esker system parallel to the axis of the valley. The base of the formation is unexposed. It represents part of the ice-sheet palaeohydrology as ice wasted from the Erne basin north-eastwards towards the previous centres of ice-dispersal in County Tyrone (McCabe 1985).

(24) Bohilbreaga Formation. Stratotype: Bohilbreaga, Co. Londonderry [C 755003]. A wide-range of talus deposits on bedrock of periglacial origin (Colhoun 1971b).

(25) Fruitfield Formation. Stratotype: Fruitfield, near Limavady, Co. Londonderry [C 6725]. It includes all of the raised late-glacial rebound shoreline deposits and deltas of northeast Ireland. At Fruitfield, cross-bedded deltaic gravels up to 26 m O.D. are modified by ice-wedge pseudomorphs (McCabe unpublished).

(26) Slieve Gallion Formation. Type area: Slieve Gallion, Co. Tyrone [H 8188]. Holocene mountain reedswamp and blanket peats (e.g. Pilcher 1973).

(27) Ballyscullion Formation. Type area: Ballyscullion, Co. Tyrone [H 9696]. Raised bog complexes, including fen-peat, wood-fen peat, open water mud and sphagnum peat. Mitchell (1986) suggested that it started to form c. 7000 BP (Edwards 1985).

(28) Bann Formation. Type area: Bann Valley, Co. Londonderry [C 8035]. Holocene aeolian, fluvial, shallow lacustrine and peat sequences along flood plains and in coastal zones (Carter 1988; Carter & Wilson 1993).

(29) Magilligan Formation. Type area: Magilligan Point, Co. Londonderry [C 6835]. Holocene coastal deposits: for example, the Lough Foyle estuarine clays (McMillan 1957). See also: Carter (1980, 1982, 1983, 1989); Carter & Orford (1980, 1984), and Carter et al. (1989). In its type area it overlies till (McMillan 1957).

The Irish Midlands

(1) Ballyline Formation. Stratotype: Ballyline, Co. Kilkenny [S 391467]. Laminated clays (25 m) infilling a limestone solution feature with their base resting on bedrock (Coxon & Flegg 1985). The pollen shows interglacial vegetation that differs from that characteristic of the Gortian; it cannot be correlated with other interglacial deposits (Coxon 1993b).

(2) Kildromin Bed. Stratotype: Kildromin, Co. Limerick [R 7141]. Freshwater interglacial organic sediments from a core (Watts 1967). Pollen analysis has identified Gortian pollen zones Gn I, Gn II and Gn IIIa (Coxon 1993b). Their base rests on a stony clay with non-local clasts.

(3) Baggotstown Bed. Stratotype: Baggotstown, Co. Limerick [R 6635]. The log of this well-hole was reconstructed from 'spoil' and requires re-investigation (Coxon 1993b). The deposits include organic sediments, including algal gyttja, shell marl, and coarser detrital organic material: Gortian pollen zones Gn I-g, Gn I, Gn II, Gn IIIa, Gn IIIb and Gn IV were recognised (Watts 1964; Coxon 1993b). The base lies on a stony deposit that may be glacial in origin (Watts 1964). They are overlain by 5 m of diamict probably till (Watts 1964).

(4) Blessington Formation. Type area: Blessington basin, Co. Wicklow [N 9815]. A large ice-contact deltaic systems deposited in water ponded between lowland ice-margins and rising ground to the east (Farrington 1957; Farrington & Mitchell 1973; Synge 1978, 1979b; Cohen 1979). It has been regarded as part of the terminal morainic accumulations (Synge 1979a) of the 'South Irish End Moraine' (Charlesworth 1928).

(5) Fedamore Formation. Type area: Fedamore, Co. Limerick [R 5944]. Deposits of moranic ridges marking the outer limit of a drumlin field (Synge 1966, 1973).

(6) Ballylanders Formation. Stratotype: Ballylanders, Co Limerick [R 763245]. Deposits of an end-moraine complex from ice originating in the central lowlands (Synge 1966). It overlies bedrock and consists largely of fluvioglacial sediment. It forms part of the South Irish End Moraine (Charlesworth 1928).

(7) Tullamore Formation. Type area: around Tullamore, Co. Offaly [N 3524]. Subglacial and proglacial sand and gravels of a west to east system of eskers in central Ireland (Farrington & Synge 1970; McCabe 1985; Delaney 1995).

(8) Galtrim Formation. Stratotype: Galtrim, Co. Meath [N 860520]. Sediments of NW to SE subglacial eskers and ice-marginal efflux delta fans associated with a halt in the north-westward recession of the ice in County Meath (Synge 1950). Their base rests on till.

(9) Kentstown Formation. Stratotype: Kentstown, Co. Meath [N 972650]. Basal till rich in limestone, overlying striated bedrock, from midland ice flow into the Irish Sea basin. This unit is associated with low streamlined topographic features.

(10) Ardee Formation. Type area: Ardee, Co. Louth [N 9690]. Gravel and sand ridges in front of the drumlin fields of counties Louth and Cavan. The ridge complexes are traced south-westwards from Ardee, through Kells, to Mullingar, and were named the 'Drumlin Readvance' by Synge (1969). It overlies limestone-rich till.

(11) Nobber Formation. Type area: Nobber, Co. Louth [N 829869]. Limestone-rich till overlying striated limestone that indicates south-easterly ice-flow and the process of drumlinisation (McCabe 1993).

(12) Fane Formation. Type area: Fane Valley, Co. Louth [J 0101]. Holocene river alluvium overlying fluvioglacial gravel.

(13) Littleton Formation. Stratotype: Littleton Bog, Co. Tipperary [S 2257]. Mud and peat of late-glacial and Holocene age, up to the 18th century AD (Mitchell 1965b). The base is placed at a depth of 750 cm in a 1954 boring (Mitchell 1965b). This is the stratotype for the Littletonian (Holocene) in Ireland (Mitchell et al. 1973).

(14) Bog of Allen Formation. Type area: Bog of Allen, Co. Kildare [N 7527]. Raised bogs in the Irish lowlands (Mitchell 1979, 1986) overlying till and fluvioglacial deposits.

Southwest Ireland

(1) Cork Harbour Formation. Stratotype: Cork Harbour, Co. Cork [W 680718]. Estuarine sediments (c. 15 m), cored in Cork Harbour, containing foraminifera, ostracoda and diatoms within organic silty clays (Scourse et al. 1992). The base rests on pebbly gravel and is probably erosional. The sequence is overlain by 17m of gravel. Pollen analysis indicates correlation with the Gn II, IIIa and IIIb zones of the Gortian. D-aIle/L-Ile ratios on *Ammonia batavus* suggests correlation with the Hoxnian of England.

(2) Kilfenora Formation. Stratotype: Kilfenora, Co. Kerry, between Spa and Fenit [Q 765149]. Lagoonal organic deposits, including peat, within a raised beach lithofacies that rests on a wave-cut platform (Mitchell 1970). Uranium-series ages between 114 000 and 123 000 BP indicate correlation with oxygen isotope stage 5 (Heijnis *et al.* 1993). Pollen evidence suggest that the organic deposits accumulated during oxygen isotope sub-stages 5d or the beginning of sub-stage 5c (Coxon 1993*b*).

(3) Feohanagh Formation. Stratotype: Feohanagh, Co. Kerry [Q 380090]. Diamicts interbedded with sand, gravel, clay, and breccia. Its base overlies beach gravel. It has been proposed that the sequence represents multiple glaciation separated by 'pollen sands' of interstadial aspect (Lewis 1974, 1977).

(4) South Cork Formation. Type area: south Cork, Co. Cork [W 4338]. It is subdivided into six members that show glacial, shallow water and beach sedimentation related to fluctuating relative sea-levels at about the maximum or during a retreat stage of the Late Devensian glaciation (O'Cofaigh unpublished). Its base overlies glacially sculptured bedrock. The **Broadstrand Member** [W 521412] consists of glaciotectonically thrust and deformed diamict overlying shallow water marine sand and gravel on a glaciated shore platform. The diamict is are part of a large apron of sediment formed as the ice withdrew north from the Celtic Sea and re-equilibrated on coastal headlands. The **Simon's Cove Member** [W 429381] consists of stacked Bed of gravel and diamict deposited from a subglacial jet efflux. The **Ballinglanna Member** [W 433381] consists of coarse-grained paraglacial breccia. The **Ballycroneen Member** [W 928616] is the plume rainout (D-aIle/L-Ile ratios of marine shell fragments from Ballycotton Bay (Bowen 1991*a*) indicate a Late Devensian age). The **Howe's Strand Member** [W 562428] consists of hummocky and swaley cross-bedded sands. The **Courtmacsherry Member** [W 562428] consists of beach gravels resting on a platform furrowed by subglacial meltwater erosion. The deposits are interbedded and form part of a submergent glaciomarine system deposited as ice re-equilibrated in this coastal zone (McCabe & O'Cofaigh 1996).

Earlier, traditional, interpretations of the members of the South Cork Formation recognised the Courtmacsherry Member as a raised beach and the Howe's Strand Member as associated blown sands. Wright & Muff (1904) proposed the beach accumulated in a cold, glacial, sea; Mitchell (1960) propose a Gortian interglacial age; and Bowen (1973*b*) proposed an Ipswichian age. The Ballinglanna Member was widely regarded as a periglacial unit deposited during the 'earlier cold stage' (Farrington 1954, 1966; Mitchell 1960), or Early Midlandian (Bowen 1973*b*). The Ballycroneen Member was interpreted as an Irish Sea till of 'Munsterian' age (Farrington 1954, 1966; Mitchell 1960, 1972), or Late Midlandian age (Bowen 1973*b*).

(5) Ballyvoyle Formation. Stratotype: Ballyvoyle, Co. Waterford [X 3494]. A redeposited breccia, diamict and coarse-grained gravel on coastal slopes that represent both ice-marginal and paraglacial sedimentation events. Its base overlies shattered bedrock. It was formerly interpreted as till from inland ice (Wright & Muff 1904; Watts 1959*b*), and correlations with till units elsewhere have been made: e.g. with Newtown, Co. Waterford (Watts 1964; Synge 1981).

(6) Glentaunatinagh Formation. Stratotype: Glenaunatinagh, Co. Waterford [S 018091]. Local cryoturbated diamict with silicified limestone erratics at *c.* 570 m in the Knockmealdown Mountains (Mitchell 1992*b*). Its base overlies the Devonian. The erratics suggest ice from the Irish midlands was moving southwards, although Farrington (1947) and Lewis (1976) considered that the summits of the Knockmealdowns above 365 m were unglaciated.

(7) Courtaparteen Formation. Stratotype: Courtaparteen, Co. Cork [W 633469]. Compact diamict, deposited by ice moving east from County Cork and County Kerry (Farrington 1966), overlying breccias and sands.

(8) Kilcummin Formation. Type area: Kilcummin, Co. Kerry [V 992950]. Deposits of morainic ridges and fluvioglacial spreads formed near the margins of a large northwards flowing piedmont glacier north of MacGillycuddy's Reeks (Warren 1979).

(9) Killumney Formation. Type area: Killumney, Co. Cork [W 5369]. Deposits of a major moraine and glaciofluvial outwash terraces (Farrington 1954, 1959) associated with local ice-cap expansion from the Cork-Kerry Mountains. It overlies till and may represent a retreat position from an ice limit farther east or a withdrawal of ice from the continental shelf.

(10) Ballybunnion Formation. Stratotype: Ballybunnion, Co.-Kerry [Q 860417]. Diamict located to the south of the Shannon, that is overlain unconformably by gravel that is overlain by periglacial slope deposits (Warren 1985). Its base has not been defined (Warren 1985).

(11) Beginish Formation. Stratotype: Beginish Island, Co. Kerry [V 420788]. Diamict that overlies a tectonically disturbed beach deposit. Mitchell (1992*a, b*) inferred two phases of ice-sheet movement.

(12) Behy Formation. Type area: Behy Valley, Co. Kerry [V 6586]. Sediments of morainic landforms deposited by valley glaciation (Lewis 1967). It overlies till and bedrock.

(13) Ballinskelligs Formation. Type area: Ballinskelligs Bay, Co. Kerry [V 4565]. Deposits of complex glaciotectonically disturbed sequences and ridge moraines overlying till in south Iveragh (Bryant 1968; 1974; Lewis 1977). Bryant (1968) proposed that involutions are contemporaneous with the local (Cummeragh) glaciation,

(14) Bantry Formation. Type area: Bantry Bay, Co. Cork [V 9849]. Deposits exposed in drumlins, overlying bedrock, that record rapid ice-flow from a major centre of ice dispersal (Farrington 1936). Lewis (1977) proposed ice-flow from SW to NE.

(15) Lee Formation. Type area: Lee and Blackwater Valleys, Co. Cork [X 0571]. Glaciofluvial outwash deposits and deltas associated with westerly retreat phases of a major glaciation centred on the Cork/Kerry Mountains (Farrington 1959). It overlies till and bedrock.

(16) Muskry Formation. Stratotype: Lough Muskry, Co. Tipperary [R 919250]. Local glacial deposits of valley moraines and cirque moraines in the Galtee Mountains (Synge 1978).

(17) Finglas River Formation. Stratotype: Finglas River, Co. Kerry [Q 701060]. A late-glacial lithostratigraphical sequence of organic muds (^{14}C: 11 950 BP) that overlie gravels, with cryoturbations, and are overlain by river gravel (Bryant 1974).

(18) Galty Formation. Type area: Galty Mountains, Counties Limerick & Tipperary [R 940205]. Periglacial slope deposits and resedimented paraglacial deposits on the northern and southern flanks of the Galty Mountains.

(19) Coomrooanig Formation. Type area: Cummerash, Co. Kerry [V 5764]. Deposits of well-defined local cirque moraines

(Bryant 1968). It overlies till and bedrock.

(20) Millstreet Bed. Stratotype: Millstreet, Co. Cork [W 273973]. Deposits representing former pingos and their infills. Deposition in the former pingo hollows commenced at *c*. 10 000 BP (Coxon 1986). They overlie till and solifluction deposits.

(21) Littleton Formation (*Irish Midlands, note 13*).

(22) Suir Formation. Type area: Suir Valley, Co. Waterford [S 4520]. Holocene river alluvium throughout the region.

Northwest and Western Ireland

(1) Pollnahallia Formation. Stratotype: Pollnahallia, Co. Galway [M 342470]. Organic deposits, on bedrock at the bottom of a limestone gorge. They contain palynomorphs indicative of a Late Tertiary or Early Pleistocene age, with some elements similar to those found in the Reuverian (Pliocene) of the Netherlands (Coxon & Flegg 1987; Coxon & Coxon in press). They are overlain by sand (8 m) and undated glacigenic deposits.

(2) Derrynadivva Bed. Stratotype: Derrynadivva, Co. Mayo [M 131954]. Organic (interglacial) sequence overlying sand and gravel. Pollen analysis identified pollen zones Gn II, Gn IIIa, Gn IIIb and Gn IV of the Gortian (Coxon & Hannon 1991; Coxon *et al*. 1994). They are overlain by diamict associated with drumlins along the Glydagh river.

(3) Gort Bed. Stratotype: Boleyneendorrish River, Co. Galway [M 5306]. Organic (interglacial) bed with a base at 670 cm depth, overlying a 'fine sandy clay' that records cold climatic conditions, and a solifluction gravel (Jessen *et al*. 1959). Pollen zones recognised are: Gn I, Gn II, Gn IIIa, Gn IIIb and Gn IV (Coxon 1993*b*). The pollen assemblage zones are similar to eleven other localities in Ireland (Coxon 1993*b*). This is the stratotype for the Gortian in Ireland (Mitchell *et al*. 1973). The Gort Bed is overlain by two lithologically distinct diamicts.

(4) Erris Formation. Type area: West County Mayo [F 7114]. A discontinuous till sheet in northwest Mayo, overlying bedrock, derived by ice movement from the south and south-east (Synge 1968).

(5) Ballycastle Formation. Type area: Ballycastle [G 0937] to Mulrany [L 8398], Co. Mayo). A till unit of regional extent with exposures in discontinuous mounds of sand aand gravel that have been traced from Ballycastle in the north, to Mulrany in the south of County Mayo. The fluvioglacial accumulations are thought to mark a western margin to ice from the Irish Midlands (Synge 1968, 1969). No drumlins are found west of this limit. Its base overlies the Erris Formation at Kinrovar, Co. Mayo [S 7114].

(6) Kilkee Formation. Stratotype: Kilkee, Co. Clare [Q 882605]. Till overlying striated bedrock and associated with offshore ice movement. Drumlins occur to the north of an associated morainic limit (Synge 1969).

(7) Barna Formation. Stratotype: Barna strand, Co. Galway [M 235227]. Drumlin deposits; base is unexposed. It indicates ice advance and till deposition over undeformed proglacial subaqeous sediments of probable glaciomarine origin. It is found at the head and northern margins of Galway Bay, where ice moved westwards onto the continental shelf (McCabe & Dardis 1989*a*, *b*).

(8) Knockfola Formation. Stratotype: Knockfola, Co. Donegal [B 815328]. Deposits of a prominent lateral moraine flanking Bloody Foreland, composed of large granite boulder gravel, and overlying bedrock. It marks a lateral margin of ice that extended on to the continental shelf (Stephens & Synge 1965).

(9) Altnapetiste Formation. Stratotype: Altnapetiste, Co. Donegal [B 830340]. Diamict sequence (12 m) underlain by stratified sand and diamict on a raised marine platform with weathered corestones. It is is overlain by boulder and cobble gravel of the Altawinny Formation and forms a large terrace feature on the north side of the Bloody Foreland. It was probably associated with ice moving northwards on to the continental shelf, followed by rapid withdrawal (McCabe 1995).

(10) Accorymore Formation. Stratotype: Accorymore, Achill Island, Co. Mayo [L 9890]. Deposits of morainic arcs, overlying bedrock, outside the Accorymore cirque (Farrington 1953; Synge 1963*b*; Gray & Coxon 1991).

(11) Fanore Formation. Stratotype: Cahir Valley, Co. Clare [M 136087]. Coarse-grained breccia, with some stratified horizons, resting on a platform across Carboniferous Limestone. It has been deformed and represents a combination of debris flows and rock falls in a paraglacial possibly marine environment overlain by till (Dardis & McCabe unpublished).

(12) Mullinasole Formation. Stratotype: Mullinasole, Co.Donegal [G 888714]. Basal till overlying a stratified ice-contact glaciomarine complex, exposed in a drumlin in Donegal Bay (Hanvey 1989). Ice flow was to the west, fed by dispersal centres in County Donegal and the Omagh basin.

(13) Buncrana Formation. Stratotype: Buncrana, Co. Donegal [C 346315]. Deposits exposed in a drumlin showing a till core that grades, distally, into a lee-side stratified sequence (Dardis *et al*. 1984). Drumlinisation was associated with ice-flow along the margins of Lough Swilly on to the continental shelf.

(14) Altawinny Formation. Stratotype: Altawinny, Co. Donegal [B 825341]. Coarse-grained cobble to boulder gravel Bed that overly the Altnapetiste Formation. It was deposited when ice retreated from the continental shelf (McCabe 1995).

(15) Clew Bay Formation. Type area: Clew Bay, Co. Mayo [L 9890]. Proglacial and subglacial deposits exposed in drumlins with complex lithostratigraphy on bedrock. The drumlins show complex cross-cutting relationships fashioned by westerly ice movement from the Irish Midlands onto the continental shelf (Hanvey 1987), followed by later ice movement to the north west (McCabe unpublished). Synge (1968) interpreted different lithofacies in the drumlins as representing separate ice-sheet advances.

(16) Drumore Formation. Type area: north County Galway [M 4661]. Sands and gravel of a large integrated system of eskers, fans and deltas that conducted meltwater northwards (McCabe 1985). Its base overlies bedrock at Lowberry.

(17) Lough Fin Formation. Stratotype: Lough Fin, Co. Donegal [B 890004]. Sediments of a lateral moraine deposited when the Donegal ice-cap decayed (McCabe unpublished). Its base overlies till.

(18) Cathedral Rocks Formation. Stratotype: Cathedral Rocks, Co. Mayo [F 659032]. Boulder to cobble gravel, breccia and sand (*c*. 25 m), deposited by mass flow processes into a subaqeous setting (Dardis & McCabe unpublished). Its base overlies rock and it is locally truncated by raised beach gravel.

(19) Falcarragh Formation. Stratotype: Falcarragh, Co. Donegal [B 939938]. Coarse-grained sediments of a glacial efflux system (McCabe 1995).

(20) Glencrow Formation. Stratotype: Glencrow, Co. Donegal [L 611387]. Sediments of an ice-pushed delta and outwash complex with drapes of red marine clay overlying till (Stephens 1963) deposited in a subaqeous environment (Stephens & Synge 1965). It represents an ice-contact glacial efflux system formed as northward moving ice from Donegal withdrew from the continental shelf.

(21) Burnfoot Formation. Stratotype: Bunrfoot, Co. Donegal [C 378228]. Fine-grained diamict with a marine molluscan fauna and microfauna at the head of Lough Swilly (Colhoun 1971). Its base overlies gravel. It was originally considered to be a till deposited by south-westerly flowing Scottish ice (Colhoun 1971). The location and form of the deposits resemble a bay head fjord delta of glaciomarine origin, fed by meltwater from an ice limit at Bridge End [C 4021]. It is truncated by Holocene beach gravels (McCabe unpublished).

(22) Tullywee Formation. Stratotype: Tullywee Bridge, Co. Galway [L 726585]. Deposits of a subglacial complex along the axis of the Kylemore trough. It leads to a dissected, flat-topped glacial efflux system. Coxon and Browne (1991) interpreted part of it as delta moraines. One delta surface occurs at 40 m O.D., and may be related to a high relative sea-level. Part of the deposit is composed of migratory gravelly bedforms (McCabe *et al.* 1992).

(23) Brockhill Formation. Stratotype: Brockhill, Co, Mayo [G 091375]. Coarse-grained gravel foreset Bed of an ice-contact glacial efflux system that prograded over sandy bedforms. The system was deposited with a water surface at *c*. 80 m O.D., controlled by a high relative sea-level (McCabe *et al.* 1986). It is correlated with the Belderg Formation. Its base overlies the Belderg Formation at Aghoo (Synge 1968).

(24) Belderg Formation. Stratotype: Belderg, Co. Mayo [F 990415]. Drape of compact to laminated glaciomarine mud and sand overlying till along the coastal fringe of north County Mayo (Synge 1968; McCabe *et al.* 1986). The muds contain an *Elphidium clavatum* and *Quinqueloculina arctica* dominated, low diversity, microfauna typical of circum-Arctic cool water assemblages. Complete valves of *Macoma calcarea* from the mud gave ^{14}C ages of: $16\,940 \pm 120$ and $17\,300 \pm 100$ BP. D-aIle-L-Ile ratios of 0.07 ± 0.007 (n = 15) (Bowen unpublished) are consistent with these and confirm the *in situ* nature of the *Macoma calcarea* fauna. The mud drape borders the drumlin

field of Donegal Bay, but does not occur within the gravel efflux system of the Brockhill Formation. It is proposed that the glaciomarine event closely followed an early phase of drumlinisation as the ice withdrew from Donegal Bay to stabilise on the coastal fringe (McCabe *et al.* 1986).

(25) Malin Beg Formation. Stratotype: Malin Beg, Co. Donegal [B 500799]. Glaciomarine mud and muddy diamict that records deposition from sediment plumes and ice-rafting. A foraminiferal assemblage, of low diversity, is ice-proximal in origin. D-aIle/L-Ile ratios of mollusc fragments indicates a Late-/Devensian age (McCabe *et al.* 1993*b*). Previously, Charlesworth (1924) and Colhoun (1973) interpreted these deposits as pre-Devensian till.

(26) Errigal Formation. Stratotype: Errigal Mountain, Co. Donegal [B 920207]. Deposits of protalus ramparts, fossil rock glaciers and talus-foot debris complexes overlying bedrock on the flanks of Errigal Mountain down to 150 m O.D. It is proposed that they date predominantly from the Nahanagan (Younger Dryas) (Wilson, 1990*a, b*, 1993).

(27) Malin Head Formation. Stratotype: Malin Head, Co. Donegal [C 381587]. Late-glacial raised beach deposits and associated landforms up to 20 m O.D. (Stephens 1963; Stephens & Synge 1965).

(28) Gortalecka Formation. Stratotype: Gortalecka, Co. Clare [R 2294]. Late-glacial deposits (Watts 1963).

(29) Drumskellan Formation. Stratotype: Drumskellan, Co. Donegal [C 5128]. Holocene raised beaches.

(30) Meanbog Formation. Type area: Meanbog, Co. Donegal [C 003085]. Blanket bog sequences on the Glendowan Mountains.

(31) Shannon Formation. Type area: the Shannon Basin [N 0474]. Holocene floodplain deposits which in part of the type area overlie fluvioglacial deposits.

(32) Attymon Formation. Type area: Attymon, Co. Galway [M 5930]. Raised lowland bog sequences.

Chapter 11

The Continental Shelf

T. D. J. CAMERON & R. HOLMES

Introduction

T. D. J. Cameron

Reconnaissance mapping of the UK's continental shelf and slope by the British Geological Survey has led complete cover at a scale of 1:250 000 illustrating the Quaternary geology. The maps and accompanying reports give a summary of the characteristics of its component stratigraphic units.

The mapping has revealed that middle Pleistocene, late Pleistocene or Holocene sediments rest unconformably on pre-Quaternary deposits across much of the continental shelf. In the North Sea Basin, pre-Anglian deposits are thin or absent for up to 100 km east of the present coastline, although they are many hundreds of metres thick locally along the international median line. North and west of Scotland and southwest of England, pre-Anglian deposits are restricted to the outer shelf and continental slope. They probably also occur in a shallow basin extending from beneath the centre of St. George's Channel into the south Irish Sea.

Subdivision of the Quaternary deposits on the continental shelf and slope has been achieved by detailed interpretation of grids of high-resolution seismic profiles, supplemented by lithological data from many thousands of shallow cores and several hundred boreholes, continuously cored for up to 210 m below the sea bed. Because only a small proportion of the shallow cores penetrated sediments older than the Late Devensian, techniques of lithostratigraphy have been mainly limited to defining formations and members within uppermost Pleistocene and Holocene sediments. Techniques of seismic stratigraphy outlined by Mitchum et al. (1977) and Vail (1987) have been applied to subdivide the remainder of the Pleistocene into seismo-stratigraphic units, and these have also been assigned formation status. The boundaries of all such formations have been mapped across many thousands of square kilometres. Boundaries between early Pleistocene formations of a southern North Sea delta complex are seismic sequence boundaries (Mitchum et al. 1977), in that they represent intervals of hiatus during which there were significant basinward shifts of coastal onlap. Boundaries between the majority of middle and late Pleistocene formations of the shelf are erosional unconformities. The lithology between the erosional unconformities may not always be clear.

Information on environment of deposition of the Quaternary formations has been derived from detailed studies of the sedimentology and biostratigraphy of the borehole sections and of selected shallow cores, supplemented by seismic facies analysis. For the marine sediments, integrated studies of the dinoflagellate cysts and benthonic foraminifera have proved particularly useful, providing evidence of contemporary oceanic water mass circulation and local environmental conditions (Harland et al. 1978). Pollen spectra have also been obtained from the marine sediments in a number of boreholes, but the evidence that they provide on terrestrial palaeoclimate is not always compatible with the marine record; the reasons for this are not yet fully understood (Cameron et al. 1984).

Information on age of the formations of the North Sea Basin has been inferred by correlation with the successions of mainland Britain and the Netherlands. Such correlations are tentative in many cases, and are particularly so for lower Pleistocene formations at the centre of the basin. Quaternary formations from west of Scotland, the Irish Sea and the Celtic Sea (Hebridean Seas and Irish Sea Basin glacial sediment systems) show many resemblances to those of western Britain and Ireland. Little is known about the Quaternary sediments of the Atlantic Margin west of Ireland.

Where possible, the correlations have been based on biostratigraphy, but many are supplemented by ages obtained from magnetic polarity studies, amino-acid geochronology (D-aIle/L-Ile), U-series or radiocarbon dating, or by tephrochronology. Results of the biostratigraphy suggest that most of the middle and late Pleistocene sediments of the central and northern North Sea and Irish Sea were deposited under arctic or boreal-arctic conditions (Sejrup et al. 1987; Knudsen & Asbjörndóttir 1991; Wingfield 1995). Post-Anglian deposits of interglacial aspect have had poor preservation potential on the continental shelf in general. Such deposits are patchily preserved beyond the limits of subsequent ice cover, or they occur as thin layers within the composite fill of overdeepened valleys eroded during the previous glaciation (Long & Stoker 1986).

The most complete record of Quaternary climatic fluctuation in north-west Europe is currently that of the Netherlands, at the southern end of the North Sea Basin. The sediments there are largely non-marine above the major regression of c. 1.8 Ma (Zagwijn 1989). Despite this, the curve of mean July temperature that Zagwijn (1985) derived by integrating the pollen spectra from many hundreds of Dutch boreholes and exposures bears many resemblances to the deep-ocean oxygen isotope stratigraphy. Zagwijn (1985) stressed that direct comparison will not be possible until absolute ages of climatic fluctuations in the Netherlands can be resolved; there may be significant gaps of unknown duration within parts of the succession.

North Sea

T. D. J. Cameron and R. Holmes

Caston (1977) first demonstrated the great thickness of Quaternary deposits beneath the North Sea, based on the records from deep wells drilled in the search for oil and gas. Subsequently, Quaternary sediments are more than 800 m thick have been proved along parts of the central axis of the North Sea (Evans 1994). Such thick sediments accumulated above a rift zone that has been subsiding intermittently since at least the Triassic period.

Table 28. *Quaternary correlations in the Southern North Sea and oxygen isotope stratigraphy. (H: Hirundo Formation; S: Sunderland Ground Formation; V: Volans Member; E: East Bank Member)*

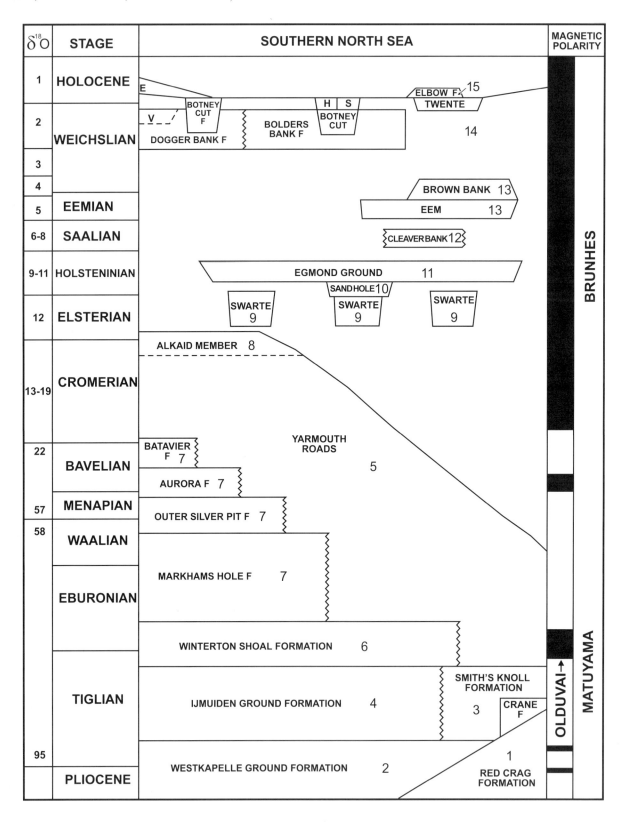

Until mid-Pleistocene times, late Cenozoic sedimentation in the southern North Sea Basin was dominated by the offshore expansion of massive peripheral delta systems. These were principally associated with former Baltic rivers and westward-flowing north German rivers during the Neogene (Gibbard 1988*b*), when much of the UK sector was either starved of sediment supply or was emergent. The eastern deltas encroached into the UK sector early in the Pleistocene (Cameron *et al.* 1987) to amalgamate with newly expanded delta systems of the Rhine, Meuse, Scheldt and Thames rivers (Zagwijn 1979). Despite continuing tectonic subsidence, this increased sediment supply rapidly filled southern parts of the North Sea Basin to near or above contemporary sea level. Lower and early Middle Pleistocene sections there and in East Anglia contain abundant evidence for an upward transition from marine to mainly fluvial sedimentary facies (Cameron *et al.* 1987). Central and northern areas of the UK sector lay beyond the delta front, but nevertheless accumulated up to 600 m of marine prodelta sediment above the Central Graben of the North Sea.

Stoker & Bent (1985) inferred proximity of ice cover to the west-central North Sea shortly after the Matuyama/Brunhes magnetic polarity reversal. However, it was the development of more widespread ice cover across northwest Europe and much of its continental shelf during the Anglian (oxygen isotope stage 12) that led to regional changes in river drainage patterns (Gibbard 1988*b*) and abandonment of the southern North Sea delta complex (Cameron *et al.* 1987). Ice cover extended across the North Sea Basin for the first time and the basin's subsequent history has alternated between periods of glacigenic sedimentation and relatively short-lived intervals of generally macrotidal marine conditions similar to those of the present day. With reduced sediment supply, continuing tectonic subsidence has enabled at least three transgressions to extend across the former delta complex in the south. Parts of the central and northern North Sea have remained a fully marine environment through much of the late Quaternary, even when sea level was about 100 m below present during the Late Devensian.

Two different systems of Quaternary stratigraphical nomenclature have evolved during the BGS mapping programme of the North Sea, south and north of 56°N. To some extent this reflects a geological contrast between the two areas. The pre-Anglian deposits are more readily divisible into delta-related seismo-stratigraphic units in the south, whereas relationships between the middle and late Pleistocene formations are more complex in the heavily glaciated northern area. The southern nomenclature evolved during close collaboration between BGS and the Geological Survey of the Netherlands (Rijks Geologische Dienst, RGD).

Southern North Sea

(south of 56°N)

(1) Red Crag Formation (Eastern England, South & East Suffolk, note 1). It forms a basin-marginal bar of shelly sands between 54°–55°N. Sampled only in well cuttings, its molluscan fauna resembles that in the Norwich Crag Formation of East Anglia (T. Meijer, pers. comm. 1991). Jeffery (1992) has correlated the sands with the Praetiglian and Tiglian.

(2) Westkapelle Ground Formation. Mainly composed of prodelta deposits that rest unconformably on late Pliocene (Red Crag) or Palaeogene sediments off East Anglia (Cameron *et al.* 1989*a*). Biostratigraphic results from three BGS boreholes suggest correlation with Thurnian deposits; the 'X' and Réunion normal polarity events were detected at 81/50A (Cameron *et al.* 1984). Results of magnetic polarity (Thompson *et al.* 1992), molluscan, and foraminiferal analyses (W. Hinsch & K. A. Jensen personal communications 1991) from borehole 89/5 have confirmed Jeffery's suggestion (1992) of a latest Pliocene-Tiglian age farther north. The base of the formation is now defined as the Gauss/Matuyama magnetic polarity reversal, and it occurs 4 ± 1 m below the Pliocene/Pleistocene boundary at 89/5 as established from the biostratigraphy. The top of the formation is poorly defined at 89/5.

(3) Smith's Knoll and Crane Formations. British-derived delta-front sediments east of East Anglia (Cameron *et al.* 1989*a*). Pollen and dinoflagellate cyst assemblages from BGS boreholes 81/50, 81/50A and 81/51 indicate correlation with Antian deposits of East Anglia (Cameron *et al.* 1984). The formation traces eastwards into the **Ijmuiden Ground Formation**.

(4) Ijmuiden Ground Formation. Delta-front deposits that extend into the UK sector from Dutch waters south of 54°N, and equivalent prodelta sediments farther west and northwest (Jeffery 1992). Pollen analysis from RGD borehole S1-63 suggested a late Tiglian age (Cameron *et al.* 1989*a*).

(5) Yarmouth Roads Formation. The transition from marine sediments to decalcified, delta-plain deposits is strongly diachronous across the southern North Sea. The earliest fluvial deposits in the south may correlate with the Waalian of the Netherlands (Cameron *et al.* 1984), whereas the transition occurred later than the Matuyama/Brunhes boundary at site 81/34 (Evans 1994). It subcrops Anglian glacigenic or younger deposits beneath a major regional unconformity. It was deposited prior to oxygen isotope stage 12.

(6) Winterton Shoal Formation. Comprises delta-front deposits between 52°N and 54°N, and prodelta sediments farther north (Jeffery 1992). Pollen analysis from BGS borehole 81/50 exhibits strong affinities with that of the Baventian East Anglia (Cameron *et al.* 1984). At site 89/5 it has normal magnetic polarity (Thompson *et al.* 1992), indicating deposition during the Olduvai Subzone and correlation with latest Tiglian or early Eburonian deposits of the Netherlands (Zagwijn 1989).

(7) Markham's Hole, Outer Silver Pit, Aurora and Batavier Formations. Ages of these units are poorly constrained. With reversed magnetic polarity at 89/5 (Thompson *et al.* 1992), the Markham's Hole Formation was deposited after the Olduvai Subzone. The Outer Silver Pit Formation has yielded cold-water, intertidal or tidal-flat foraminiferal assemblages at site 89/5 (K. A. Jensen pers. comm. 1991), suggesting correlation with a cold phase of the Waalian or, more likely, with the Menapian of the Netherlands. The Matuyama/Brunhes magnetic polarity reversal may lie close above the top of the Batavier Formation at site 81/34 (Evans 1994).

(8) Alkaid Member. This is considered by Evans (1994) to be a delta-top facies at the Dogger Bank, and possibly coeval with Cromerian deposits in East Anglia. Its relationship with the stratigraphy north of 56°N is unclear. Possible equivalent sediments there include the Ling Bank Formation, which has yielded a Cromerian pollen assemblage at site 81/34 (Ansari 1992), and the Fisher Formation of likely 'Saalian' age. The Alkaid Member may span all or part of oxygen isotope stages 6–16.

(9) Swarte Bank Formation. Partially or completely filling an anastomosing swarm of Anglian glacial palaeovalleys, this unit includes diamicts, glacifluvial sand, and commonly thick glacilacustrine muds that are overlain by glaciomarine clays at 79/8 (Jeffery 1992). Because it also includes an uppermost member of warm-temperate marine sediments in some palaeovalleys (Jeffery 1991) its age may extend from oxygen isotope stage 12 into Stage 11.

(10) Sand Hole Formation. This unit has yielded a warm-temperate, shallow-water foraminiferal assemblage (Fisher *et al.* 1969). Its pollen assemblage resembles that of the Nar Valley Clay (North West Norfolk) (Ansari 1992). D-aIle/L-Ile ratios indicate that it was deposited during oxygen isotope stage 11 (Scourse *et al.* 1993).

(11) Egmond Ground Formation. This unit has not been adequately sampled in the UK sector. Equivalent sediments have an open-marine aspect in the Dutch sector, where they are demonstrably younger than Elsterian and older than Saalian glacigenic deposits (Cameron *et al.* 1989b). It is probably younger than the Sand Hole Formation of the UK sector (Jeffery 1992) and may be correlated with oxygen isotope stage 9.

(12) Cleaver Bank Formation. This comprises proglacial, partly glaciomarine diamicts and micaceous sands that is traced laterally into till (Borkumriff Formation) of Saalian age in the eastern Dutch sector (Joon *et al.* 1990). Hence this unit correlates with oxygen isotope stages 6 or 8.

(13) Eem and Brown Bank Formations. Probably with a restricted distribution in the UK sector (Jeffery 1992), marine sands of the Eem Formation correlate with oxygen isotope sub-stage 5e (Zagwijn 1989). The overlying largely unfossiliferous silty clays of the Brown Bank Formation were deposited in a brackish-water lagoon of the Southern Bight after sea level had fallen to about 40 m below present (Cameron *et al.* 1989b). Parts of the latter formation may correlate with oxygen isotope stage 4.

(14) Dogger Bank, Bolders Bank, Botney Cut, Hirundo, Sunderland Ground and Twente Formations. This resembles Late Devensian diamicts in eastern England (Jeffery 1992). At least the upper part of the **Dogger Bank Formation** accumulated under glaciomarine conditions (Jeffery 1992), but its Volans Member fills channels that were possibly eroded close to a grounded ice-sheet limit (Evans 1994). Occurring within Late Devensian glacial palaeovalleys, the **Botney Cut Formation** comprises diamicts overlain by glaciolacustrine and glaciomarine clays. Overlying these west of the Dogger Bank are reddish brown clays, designated the **Hirundo Formation (Volans and East Bank members)**, or proglacial water-laid muds of the **Sunderland Ground Formation** (Evans 1994). Periglacial sands of the **Twente Formation** have been preserved from Holocene marine reworking at only a few localities (Cameron *et al.* 1989b). All the formations are correlated with oxygen isotope stage 2.

(15) Elbow Formation. Deposited early in the Holocene transgression, the Elbow Formation may be coeval with an East Bank Deposit described by Jansen *et al.* (1979) from west of the Dogger Bank. Composed largely of muddy sands, where these locally overlie brackish-water clay and a basal peat, such are also included within the formation (Cameron *et al.* 1989b). The peat has yielded radiocarbon ages of: 8425 ± 70 BP at Leman Bank (Godwin 1960), 9374 ± 90 BP and 9949 ± 125 BP from the centre of the Southern Bight (Kirby & Oele 1975), and 9530 ± 140 BP (SRR-2534) from a site on the Dogger Bank.

On jointly published Sea Bed Sediment maps, the BGS and the RGD subdivided fully marine Holocene deposits into the four formations and two members defined by Cameron *et al.* (1989b) and Balson (1992).

Central North Sea, Firth of Forth and Moray Firth

R. Holmes

(1) Aberdeen Ground Formation. The magnetostratigraphy, lithostratigraphy, and biostratigraphy of 75/33, 81/27, 81/29, and stratotype 81/34 indicate that delta-front to open shelf marine environments forming the bulk of the Aberdeen Ground Formation are coeval with principal delta expansion in the southern North Sea during the Matuyama Polarity Chron (Bent 1986). The Pliocene-Pleistocene boundary at 771 m below sea level in 30/13-2X is biostratigraphically defined by the last common occurrence of *Cibicides grossa* and correlated with events at approximately 2.3 Ma (Knudsen & Asbjörnsdottir 1991). Seismic reflection profiles in areas of the thickest Quaternary sedimention adjacent to 30/13-2x indicate that the deposition of the Aberdeen Ground Formation appears to be continuous across the Pliocene/Pleistocene boundary. Upwards decreasing frequencies of *Cassidulina teretis* occur in the early Pleistocene of 30/13-2X (Knudsen & Asbjörnsdottir 1991) and extremely high percentages of *Cassidulina teretis* preceding the Jaramillo Polarity Subchron at approximately 215 m below the sea bed in 81/34 (Stoker *et al.* 1983) are correlated with the Tiglian/Praetiglian (Knudsen & Sejrup 1993). North of 56.5°N the base of the Aberdeen Ground Formation is defined on the seismic reflection profiles by a regional unconformity, the 'Crenulate Reflector' buried more than 310 m below seabed in the Fladen Ground at approximately 58.5°N (Holmes 1977). Closed small-scale incisions on the unconformity are sub-parallel to the basin margins (Long, unpublished) consistent with geometry originating from ice scour (Gipp 1993) The unconformity is in use by commerce as a regional marker geotechnical horizon and is correlated with the earliest Pleistocene or the Pliocene. The unconformity is more than 150 m below a diamict, tentatively correlated in 81/26 with a glacial event within the Netherlands Bavelian, possibly oxygen isotope stage 22 (Sejrup *et al.* 1987). An overlying ameliorative interval with dominant species *Bulimina marginata*, also within the Matuyama Reversed Polarity Chron, is correlated with the Leerdam Interglacial of the Netherlands, possibly oxygen isotope stage 21. Tills were deposited from a tidewater grounded ice sheet in the Forth Approaches and Moray Firth and are tentatively correlated with the Cromerian 'Glacial A' (Stoker & Bent 1985; Bent 1986), oxygen isotope stage 20. Arctic, Boreal-Arctic and non-marine environments at the formation top in stratotype 81/34 are correlated with the Cromerian Complex in the Brunhes Normal Polarity Chron (Knudsen & Sejrup 1993). Warm-water foraminiferal assemblages at the formation top also in the Brunhes Normal Polarity Chron and between 106 and 130 m below the seabed in 81/26 are correlated with the Devil's Hole Interglacial (Sejrup & Knudsen 1993) at some point in the Cromerian (oxygen isotope stages 19 to 15).

(2) Ling Bank Formation. This is confined to the Brunhes Normal Polarity Chron and fills and in place joins differing styles of isolate, anastomosing and stacked channels. Correlation of its earliest sediments with the Cromerian is made by D-aIle/L-Ile ratios of *Elphidium excavatum* deposited in marine Arctic conditions in 81/29 and stratotype 81/34 (Knudsen &

Table 29. *Quaternary correlations in the Central North Sea, Firth of Forth and Moray Firth and oxygen isotope stratigraphy (a, Largo Bay; b, Fitzroy; c, St Andrews Bay; d, Whitethorn Members)*

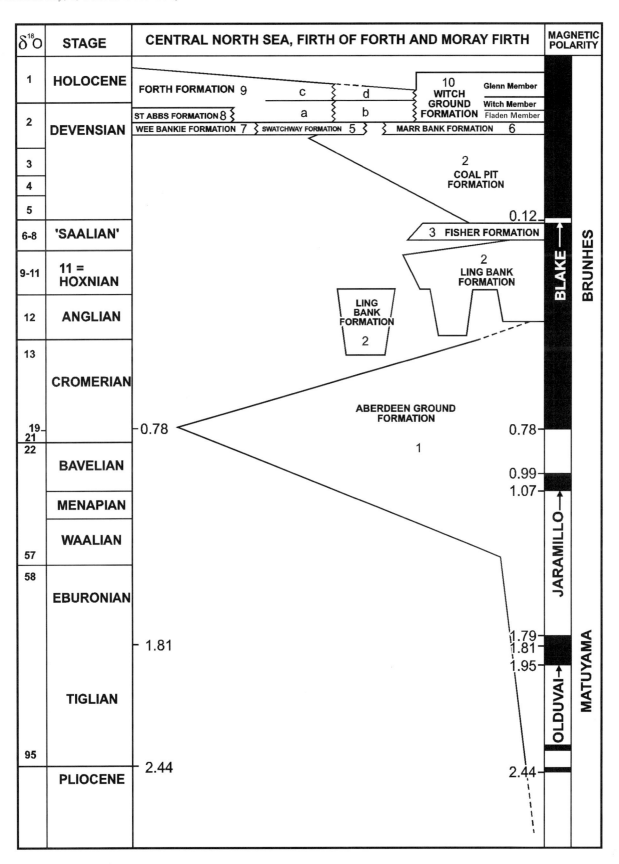

Sejrup 1993; Sejrup & Knudsen 1993); on pollen assemblages with higher frequencies of *Picea* than *Abies* in 81/34 (Ansari 1992); and the occurrence of Arctic brackish water ostracod *Scottia brownia* in 81/29 (Penney 1990). Similarly, the earliest Arctic deposits of the Ling Bank Formation appear correlative with the Cromerian in the Brunhes Normal Polarity Chron, range oxygen isotope stages 18-16. This contrasts with the ascription by Cameron *et al.* (1987) of the channelling and the bulk of the channel infill to the first regional shelf glaciation of the central North Sea during the Anglian. Boreal foraminiferal assemblages near the base of the Ling Bank Formation in 81/ 34 are assigned to the Devil's Hole Interglacial, and are correlated by D-aIle/L-Ile ratios from *Bulmina marginata* with the 'late' Cromerian (Knudsen & Sejrup 1993). However, in 81/26 D-aIle/L-Ile ratios that are also assigned to the Devils Hole Interglacial occur in the Brunhes Normal Polarity Chron in a section correlated seismostratigraphically with the top of the Aberdeen Ground Formation (Sejrup & Knudsen 1993). The apparent conflict between the regional seismostratigraphy and aminostratigraphy may originate, for example, if the D-aIle/L-Ile ratios does not resolve Cromerian stages within the Brunhes Normal Polarity Chron, or insufficient D-aIle/L-Ile ratios are available. Arctic glaciomarine dense silts, silty sands and interbeds of silt and clay that dominate the middle of the stratotype in 81/34 are tentatively correlated on the basis of the aminostratigraphy (Sejrup & Knudsen 1993) with the Anglian (oxygen isotope stage 12). D-aIle/L-Ile ratios from Boreal Foraminiferal Zone E approximately 81 to 90 m below the seabed, near the top of section in stratotype 81/34, are correlated with those from the Holsteinian (oxygen isotope stage 11) at onshore sections in Denmark and Germany (Knudsen & Sejrup 1993). Although higher frequencies of *Picea* than *Abies* in the same interval are a characterisitic of the Cromerian (Ansari 1992), pollen was deposited well away from fluvial sources, so that the foraminifera appear to be Hoxnian (Scourse personal communication). Tentative correlation of the top of the stratotype in 81/34 with the 'Saalian' is constrained by the aminostratigraphy of *Elphidium excavatum* sampled from a dominantly marine Arctic foraminiferal assemblage (Knudsen & Sejrup 1993).

(3) Fisher Formation. Interbedded pebbly clays and silty sands deposited following a marine transgression (Jensen & Knudsen 1988; Long 1993). The arctic glaciomarine Fisher Formation is contemporaneous with sub-glacial erosion and deposition north of 58.5°N and in the Inner Moray Firth (Bent 1986). D-aIle/L-Ile ratio on *Elphidium excavatum* in 81/34 (stratotype in Stoker *et al.* 1985) and 81/29 is correlated with the 'Saalian' (Knudsen & Sejrup 1993), while a TL age from 81/29 of 182 000 ± 18 000 (Jansen & Knudsen 1988) places it in oxygen isotope stage 6. It indicates that the marine transgression at the base of the formation may correlate with oxygen isotope stage 7 Seismic facies in the stratotype are traceable laterally for 15 km southwards to 55°N and correlate with the Alkaid Member of the Yarmouth Roads Formation, as defined by Jeffery (1992).

(4) Coal Pit Formation. Mostly glaciomarine sediments deposited in pulses of rapid sedimentation (Sejrup *et al.* 1987). It fills extends beyond channels cut during 'Saalian' times (Evans 1993). Approximately 7.4 m above the formation base in 75/47 (previously 75/33) a reversed magnetic interval in the Brunhes Normal Polarity Chron is attributed to the Blake Event (Stoker *et al.* 1985a) and correlated with the transition between oxygen isotope sub-stages 5e and 5d at approximately 117–120 ka. (Tucholka *et al.* 1987). In 75/47 the event occurs

with foraminiferal assemblages that confirm correlation with the Ipswichian (Cameron *et al.* 1987) or an ameliorative event in the earliest Devensian. Ameliorative foraminiferal and pollen assemblages in the Tartan Field (58°22.2′N, 0°04.4′E) are also correlated with Ipswichian or older ages (Jansen & Hensey 1981) in sediments that are seismostratigraphically equivalent to the Coal Pit Formation (Stoker *et al.* 1985a). A reversed magnetic polarity interval in the Brunhes Chron at the top of 77/3 is tentatively correlated with the Laschamp excursion (Stoker *et al.* 1985) assigned a mean age of 42 900 ± 7.8 BP (Levi *et al.* 1990). The younger formation ages are constrained by AMS dates from approximately 18.5–19.2 m below seabed in 77/2 yielding 20 860 ± 430 BP from *Portlandia arctica*, 22 630 ± 335 BP from *Elphidium* spp., and 19 740 ± 330 BP from *Elphidium* spp. An AMS date of 42 300 ± 1900 BP, a maximum age, was obtained from mixed arctic benthic foraminifera at 20.85 m below seabed in a re worked diamict . Possibly originating as a till, the diamict is correlated with maximum glaciation of the central North Sea between approximately 29 000 BP and 22 000 BP (Sejrup *et al.* 1994). The eastern boundary of the Bosies Bank Moraine, part of the Coal Pit Formation (Bent 1986), together with the eastern boundary of the Wee Bankie Formation, are correlated with a Late Devensian ice limit maximum at around 18 000 BP (Bent 1986). The Coal Pit Formation is correlated with the 'Saalian' to the Late Devensian.

(5) Swatchway Formation. Consists of well sorted medium sands that merge northwards into silts and sandy clays correlative with High Arctic foraminiferal assemblages in zone IV of the Tartan Field (Jansen & Hensey 1981) and in the stratotype 75/33 (Stoker *et al.* 1985). To the west parts of it are correlated seismostratigraphically with the Marr Bank Formation (Stoker *et al.* 1985). In 77/2 AMS dates of 16 100 ± 185 BP from *Elphidium asklundi* and *Nonion orbiculare* near the base of the Swatchway Formation and 14 730 ± 115 BP from *Elphidium asklundi* in mid-formation (Sejrup *et al.* 1994) are correlated with the later part of oxygen isotope stage 2.

(6) Marr Bank Formation. Interfingering to the west with the Wee Bankie Formation, the Arctic to High Boreal estuarine to inner shelf pebbly and sandy deposits of the Marr Bank Formation (Thomson 1978) rest on a planar regional surface dipping from 60 m below mean sealevel to more than 100 m below mean sea-level to the east (Holmes 1977; Stewart 1991). Radiocarbon ages of 17 734 ± 480 and 21 707 ± 680 BP (Holmes 1977) are from lignitised wood in stratotype 74/7, but a radiocarbon age of 13 171 ± 40 BP from lignitised wood below the stratotype possibly indicate insecure radiocarbon ages for the stratotype (Stoker *et al.* 1985). On the basis of its extension from the Wee Bankie Formation, the the Marr Bank Formation is correlated with late oxygen isotope stage 2.

(7) Wee Bankie Formation. Comprised of Late Devensian tills and glaciomarine diamict with interbeds of sand, pebbly sand and silty clay. It extends from approximately 56°N to 57.5°N along the east coast of Scotland to a longitude of 1° 15″W. It may mark the limit of the Late Devensian ice sheet (Holmes 1977; Stewart 1991).

(8) St. Abbs Formation. This consists of glaciomarine pebbly muds and pebbly silty muds in stratotype 73/11, and occurs mainly in the Tay-Forth area. Correlation with the Errol Member (Scotland: Tay-Earn, note 2) of the Forth and Tay estuaries is based on ostracod assemblages.

(9) Forth Formation. Subdivision of the Forth Formation is based on seismic stratigraphy (Stoker *et al.* 1985). Estuarine to shallow marine muds and silty muds of the basal **Largo Bay**

Member are confined to the Tay-Forth area. In stratotype 74/1, mid-unit foraminiferal assemblages indicate cooling correlated with the onset of the Younger Dryas (Gregory *et al.* 1978) while coeval silts-and-sands of the **Fitzroy Member** from the stratotype in 81/39 were deposited farther offshore. Holocene fluvial, estuarine and shallow marine sands and silts of the **St Andrews Bay Member** in stratotype 71/33 are restricted to nearshore areas between 56mN and 58mN. Coeval with the St Andrews Bay Member, the **Whitethorn Member** nearshore sands in stratotype 81/39 locally prograde towards to the east while farther offshore the Whitethorn Member is essentially a channel fill deposit. The Forth Formation and the Witch Ground Formation are correlated with the late oxygen isotope stage 2 and with oxygen isotope stage 1 (Holocene).

(10) Witch Ground Formation. Subdivision is based on lithology and seismostratigraphy (Stoker *et al.* 1985). In stratotype 75/33 the basal **Fladen Member** consists of gravelly multi-layered glaciomarine silty clays and sands. AMS ages from 77/2 yielded: $13\,120 \pm 460$ BP from *Yoldiella lenticula*, $14\,295 \pm 460$ BP from *Elphidium asklundi*, $14\,170 \pm 165$ BP from *Elphidium* spp and $14\,370 \pm 200$ BP from *Portlandia arctica* (Sejrup *et al.* 1994). Radiocarbon ages of $13\,255 \pm 185$, $13\,215 \pm 185$ and $13\,055 \pm 155$ from *Portlandia arctica* in $58 + 00/111$ indicate polar water in the central North Sea until at least 13 200–13 100 BP (Peacock & Harkness 1990) during the Late Devensian (oxygen isotope stage 2). The boundary with the overlying **Witch Member** exhibits evidence in the form of buried pockmarks for fluid release to the seabed, correlated with seawater warming and methane emission at seabed at the start of the Windermere interstadial at approximately 13 000 BP (Peacock & Harkness 1990) approximating to the beginning of oxygen isotope stage 1. The **Mid-Witch Member** contains volcanic shards that are correlated with the Vedde Ash Bed and the Younger Dryas (Long & Morton 1987), the return of marine polar waters to Scottish seas occurred between approximately 10 800–10 100 BP (Peacock & Harkness 1990). Silts and sands of the **Glenn Member** (Holocene) extend to the seabed in stratotype $57 + 00/9$ and the foraminiferal assemblages indicate relatively deep water conditions. The Glenn Member in the Fladen Ground yielded steadily upwards decreasing conventional radiocabon ages ranging from 7000 to 5000 BP (Erlenkeuser 1979).

East Shetland Shelf and Norwegian Channel & Northern North Sea

R. Holmes

The East Shetland Shelf, also known as the northern North Sea, is defined for this report as the UK designated shelf between approximately 59.5°N to 62°N. The north and west margins of the Norwegian Channel are included as they are within the UK-designate zone. Seismostratigraphical correlation of the study area with the central North sea is possible across Quaternary sediments that thin over the East Shetland Ridge (Long 1993). The division between the central North Sea environment from the generally more open shelf environment east of Shetland, also glaciated from Norway, is reflected in the different depositional styles and different separate formations. Pliocene and older sediments adjacent to Norway are truncated (Rise *et al.* 1984) but an interpretation of the

depth to the base of the Pleistocene (Holmes *et al.* 1993) indicates that during the earliest Pleistocene a broad re-entrant, essentially a proto-Norwegian Channel, extended south from the north Atlantic into the North Sea. The re-entrant was subsequently eroded during glaciations but vertical shelf aggradation and progradation eastwards, for example at approximately 60.5°N in the UK-designate zone, also narrowed the Norwegian Channel by approximately 40 km since the earliest Pleistocene. Within the outer (northern) Norwegian Channel prograding and vertically aggrading packages deposited above a regional angular unconformity, formerly correlated with the Pliocene are now correlated with the Quaternary (King *et al.* 1996). The erosional boundaries to the packages are probably glacigene in origin, the oldest package corresponding to an approximate age of 1.1 Ma and the Fedje Glaciation of Sejrup *et al.* (1995). However, as the topographic boundary dividing the western margin of the Norwegian Trench from the North Sea defines the approximate eastern limit of this correlation, and correlation between the shelf edge and deeper channel margins are complicated by erosion of late unconformities down to older units, correlation of the UK shelf with the Norwegian Channel is restricted in this report to units within the Brunhes Chron. Correlations are made using published work together with the information available from maps published by the BGS.

The following should be followed with the table relating to both East and West Shetland Shelves where common units have the same numbers.

(1) Shackleton Formation. In the western part of the region its base and that of the Quaternary are the same and lie unconformably on Palaeogene and older sediments. In the eastern part of the region it extends without lithological break into the Pliocene. Reversed magnetic polarity profiles in 78/09, 80/01 and 81/18 (that did not penetrate the base of the formation) are assigned to the Matuyama Reversed Polarity Chron (Stoker *et al.* 1983). Foraminiferal assemblages, indicative of the Pliocene/Lower Pleistocene, occur in 81/18, while in 81/16 brackish water foraminiferal assemblages are comparable to Praetiglian assemblages in the Netherlands (Long 1993). Dinoflagellate assemblages in 84/10 are probably comparable to those in the southern North Sea spanning the Tiglian and Eburonian. A normal polarity event in 78/09 is correlated with the Jaramillo Normal Polarity Subchron (Stoker *et al.* 1983): oxygen isotope stages 27 to 32. South of the East Shetland Ridge, a mid-unit regional acoustic reflector in 81/18 divides lower sands from sandy clay above, and may be the result of marine erosion associated with early Pleistocene glaciation (Long *et al.* 1988).

(2) Mariner Formation. Its base is regionally defined on seismic reflection profiles by an irregular Cromerian glacigenic erosion surface locally overlain by diamict (Long 1993). However, in 78/09 sediments near the base of the formation and placed in the Matuyama Reversed Polarity Chron, are coeval with warmer foraminiferal assemblages, including *Elphidium* cf *selseyense*, and are correlated with the Cromerian (Skinner *et al.* 1986). The warm assemblages extend without apparent break into the Brunhes Polarity Chron, thus may, in part, be correlated with oxygen isotope stage 19. Mid-formation erosion, correlated with the 'Saalian' appears to have removed evidence for the Hoxnian (Skinner & Gregory 1983; Skinner *et al.* 1986). The paucity of evidence makes correlation of the Mariner Formation with oxygen isotope stages 19 to 8 provisional.

(3) Ferder Formation. Its basal sediments fill deep glacial

Table 30. *Quaternary correlations in the East Shetland Shelf and Norwegian Channel and the Northern North Sea and oxygen isotope stratigraphy*

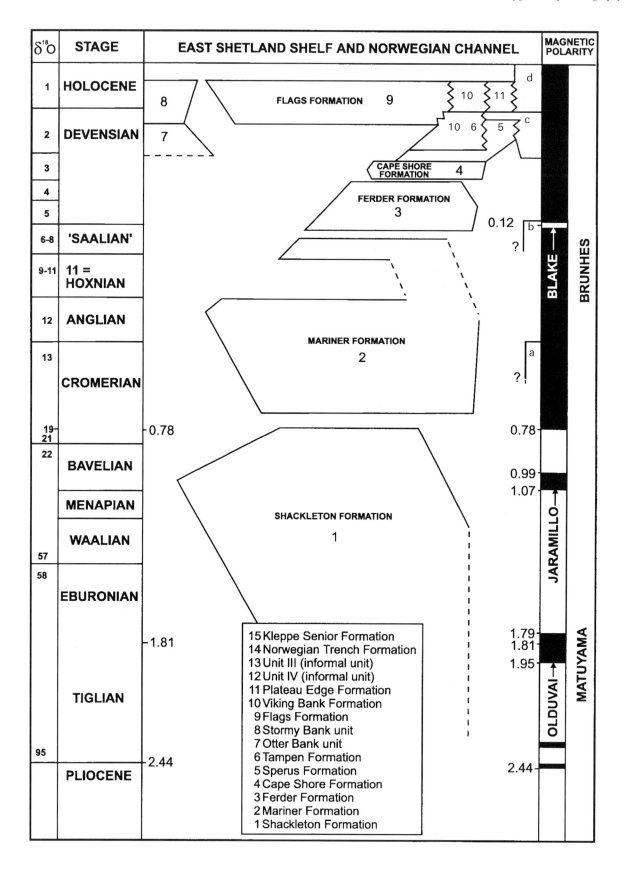

channels that increase in size and frequency to the south. These channels are ascribed to the late 'Saalian' (Skinner *et al.* 1986) during oxygen isotope stage 6. Ameliorative foraminiferal assemblages, coeval with the Blake Event in 80/1 (Stoker *et al.* 1983; Skinner *et al.* 1986) and in 78/09 (Skinner & Gregory 1983; Stoker *et al.* 1983; Skinner *et al.* 1986), are correlated with the Eemian–Devensian transition between oxygen isotope sub-stages 5e and 5d, at approximately 117 ka (Tucholka *et al.* 1987). However, in 81/18 a magnetic reversal coeval with foraminiferal assemblages that indicate an unfavourable environment is also correlated with the Blake Event. Intra-formational channels both within, and regionally truncating the top of the formation, are speculatively attributed to an origin under ice sheets extending from Scandinavia and Shetland during oxygen isotope stage 4 (Long 1993). The Ferder Formation probably spams oxygen isotope stages 6 to 4

(4) Cape Shore Formation. The base is defined by an erosion surface. It is correlated with deglaciation and climatic warming at the transition between oxygen isotope stages 4 and 3 (Long 1993). In 78/9 ameliorative foraminiferal assemblages are correlated with the Upton Warren Interstadial on the basis of chroneity with the Laschamp Reversed Polarity Subchron (Skinner *et al.* 1986) with an estimated mean age of $42\,900 \pm 7.8$ BP (Levi *et al.* 1990) (oxygen isotope stage 3). Radiocarbon ages of $31\,150 \pm 1200$ BP from shell fragments deposited in an Arctic environment, approximately 17.5 m below seabed in Brent Soil boring 1 (Milling 1975), and down-hole AMS ages of: $29\,430 \pm 390$, $29\,930 \pm 460$, $30\,190 \pm 360$ BP on *Macoma calcarea* in A79-156, are associated with Arctic foraminiferal assemblages (Rise & Rokoengen 1984; Sejrup *et al.*1994) correlative with the closing events of oxygen isotope stage 3. Strongly ameliorative foraminiferal assemblages near the formation top in Statfjiord B 3506 ('BH Statfjord Area' in Skinner *et al.* 1986) are correlated with the late Eemian (Feyling-Hanssen 1982) oxygen isotope sub-stage 5e or early Devensian (oxgen isotope stage 5)(Feyling-Hanssen & Knudsen 1986). However, if the D-aIle/L-Ile ratios of 0.036 from *Elphidium excavatum* and 0.048 from *Cibicides lobatulus* are correlated with the Late Devensian then the ameliorative foraminiferal assemblages must precede the late Devensian glaciation during oxygen isotope stage 2. Correlation of the Cape Shore Formation with part of oxygen isotope stage 3 is sure, but is less certain with the latter part of oxygen isotope stage 4 and the earliest part of oxygen isotope stage 2.

(5) Sperus Formation. Sandy gravelly clay glaciomarine deposits 23 m below the seabed in the Sperus Formation at Statfjord B 3506 (Skinner *et al.* 1986) are in foraminiferal Zone 3 (Feyling-Hanssen & Knudsen1986). It is correlated by D-aIle/L-Ile ratios on *Elphidium excavatum* with the Late Devensian (Knudsen & Sejrup 1988).

(6) Tampen Formation. A maximum age is derived from radiocarbon ages on mixed shell fragments, approximately 1.24–1.75 m below seabed in A79-146, of $18\,860 \pm 260$ BP (Rokoengen *et al.* 1982). It probably originated as a lodgement till (Carlsen *et al.*. 1986) and is coeval with the Norwegian Trench Formation (Rise *et al.* 1984). It is overconsolidated, so that between seabed and approximately 5 m below seabed it is unresolved on the seismic reflection profiles. Samples from approximately 0.2 to 3 m below seabed are radiocarbon dated between $12\,090 \pm 170$ to $10\,330 \pm 120$ BP (in: A79-135, -137,-138,-146,-159); and there is also a radiocarbon age of 10, 330 110 BP on *Mya Truncata* 200 mm below seabed (in A79-135) (Rise & Rokoengen 1984).

(7) Otter Bank Unit (informal). Comprises diamicts in mounded units that originated as submarine moraines. They are correlated on the basis of regional seismostratigraphy with the Tampen and Sperus Formations (Long 1993). Diamicts are widespread on the seafloor adjacent to Shetland, but are commonly too thin or discontinuous to be resolved on the seismic reflection profiles. They are tentatively correlated seismostratigraphically with the Otter Bank unit. Such diamict in $60/ + 00/49$, interpreted as a soft-sediment deformation till or a subaqueous glacigenic debris flow, yielded AMS radio-carbon ages of $13\,180 \pm 120$ from *Hiatella arctica*;and $13\,720 \pm 150$ from *Portlandia arctica*. These ages possibly indicate a later deglaciation around Shetland than on mainland Scotland (Peacock & Long 1994).

(8) Stormy Bank Unit (informal). This is separated spatially from the Witch Ground Formation and is insecurely correlated on the basis of seismic facies, and crop under seabed, with the Witch ground Formation (Long 1993).

(9) Flags Formation. Glaciomarine pebbly clays and silts that were deposited in isolated hollows on the seabed are seismostratigraphically correlated with the Witch Ground Formation (Long 1993) and with oxygen isotope stages 2 and 1.

(10) Viking Bank Formation. A lower muddy lower unit is undated but together with a predominantly sandy marine upper unit is seismostratigraphically correlated with the Plateau Edge Formation (Long 1993). Shell fragments in a channel-fill in the upper unit occur 1.2 m below seabed in A79-173 are AMS dated as $11\,350 \pm 120$ BP; they are associated with predominantly Arctic foraminiferal assemblages (Rise & Rokoengen 1984). Poor foraminiferal assemblages occur with shell fragments that are AMS dated to: $10\,420 \pm 80$ BP approximately 2.7 m below seabed in A79-178; and 8530 ± 110 BP 0.2 m below seabed in A79-177. Sands with a dominant Boreal foraminiferal assemblages contain shell fragments dated to 9770 ± 140 BP, 0.2 m below seabed in A79-173; and 5250 ± 120 BP approximately 0.4 m below seabed in A79-178 (Rise & Rokoengen 1984).

(11) Plateau Edge Formation. Comprising a sandy and gravelly deposit that extends as a narrow wedge for more than 50 km along the western shelfbreak of the Norwegian Trench. Textures on quartz sand grains indicate a littoral and aeolian origin. Radiocarbon ages are: $12\,310 \pm 170$ and $11\,090 \pm 170$ from shell material in mid-formation; and $10\,820 \pm 140$ at the top of the formation in A79-162 (Rokoengen *et al.* 1982) A radiocarbon age of 140 ± 130 BP, 350 mm below seabed in A79-162 comes from a horizon with deep-water mainly boreal foraminiferal assemblages (Rise & Rokoengen 1984). An AMS radiocarbon age of $12\,670 \pm 130$ from *Hiatella arctica*, comes from shelly sands above a diamict, but below a superficial cover of seabed sand, in $60/ + 00/49$ – some 60 km east of Shetland (Peacock & Long 1984). The enclosing sediments are interpreted as shelly bed of 'Late-glacial interstadial' age that are typical of shallow shelly gravel, shelly sand and shell hash in scdiments some 0.5 to 1.0 or so thick over much of the northern North Sea. These sediments cannot be resolved on seismic reflection records, but may be correlated as a thin unit of the Plateau Edge Formation (Peacock & Long 1994).

Norwegian Channel

(a) Unit IV (informal unit). This unit was only sampled in the top few metres of marine sediments in Troll boreholes 5.1/5,2. It contained High-Boreal to Low-Arctic foraminifera that are assigned to the Norwegian Trench Interglacial. On the the basis of their D-aIle/L-Ile ratios, they appear to post-date the Devil's Hole Interglacial in the Brunhes Normal Polarity Chron (Knudsen & Sejrup 1993; Sejrup & Knudsen 1993). If that interglacial is Cromerian (Sejrup & Knudsen 1993), then the top of the unit be correlated with oxygen isotope stages 17 or 15.

(b) Unit III (informal unit). The lower till or glaciomarine sequence in the informal unit III of Sejrup & Brigham-Grette (1989) is correlated tentatively with the 'Saalian'. Warm foramineral assemblages at the unit top in the Troll borehole 5.1/5.2 are informally assigned to the Troll Interglacial. This is based on D-aIle/L-Ile ratios on *Bulimina marginata*, and the incoming of sub-polar planktonic faunas which entered the Norwegian Sea only twice during the last 450 ka. The top of unit III is correlated with the Eemian and oxygen isotope sub-stage 5e.

(c) Norwegian Trench Formation. This consists of till deposited from north-flowing ice in the Norwegian Trench (Rise *et al.* 1984). In the Troll 5.1/5.2 borehole the biostratigraphy and aminostratigraphy of sediments underlying the Norwegian Trench Formation is correlated with the Ipswichian (oxygen isotope sub-stage 5e) (Serjup *et al.* 1989). Demonstrably younger than parts of the Sperus Formation (5) (section CC' in Rise *et al.*1984), the west margin of the Norwegian Trench Formation (L2 in Sejrup *et al.* 1989) post-dates the transition from oxygen isotope stage 3 to 2. An AMS date, from mixed derived arctic and boreal foraminifera in the sandy and gravelly glacigene sediments at the top of the Norwegian Trench Formation, is infinite (Lehman *et al.* 1991) although an AMS date 15 145 ± 205 from mixed benthonic foraminifera in 89.03 0.1 m above the base of the overlying Kleppe Senior Formation in the Norwegian Trench (Sejrup *et al.* 1994) locally constrains a minimum formation age. The lithostratigraphy and seismic stratigraphy indicate that the upper part of the Norwegian Trench Formation is coeval with the Tampen Formation and is therefore securely correlated with oxygen isotope stage 2. There is, however, no evidence for correlation of the Norwegian Trench Formation with the Early and Middle Devensian (oxygen isotope sub-stages 5d-5a, and oxygen isotope stages 4 and 3).

(d) Kleppe Senior Formation. In muds of the Troll 3.1 borehole, decreasing δ^{18}O isotope values from *Nonion labradoricum* and AMS dates of 14 690 ± 120 BP from *Nonion labradoricum* (Lehman *et al.* 1991), and 15 145 ± 205 from mixed benthonic foraminifera in 89.03 (Sejrup *et al.*1994) 0.1 m above the base of the formation (L1 in Sejrup *et al.* 1989), post-date the initiation of Fennoscandian ice-sheet retreat at approximately 15 000 BP. Correlation of sands in the Plateau Edge Formation (11) and the Viking Bank Formation (10) with mid-formation sands and muddy sands in the Kleppe Senior Formation (Rise *et al.* 1984) is confirmed by AMS dates from shell fragments of 12 450 ± 140 and 12 370 ± 170 BP in 1005 (Rokoengen *et al.* 1982), and in 89.03 with AMS dates of 11 155 ± 90 and 12 040 ± 145 BP from *Nonion labradoricum* (Sejrup *et al.* 1994). Cooling, indicated by δ^{18}O isotope values from *Nonion labradoricum*, is constrained by AMS dates between 11 160 ± 120 and 10 510 ± 120 BP from *Nonion labradoricum* and is correlated with the first half of the Younger Dryas (Lehman *et al.* 1991). Abrupt changes to the lowest values of δ^{18}O isotopes from *Cassidulina laevigata* near the formation top are correlated with the flow of warmer Atlantic water from the English Channel that preceded an AMS date of 7060 ± 90 on *Uvigerina peregrina* (Lehman *et al.* 1991).

The West Shetland Shelf

R. Holmes

Seismostratigraphical correlation of the Quaternary of the West Shetland Shelf with that of the northern North Sea is prevented south of approximately 61.25°N by the submarine platform surrounding the Orkney and Shetland islands. The platform is characterised by rock cropping out at seabed through Quaternary deposits generally less than 5 m thick, or by undifferentiated Quaternary deposits, exceptionally up to 50 m thick (Holmes *et al.* 1993). However, a ramp-style and poorly-defined shelfbreak divides the northern West Shetland Shelf from the NE Atlantic slope and in this environment Quaternary units underlying the deeper-water areas are readily seismostratigraphically correlated with those from the northern North Sea. South of approximately 61°N a sharp shelfbreak forms a suitable morphological boundary for the limit of Quaternary correlation on the Shetland Shelf.

Except where the formally-defined formations extend from the northern North Sea, the Quaternary deposits north and west of Shetland are subdivided into informal seismostratigraphical units that are mapped as 'sequences' on the published BGS 1:250 000 maps. The shelf sequence boundaries are typified by unconformities and changes of seismic facies. For this report the BGS sequence is replaced by the term unit.

Compared to the North Sea much less sediment-sample research has been completed for the Quaternary units on the West Shetland Shelf. Precise age ranges are not available for units pre-dating the Devensian, so that their correlation is insecure. The uncertainties are highlighted in the following.

(1) Sinclair Unit *(informal)*. North of Shetland the regional seismostratigraphical evidence shows a pre-Shackleton Formation age, possibly Pliocene or older, for the Sinclair Formation (Stevenson 1991*a*). In 82/11and 84/04 west of Shetland it consists of Arctic shelly, pebbly muds and prodeltaic to shallow marine sands correlated with Unit 3 of Cockcroft (1987). In 82/10, sandy and gravelly muds mostly barren of dinoflagellate cyts rest on dominantly sands, sometimes glauconitic, with biostratigraphical evidence for an ameliorative climate near the base, and it overlies glauconitic sands of likely Middle to Upper Miocene age (BGS unpublished). In 81/29, sands and muds of west-prograding and deltaic sediments, are correlated with Unit 3 of Cockcroft (1987), are ascribed biostratigraphically to the Pliocene-Pleistocene (BGS unpublished). In 84/01, supposed Pliocene glauconitic sands, and in 205/21-1A and 84/02 Miocene to late Pliocene glauconitic sands, are provisionally correlated with the Sinclair unit (Stoker *et al.* 1993). This suggests that the Sinclair unit may be diachronous across the Neogene into the Lower Pleistocene.

(2) Shackleton Formation. North of approximately 61.5N° its base consists of offlapping reflectors on the seismic reflection profiles. Without borehole control the identification of its base and that of the Pliocene-Pleistocene in this area is uncertain (Stevenson 1991). It is, however, correlated with the Lower Pleistocene (East Shetland Shelf and Norwegian Channel).

(3) Morrison Formation (informal). In the inner-to-middle shelf environments a regional unconformity at approximately 160–200 m below sealevel separates sub-horizontal shelf Quaternary units from the west-prograding Morrison Formation below. Except where it interdigitates with or overlies the

Table 31. *Quaternary correlations in the West Shetland Shelf and oxygen isotope stratigraphy*

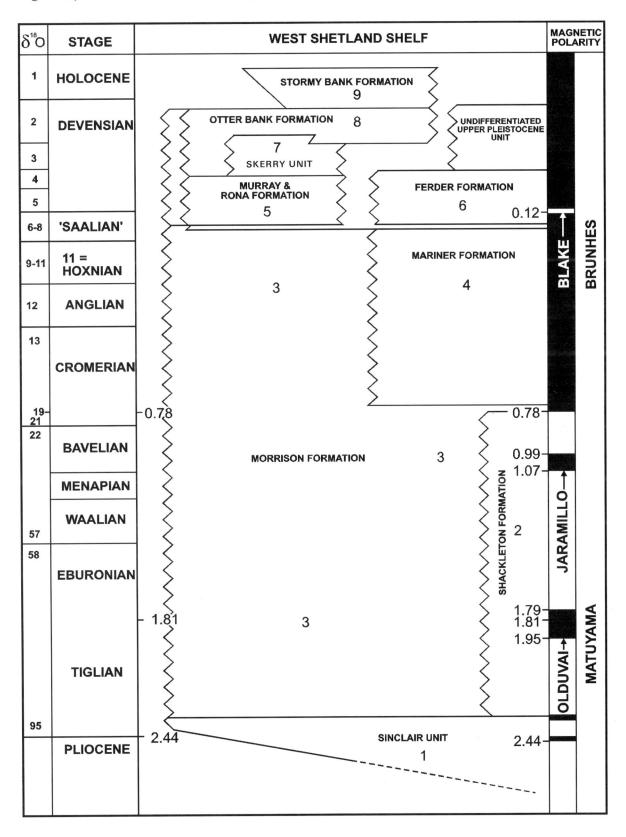

Sinclair Formation, the base of the Morrison Formation defines the base of the Pliocene-Pleistocene. It forms an outer-shelf-to-slope thinning sediment wedge, in places more than 200 m thick. North of Shetland, the base of the Morrison Formation is seismostratigraphically correlated with the base of the Shackleton Formation (Stevenson 1991). In 208/15-1A Pliocene, and possibly Pleistocene, muds and sands of the Morrison Formation onlap glauconitic Miocene sands at an intra-Neogene unconfomity. In the mid-shelf west of Shetland, muddy, sandy and gravelly sub-glacial to ice-proximal sediments in 84/04 (Cockcroft 1987), near the top of the Formation Morrision, are barren of dinoflagellate cysts, but mid-unit species, dominated by *Bitectatodinium tepikiense*, *Operculodinium centrocarpum* and *Spiniferites* (species indeterminate), are characteristic of deposition in cold conditions during the middle Pleistocene (Harland communication 1989). Pliocene strata near the base of the Morrison Formation have been proved in 204/30-1 and 208/15-1A on the outer shelf south of 62°N (Stoker *et al.* 1993). At the outer shelf and upper slope the top of the Morrison Formation comprises distal components of the Ferder, Murray, Otter Bank formations. The shelf break defines a morphological boundary between the units. There is no evidence for correlating the lowermost elements in the Morrison Formation.

(4) Mariner Formation. This is extended by seismostratigraphical correlation to the shelf north and west of Shetland (Stevenson 1991). It is correlated with the Cromerian to Saalian (oxygen isotope stages 19 to 8) (East Shetland Shelf and Norwegian Channel).

(5) Murray and Rona Formations. Comprises subhorizontal units up to 60 m or more thick on the outer shelf that extend over the shelfbreak onto the slope as overconsolidated muddy sediments where they are acoustically indistinguishable from the top of the Morrison Formation (Holmes 1991). Mid-shelf, at site 84/04, an interpretation of sediment fabric and micropalaeontological analyses indicates deposition of gravelly to sandy muds in glaciomarine-to-brackish-water environments (Unit 1 of Cockcroft 1987). Currently there is no basis for precise correlation of these with Devensian or Saalian events. The Ferder Formation in the northern North Sea is tentatively correlated with the 'Saalian' to early Devensian, oxygen isotope stages 6 to 4 (East Shetland Shelf and Norwegian Channel) and extended seismostratigraphically to the north and west of Shetland (Stevenson 1991; Holmes 1991).

(6) Ferder Formation. The Murray unit is restricted to areas south of the Foula Bight. It consists of ice-proximal acoustically chaotic diamicts in 82/10 (Unit 2 of Cockcroft 1987). Sheet-form to mounded diamicts, up to 40 m or more thick are thought, on the basis of their regional seismostratigraphy to be partly coeval with an internally eroded but dominantly well-layered seismic facies occurring to the south-west. The lowermost well-layered seismic facies is interpreted as ice-distal glaciomarine sediments in 78/07 and 72/36 and attributed to the Rona unit (Holmes 1990). The Murray unit and to the north the Ferder Formation are truncated and spatially separated by the north-east trending Papa Basin. The Ferder Formation and the Murray unit are provisionally correlated across the Foula Bight and Papa Basin on the basis of their occurrence at similar topographic levels and their regionally unconformable relationships with the underlying Morrison and the overlying Otter Bank units (Holmes 1991). A provisional basis, therefore, exists for correlating the

Murray unit diamicts and the Rona unit glaciomarine sediments with oxygen isotope stages 6 to 4.

(7) Skerry Unit *(Informal)*. North of Orkney, in a mid-shelf basin, the chaotic and acoustically transparent seismic facies at the base of the Otter Bank Formation appears to interdigitate with a well-layered seismic facies at the the the top of the Skerry Formation (Holmes 1990). Arctic foraminifera at the top of the formation in 82/04 are correlated with the Late Devensian, but only on the basis of regional seismostratigraphy (Stoker *et al.* 1993). Dinoflagellates in 82/03 and foraminifera in 82/04 indicate a mid-unit amelioration in dominantly glaciomarine muds (Holmes 1990). They are provisonally correlated with a Middle Devensian interstadial.

Undifferentiated Upper Pleistocene unit. This is unsampled and it occurs north of 61°N 20'N. Seismostratigraphically it is correlated with the Tampen, Sperus and Cape Shore Formations (East Shetland Shelf and Norwegian Channel) (Stevenson 1991), and is, therefore, correlated with oxygen isotope stages 3 to 2. Although spatially separated from the Otter Bank unit the Undifferentiated Upper Pleistocene unit is also seismostratigraphically correlated with the Otter Bank unit (Stevenson 1991) and therefore with the Late Devensian.

(8) Otter Bank Formation (**informal**). Diamicts, sometimes more than 30 m occur west of Shetland. These were deposited proximal to grounded shelf-glacier ice (Cockcroft 1987). The diamicts locally extend over the shelf-edge to the upper slope where they were reworked by iceberg scour and their seismic facies are indistinguishable from those at the top of the Morrison Formation (3) (Holmes 1991). South of 61°N, outer-to-mid-shelf ridges are interpreted as still-stand submarine moraines formed as shelf-ice retreated to the east (Holmes 1991; Stoker & Holmes 1991). In 72/36, 84/2, 82/10 and 84/04 shelly gravelly sands on the Otter Bank Formation indicate deposition in high-energy shallow marine, glaciomarine and deltaic environments (Cockcroft 1987). Underlying the Otter Bank Formation middle-to-outer-shelf units, units of the Ferder Formation, correlated with oxygen isotope stage 4 (below), extend from the shelf north of Shetland (Stevenson 1991) to the shelf west of Shetland (Holmes 1991) and provide a regional basis for correlation of the diamicts of the Otter Bank Formation on the middle and outer shelf, with the Late Devensian. The lateral continuity of the overconsolidated diamict units, generally less than 10 m thick, is not resolvable on the seismic reflection profiles, so that mapping of the thinner sections of the Otter Bank Formation on the inner shelf adjacent to Shetland is on the basis of correlation of information from shallow cores and similar seabed topographical styles to those on the middle shelf (Stevenson 1991). From site 61-01/66 in this area a sample of *Trodonta elliptica*, from glaciomarine or sub-glacial diamict approximately 2.8 m below seabed in the Otter Bank Formation, yielded a radiocarbon age of 18 230 ± 280 BP. *Hiatella arctica*, from sandy muds approximately 2.2 m below the seabed, yielded a radiocarbon age 13 390 ± 190 BP (Ross 1996). The radiocarbon ages support correlation of the Otter Bank Formation with the late Devensian.

(9) Stormy Bank Formation (informal). Glaciomarine muds and sands in 77/07, 80/08, 84/3, 84/02, 82/11, 77/9, 82/02, and 82/05 are undated but are correlated seismostratigraphically with the Stormy Bank Formation on the shelf east of Shetland, and with the Witch Ground Formation in the North Sea (Long 1993).

Irish Sea, St George's Channel and North Celtic Sea

T. D. J. Cameron

Following Neogene uplift, the Irish Sea and much of the continental shelf south-west of mainland Britain remained an area of net erosion from late Neogene to mid-Pleistocene times (Wingfield 1994, 1995; Evans 1990). Consequently, Middle and Late Pleistocene, and Holocene sediments rest unconformably on strata ranging from Precambrian to Neogene in age across much of this area.

The Quaternary deposits between England, Wales and Ireland are mostly less than 100 m but, exceptionally, are up to 375 m thick. Based on seismic interpretation, these deposits have been subdivided by Hession (1988) and Wingfield (1994, 1995) into six formations that are mainly separated by erosion surfaces. The oldest formation includes both terrestrial and marine sediments, and is mainly preserved in shallow basins beneath the present deep-water areas. Three of the overlying formations record episodes of regional glaciation that have been correlated by Wingfield (1994, 1995) with the Elsterian (Anglian), Saalian (Wolstonian) and late Weichselian (Late Devensian) glaciations of northwest Europe. All three formations display complex internal relationships between informal members and seismic facies that include unstratified diamicts and the infill of glacial depressions termed incisions by Wingfield (1990). A fifth formation of mainly glaciomarine sediments may have been deposited during an early phase of the 'Saalian' glaciation (Wingfield 1994). Superficial sediments include deposits of the end-Devensian-early Holocene marine transgression, and those of the present-day macrotidal environment (Wingfield 1994, 1995).

(1) Bardsley Loom Formation. Comprises clay, sand, pebbly sand and gravel, with layers of peat (Wingfield 1994). These sediments have yielded a sparse, cold-water marine microfauna (Harland & Wilkinson unpublished), but their general disposition beneath the oldest known glacial deposits of the region suggests deposition at least partly during a cold phase of the Cromerian (oxygen isotope stages 13,15,17 or 19).

(2) Caernarfon Bay Formation. Resting on an unconformity or on bedrock, basal beds comprise diamict and laterally equivalent sediments. These were deposited prior to erosion and infill of a suite of glacial incisions (Wingfield 1994, 1995). Although unsampled, all of these sediments have been ascribed by Wingfield (1994, 1995) to the Anglian glaciation, although marine deposits of a succeeding interglacial could also be present within the incisions. At the top of the formation is a diamict that yields a sparse, cold-water dinoflagellate cyst assemblage. As this unit has been correlated by Wingfield (1994) with the 'Saalian' glaciation, the formation may span oxygen isotope stages 12 to 6.

(3) St. George's Channel Formation. Composed of muds with minor shell debris and rare pebbles at 71/56, 73/41 and 89/10 (Wingfield 1994). The marine microfauna indicate deposition in mainly boreal or cold waters (Gregory & Harland unpublished), but a horizon at 7 m depth at 89/10 has yielded a rich warm-temperate foraminiferal assemblage of Hoxnian affinity (C. Dickson unpublished). Knudsen & Sejrup (1988) cited an age of 377 ka for a single D-aIle/L-Ile ratio from this interval. Part of the formation is coeval with uppermost beds of the Caernarfon Bay Formation (Wingfield 1994). Hence, it may span oxygen isotope stages 12 to 6.

(4) Cardigan Bay Formation. This can often be separated into two units in the west. It is partly coeval with incision infill and

upper diamict members of the Cardigan Bay Formation (Wingfield 1995). The lower unit includes the infill of glacial incisions and overlying stratified deposits: muds, cored at 89/15, have yielded a cold-water dinoflagellate cyst assemblage (Harland unpublished), with foraminifera dated from their D-aIle/L-Ile ratios as Early Devensian (Wingfield 1995). This unit may span much of oxygen isotope stages 6–2. Resting on an erosion surface, and more widespread, the upper unit includes the infill of Late Devensian glacial incisions with overlying stratified deposits (Wingfield 1994, 1995). These sediments either contain very sparse marine microfossil assemblages of arctic affinity, or they are unfossiliferous (D. M. Gregory & R. Harland unpublished). Substantial thicknesses of shelly muds and silts occur locally with scattered dropstones. Marine microfossil assemblages from these indicate a downward transition from temperate to cold, boreal conditions at many western sites, though comparable deposits in the east accumulated in cold water (R. Harland & D. M. Gregory *op cit.*). The upper unit may extend from oxygen isotope stage 2 to very early in stage 1.

(5) Western Irish Sea Formation. Basal diamicts, interpreted by Wingfield (1994, 1995) as lodgement tills, rest with laterally equivalent glaciomarine beds on an erosion surface. Overlying beds include the infill of a suite of deep glacial incisions. These have yielded a sparse marine microfauna of arctic or boreal affinity (Gregory & Harland unpublished), suggesting deposition during deglaciation (Wingfield 1995). They may be partly coeval with the Ayre Marine Silts of the northern Isle of Man (Lamplugh 1903; Smith 1930; Thomas Chapter 8, this volume). Warm-temperate microfaunas have not been recovered, but a single D-aIle/L-Ile ratio from 89/10 yielded an Ipswichian age of (Knudsen & Sejrup 1988). The uppermost beds comprise a widespread diamict that has been correlated by Wingfield (1994, 1995) with the 'Irish Sea Drift' of Late Devensian age. Hence the formation is likely to span oxygen isotope stages 6-2.

(6) 'Surface Sands' (informal unit). Includes the products of Holocene and present-day marine processes with sediments laid down in shallower water or subaerially (Wingfield 1994, 1995). Its marine fossil assemblages mainly indicate deposition under temperate conditions. Ice-rafted glacial debris occurs within equivalent deposits in the Celtic Sea (Pantin & Evans 1984) indicating that in some areas its basal sediments were deposited late in oxygen isotope stage 2.

The English Channel & its Western Approaches

T. D. J. Cameron

Quaternary deposits are no more than a few metres thick beneath much of the English Channel and its western approaches. They are exceptionally up to 180 m thick where they have partially or completely filled palaeovalleys such as the Hurd Deep, and they are up to 60 m thick in tidal sand ridges (Evans 1990). If pre-Devensian glacial deposits once extended south of the central Celtic Sea, then they have been completely eroded (Evans 1990). Devensian glacial deposits are largely absent too, though a tongue of the last Devensian ice sheet may have extended at least as far south as the Scilly Isles (Scourse 1990) and to 49°30'N in the outer shelf (Scourse *et al.* 1990). Ice-rafted glacial erratics and isolated mounds of glaciomarine sediment have been encountered at only 12 sites farther south. As a result, Holocene deposits rest on pre-

Table 32. *Quaternary correlations and oxygen isotope stratigraphy in the Irish Sea, St. George's Channel, North Celtic Sea, English Channel and its Western Approaches*

$\delta^{18}O$	STAGE	IRISH SEA, ST. GEORGES CHANNEL, NORTH CELTIC SEA	WESTERN ENGLISH CHANNEL AND ITS WESTERN APPROACHES
1	HOLOCENE	SURFACE SANDS 6	UNITS A & B 3
2	DEVENSIAN	WESTERN IRISH SEA FM 5	MELVILLE FM 3
3		CARDIGAN BAY FORMATION 4	
4			
5			
6-8	'SAALIAN'		
9-11	11 = HOXNIAN	ST. GEORGES CHANNEL FORMATION 3	
12	ANGLIAN	CAERNARFON BAY FM 2	
13	CROMERIAN	BARDSLEY LOOM FM 1	
19-21			
22	BAVELIAN		
	MENAPIAN		
	WAALIAN		
57			
58	EBURONIAN		
	TIGLIAN		
95			LITTLE SOLE FM
	PLIOCENE		

Quaternary bedrock across much of this area.

Two Quaternary formations were formally defined by Evans & Hughes (1984) for the area west of 6°W. One of these is mainly Neogene in age, while deposits of the other straddle the Late Devensian-Holocene boundary. Overlying sea-bed sediments and their basal lag were informally designated Layers A and B respectively by Pantin & Evans (1984).

Quaternary deposits of the English Channel have not been formally subdivided. Sediments older than the Holocene transgression are confined to the complex network of palaeovalleys that extends from the Dover Strait to the Hurd Deep, and to isolated valleys farther west, and have not been sampled. The origin of the valleys is a subject of controversy. Hamblin (1992) considers that many evolved in river systems that drained the English Channel during at least four periods of low eustatic sea level; the earliest of these may have been during the Cromerian. Smith (1985a) and Gibbard (1988b) suggested that others initiated by southward overflow of an Anglian ice-dammed southern North Sea lake through a precursor of the Dover Strait. Wingfield (1990) invoked scouring by outbursts from late Weichselian englacial lakes to account for the deepest valleys, although there is no evidence for glaciation of the English Channel (Hamblin 1991).

(1) Little Sole Formation. The uppermost beds, largely confined to the outer continental shelf, contain early Pleistocene foraminiferal assemblages (Curry et al. 1965; Evans & Hughes 1984), similar to those described by Jenkins (1982) and Jenkins et al. (1986) from the St Erth Beds, Cornwall. The St. Erth Beds were regarded as being 1.9 Ma to 2.1 Ma in age but, as on the Goban Spur (de Graciansky & Poag 1985), sedimentation may have been continuous from the Pliocene through to later in the Pleistocene on parts of the continental slope (Evans 1990).

(2) Melville Formation. Deposits of tidal sand ridges. This unit includes sediment lenses of glacial aspect proved between the ridges (Pantin & Evans 1984). Resting on the flanks of a tidal sand ridge at one site, a lens of ice-rafted glaciomarine silty clay has yielded an arctic molluscan fauna (Scourse et al. 1990). Hence the sand ridges were at least coeval with glaciation a greater or lesser distance away from them (Evans 1990). This occurred in the latter part of the Late Devensian glaciation (Scourse et al. 1990).

(3) Units A & B. Lag deposits of the late Devensian to early Holocene marine transgression and their reworked sediments.

Late Devensian and early Holocene transgressive deposits and overlying fully marine sediments are widespread across the floor of the English Channel. Older sediments are restricted to the network of palaeovalleys illustrated by Auffret et al. (1990). They have not yet been sampled and their age is uncertain.

References

AALTO, M. M., COOPE, G. R. & GIBBARD, P. L. 1984. Late Devensian river deposits at Thrupp House Farm, Abingdon, Berkshire, England. *Proceedings of the Geologists' Association,* **95,** 65–79.

ABBOTT, W. J. L. 1890. Notes on some Pleistocene sections in and near London. *Proceedings of the Geologists' Association,* **11,** 473–480.

—— 1911. On the classification of the British Stone Age industries and some new, and little known well marked horizons and cultures. *Journal of the Royal Anthropological Institute,* **41,** 458–481.

ABD-ALLA, M. A. A. 1988. *Mineralogical and geochemical studies of tills in south-western Scotland.* PhD thesis, University of Glasgow.

ADDISON, K. & EDGE, M. J. 1992. Early Devensian interstadial and glacigenic sediments in Gwynedd, North Wales. *Geological Journal,* **27,** 181–190.

AGUIRRE, E. & PASSINI, G. 1985. The Pliocene-Pleistocene boundary. *Episodes,* **8,** 116–120.

AITKEN, A. M., MERRITT, J. W. & SHAW, A. J. 1979. The sand and gravel resources of the country around Garmouth, Grampian Region. Description of 1: 25,000 resource sheet NJ36. *Mineral Assessment Report of the Institute of Geological Sciences,* **No. 41.**

ALABASTER, C. & STRAW, A. 1976. The Pleistocene context of faunal remains and artefacts discovered at Welton-Le-Wold, Lincolnshire. *Proceedings of the Yorkshire Geological Society,* **41,** 75–94.

ALDHOUSE-GREEN, S. H. R. 1995. Pontnewydd Cave, Wales: a later Middle Pleistocene hominid and archaeological site: a review of stratigraphy, dating, taphonomy and interpretation. *In:* BERMUDEZ, J. M., ARSUAGA, J. L. & CARBONELL, E. (eds) *Human Evolution in Europe and the Atapuerca Evidence (Junta de Castilla y Leon),* 37–55.

—— & SCOTT, K. in press. Coygan Cave, Laugharne, South Wales: A Mousterian site and hyaena den: a report on the University of Cambridge excavations *Proceedings of the Prehistoric Society,* **61.**

ALDISS, D. T. 1992a. Geological notes and local details for 1:10,000 sheet TL12NE (Hitchin). *British Geological Survey Technical Report,* WA/92/61.

—— 1992b. Geological notes and local details for 1:10,000 sheet TL12NW (Little Wymondley). *British Geological Survey Technical Report,* WA/92/62.

ALLEN, J. R. L. 1982. Late Pleistocene (Devensian) glaciofluvial outwash at Banc-y-Warren, near Cardigan (West Wales). *Geological Journal,* **17,** 31–47.

—— 1987. Late Flandrian Shoreline Oscillations in the Severn Estuary: the Rumney Formation at its Typesite (Cardiff area). *Philosophical Transactions of the Royal Society of London,* B **315,** 157–174.

—— 1991. *The evolution of the Solent River during the Pleistocene.* PhD thesis, University of Cambridge.

—— & GIBBARD, P. L. 1994. Pleistocene evolution of the Solent River of southern England. *Quaternary Science Reviews,* **12,** 503–528.

——, ——, PREECE, R. C. & ROBINSON, J. E. 1996. Late Pleistocene interglacial deposits at Pennington Marches, Lymington, Hampshire, England. *Proceedings of the Geologists' Association,* **107,** 39–50.

ALLEN, P. 1982. Great Blakenham and Creeting St Mary. *In:* ALLEN, P. (ed.) *Field meeting guide. Suffolk.* Section **2,** 1–18. London: Quaternary Research Association.

—— 1983. *Middle Pleistocene stratigraphy and landform development in south-east Suffolk.* PhD thesis, University of London.

—— 1984. *Field Guide to the Gipping and Waveney Valleys,* Quaternary Research Association.

—— 1991. Deformation structures in British Pleistocene sediments. *In:* EHLERS, J., GIBBARD, P. L. & ROSE, J. (eds) *Glacial Deposits in Great Britain and Ireland.* Balkema, Rotterdam, 455–469.

—— & JACKSON, A. A. 1985. Geology of the country around Harlech. *Memoir British Geological Survey.*

—— & ROSE, J. 1986. A glacial meltwater drainage system between Whittonstall and Ebchester, Northumberland *In:* MACLIN, M. G. & ROSE, J. (eds) *Quaternary River Landforms and Sediments in the Northern Pennines, England.* Field Guide. British Geomorphological Research Group/Quaternary Research Association, 69–88.

——, CHESHIRE, D. A. & WHITEMAN, C. A. 1991. Glacial Deposits of southern East Anglia. *In:* EHLERS, J., GIBBARD, P. L. & ROSE, J. (eds) *Glacial Deposits in Great Britain and Ireland.* Balkema, Rotterdam, 255–278.

ALLEN, T. 1977. Interglacial sea-level change: evidence for brackish water sedimentation at Purfleet, Essex. *Quaternary Newsletter,* **22,** 1–3.

ALLEN, T. J. 1978. Disposition of the terraces of the River Thames in the vicinity of Yiewsley. *In:* COLLINS, D. (ed.) *Early Man in West Middlesex,* HMSO, London, 5–10.

ALLEY, R. B. & CLARK, P. U. in press. The deglaciation of the Northern Hemisphere

ALMAINE, H. G. W. D. 1922. Palaeolithic gravel near Abingdon. *Antiquaries Journal,* **2,** 257–258.

AMBROSE, J. D. 1973. The sand and gravel resources of the country around Maldon, Essex. *Report of the Institute of Geological Sciences,* 73/1.

AMBROSE, K. & HORTON, A. 1991. The origin of Ot Moor, Oxfordshire. *Proceedings of the Geologists' Association,* **102,** 265–274.

——, MOORLOCK, B. S. P. & CANNELL, B. 1985. *The geology of sheet SO84.* British Geological Survey, Keyworth.

ANDREWS, J. T., BOWEN, D. Q. & KIDSON, C. 1979. Amino acid ratios and the correlation of raised beach deposits in south-west England and Wales. *Nature,* **281,** 556–558.

——, GILBERTSON, D. D. & HAWKINS, A. B. 1984. The Pleistocene succession of the Severn Estuary: a revised model based on amino-acid racemization studies. *Journal of the Geological Society, London,* **141,** 967–974.

ANON, 1906. Flint Implements and Fossils from Clacton. *Essex Naturalist,* **14,** 164.

—— 1908. Palaeolithic flint implement from a gravel pit, Handborough, Oxon. *Oxford University Gazette,* **38,** 752.

—— 1911a. Visit to Clacton-on-Sea, and 301st ordinary meeting. Saturday, 30th September 1911. *Essex Naturalist,* **16,** 322–324.

—— 1911b. Exhibition by S. H. Warren of plaster casts of Palaeolithic wooden spear (?) and some flint-flakes from a Pleistocene deposit at Clacton-on-Sea. *Essex Naturalist,* **16,** 326.

—— 1913. Excursion to Mersea Island (the 427th Meeting), Saturday, 20th September 1913. *Essex Naturalist,* **17,** 229–234.

—— 1931. The Newton Collection. *Antiquaries Journal,* **11,** 420–421.

—— 1966. The Aveley elephants. *Report of the British Museum (Natural History)* (for 1963-1965), 30–31.

—— 1982a. Waltham Cross, Hertfordshire. *Earth Science Conservation,* **19,** 35.

—— 1982b. Hornchurch, Essex. *Earth Science Conservation,* **19,** 35.

—— 1984a. Hornchurch Railway cutting. *Earth Science Conseervation,* **21,** 42.

—— 1984b. Globe Pit SSSI, Essex. *Earth Science Conservation,* **21,** 39–40.

ANSARI, M. H. 1992. *Stratigraphy and palaeobotany of Middle Pleistocene interglacial deposits in the North Sea.* PhD thesis, University of Wales.

ApSIMON, A. M. & DONOVAN, D. T. 1956. Marine Pleistocene deposits in the Vale of Gordano, Somerset. *Proceedings, University of Bristol Spelaeological Society,* **7,** 130–136.

——, —— & TAYLOR, H. 1961. The stratigraphy and archaeology of the Late-Glacial and Post-Glacial deposits at Brean Down, Somerset. *Proceedings,University of Bristol Spelaeological Society,* **9,** 67–136.

——, GAMBLE, C. S. & SHAKLEY, M. I. 1977. Pleistocene raised beaches on Ports Down, Hampshire. *Proceedings of the Hampshire Field Club Archaeology Society,* **33.**

ARKELL, W. J. 1943. The Pleistocene rocks at Trebetherick Point, North Cornwall: their interpretation and correlation. *Proceedings of the Geologists' Association,* **54,** 141–170.

—— 1945. Three Oxfordshire palaeoliths and their significance for Pleistocene correlation. *Proceedings of the Prehistoric Society,* **2,** 20–31.

—— 1947a. *The Geology of Oxford,* Clarendon, Oxford.

—— 1947b. The geology of the Evenlode Gorge, Oxfordshire. *Proceedings of the Geologists' Association*, **58**, 87–113.

—— 1947c. A palaeolith from the Hanborough Terrace. *Oxoniensia*, **11–12**, 1–4.

—— & OAKLEY, K. P. 1948. The implements in the Treacher Collection. *In:* On the ancient channel between Caversham and Henley, Oxfordshire, and its contained flint implements. *Proceedings of the Prehistoric Society*, **14**, 126–154.

ARMSTRONG, M., PATERSON, I. B. & BROWNE, M. A. E. 1985. Geology of the Perth and Dundee District. *Memoir of the British Geological Survey*.

ARTHURTON, R. S., BOOTH, S. J., MORIGI, A. N. & ABBOTT, M. A. W. 1994. Geology of the country around Great Yarmouth. *Memoir of the British Geological Survey*.

ASHTON, N. M. 1992. The High Lodge flint industries. *In:* ASHTON, N. M., COOK, J., LEWIS, S. G. & ROSE, J. (eds) *High Lodge. Excavations by G. de G. Sieveking, 1962-8 and J. Cook, 1988.* British Museum Press, London, 124–163.

ASHTON, N., BOWEN, D. Q., HOLMAN, A., HUNT, C., IRVING, B., KEMP, R. A., LEWIS, S. G., McNABB, J., PARFITT, S. & SEDDON, M. B. 1994a. Excavations at the Lower Palaeolithic site at East Farm, Barnham, Suffolk, 1989-1992. *Journal of the Geological Society, London*, **151**, 599–607.

——, McNABB, J., IRVING, B., LEWIS, S. G. & PARFITT, S. 1994b. Contemporaneity of Clactonian and Acheulian flint industries at Barnham, Suffolk. *Antiquity*, **68**, 585–589.

ATKINSON, T. C., HARMON, R. S., SMART, P. L. & WALTHAM, A. C. 1978. Palaeoclimatic and geomorphic implications of ^{230}Th/^{234}U dates on speleothems from Britain. *Nature*, **272**, 24–28.

AUFFRET, J. P., ALDUC, D., LARSONNEUR, C. & SMITH, A. J. 1990. Cartographie du réseau de palléovallées et de l'épaisseur des formations superficielles meubles de la Manche orientale. *Annales Institut Oceanographie*, **56**, 21–35.

AUSTEN, R. A. C. 1851. On the superficial accumulations of the coasts of the English Channel, and the changes they indicate. *Proceedings of the Geological Society*, **7**, 118–136.

AUTON, C. A. 1982. The sand and gravel resources of the country around Redgrave, Suffolk. Description of 1 : 25000 resource sheet TM07 and part of TM08. *Mineral Assessment Report*, 117.

——, MORIGI, A. N. & PRICE, D. 1985. The sand and gravel resources of the country around Harleston and Bungay, Norfolk and Suffolk. Description of 1 : 25000 resource sheets comprising parts of TM 27, 28, 38 and 39. *Mineral Assessment Report British Geological Survey*, 145.

AVERY, B. W. & CATT, J. A. 1983. Northaw Great Wood. *In:* ROSE, J. (ed.) *The Diversion of the Thames*, Field Guide, Quaternary Research Association, Cambridge, 96–101.

BADEN-POWELL, D. F. W. 1930. Notes on raised beach mollusca from the Isle of Portland. *Proceedings of the Malacological Society*, **19**, 67–76.

—— 1948. The chalky boulder clays of Norfolk and Suffolk. *Geological Magazine*, **85**, 279–296.

—— 1949. Experimental Clactonian technique. *Proceedings of the Prehistoric Society*, **15**, 38–41.

—— 1950. The Pliocene-Pleistocene boundary in the British deposits. *In:* OAKLEY, K. P. (ed.) *The Pliocene-Pleistocene boundary*. International Geological Congress 18th session (G. B., 1948), Volume 9, 8–10.

—— 1951. The age of interglacial deposits at Swanscombe. *Geological Magazine*, **88**, 344–56.

—— 1955. Appendix B: Report on the marine fauna of the Clacton Channels. *In:* WARREN, S. H. The Clacton Channel deposits. *Quarterly Journal of the Geological Society, London*, **111**, 301–305.

BAKER, C. A. 1971. A contribution to the glacial stratigraphy of west Essex. *Essex Naturalist*, **32**, 318–330.

—— 1977. *Quaternary stratigraphy and environments in the Upper Cam valley*. PhD thesis, University of London.

—— 1983. Glaciation and Thames Diversion in the mid-Essex Depression. *In:* ROSE, J. (ed.) *The Diversion of the Thames*, Field Guide, Quaternary Research Association, Cambridge, 39–49.

—— & JONES, D. K. C. 1980. Glaciation of the London Basin and its influence on the drainage pattern: a review and appraisal. *In:* JONES, D. K. C. (ed.) *The Shaping of Southern England*, Institute of British Geographers Special Publication 11, Academic,

London, 131–176.

BALSON, P. S. 1992. Holocene. *In:* CAMERON, T. J. D. *et al.* (eds) United Kingdom offshore regional report: the geology of the southern North Sea. *British Geological Survey*, 116–130.

BANHAM, P. H. 1971. Pleistocene beds at Corton, Suffolk. *Geological Magazine*, **108**, 281–285.

—— 1988. Polyphase glaciotectonic deformation in the Contorted Drift of Norfolk. *In:* CROOT, D. (ed.) *Glaciotectonics; forms and processes*. Balkema, Rotterdam, 27–32.

BARBER, K. E. & BROWN, A. G. 1987. Late Pleistocene organic deposits beneath the floodplain of the River Avon at Ibsley, Hampshire. *In:* BARBER, K. E. (ed.) *Wessex and the Isle of Wight*. Quaternary Research Association Field Guide, Cambridge, 65–74.

——, CHAMBERS, F. M. & MADDY, D. 1994. Sensitive high resolution records of Holocene palaeoclimate from ombrotophic bogs. *Palaeoclimate of the last glacial/interglacial cycle*. Natural Environment Research Council, Swindon.

BARCLAY, W. J., BRANDON, A., ELLISON, R. A. & MOORLOCK, B. S. P. 1992. Pleistocene palaeovalley-fill west of the Malvern Hills. *Journal of the Geological Society, London*, **149**, 75–92.

——, AMBROSE, K., CHADWICK, R. A. & PHARAOH, T. C. in press. *Geology of the Country Around Worcester*. Memoir British Geological Survey.

BARNOSKY, A. D. 1985. Taphonomy and herd stucture of the extinct Irish Elk *Megaloceros giganteus*. *Science*, **22**, 340–344.

BARROW, G. 1906. *The Geology of the Isles of Scilly*. Memoir of the Geological Survey of Great Britain.

—— 1919a. Some future work for the Geologists' Association. *Proceedings of the Geologists' Association*, **30**, 1–48.

—— 1919b. Notes on the correlation of the deposits described in Mr C J. Gilbert's paper with the high-level gravels of the south of England (or the London Basin). *Quarterly Journal of the Geological Society, London*, **75**, 44–50.

—— 1919c. Excursion to Stanmore Hill and Bushey Heath. *Proceedings of the Geologists' Association*, **30**, 122–126.

BARTLEY, D. D. 1960a. Rhosgoch Common, Radnorshire: stratigraphy and pollen analysis. *New Phytologist*, **59**, 238–262.

—— 1962. The stratigraphy and pollen analysis of lake deposits near Tadcaster, Yorkshire. *New Phytologist*, **61**, 277–287.

—— 1966. Pollen analysis of some lake deposits near Bamburgh in Northumberland. *New Phytologist*, **65**, 141–156.

——, CHAMBERS, C. & HART-JONES, B. 1976. The vegetational history of parts of south and east Durham. *New Phytologist*, **77**, 437–468.

BARTON, M. E. 1963. Pleistocene geology of the country around Bromsgrove. *Proceedings of the Geologists' Association*, **71**, 139–155.

BATEMAN, R. M. & ROSE, J. 1994. Fine sand mineralogy of the early and middle Pleistocene Bytham Sands and Gravels of midland England and East Anglia. *Proceedings of the Geologists' Association*, **105**, 33–39.

BATES, M. R. 1993. Quaternary Aminostratigraphy in Northwestern France. *Quaternary Science Reviews*, **12**, 793–810.

——, PARFITT, S. A. & ROBERTS, M. B. 1997. The chronology, palaeogeography and archaeological significance of the marine Quaternary record of the West Sussex Coastal Plain, southern England, UK. *Quaternary Science Reviews*, **16**, 1227–1252.

BEAUMONT, P. 1968. A history of glacial research in Northern England from 1860 to the present day. *University of Durham Occasional Papers*, **9**, 1–21.

——, TURNER, J. & WARD, P. F. 1969. An Ipswichian peat raft in glacial till at Hutton Henry, Co. Durham. *New Phytologist*, **68**, 779–781.

BELL, A. M. 1894a. Palaeolithic remains at Wolvercote, Oxfordshire I and II. *Antiquary*, **30**, 148–152 and 192–198.

—— 1894b. On the Pleistocene gravels at Wolvercote near Oxford. *Report of the British Association, Oxford*, 663–664.

BELL, A. M. 1904. Implementiferous sections at Wolvercote, Oxfordshire. *Quarterly Journal of the Geological Society, London*, **60**, 120–132.

BELL, F. G. 1969. The occurrence of southern, steppe and halophyte elements in Weichselian (last glacial) floras from southern Britian. *New Phytologist*, **68**, 913–922.

—— & DICKSON, C. A. 1971. The Barnwell Station arctic flora: a reappraisal of some plant identifications. *New Phytologist*, **70**,

627–638.

——, COOPE, G. R., RICE, R. J. & RILEY, T. H. 1972. Mid-Weichselian fossil-bearing deposits at Syston, Leicestershire. *Proceeedings of the Geologists' Association,* **83,** 197–211.

BELL, J. A. 1917. The shells of the Holderness Basement Clays. *The Naturalist,* **95–98,** 135–138.

—— 1919. Fossils of the Holderness Clays. *The Naturalist,* **57–59.**

BELL, M. 1983. Valley sediments as evidence of prehistoric land-use on the South Downs. *Proceedings of the Prehistoric Society,* **49,** 119–150.

BEMROSE, H. H. A. & DEELEY, R. M. 1886. Discovery of mammalian remains in the old river gravels of the Derwent near Derby. *Quarterly Journal of the Geological Society, London,* **52,** 497–510.

—— & NEWTON, E. T. 1905. On a fossiliferous cavern of Pleistocene age at Hoe Grange Quarry, Longcliffe, near Brassington (Derbyshire). *Quarterly Journal of the Geological Society, London,* **61,** 43–63.

BENNETT, K. D., PEGLAR, S. M. & SHARPE, M. J. 1991. Holocene lake sediments in central East Anglia. *In:* LEWIS, S. G., WHITEMAN, C. A. & BRIDGLAND, D. R. (eds) *Central East Anglia and the Fen Basin* Field Guide, Quaternary Research Association, London, 111–118.

BENT, A. J. A. 1986. *Aspects of Pleistocene Glaciomarine Sequences in the Northern North Sea.* PhD thesis, University of Edinburgh.

BERCKHEMER, F. 1933. Ein Menschen-Schadel aus den diluvialen Schottern von Steinheim a. d. Murr. *Anthropologische Anzeiger,* **10,** 318–321.

BERRY, F. G. & SHEPHARD-THORN, E. R. 1982. Geological notes and local details for 1:10000 sheets SZ 98 NW, NE, SW and SE, SZ 99 NW and NE (West Sussex Coastal Plain between Selsey and Bognor). *Institute of Geological Sciences.*

BIRKS, H. J. B. 1993. Loch Cill an Aonghais. *In:* GORDON, J. E. & SUTHERLAND, D. G. (eds) *Quaternary of Scotland,* Chapman and Hall, London, 350–351.

—— & PEGLAR, S. M. 1979. Interglacial pollen spectra from Sel Ayre, Shetland. *New Phytologist,* **83,** 559–575.

—— & RANSOM, M. E. 1969. An interglacial peat at Fugla Ness, Shetland. *New Phytologist,* **68,** 777–796.

BIRNIE, J. 1983. Tolsta Head: further investigations of the interstadial deposit. *Quaternary Newsletter,* **41,** 18–25.

BISAT, W. S. 1932. On the subdivision of the Holderness boulder clays. *The Naturalist,* **215–219.**

—— 1939. The relationship of the 'Basement Clays' of Dimlington, Bridlington and Filey bays. *The Naturalist,* **133–135,** 161–168.

—— 1940. Older and newer drift in East Yorkshire. *Proceedings of the Yorkshire Geological Society,* **24,** 137–151.

—— 1948. Interglacial moss at Dimlington, Yorkshire. *The Naturalist,* Hull, **1.**

—— & BELL, J. A. 1941. The occurence of a bed containing moss in the boulder clays of Dimlington. *Proceedings of the Yorkshire Geological Society,* **24,** 219–222.

BISHOP, M. J. 1974. A preliminary report on the Middle Pleistocene mammal bearing deposits of Westbury-sub-Mendip, Somerset. *Proceedings, University of Bristol Spelaeological Society,* **13,** 301–318.

—— 1982. The mammal fauna of the early Middle Pleistocene cavern infill site of Westbury-sub-Mendip, Somerset. *Special Papers in Palaeontology,* **28,** 1–108.

BISHOP, W. W. 1958. The Pleistocence geology and geomorphology of three gaps in the Middle Jurassic escarpmet. *Philosophical Transactions of the Royal Society of London,* **B241,** 255–306.

—— & COOPE, G. R. 1977. Stratigraphical and faunal evidence for Lateglacial and early Flandrian environments in south-west Scotland. *In:* GRAY, J. M. & LOWE, J. J. (eds) *Studies in the Lateglacial Environment.* Pergamon, Oxford, 61–88.

BLACKBURN, K. B. 1952. The dating of a deposit containing an elk skeleton found at Neasham near Darlington, County Durham. *New Phytologist,* **51,** 364–377.

BLAIR, K. G. 1923. Some Coleopterous remains from the peat-bed at Wolvercote, Oxfordshire. *Transactions of the Royal Entomological Society of London,* **71,** 558–563.

BLAKE, J. H. 1891. Excursion to Henley-on-Thames and Nettlebed. *Proceedings of the Geologists' Association,* **12,** 204–206.

—— 1900. Excursion to Silchester. *Proceedings of the Geologists' Association,* **16,** 513–516.

—— 1903. The Geology of the Country around Reading. *Memoir of the Geological Survey of Great Britain.*

BLEZARD, R. G. 1966. Field meeting at Aveley and West Thurrock. *Proceedings of the Geologists' Association,* **77,** 273–276.

—— 1973. South Essex. *In: The Estuarine Region of Suffolk and Essex* (eds GREENSMITH, J. T., BLEZARD, R. G., BRISTOW, C. R. *et al.*), *Geologists' Association Guide.* Benham, Colchester, 35–41.

BOARDMAN, J. 1985. The Troutbeck Paleosol, Cumbria, England. *In:* BOARDMAN, J. (ed.) *Soils and Quaternary landscape evolution.* 231–260. Wiley, Chichester.

—— 1991. Glacial deposits of the English Lake District. *In:* EHLERS, J., GIBBARD, P. L. & ROSE, J. (eds) *Glacial Deposits in Great Britain and Ireland.* Balkema, Rotterdam. 175–184.

BOLTON, J. 1862. On a deposit with insects, leaves, etc near Ulverston. *Quarterly Journal of the Geological Society, London,* **18,** 274–277.

BOND, G. & LOTTI, R. 1995. Iceberg discharges into the North Atlantic on millennial time scales during the last deglaciation. *Science,* **267,** 1005–1010.

BONNY, A. P., MATHERS, S. J. & HAYWORTH, E. Y. 1986. Interstadial deposits with Chelford affinities from Burland, Cheshire. *The Mercian Geologist,* **10,** 151–160.

BOREHAM, S. & GIBBARD, P. L. 1995. Middle Pleistocene Hoxnian Stage interglacial deposits at Hitchin, Hertfordshire, England. *Proceedings of the Geologists' Association,* **106,** 259–270.

BOSWELL, P. G. H. 1940. Climates of the past: a review of the geological evidence. *Quarterly Journal of the Royal Meteorological Society of London,* **66,** 249–274.

—— 1952. The Pliocene-Pleistocene boundary in the East of England. *Proceedings of the Geologists' Association,* **63,** 301–312.

BOULTER, M. C. & MITCHELL, I. 1977. Middle Pleistocene (Gortian) deposits from Benburb, Northern Ireland. *Irish Naturalists' Journal,* **19,** 2–3.

BOULTON, G. S. 1977. A multiple till sequence formed by a Late Devensian Welsh ice-cap: Glanllynnau, Gwynedd. *Cambria,* **4,** 10–31.

—— & WORSLEY, P. 1965. Late Weichselian glaciation in the Cheshire-Shropshire Basin. *Nature,* **207,** 704–706.

BOULTON, W. S. 1917. Mammalian remains in the glacial gravels at Stourbridge. *Proceedings of the Birmingham Natural History and Philosophical Society,* **14,** 107–112.

BOWEN, D. Q. 1969*a*. A new interpretation of the Pleistocene succession in the Bristol Channel area (Abstract). *Proceedings of the Ussher Society,* **2,** 86.

—— 1969*b*. Port-Eynon Bay north side: Horton to Western Slade to Eastern Slade. *In:* BOWEN, D. Q. (ed.) *Coastal Pleistocene deposits in Wales.* Quaternary Research Association Field Guide 1969, 12–15.

—— 1970. South-east and central Wales. *In:* LEWIS, C. A. (ed.) *The glaciations of Wales and adjoining regions.* Longman, London, 197–228.

—— 1971*a*. The Quaternary succession of south Gower. *In:* BASSETT, D. A. & BASSETT, M. G. (eds) *Geological excursions in South Wales and the Forest of Dean.* Geologists' Association, South Wales Group, Cardiff, 135–142.

—— 1971*b*. The Pleistocene succession and related landforms in north Pembrokeshire and south Cardiganshire. *In:* BASSETT, D. A. & BASSETT, M. G. (eds) *Geological excursions in South Wales and the Forest of Dean.* Geologists' Association, South Wales Group, Cardiff, 260–266.

—— 1973*a*. The Pleistocene history of Wales and the borderland. *Geological Journal,* **8,** 207–224.

—— 1973*b*. The Pleistocene succession of the Irish Sea. *Proceedings of the Geologists' Association,* **84,** 249–272.

—— 1973*c*. The Excavation at Minchin Hole 1973. *Journal of the Gower Society,* **24,** 12–18.

—— 1974. The Quaternary of Wales. *In:* OWEN, T. R. (ed.) *The Upper Palaeozoic and post-Palaeozoic rocks of Wales.* University of Wales Press, Cardiff, 373–426.

—— 1977*a*. The coast of Wales. *Geological Journal* (special issue), **7,** 223–256.

—— (ed.) 1977*b*. *Wales and the Cheshire-Shropshire Lowland.* X INQUA Congress Guidebook for Excursions A8 and C8.

—— 1978. *Quaternary Geology: A Stratigraphic Framework for Multidisciplinary Work,* Pergamon, Oxford.

—— 1981a. The 'South Wales end moraine': fifty years after. *In:* NEALE, J. & FLENLEY, J. (eds) *The Quaternary of Britain.* Pergamon, Oxford, 60–67.

—— 1981b. Sheet 1. 3. *In:* CARTER, H. & GRIFFITHS, H. M. (eds) *National Atlas of Wales.* University of Wales Press, Cardiff.

—— 1982. Pleistocene deposits and fluvioglacial landforms of north Preseli. *In:* BASSETT, M. G. (ed.) *Geological excursions in South-West Wales.* Geologists' Association, South Wales Group, Cardiff, 289135–142.

—— 1989. The last interglacial-glacial cycle in the British Isles. *Quaternary International, 3/4,* 41–47.

—— 1991. Amino acid geochronology. *In:* LEWIS, S. G., WHITEMAN, C. A. & BRIDGLAND, D. R. (eds) *Central East Anglia and the Fen Basin,* Field Guide, Quaternary Research Association, London, 21–24.

—— 1992. Aminostratigraphy of non-marine mollusca in South Britain. *Sveriges Geologiska Undersokning,* **81,** 65–67

—— 1994a. The Pleistocene History of North West Europe. *Science Progress,* **76,** 209–223.

—— 1994b. Late Cenozoic Wales and South-West England. *Proceedings of the Ussher Society,* **8,** 209–213.

—— in press. Only Four Major '100 ka' Glaciations during the Brunhes? *Geologische Rundschau.*

—— & HENRY, A. 1984. *Wales: Gower, Preseli and Fforest Fawr.* Quaternary Research Association Field Guide, Cambridge.

—— & LEAR, D. L. 1982. The Quaternary geology of the lower Teifi Valley. *In:* BASSETT, M. G. (ed.) *Geological excursions in Dyfed, south-west Wales,* National Museum of Wales, Cardiff, 297–302.

—— & SYKES, G. A. 1988. Correlation of marine events and glaciations in the northeast Atlantic margin. *Philosophical Transactions of the Royal Society,* **B318,** 619–635.

—— & SYKES, G. A. 1991. Discussion of 'The correlation of the Speeton Shell Bed, Filey Bay, Yorkshire, to an oxygen isotope stage'. *Proceedings of the Yorkshire Geological Society,* **48(3),** 223–226.

—— & —— 1994. How old is 'Boxgrove man'? *Nature,* **371,** 751.

——, ——, REEVES, A., MILLER, G. H., ANDREWS, J. T., BREW, J. S. & HARE, P. E. 1985. Amino acid geochronology of raised beaches in south-west Britain. *Quaternary Science Reviews,* **4,** 279–318.

——, ROSE, J., MCCABE, A. M. & SUTHERLAND, D. G. 1986. Quaternary Glaciations in England, Ireland Scotland and Wales. *Quaternary Science Reviews,* **5,** 299–340.

——, HUGHES, S., SYKES, G. A. & MILLER, G. H. 1989. Land-sea correlations in the Pleistocene based on isoleucine epimerization in non-marine molluscs. *Nature,* **340,** 49–51.

——, SMITH, D. B. & SYKES, G. A. 1991. The age of the Easington Raised Beach, County Durham. *Proceedings of the Yorkshire Geological Society,* **48(4),** 415–420.

——, PHILLIPS, F. M. & ELMORE, D. 1994. [36]Cl dating British Ice Sheets. *EOS,* (Nov 7) American Geophysical Union.

BOYD, W. E. 1986a. Late Devensian shoreline position in north Ayrshire. *Scottish Journal of Geology,* **22,** 412–416.

—— 1986b. Fossil *Lithothamnium* (calcareous algae) rhodoliths from Late Quaternary raised coastal sediments, Irvine, Ayrshire. *Scottish Journal of Geology,* **22,** 165–177.

—— 1986c. Vegetation history at Linwood Moss, Renfrewshire, central Scotland. *Journal of Biogeography,* **13,** 207–223.

—— 1988. Early Flandrian vegetational development on the coastal plain of north Ayrshire, Scotland: evidence from multiple pollen profiles. *Journal of Biogeography,* **15,** 325–337.

BOYLAN, P. 1966. The Pleistocene deposits of Kirmington, Lincolnshire. *Mercian Geologist,* **1,** 339–350.

—— 1972. The scientific significance of the Kirkdale Cave hyaenas. *Yorkshire Philosophical Society Annual Report for 1971,* 38–47.

—— 1977a. Kirkdale Cave. *In:* CATT, J. A. (ed.) *Guidebook for Excursion C7. Yorkshire and Lincolnshire.* INQUA X Congress, United Kingdom. Norwich. Geo Abstracts. 26–27.

—— 1977b. Victoria Cave. *In:* CATT, J. A. (ed.) *Guidebook for Excursion C7. Yorkshire and Lincolnshire.* INQUA X Congress, United Kingdom. Norwich. Geo Abstracts. 52–53.

BRAMWELL, D. 1964. The excavations at Elder Bush Cave, Wetton, Staffordshire. *North Staffordshire Journal of Field Studies,* **4,** 46–59.

BRANDON, A. 1984. Sheet SO 55 (Leominster south-east). Geology with special emphasis on potential resources of sand and gravel. *Geological reports for DoE: Land Use-Planning. British Geological Survey.*

—— 1989. Geology of the country between Hereford and Leominster. *Memoir of the British Geological Survey.*

—— 1982. Quaternary deposits of Sheet SO54 (Hereford north-east). *Institute of Geological Sciences.*

—— 1987. Geological notes and local details of the 1 : 10 000 sheets: SK 94 NW (Caythorpe). *British Geological Survey.*

—— 1991. *1 : 10 000 Geological sheet SK 84 SE (Foston). British Geological Survey.*

—— 1992. 1 : 10 000 Geological Sheet SK 84 NW (Bottlesford). *British Geological Survey.*

—— 1994. Geology of the Normanton on Soar area: 1 : 10 000 Sheet SK 52 SW. *British Geological Survey Technical Report WA/94/60.*

—— 1995. Geology of the Lower Derwent valley: 1 : 10 000 Sheets SK 33 SE, SK 43 SW and SK 43 SE. *British Geological Survey Technical Report.*

—— 1996. Geology of the lower Derwent valley: 1 : 10 000 sheets SK 33 SE, 43 SW & 43 SE. *Technical Report WA/96/07. British Geological Survey.*

—— in prep. Geology of the Etwall-Willington area: 1 : 10 000 Sheets SK 23 SE and SK 22 NE. *Technical Report. British Geological Survey.*

—— & HAINS, B. A. 1981. Geological notes and local details for 1 : 10 000 Sheets SO 43 NE, SO 44 SE, SO 53 NW, SO 54 SW (Hereford City). *Institute of Geological Sciences.*

—— & SUMBLER, M. G. 1988. An Ipswichian fluvial deposit at Fulbeck, Lincolnshire and the chronology of the Trent terraces. *Journal of Quaternary Science,* **3,** 127–133.

—— & SUMBLER, M. G. 1991. The Balderton Sand and Gravel: pre-Ipswichian cold stage fluvial deposits near Lincoln, England. *Journal of Quaternary Science,* **6,** 117–138.

—— & —— in prep. Middle Pleistocene deposits of the rivers Trent and Bain, east of Lincoln, England.

——, COOPE, G. R., FIELD, H. F. & PREECE, R. C. in prep. A. A Middle Pleistocene interglacial deposit beneath the Balderton Sand and Gravel at Whisby, Lincolnshire.

——, ——, —— & GIBBARD, P. L. in prep. B. Pre-Anglian and Anglian deposits of the Mathon River at The Brays Pit, Mathon, Herefordshire.

BRAZIER, V. B., WHITTINGTON, L. & BALLANTYNE, C. K. 1988. Holocene debris cone formation in Glen Etive, Western Grampian Highlands, Scotland. *Earth Surface Processes and Landforms,* **13,** 525–531.

BREITINGER, E. 1952. Zur Morphologie und systematischen Stellung des Schadelfragmentes von Swanscombe. *Homo,* **3,** 131–3.

—— 1955. Das Schadelfragment von Swanscombe und das 'Praesapiensproblem'. *Mitteilungen der Anthropologischen Gesellschaft Wien,* **84/85,** 27–38.

—— 1964. Reconstruction of the Swanscombe Skull. *In:* OVEY, C. D. (ed.) *The Swanscombe Skull,* Royal Anthropological Institute, Occasional Paper No. 20, 161–72. Translated by Watson, D. M. from: Das Schadelgragment von Swanscombe und das 'Praesapiensproblem'. *Mitteilunger der Anthropologischen Gesellschaft Wien,* **84/85,** 27–38.

BREUIL, H. 1932a. Appendix in Sandford, K. S., The Pleistocen succession in England. *Geological Magazine,* **69,** 17–18.

—— 1932b. Les Industries a eclats du Palaeolithique ancien, I: Le Clactonien. *Prehistoire, Paris,* **1,** 148–57.

—— 1934. De l'importance de la solifluction dans l'etude des terrains Quaternaires de la France et des pays voisins. *Revue de Geographie Physique et de Geologie Dynamique,* **7,** 269–331.

—— 1947. Age of the Baker's Hole Coombe Rock, Northfleet, Kent. *Nature, London,* **160,** 831.

BRIDGE, D. MCC. & HOPSON, P. M. 1985. Fine gravel, heavy mineral and grain-size analyses of mid-Pleistocene glacial deposits in the lower Waveney valley, East Anglia. *Modern Geology,* **9,** 129–144.

BRIDGE, M. C., HAGGART, B. A. & LOWE, J. J. 1990 The history and palaeoclimatic significance of subfossil remains of *Pinus sylvestris* in blanket peats from Scotland. *Journal of Ecology,* **78,** 77–99.

BRIDGLAND, D. R. 1980. A reappraisal of Pleistocene stratigraphy in north Kent and eastern Essex, and new evidence concerning the former courses of the Thames and Medway. *Quaternary News-*

letter, **32**, 15–24.

—— 1983*a*. *The Quaternary fluvial deposits of north Kent and eastern Essex*. PhD thesis, City of London Polytechnic.

—— 1983*b*. Eastern Essex. *In: Diversion of the Thames. In:* ROSE, J. (ed.), Field Guide, Quaternary Research Association, Cambridge, 170–184.

—— 1985*a*. Pleistocene sites in the Thames-Avon system. *Earth Science Conservation*, **22**, 36–39.

—— 1985*b*. Uniclinal shifting; a speculative reappraisal based on terrace distribution in the London Basin. *Quaternary Newsletter*, **47**, 26–33.

—— 1986*a*. Discussion of procedures and recommendations. *In:* BRIDGLAND, D. R. *Clast Lithological Analysis* Technical Guide No. 3 Quaternary Research Association, Cambridge, 1–33.

—— 1986*b*. The rudaceous components of the East Essex gravel; their characteristics and provenance. *Quaternary Studies*, **2**, 34–44.

BRIDGLAND, D. R. 1986*c*. The provenance of gravel at Great Fanton Hall, near Wickford, Essex. *In: Clast Lithological Analysis* (ed. Bridgland, D. R.), Technical Guide No. 3, Quaternary Research Association, Cambridge, 147–152.

—— 1988*a*. The Pleistocene fluvial stratigraphy and palaeogeography of Essex. *Proceedings of the Geologists' Association*, **99**, 291–314.

—— 1988*b*. Problems in the application of lithostratigraphic classification to Pleistocene terrace deposits. *Quaternary Newsletter*, **55**, 1–8.

—— 1988*c*. The Quaternary derivation of quartzites used by palaeolithic Man in the Thames Basin for tool manufacture. *In:* Non-flint Stone Tools and the Palaeolithic Occupation of Britain, *British Archaeological Report, British Series*, **189**, 187–198

—— 1989. Analysis of the gravel deposits. *In:* CRUSE, R. J. Further investigation of the Acheulian site at Cuxton. *Archaeologia Cantiana*, **104**, 39–81.

—— 1990*a*. Pleistocene stratigraphy and river basin sediments: a reply to Maddy, D. & Green, C. P. *Quaternary Newsletter*, **60**, 10–12.

—— 1990*b*. Little Oakley (TM 223294), *In:* TURNER, C. (ed.) *The Cromer Symposium Field Excursion Guidebook*, Symposium of European Quaternary Stratigraphy/Quaternary Research Association, Cambridge, 48–57.

—— 1994. *Quaternary of the Thames*. Chapman & Hall, London.

—— & CHESHIRE, D. A. 1994. Westmill Quarry. *In:* BRIDGLAND, D. R. (ed.) *The Quaternary of the Thames*. Joint Nature Conservation Committee, Chapman and Hall, London, 121–129.

—— & D'OLIER, B. 1987. Attempted correlation of onshore and offshore Thames Channels and terraces in the eastern London Basin and the southern North Sea. *Programme and Abstracts XII INQUA Congress* July 1987.

—— & —— 1989. A preliminary correlation of the onshore and offshore courses of the Rivers Thames and Medway during the Middle and Upper Pleistocene. *In: Quaternary and Tertiary Geology of the Southern Bight, North Sea* (eds HENRIET, J. P. & DE MOORE, G.), Belgian Ministry of Economic Affairs, Geological Survey, 161–172.

—— & —— 1995. The Pleistocene evolution of the Thames and Rhine drainage systems in the southern North Sea Basin. *In:* PREECE, R. C. (ed.) *Island Britain: a Quaternary perspective*. Geological Society, London, Special Publications No. 96, 27–45

—— & GIBBARD, P. L. 1990. Ardleigh (Martell's Quarry) TM 053280. *In:* TURNER, C. (ed.) *The Cromer Symposium Field Excursion Guidebook*, Symposium of European Quaternary Stratigraphy/Quaternary Research Association, Cambridge, 57–62.

—— & HARDING, P. 1985. Palaeolithic artifacts from the gravels of the Hoo Peninsula. *Archaeologia Cantiana*, **101**, 41–55.

—— & HARDING, P. 1986. An attempt to locate the 'Wolvercote Channel' in the railway cutting adjacent to Wolvercote Brick Pit. *Quaternary Newsletter*, **48**, 12–16.

—— & LEWIS, S. G. 1991. Introcution to the Pleistocene geology and drainage history of the Lark valley. *In:* LEWIS, S. G., WHITEMAN, C. A. & BRIDGLAND, D. R. (eds) *Central East Anglia and the Fen Basin*, Field Guide, Quaternary Research Association, London, 37–44.

——, GIBBARD, P. L., HARDING, P., KEMP, R. A., & SOUTHGATE, G. 1985. New information and results from recent excavations at Barnfield Pit, Swanscombe. *Quaternary Newsletter*, **46**, 25–38.

——, KEEN, D. H. & MADDY, D. 1986. A reinvestigation of the Bushley Green Terrace typesite, Hereford and Worcester. *Quaternary Newsletter*, **50**, 1–6.

——, GIBBARD, P. L. & WHITEMAN, C. A. 1988*a*. A preliminary Report on the Stratigraphy of the Lower Thames Valley. *Quaternary Newsletter*, **56**, 1–8.

——, ALLEN, P., CURRANT, A. P., *et al.* 1988*b*. Report of the Geologists' Association field meeting in north-east Essex, May 22nd-24th, 1987. *Proceedings of the Geologists' Association*, **99**, 315–333.

——, KEEN, D. H. & MADDY, D. 1989. The Avon terraces: Cropthorne, Ailstone and Eckington. *In:* KEEN, D. H. (ed.) *The Pleistocene of the West Midlands: Field Guide*. Quaternary Research Association, Cambridge 51–67.

——, GIBBARD, P. L. & PREECE, R. C. 1990. The geology and significance of the interglacial sediments at Little Oakley, Essex. *Philosophical Transactions of the Royal Society of London*, **B328**, 307–339.

——, KEEN, D. H. & DAVEY, N. D. W. 1991. The Pleistocene sequence in the Peterborough district: possible correlations with the deep-sea ocean record. *In:* LEWIS, S. G., WHITEMAN, C. A. & BRIDGLAND, D. R. (eds) *Central East Anglia and the Fen Basin*, Field Guide, Quaternary Research Association, London, 209–212.

——, D'OLIER, B., GIBBARD, P. L. & ROE, H. M. 1993. Correlation of Thames terrace deposits between the lower Thames, eastern Essex and the submerged offshore continuation of the Thames-Medway valley. *Proceedings of the Geologists' Association*, **104**, 51–58.

——, KEEN, D. H., GREEN, C. P., BOWEN, D. Q. & SYKES, G. A. 1995*a*. Last Interglacial deposits at Folkestone, Kent. *Proceedings of the Geologists' Association*, **106**, 183–193.

——, GIBBARD, P. L., HARDING, P., KEMP, R. A. & SOUTHGATE, G. 1995*b*. New information and results from recent excavations at Barnfield Pit, Swanscombe. *Quaternary Newsletter*, **46**, 25–38.

BRIGGS, D. J. 1973. *Quaternary Deposits of the Evenlode Valley and Adjacent Areas*. PhD thesis, University of Bristol.

—— 1976*a*. River terraces of the Oxford area. *In:* ROSE, J. (ed.) *Field Guide to the Oxford Region*, Quaternary Research Association, Oxford, 8–15.

—— 1976*b*. Some Quaternary problems in the Oxford area. *In:* ROSE, J. (ed.) *Field Guide to the Oxford Region*, Quaternary Research Association, Oxford, 6–7.

—— 1988. The environmental background to human occupation in the Upper Thames valley during the Quaternary Period. *In:* MACRAE, R. J. & MOLONEY, N. *Non-flint Stone Tools and the Palaeolithic Occupation of Britain British Archaeological Report, British Series*, **189**, 167–186.

—— & GILBERTSON, D. D. 1973. The age of the Hanborough Terrace of the River Evenlode, Oxfordshire. *Proceedings of the Geologists' Association*, **84**, 155–173.

—— & —— 1974. Recent studies of Pleistocene deposits in the Evenlode valley and adjacent areas of the Cotswolds. *Sound (Journal of the Plymouth Polytechnic Geological Society)*, **3**, 7–22.

—— & —— 1980. Quaternary processes and environments in the Upper Thames basin. *Transactions of the Institute of British Geographers*, **5**, 53–65.

——, COOPE, G. R. & GILBERTSON, D. D. 1975*a*. Late Pleistocene terrace deposits at Beckford, Worcestershire, England. *Geological Journal*, **10**, 1–16.

——, GILBERTSON, D. D., GOUDIE, A. S., *et al.* 1975*b*. New interglacial site at Sugworth. *Nature, London*, **257**, 477–479.

——, COOPE, G. R. & GILBERTSON, D. D. 1985. The Chronology and Environmental Framework of Early Man in the Upper Thames Valley: A New Model. *British Archaeological Report, British Series*, **137**, 176.

——, GILBERTSON, D. D. & HAWKINS, A. B. 1991. The raised beach deposits at Swallow Cliff, Middle Hope. *Proceedings of the Bristol Naturalists' Society*, **51**, 63–71.

BRISTOW, C. R. 1985. *The Geology of the Country around Chelmsford*. Memoir of the Geological Survey.

—— 1990. *Geology of the country around Bury St Edmunds*. Memoir of the British Geological Survey.

—— & COX, F. C. 1973. The Gipping Till: a reappraisal of East Anglian glacial stratigraphy. *Journal of the Geological Society, London*, **129**, 1–37.

——, FRESHNEY, E. C. & PENN, I. E. 1991. *Geology of the Country Around Bournemouth*. Memoir British Geological Survey.

BROMEHEAD, C. E. N. 1912. On diversions of the Bourne near Chertsey. *Summary of Progress, Geological Survey of Great Britain* (for 1911), 74–77.

—— 1925. *The Geology of North London*. Memoir of the Geological Survey of Great Britain, 63.

BROWN, A. P. 1977. Late-Devensian and Flandrian vegetational history of Bodmin Moor, Cornwall. *Philosophical Transactions of the Royal Society of London*, **B276**, 251–220.

—— 1980. Deposits at Hawks Tor, Bodmin Moor. *In:* SIMS, P. C. (ed.) *West Cornwall*. Quaternary Research Association Field Handbook, West Cornwall Field eeting, September 1980. 37–40.

BROWN, E. H. 1975. The Quaternary terraces of the River Thames. *In: L'evolution Quaternaire des Bassins Fluviaux de la Mer du Nord Meridionale* (ed. MACAR, P.), Societe Geologique de Belgique, Leige, 318.

—— & COOKE, R. U. 1977. Landforms and related glacial deposits in the Wheeler Valley area, Clwyd. *Cambria*, **4**, 32–45.

BROWN, I. M. 1994. Former glacial lakes in the Dee valley: origin, drainage and significance. *Scottish Journal of Geology*, **30**, 147–158.

BROWN, J. 1838. Discovery of a large pair of fossil horns in Essex. *Magazine of Natural History, Series 2*, **2**, 163–164.

—— 1839. Fossil Bones at Clacton. *Essex Literary Journal* (for 1839), 29.

—— 1840. Notice of a fluvio-marine deposit containing mammalian-remains occurring in the parish of Little Clacton on the Essex coast. *Magazine of Natural History, Series 2*, **4**, 197–201.

—— 1841. A list of the fossil shells found in a fluvio-marine deposit at Clacton in Essex. *Annals and Magazine of Natural History, Series 1*, **7**, 427–429.

—— 1845. On certain conditions and appearances of the strata on the coast of Essex near Walton. *Quarterly Journal of the Geological Society, London*, **1**, 341–342.

—— 1847. Note on bovine remains, lately found at Clacton, Essex. *Annals and Magazine of Natural History, Series 2*, **20**, 397–398.

BROWN, M. J. F. 1971. *Glacial Geomorphology of Montgomeryshire and West Shropshire*. PhD thesis, University of London.

BROWN, R. C., GILBERTSON, D. D., GREEN, C. P. & KEEN, D. H. 1975. Stratigraphy and environmental significance of Pleistocene deposits at Stone, Hampshire. *Proceedings of the Geologists' Association*, **86**, 349–363.

BROWNE, M. A. E. & McMILLAN, A. A. 1989. Quaternary geology of the Clyde Valley. *British Geological Survey Research Report* SA/89/1. Onshore Geology Series, 63.

——, —— & HALL, I. H. S. 1983. Blocks of marine clay in till near Helensburgh, Strathclyde. *Scottish Journal of Geology*, **19**, 321–325.

——, GRAHAM, D. K. & GREGORY, D. M. 1984. Quaternary estuarine deposits in the Grangemouth area, Scotland. *Report of the Geological Survey*, **16/3**, 14.

——, HARKNESS, D. D., PEACOCK, J. D. & WARD, R. G. 1977. The date of deglaciation of the Paisley–Renfrew area. *Scottish Journal of Geology*, **13**, 301–303.

BRUNNACKER, K. 1986. Quaternary stratigraphy in the Lower Rhine area and northern Alpine foothills. *Quaternary Science Reviews*, **5**, 373–379.

——, LOSCHER, M., TILLMANNS, W. *et al.* 1982. Correlation of the Quaternary terrace sequences in the Lower Rhine valley and northern Alpine foothills of central Europe. *Quaternary Research*, **18**, 152–173.

BRYANT, I. D. 1983. Facies sequences associated with some braided river deposits of late-Pleistocene age from southern Britain. *In:* COLLINSON, J. D. & LEWIN, J. *Modern and Ancient Fluvial Systems: Sedimentology and Processes* International Association of Sedimentologists, Special Publication, No. **6**, 267–275.

——, HOLYOAK, D. T. 1980. Devensian deposits at Brimpton, Berkshire. *Quaternary Newsletter*, **30**, 17.

——, GIBBARD, P. L., HOLYOAK, D. T., SWITSUR, V. R. & WINTLE, A. G. 1983a. Late Pleistocene river deposits at Alton Road, Farnham, Surrey. *Geological Magazine*, **120**, 587–606.

——, HOLYOAK, D. T. & MOSELEY, K. A. 1983b. Late Pleistocene deposits at Brimpton, Berkshire, England. *Proceedings of the*

Geologists' Association, **94**, 321–343.

BRYANT, R. H. 1968. *A Study of the Glaciation of South Iveragh, County Kerry*. PhD Thesis, University of Reading.

—— 1974. A late-Midlandian section at Finglas river, near Waterville, Kerry. *Proceedings of the Royal Irish Academy*, **74B**, 161–178.

BUCKLAND, W. 1823. *Reliqiae Diluvianae: or Observation on the Organic remains Contained in Caves, Fissures and Diluvial Gravel and on Other Geological Phenomena, Attesting the Action of a Universal Deluge*. John Murray, London.

—— 1842. On the glacia-diluvial phenomena in Snowdonia and the adjacent parts of North Wales. *Proceedings of the Geological Society of London*, **3**, 579–584.

—— & CONYBEARE, W. D. 1824. Observations on the South-western Coal District of England. *Transactions of the Geological Society, Series 2*, **1**, 210–316.

BUCKMAN, S. S. 1897. Deposits of the Bajocian Age in the northern Cotteswolds: The Cleeve Hill Plateau. *Quarterly Journal of the Geological Society, London*, **53**, 607–629.

—— 1899a. Gravel at Moreton-in-March, Gloucestershire. *Quarterly Journal of the Geological Society, London*, **55**, 220–223.

—— 1899b. The development of rivers; and particularly the genesis of the Severn. *Natural Science*, **14**, 273–289.

—— 1900. Excursion notes: chiefly on river features. Salisbury meeting. *Proceedings of the Cotteswold Naturalists Field Club*, **13**, 175–192.

BULL, A. J. 1942. Pleistocene chronology. *Proceedings of the Geologists' Association*, **53**, 1–45.

BULLEID, A. & JACKSON, J. W. 1937. The Burtle sand beds of Somerset. *Proceedings of the Somerset Archeological and Natural History Society*, **83**, 171–195.

—— & JACKSON, J. W. 1941. Further notes on the Burtle sand-beds of Somerset. *Proceedings of the Somerset Archeological and Natural History Societies*, **87**, 111–116.

BURCHELL, J. P. T. 1931. Early Neanthropic Man and his relation to the Ice Age. *Proceedings of the Prehistoric Society of East Anglia*, **6**, 253–303.

—— 1933. The Northfleet 50-foot submergence later than the Coombe Rock of the post-Early Mousterian times. *Archaeologia*, **83**, 67–91.

—— 1934a. The Middle Mousterian Culture and its relation to the Coombe Rock of post-Early Mousterian times. *Antiquaries Journal*, **14**, 33–39.

—— 1934b. Fresh facts relating to the Boyn Hill Terrace of the Lower Thames valley. *Antiquaries Journal*, **14**, 163–166.

—— 1935a. Evidence of a further glacial episode within the valley of the Lower Thames. *Geological Magazine*, **72**, 90–91.

—— 1935b. Some Pleistocene deposits at Kirmington and Crayford. *Geological Magazine*, **72**, 327–331.

—— 1936a. A final note on the Ebbsfleet Channel series. *Geological Magazine*, **73**, 550–554.

—— 1936b. Hand-axes later than the main Coombe Rock of the Lower Thames valley. *Antiquaries Journal*, **16**, 260–264.

—— 1936c. Evidence of a Late Glacial episode within the valley of the Lower Thames. *Geologiae Magazine*, **73**, 91–92.

—— 1954. Loessic deposits in the fifty-foot terrace post dating the main Coombe Rock of Baker's Hole, Northfleet, Kent. *Proceedings of the Geologists' Association*, **65**, 256–261.

—— 1957. A temperate bed of the last interglacial period at Northfleet, Kent. *Geological Magazine*, **94**, 212–214.

BUREK, C. V. 1991. Quaternary history and glacial deposits of the Peak District. *In:* EHLERS, J., GIBBARD, P. L. & ROSE, J. (eds) *Glacial Deposits in Great Britain and Ireland*. Balkema, Rotterdam, 193–202.

BURLEIGH, R., EVANS, J. G. & SIMPSON, D. D. A. 1973. Radiocarbon dates from Northton, Outer Hebrides. *Antiquity*, **47**, 61–64.

BURY, H. 1923. Some aspects of the Hampshire Plateau Gravels. *Proceedings of the Prehistoric Society of East Anglia*, **4**, 15–41.

BURRIN, P. J. 1985. Holocene alluviation in southeast England and some implications for palaeohydrological studies. *Earth Surface Processes and Landforms*, **10**, 257–271.

—— 1988. The Holocene floodplain and alluvial deposits of the Rother valley and their bearing on the evolution of Romney Marsh. *In:* EDDISON, J. & GREEN, C. (eds) *Romney Marsh. Evolution. Occupation. Reclamation*. Oxford University Committee for Archaeology Monograph No. 34, Oxford, 31–52.

—— & SCAIFE, R. G. 1984. Aspects of Holocene valley sedimentation and floodplain developments in southern England. *Proceedings of the Geologists' Association*, **95**, 81–96.

BUSH, M. B. & ELLIS, S. 1987. The sedimentological and vegetational history of Willow Garth. *In:* ELLIS, S. (ed.) *East Yorkshire Field Guide.* 42–52. Cambridge, Quaternary Research Association.

—— & FLENLEY, J. R. 1987. The age of the British Chalk grassland. *Nature*, **329**, 434–436.

CALKIN, J. B. 1934. Implements from the higher raised beaches of Sussex. *Proceedings of the Prehistoric Society of East Anglia*, **7**, 33–47.

—— & GREEN, J. N. F. 1949. Palaeoliths and terraces near Bournemouth. *Proceedings of the Prehistoric Society*, **15**, 21–37.

CALLAWAY, C. 1905. The occurrence of glacial clay on the Cotteswold Plateau. *Geological Magazine*, **2**, 216–219.

CALLOW, P. & CORNFORD, J. M. (eds) 1986. *La Cotte de St Brelade, Jersey: excavations by C. B. M. McBurney 1962–1980.* Geobooks, Norwich.

CALLOW, W. J., BAKER, M. J. & HASSALL, G. I. 1966. National Physical Laboratory Radiocarbon Measurements IV. *Radiocarbon* **8**, 340–347.

CAMERON, T. D. J., BONNY, A. P., GREGORY, D. M. & HARLAND, R. 1984. Lower Pleistocene dinoflagellate cyst, foraminiferal and pollen assemblages in four boreholes in the Southern North Sea. *Geological Magazine*, **121**, 85–97.

——, STOKER, M. S. & LONG, D. 1987. The history of Quaternary sedimentation in the UK sector of the North Sea Basin. *Journal of the Geological Society, London*, **144**, 43–58.

——, LABAN, C. & SCHÜTTENHELM, R. T. E. 1989a. Upper Pliocene and Lower Pleistocene stratigraphy in the Southern Bight of the North Sea. *In:* HENRIET, J-P. & DE MOOR, G. (eds) *The Quaternary and Tertiary geology of the Southern Bight, North Sea.* Belgian Geological Survey, Brussels, 97–110.

——, —— & LABAN, C. 1989b. Middle and Upper Pleistocene and Holocene stratigraphy in the Southern Bight of the North Sea. *In:* HENRIET, J-P. & DE MOOR, G. (eds) *The Quaternary and Tertiary geology of the Southern Bight, North Sea.* Belgian Geological Survey, Brussels, 119–135.

CAMBRIDGE, P. G. 1977. Whatever happened to the Boytonian? A review of the marine Plio-Pleistocene of the southern North Sea Basin. *Bulletin of the Geological Society of Norfolk*, **29**, 23–45.

CAMPBELL, J. B. 1977. *The Upper Palaeolithic of Britain: a study of man and nature in the late Ice Age.* Oxford, Clarendon, 264 & 376 (2 vols).

—— & SAMPSON, C. G. 1971. *A new analysis of Kent's Cavern, Devonshire, England.* University of Oregon Occasional Paper No. **3**.

CAMPBELL, S. 1984. *The Nature and Origin of the Pleistocene Deposits around Cross Hands and on West Gower, South Wales.* PhD thesis, University of Wales.

—— & BOWEN, D. Q. 1989. *Quaternary of Wales.* Geological Conservation Review Series, 2. Nature Conservancy Council, Peterborough.

——, HUNT, C. O., SCOURSE, J. D., KEEN, D. H. & STEPHENS, N. 1998 *Quaternary of South-West England.* Geological Conservation Review Series. Chapman and Hall, London. 439.

——, ANDREWS, J. T. & SHAKESBY, R. A. 1982. Amino acid evidence for Devensian ice, west Gower, South Wales. *Nature*, **300**, 249–251.

—— & SHAKESBY, R. A. 1985. Wood fragments of possible Chelford Interstadial age from till at Broughton Bay, Gower, South Wales. *Quaternary Newsletter*, **47**, 33–36.

—— & —— 1986a. Comments on the note by Bowen, D. Q., Reeves, A. & Sykes, G. A. *Quaternary Newsletter*, **49**, 14–16.

—— & —— 1986b. Comments on the note by Worsley, P. *Quaternary Newsletter*, **49**, 19–20.

—— & —— 1994. Late Pleistocene deposits at Broughton Bay, Gower, South Wales: evidence for deposition at a non-marine Devensian ice margin. *Proceedings of the Geologists' Association*, **105**, 167–185.

—— & THOMPSON, I. C. 1991. The palaeoenvironmental history of Late Pleistocene deposits at Moel Trfyan, North Wales: evidence from Scanning Electron Microscopy (SEM). *Proceedings of the Geologists' Association*, **102**, 123–134.

——, WOOD, M., ADDISON, K. SCOURSE, J. D. & JONES, R. E. 1995. Notice of raised beach deposits at Llanddona, Anglesey, North Wales. *Quaternary Newsletter*, **77**, 1–5.

CANTRILL, T. C., DIXON, E. E. L., THOMAS, H. H. & JONES, O. T. 1916. The geology of the South Wales Coalfield, Part 7. The country around Milford. *Memoir of the Geological Survey of Great Britain.*

CARLSEN, R., LfKEN, T., and ROALDSET, E. 1986. Late Weichselian transgression, erosion and sedimentation at Gullfaks, northern North Sea. *In:* SUMMERHAYES, C P, & SHACKLETON, N J (eds) North Atlantic Palaeoceanography. *Geological Society, London, Special Publications*, No. **21**.

CARPENTER, C. P. & WOODCOCK, M. P. 1981. A detailed investigation of a pingo remnant in western Surrey. *Quaternary Studies*, **1**, 1–26.

CARR, A. P. & BLACKLEY, M. W. L. 1973. Investigations bearing on the age and development of Chesil Bank, Dorset and the associated area. *Transactions of the Institute of British Geographers*, **58**, 99–112.

CARRECK, J. N. 1964. Field meeting to the Medway Valley, Kent, from Maidstone to Rochester. *Proceedings of the Geologists' Association*, **75**, 357–360.

—— 1972. *Chronology of the Quaternary deposits of south-east England, with special reference to their vertebrate faunas.* M. Phil. thesis, University of London.

—— 1976. Pleistocene mammalian and molluscan remains from 'Taplow' Terrace deposits at West Thurrock, near Grays, Essex. *Proceedings of the Geologists' Association*, **87**, 83–92.

CARRUTHERS, R. G. 1953. *Glacial Drifts and the Undermelt Theory.* H. Hill, Newcastle, 42.

CARTER, P. A., JOHNSON, G. A. L. & TURNER, J. 1978. An interglacial deposit at Scandal Beck, N. W. England. *New Phytologist* **81**, 785–790.

CARTER, R. W. G. 1980. Longshore variations in nearshore wave processes at Magilligan Point, Northern Ireland. *Earth Surface Processes*, **5**, 81–89.

—— 1982. Sea-level changes in Northern Ireland. *Proceedings of the Geologists' Association*, **93**, 7–23.

—— 1983. Raised coastal landforms as products of modern process variations, and their elevance in eustatic sea-level studies: examples from eastern Ireland. *Boreas*, **12**, 167–182.

—— 1988. *Coastal Environments.* Academic, London.

—— 1989. Resources and management of Irish coastal waters and adjacent coasts. *In:* CARTER, R. W. G. & PARKER, A. J. (eds) *Ireland: a Contemporary Geographical Perspective.* Routledge, London, 393–419.

—— & ORFORD, J. D. 1980. Gravel barrier genesis and management: a contrast. Coastal Zone 180. *American Society Civil Engineers*, **11**, 1304–1320.

—— & —— 1984. Coarse clastic barrier beach: a discussion of distinctive dynamic and morphosedimentary characteristics. *Marine Geology*, **60**, 377–389.

—— & WILSON, P. 1993. Aeolian processes and deposits in northwest Ireland. *In:* PYE, K. (ed.) *The Dynamics and Environmental Content of Aeolian Sedimentary Systems.* Geological Society, London, Special Publications, **11**, 173–190.

——, DEVOY, R. J. & SHAW, J. 1989. Late Holocene sea levels in Ireland. *Journal of Quaternary Science*, **4**, 7–24.

CASE, D. J. 1983. *Quaternary Airfall deposits in South Wales: Loess and Coversands.* PhD thesis, University of Wales.

—— 1984. Port Eynon Silt (Loess). *In:* BOWEN, D. Q. & HENRY, A. (eds) *Preseli, Fforest Fawr.* Quaternary Research Association Field Guide, April 1984, 51–54.

—— 1993. Evidence for temperate soil development during the Early Devensian in Gower, South Wales. *Geological Magazine*, **130** (1), 113–115.

CASE, H. J. & KIRK, J. R. 1952. Notes and News: Henley-on-Thames. *Oxoniensia*, **15**, 107.

—— & KIRK, J. R. 1955. Notes and News: Rotherfield Peppard. *Oxoniensia*, **19**, 118.

CASTELL, C. P. 1964. The non-marine Mollusca. *In:* OVEY, C. D. (ed), *The Swanscombe Skull*, Royal Anthropological Institute of London, 77–83.

CASTLEDEN, R. 1976. The floodplain gravels of the River Nene. *Mercian Geologist*, **6**, 33–47.

—— 1980. The Second and Third terrace of the River Nene. *Mercian Geologist*, **8**, 29–46.

CASTON, V. N. D. 1977. Quaternary sediments of the central North Sea. A new isopach map of the Quaternary of the North Sea. *Report Institute of Geological Sciences*, 77/11, 1–8.

CATT, J. A. 1977a. Loess and coversands. *In:* SHOTTON, F. W. (ed.) *British Quaternary Studies: Recent Advances.* Clarendon, Oxford, 221–229.

—— 1977b. *Guidebook for Excursion C7. Yorkshire and Lincolnshire.* INQUA X Congress, United Kingdom. Norwich. Geo Abstracts.

—— 1978. The contribution of Loess to soils in lowland Britain. *In:* IMBREY, S. & EVANS, J. G. *The Effect of Man on the Landscape: the Lowland Zone* Council for British Archaeological Resources, Report No. 21, 12–20.

—— 1979. Soils and Quaternary geology in Britain. *Journal of Soil Science*, **30**, 607–642.

—— 1981. British Pre-Quaternary glaciations. *In:* NEALE, J. & FLENLEY, J. (eds) *The Quaternary in Britain.* Pergamon, Oxford, 9-19.

—— 1991. Quaternary history and glacial deposits of East Yorkshire. *In:* EHLERS, J., GIBBARD, P. L. & ROSE, J. (eds) *Glacial Deposits in Great Britain and Ireland.* Balkema, Rotterdam, 185–192.

—— & HODGSON, J. M. 1976. Soils and geomorphology of the chalk in south-east England. *Earth Surface Processes*, **1**, 181–193.

—— & MADGETT, P. A. 1981. The work of W. S. Bisat F. R. S. on the Yorkshire Coast. *In:* NEALE, J. & FLENLEY, J. (eds) *The Quaternary in Britain.* Pergamon, Oxford, 119–136.

—— & PENNY, L. F. 1966. The Pleistocene deposits of Holderness, East Yorkshire. *Proceedings of the Yorkshire Geological Society,* **35**, 375–420.

—— & STAINES, S. J. 1982. Loess in Cornwall. *Proceedings of the Ussher Society,* **5**, 368–375.

——, CORBETT, W. M., HODGE, C. A. H. *et al.* 1971. Soils of north Norfolk. *Journal of Soil Science,* **22**, 444–452.

——, WEIR, R. A. & MADGETT, P. A. 1974. The loess of eastern Yorkshire and Lincolnshire. *Proceedings of the Yorkshire Geological Society,* **40**, 23–34.

CAVE, R. & HAINS, A. 1986. Geology of the Country between Aberystwyth and Machynlleth. *Memoir British Geological Survey.*

CEPEK, A. G. 1986. Quaternary stratigraphy of the German Democratic Republic. *Quaternary Science Reviews,* **5**, 359–364.

—— & ERD, K. 1982. Classification and stratigraphy of the Holsteinian and Saalian complex in the Quaternary of the German Democratic Republic. *In:* EASTERBROOK, D. J., HANSLIEK, P., JAGER, K. D. & SHOTTON, F. W. *Quaternary Glaciations in the Northern Hemisphere* UNESCO -International Geological Correlation Programme, Project 73/1/24 Report 7, Prague 1981, 50–7.

CHAMBERS, F. M., ADDISON, K., BLACKFORD, J. J. & EDGE, M. J. 1995. Palynology of organic beds below Devensian glacigenic sediments at Oen-y-Bryn, Gwynedd, North Wales. *Journal of Quaternary Science,* **10** (2), 157–173.

CHANDLER, R. H. 1914. The Pleistocene deposits of Crayford. *Proceedings of the Geologists' Association,* **25**, 61–70.

—— 1916. The implements and cores of Crayford. *Proceedings of the Prehistoric Society of East Anglia,* **2**, 240–248.

—— 1930. On the Clactonian Industry at Swanscombe. *Proceedings of the Prehistoric Society of East Anglia,* **6**, 79–116.

—— 1931. On the Clactonian Industry and report of field meeting at Swanscombe. *Proceedings of the Geologists' Association,* **42**, 175–177.

—— 1932a. Notes on types of Clactonian implements at Swanscombe. *Proceedings of the Prehistoric Society of East Anglia,* **6**, 377–378.

—— 1932b. The Clactonian industry and report of field meeting at Swanscombe (II), *Proceedings of the Geologists' Association,* **43**, 70–72.

—— & LEACH, A. L. 1907. Excursion to Crayford and Dartford Heath. *Proceedings of the Geologists' Association,* **20**, 122–126.

—— & —— 1911. Excursion to Dartford Heath. *Proceedings of the Geologists' Association,* **22**, 171–175.

—— & —— 1912. On the Dartford Heath Gravel and on a Palaeolithic implement factory. *Proceedings of the Geologists' Association,* **23**, 102–111.

CHAPELHOWE, R. 1965. On glaciation in North Roe, Shetland. *Geographical Journal,* **131**, 60–71.

CHARLESWORTH, J. K. 1924. The glacial geology of the north-west of Ireland. *Proceedings of the Royal Irish Academy,* **36B**, 174–314.

—— 1928. The glacial retreat from central and southern Ireland. *Quarterly Journal of the Geological Society, London,* **84**, 293–342.

—— 1929. The South Wales end moraine. *Quarterly Journal of the Geological Society, London,* **85**, 335–358.

—— 1939. Some observations on the glaciation of north-east Ireland. *Proceedings of the Royal Irish Academy,* **45B**, 255–295.

—— 1957. *The Quaternary Era* (2 vols). London.

CHARSLEY, T. J., RATHBONE, P. A. & LOWE, D. J. 1990. Nottingham: a geological background for planning and development. *British Geological Survey Technical Report,* WA/90/1.

CHARTRES, C. J. 1975. *Soil Development on the Terraces of the River Kennet.* PhD thesis, University of Reading.

—— 1980. A Quaternary soil sequence in the Kennet valley, central southern England. *Geoderma,* **23**, 125–146.

—— 1981. The mineralogy of Quaternary deposits in the Kennet valley, Berkshire. *Proceedings of the Geologists' Association,* **92**, 93–103.

—— 1984. The micromorphology of Quaternary river terrace deposits in the Kennet valley, Berkshire, England. *Earth Surface Processes and Landforms,* **9**, 343–355.

——, CHEETHAM, G. H. & FENWICK, I. M. 1976. Excursion to the Kennet valley. *In:* ROE, D. *Field Guide to the Oxford Region,* Quaternary Research Association, Oxford, 23–31.

CHATWIN, C. P. 1927. Fosils from the ironsands on Netley Heath (Surrey), *Summary of Progress, Geological Survey of Great Britain* (for 1926), 154–157.

CHEETHAM, G. H. 1980. Late Quaternary palaeohydrology: the Kennet valley case study. *In:* JONES, D. K. C. (ed.) *The Shaping of Southern England,* Institute of British Geographers Special Publication **11**, Academic, London, 203–223.

CHESHIRE, D. A. 1978. *The Glaciation of the Lea valley between Hertford and Enfield.* MSc thesis, City of London Polytechnic and Polytechnic of North London.

—— 1981. A contribution towards a glacial stratigraphy of the lower Lea valley, and implications for the Anglian Thames. *Quaternary Studies,* **1**, 27–69.

—— 1983a. Till lithology in Hertfordshire and West Essex. *In:* ROSE, J. (ed.) *Diversion of the Thames,* Field Guide, Quaternary Research Association, Cambridge, 50–59.

—— 1983b. Westmill. *In:* ROSE, J. (ed.) *Diversion of the Thames,* Field Guide, Quaternary Research Association, Cambridge, 50–59.

—— 1983c. Hoddesdon, St Albans Sand and Gravel Co. Quarry and Hoddesdon, Nursery Grove Pits. *In:* ROSE, J. (ed.) *Diversion of the Thames,* Field Guide, Quaternary Research Association, Cambridge, 140–148.

—— 1986a. *The Lithology and Stratigraphy of the Anglian deposits of the Lea Basin.* PhD thesis, Hatfield Polytechnic.

—— 1986b. The use of small clast counts as a means of till differentiation in Hertfordshire and western Essex. *In:* BRIDGLAND, D. R. (ed.) *Clast Lithological Analysis.* Technical Guide 3, Quaternary Research Association, Cambridge, 129–143.

—— & BRIDGLAND, D. R. 1994. Ugley Park Quarry. *In:* BRIDGLAND, D. R. (ed.) *The Quaternary of the Thames.* Joint Nature Conservation Committee, Chapman and Hall, London, 134–138.

—— & GIBBARD, P. L. 1983. Harper Lane. *In:* ROSE, J. (ed.) *Diversion of the Thames,* Field Guide, Quaternary Research Association, Cambridge, 102–109.

CHISHOLM, N. W. T. 1996. Morphological changes at Braunton Burrows, north-west Devon. *Proceedings of the Ussher Society,* **9**, 25–30.

CLARK, M. J. & BARBER, K. E. 1987. Mire development from the Devensian Lateglacial to present at Church Moor, Hampshire. *In:* BARBER, K. E. (ed.) *Wessex and the Isle of Wight.* Quaternary Research Association Field Guide, Cambridge, 23–32.

CLARK, W. E. LeG. 1955. *The Fossil Evidence for Human Evolution.* Chicago University Press.

CLARKE, B. B. 1969. The problem of the nature, origin and stratigraphical position of the Trebetherick boulder gravel. *Proceedings of the Ussher Society,* **2**, 87–91.

—— 1973. The Camel Estuary Pleistocene section west of Tregunna House. *Proceedings of the Ussher Society,* **2**, 551–553.

CLARKE, M. R. 1981. The sand and gravel resources of the country north of Bournemouth, Dorset. Description of parts of 1:25,000 sheets SU 00, 10, 20, SZ 09, 19 and 29. *Mineral Assessment Report Institute of Geological Sciences*, No. 51.

—— & DIXON, A. J. 1981. The Pleistocene braided river deposits in the Blackwater area of Berkshire and Hampshire, England. *Proceedings of the Geologists' Association*, **92**, 139–57.

—— & AUTON, C. A. 1982. The Pleistocene history of the Norfolk-Suffolk borderlands. *Institute of Geological Sciences Report*, 82/1, 23–29.

—— & AUTON, C. A. 1984. Ingham Sand and Gravel. *In:* ALLEN, P. (ed.) *Field guide to the Gipping and Waveney valleys, Suffolk.* Quaternary Research Association, Cambridge, 71–72.

—— & FISHER, P. F. 1983. The Caesar's Camp Gravel – an early Pleistocene fluvial periglacial deposit in Southern England. *Proceedings of the Geologists' Association*, **94**, 345–355.

—— & GREEN, C. P. 1987. The Pleistocene terraces of the Bournemouth Fordingbridge area. *In:* BARBER, K. E. (ed.) *Wessex and the Isle of Wight.* Quaternary Research Association Field Guide, 58–64.

CLAYDEN, B. 1977a. Hunts Bay Plateau. *In:* BOWEN, D. Q. (ed.) *Wales and the Cheshire-Shropshire Lowlands.* INQUA X Congress. Guidebook for excursions A8 and C8, Geo Abstracts, Norwich, 25–26.

CLAYTON, A. R. 1983. The sand and gravel resources of the country between Mildenhall and Barrow, Suffolk: description of 1:25,000 sheets TL76, TL77 and part of TL87. *Mineral Assessment Report*, 123, Institute of Geological Sciences, London.

CLAYTON, K. M. 1953. The glacial chronology of part of the middle Trent basin. *Proceedings of the Geologists' Association*, **64**, 198–207. —— 1957a. The differentiation of the glacial drifts of the East Midlands. *East Midlands Geographer*, **7**, 31–40.

—— 1957b. Some aspects of the glacial deposits of Essex. *Proceedings of the Geologists' Association*, **68**, 1–19.

—— 1960. The landforms of parts of southern Essex. *Transactions of the Institute of British Geographers*, **28**, 55–74.

—— 1964. The glacial geomorphology of southern Essex. *In:* CLAYTON, K. M. (ed.) *Guide to London Excursion.* International Geographical Congress (London 1964), **20**, 123–128.

—— 1977. River Terraces. *In:* SHOTTON, F. W. (ed.) *British Quaternary Studies: Recent Advances*, Clarendon, Oxford, 153–168.

—— & BROWN, J. C. 1958. The glacial deposits around Hertford. *Proceedings of the Geologists' Association*, **69**, 103–119.

CLIFFORD, M. H. 1936. A Mesolithic flora in the Isle of Wight. *Proceedings of the Isle Wight Natural History and Archaeological Society*, **2**, 582–594.

CLINCH, G. 1908. Early Man. *In: The Victorian History of the County of Kent* (ed. Page, W.), Vol. 1, Archibald Constable Ltd., Westminster, 307–338.

CLOUTMAN, E. W. 1988. Palaeoenvironments in the Vale of Pickering. Part 2: environmental history at Seamer Carr. *Proceedings of the Prehistoric Society*, **54**, 21–36.

COCKCROFT, D. N. 1987. *The Quaternary sediment of the Shetland Platform and adjacent continental shelf margin.* PhD thesis, University of Keele.

CODRINGTON, T. 1870. On the superficial deposits of the South of Hampshire and the Isle of Wight. *Quarterly Journal of the Geological Society, London*, **26**, 528–551.

COHEN, J. M. 1979. Deltaic sedimentation in glacial lake Blessington, County Wicklow, Ireland. *In:* SCHLUCHTER, C. (ed.) *Moraines and Varves.* Balkema, Rotterdam, 357–367.

COLBOURNE, G. GILBERTSON, D. D. & HAWKINS, A. B. 1974. Temporary drift exposures on the Failland Ridge. *Proceedings Bristol Naturalists' Society*, **33**, 91–97.

COLENUTT, G. W. 1896. The Plateau and Valley gravels of the Isle of Wight. *Papers and Proceedings of the Hampshire Field Club*, **3**, 143–153.

COLES, G., HUNT, C. O. & JENKINSON, R. D. S. 1985. Robin Hood's Cave: palynology. *In:* BRIGGS, D. J., GILBERTSON, D. D. & JENKINSON, R. D. S. (eds) *Peak District and Northern Dukeries Field Guide.* Cambridge. Quaternary Research Association. 178–182.

COLES, R. 1934. The evolution of the coastal drainage of Essex. *Essex Naturalist*, **25**, 36–49 and 65–70.

COLHOUN, E. A. 1970. On the nature of the glaciations and final deglaciation of the Sperrin Mountains and adjacent areas in the north of Ireland. *Irish Geography*, **6**, 162–185.

—— 1971b. Late Weichselian periglacial phenomena of the Sperrin Mountains. *Proceedings of the Royal Irish Academy*, **71B**, 53–71.

—— 1972. The deglaciation of the Sperrin Mountains and adjacent areas in Counties Tyrone, Londonderry and Donegal. *Proceedings of the Royal Irish Academy*, **72B**, 92–147.

—— 1973. Two Pleistocene sections in south-western Donegal and their relation to the last glaciation of the Glengesh plateau. *Irish Geography*, **6**, 594–609.

—— 1979a. The glacial stratigraphy of the Sperrin Mountains and its relation to the glacial stratigraphy of north-west Ireland. *Proceedings of the Royal Irish Academy*, **71B**, 37–52.

—— & McCABE, A. M. 1973. Pleistocene glacial, glaciomarine and associated deposits of Mell and Tullyallen townlands, near Drogheda, eastern Ireland. *Proceedings of the Royal Irish Academy*, **73B**, 164–206.

—— & MITCHELL, G. F. 1971, Interglacial marine formation and freshwater formation in Shortalstown Townland, County Wexford. *Proceedings of the Royal Irish Academy*, **71B**, 211–245.

—— & SYNGE, F. M. 1980. The cirque moraines at Lough Nahanagan, County Wicklow. *Proceedings of the Royal Irish Academy*, **80B**, 25–45.

——, DICKSON, J., McCABE, A. M. & SHOTTON, F. W. 1972. A Middle Midlandian freshwater series at Derryvree, Maguiresbridge, County Fermanagh, Northern Ireland. *Proceedings of the Royal Society of London*, **180B**, 274–292.

COLLINS, D. 1969. Culture, traditions and environment of early Man. *Current Anthropologist*, **10**, 267–316.

COLLINS, P. E. F., FENWICK, I. M., KEITH-LUCAS, D. M. & WORSLEY, P. 1966. Late Devensian river and floodplain dynamics and related environmental change in northwest Europe with particular reference to a site at Woolhampton, Berkshire, United Kingdom. *Journal of Quaternary Science.*

CONNELL, E. R. & HALL, A. M. 1984. Kirkhill Quarry: correlation. *In:* HALL, A. M. (ed.) *Buchan Field Guide*, Quaternary Research Association, Cambridge, 80.

—— & ROMANS, J. C. C. 1984. Kirkhill. Palaeosols. *In:* HALL, A. M. (ed.) *Buchan Field Guide*, Quaternary Research Association, Cambridge, 70–76.

——, EDWARDS, K. J. & HALL, A. M. 1982. Evidence for two pre-Flandrian palaeosols in Buchan, Scotland. *Nature*, **297**, 570–2.

CONOLLY, A. P., GODWIN, H. & MEGAW, E. M. 1950. Studies in the post-glacial history of British vegetation XI: late-glacial deposits in Cornwall. *Philosphical Transactions of the Royal Society of London*, **B234**, 397–469.

CONWAY, B. W. 1969. Preliminary geological investigation of Boyn Hill Terrace deposits at Barnfield Pit, Swanscombe, Kent during 1968. *Proceedings of the Royal Anthropological Institute* (for 1968), 59–61.

—— 1970a. Geological investigation of Boyn Hill Terrace deposits at Barnfield Pit, Swanscombe, Kent, during 1969. *Proceedings of the Royal Anthropological Institute* (for 1969), 90–93.

—— 1970b. Written discussions on West, R. G. 1969. Pollen analysis from interglacial deposits at Aveley and Grays, Essex. *Proceedings of the Geologists' Association*, **81**, 177–179.

—— 1971. Geological investigation of Boyn Hill Terrace deposits at Barnfield Pit, Swanscombe, Kent during 1970. *Proceedings of the Royal Anthropological Institute* (for 1970), 60–64.

—— 1972. Geological investigation of Boyn Hill Terrace deposits at Barnfield Pit, Swanscombe, Kent during 1971. *Proceedings of the Royal Anthropological Institute* (for 1971), 80–85.

—— 1985. Research history and geology of Barnfield Pit. *In:* DUFF, K. L. (ed.) *The story of Swanscombe Man* Duff, K. L.), Kent County Council and Nature Conservancy, 6–13.

—— & WAECHTER, J. d'A. 1977. Lower Thames and Medway valleys - Barnfield Pit, Swanscombe. *In:* SHEPHARD-THORN, E. R. & WYMER, J. J. (eds) *South East England and the Thames Valley* Guide Book for Excursion A5, X INQUA Congress, Birmingham, Geoabstracts, Norwich, 38–44.

CONWAY, V. M. 1947. Ringinglow Bog, near Sheffield. *Journal of Ecology*, **34**, 149–181.

—— 1954. Stratigraphy and pollen analysis of southern Pennine blanket peats. *Journal of Ecology*, **42**, 117–147.

CONYBEARE, W. D. & PHILLIPS, W. 1822. *Outline of the Geology of England and Wales.* London.

COOK, W. H. & KILLICK, J. R. 1924. On the discovery of a flint-working site of Palaeolithic date in the Medway Valley at Rochester, Kent, with notes on the drift stages of the Medway. *Proceedings of the Prehistoric Society of East Anglia,* **4,** 133–149.

COOK, J., STRINGER, C. B., CURRANT, A. P. et al. 1982. A middle review of the chronology of the European Middle Pleistocene hominid record. *Yearbook of Physical Anthropology,* **25,** 19–65.

COOMBE, D. E., FROST, L. C., Le BAS, M. & WATTERS, W. 1956. The nature and origin of the soils over the Cornish Serpentine. *Journal of Ecology,* **44,** 605–615.

COOPE, G. R. 1962. A Pleistocene Coleopterous fauna with Arctic affinities from Fladbury, Worcestershire. *Quarterly Journal of the Geological Society, London,* **118,** 103–123.

—— 1968. An insect fauna from the Mid-Weichselian deposits at Brandon, Warwickshire. *Philosophical Transactions of the Royal Society of London,* **B254,** 425–456.

—— 1974. Interglacial coleoptera from Bobbitshole, Ipswich, Suffolk. *Journal of the Geological Society, London,* **130,** 333–340.

—— 1982. Coleoptera from two Late Devensian sites in the Lower Colne Valley, West London, England. *Quaternary Newsletter,* **38,** 1–6.

—— 1987. The response of late Quaternary insect communities to sudden climatic changes. *In:* GEE, J. H. R. & GILLER, P. S. (eds) *Organisation of Communities, Past and Present* Blackwell Scientific, Oxford, 421–38.

—— & ANGUS, R. B. 1975. An ecological study of a temperate interlude in the middle of the last glaciation, based on fossil Coleoptera from Isleworth, Middlesex. *Journal of Animal Ecology,* **44,** 365–391.

—— & BROPHY, J. A. 1972. Late-glacial environmental changes indicated by a coleopteran succession from North Wales. *Boreas,* **1,** 97–142.

—— & JOACHIM, M. J. 1980. Lateglacial environmental change interpreted from fossil coleoptera from St Bees, Cumbria, NW England. *In:* LOWE, J. J., GRAY, J. M. & ROLINSON, J. E. *Studies in the Lateglacial of north-west Europe.* Pergamon, Oxford. 55–68.

—— & JONES, P. 1977. Church Wilne. *In:* SHOTTON, F. W. (ed.) *The English Midlands. Guidebook for Excursion A2. International Union for Quaternary Research. X Congress. Birmingham.* Norwich Geo Abstracts.

—— & PENNINGTON, W. 1977. The Windermere Interstadial of the Late Devensian. *Philosophical Transactions of the Royal Society of London.* **B280,** 337–339.

——, SHOTTON, F. W. & STRACHAN, I. 1961. A Late Pleistocene fauna and flora from Upton Warren, Worcestershire. *Philosophical Transactions of the Royal Society,* **B244,** 379–421.

——, JONES, R. L. & KEEN, D. H. 1980. Stratigraphy and palaeoecology of peat at Fliquet, Jersey, Channel Islands. *Journal of Biogeography,* **7,** 187–195.

COOPER, J. 1972. Last Interglacial (Ipswichian) non-marine Mollusca from Aveley, Essex. *Essex Naturalist,* **33,** 9–14.

CORNWALL, I. W. 1950. Pleistocene and Holocene sections in deposits of the Lower Thames. *University of London Institute of Archaeology, 6th Annual Report,* 34–43.

—— 1958. *Soils for the Archaeologist,* Phoenix House, London.

COTTON, R. P. 1847. On the Pliocene deposits of the valley of the Thames at Ilford. *Annals and Magazine of Natural History, Series 1,* **20,** 164–169.

COXON, P. 1979. *Pleistocene environmental history in central East Anglia.* PhD thesis, University of Cambridge.

—— 1984. The Waveney valley. *In:* ALLEN, P. (ed.) Field Guide to the Gipping and Waveney valleys, Suffolk. Quaternary Research Association, Cambridge, 78–107.

—— 1985. A Hoxnian interglacial site at Athelington, Suffolk. *New Phytologist,* **99,** 611–621.

—— 1986. A radiocarbon dated Early Post Glacial pollen diagram from a pingo remnant near Millstreet, County Cork. *Irish Journal of Earth Sciences,* **8,** 9–20.

—— 1993a. The Geomorphological History of the Waveney Valley and the Interglacial deposits. *In:* SINGER, R., GLADFELTER, B. G. & WYMER, J. J. *The Lower Paleolithic site at Hoxne, England.* University of Chicago Press, Chicago, 67–73.

—— 1993b. Irish Pleistocene biostratigraphy. *Irish Journal of Earth Sciences,* **12,** 83–105.

—— & BROWNE, P. 1991. Glacial deposits and landforms of central and western Ireland. *In:* EHLERS, J., GIBBARD, P. L. & ROSE, J. (eds) *Glacial Deposits of Great Britain and Ireland.* Balkema, Rotterdam, 355–366.

—— & COXON, C. E. 1997. A pre-Pliocene land surface in County Galway, Ireland. *In:* WIDDOWSON, M. (ed.) *Palaeosurfaces: Recognition, Reconstruction and Palaeoenvironmental Interpretation.* Geological Society, London, Special Publications, **120,** 37–56.

—— & FLEGG, A. 1985. A middle Pleistocene interglacial deposit from Ballyline, County Kilkenny. *Proceedings of the Royal Irish Academy,* **85B,** 107–120.

—— & FLEGG, A. 1987. A late Pliocene/Early Pleistocene deposit at Pollnahallia, near Headford, County Galway. *Proceedings of the Royal Irish Academy,* **87B,** 15–42.

—— & HANNON, G. 1991. The interglacial deposits at Derrynadivva and Bunen townland. *In:* COXON, P. *(ed.) Field Guide to the Quaternary of North Mayo. Irish Association for Quaternary Studies, Dublin,* 24–36.

——, —— & FOSS, P. 1994. Climatic deterioration and the end of the Gortian interglacial in sediments from Derrynadivva and Bunen townland, near Castlebar, County Mayo, Ireland. *Journal of Quaternary Science,* **9,** 33–46.

CRABTREE, K. 1972. Late-glacial deposits near Capel Currig, Caernarvonshire. *New Phytologist,* **71,** 1233–1243.

CRAIG, A. J. 1978. Pollen percentage and influx analysis in northeast Ireland: A contribution to the ecological history of the late glacial period. *Journal of Ecology,* **66,** 297–324.

CRANSHAW, S. 1983. Handaxes and cleavers: selected English Acheulian industries. *British Archaeological Report, British Series,* **113,** 283.

CRAWFORD, I. & SWITSUR, R. 1977. Sandscaping and ^{14}C: the Udal, North Uist. *Antiquity,* **51,** 124–136.

CREIGHTON, J. R. 1974. *A study of the Late Pleistocene geomorphology of north central Ulster.* PhD Thesis, The Queen's University, Belfast.

CROSS, P & HODGSON, J. M. 1975. New evidence for the glacial diversion of the River Teme near Ludlow, Salop. *Proceedings of the Geologists' Association,* **3,** 313–331.

CULLETON, E. B. 1978a. Characterisation of glacial deposits in south Wexford. *Proceedings of the Royal Irish Aademy,* **78B,** 293–308.

—— 1978b. Limits and Directions of the movement in south County Wexford. *Journal of Earth Sciences Royal Dublin Society,* **1,** 33–39.

—— 1978c. Infilled till cracks in southeast Ireland. *Proceedings of the Royal Irish Academy,* **82B,** 109–113.

—— & CREIGHTON, J. R. 1979. A three-till sequence at Stillorgan, County Dublin. *Journal of Earth Sciences, Royal Dublin Society,* **2,** 11–14.

CULLINGFORD, R. A. 1972. *Lateglacial and postglacial shoreline displacement in the Earn-Tay Area and Eastern Fife.* PhD thesis, University of Edinburgh.

——, CASELDINE, C. J. & GOTTS, P. E. 1980. Early Flandrian land and sea-level changes in lower Strathearn. *Nature,* **184,** 159–161.

CURRANT, A. P. 1986. Man and Quaternary interglacial faunas in Britain. *In:* COLLCUTT, S. N. (ed.) *The Palaeolithic of Britain and Its Nearest Neighbours; Recent Trends,* J. R. Collis Publications, Department of Archaeology and Prehistory, Sheffield University, 50–52.

—— 1989. The Quaternary origins of the modern British mammal fauna. *Biological Journal of the Linnean Society,* **38,** 23–30.

——, STRINGER, C. B. & COLLCUTT, S. N. 1984. Bacon Hole. *In:* BOWEN, D. Q. & HENRY, A. (eds) *Wales: Gower, Preseli, Fforest Fawr.* Field Guide Quaternary Research Association, 38–44.

CURRY, D., MURRAY, J. W. & WHITTARD, W. F. 1965. The geology of the Western Approaches of the English Channel. III. The Globigerina Silts and associated rocks. *In:* WHITTARD, W. F. & BRADSHAW, R. (eds) *Submarine Geology and Geophysics.* Butterworths. London, 239–264.

——, ADAMS, C. G., BOULTER, M. C., et al. 1978. *A Correlation of Tertiary Rocks in the British Isles.* Geological Society, London, Special Reports, **12,** 72.

CWYNAR, L. C. & WATTS, W. A. 1989. Accelerator-mass spectrometer ages for lateglacial events at Ballybelagh, Ireland. *Quaternary Research*, **31**, 377–380.

DACKOMBE, R. V. & THOMAS, G. S. P. 1991. Glacial deposits and Quaternary stratigraphy of the Isle of Man. *In:* EHLERS, J., GIBBARD, P. L. & ROSE, J. (eds) *Glacial Deposits in Great Britain and Ireland.* Balkema, Rotterdam, 333–344.

DALRYMPLE, J. B. 1958. The application of soil micromorphology to fossil soils and other deposits from archaeological sites. *Journal of Soil Science*, **9**, 199–209.

DALTON, W. H. 1880. *The Geology of the Neighbourhood of Colchester.* Memoir of the Geological Survey of Great Britain.

—— 1890. Note on the Upminster Brickyard. *Essex Naturalist*, **4**, 186–187.

—— 1908. Post-glacial beds in Mersea, Essex. *Essex Naturalist*, **15**, 136–137.

DARDIS, G. F. 1985A. Till facies associations in drumlins and some implications for their mode of formation. *Geografiska Annaler*, **67A**, 13–22.

—— 1985b. Genesis of Late Pleistocene cross-valley moraine ridges, south-central Ulster, Northern Ireland. *Earth Surface Processes and Landforms*, **10**, 483–495.

—— 1985c. Late Pleistocene glacial lakes in south-central Ulster, Northern Ireland. *Irish Journal of Earth Sciences*, **7**, 133–144.

—— 1987. Sedimentology of Late Pleistocene drumlins in south central Ulster, Northern Ireland. *In:* MENZIES, J. & ROSE, J. (eds) *Drumlin Symposium.* Balkema, Rotterdam, 15–24.

—— & MCCABE, A. M. 1983. Facies of subglacial channel sedimentation in Late Pleistocene drumlins, Northern Ireland. *Boreas*, **12**, 263–278.

—— & MCCABE, A. M. 1987. Subglacial sheetwash and debris flow deposits in Late Pleistocene drumlins, Northern Ireland. *In:* MENZIES, J. & ROSE, J. (eds) *Drumlin Symposium.* Balkema, Rotterdam, 225–240.

——, —— & MITCHELL, W. I. 1984. Characteristics and origins of lee-side stratification sequences in Late Pleistocene drumlins, Northern Ireland. *Earth Surface Processes and Landforms*, **9**, 409–424.

——, MITCHELL, W. I. & HIRONS, K. R. 1985. Middle Midlandian interstadial deposits at Greenagho, near Belcoo, County Fermanagh, Northern Ireland. *Irish Journal of Earth Sciences*, **7**, 1–6.

DAVEY, N. D. W., KEEN, D. H. & BRIDGLAND, D. R. 1991. Maxey Gravel Pit, near Peterborough. *In:* LEWIS, S. G., WHITEMAN, C. A. & BRIDGLAND, D. R. (eds) *Central East Anglia and the Fen Basin.* Quaternary Research Association Field Guide, Cambridge, Quaternary Research Association.

DAVID, J. W. E. 1883. On the evidence of glacial action in south Brecknoclshire and east Glamorgan. *Quarterly Journal of the Geological Society, London*, **39**, 39–54.

DAVIDSON, C. F. 1932. The arctic clay of Errol, Perthsire. *Transactions of the Perth Society for Natural Science*, **9**, 55–68.

DAVIES, G. M. 1915. The rocks and minerals of the Croydon Regional Survey area. *Proceedings and Transactions of the Croydon Natural History and Scientific Society*, **8**, 53–96.

—— 1917. Excursion to Netley Heath, Newlands Corner and the Silent Pool. *Proceedings of the Geologists' Association*, **28**, 48–51.

DAVIES, J. A. & FRY, T. R. 1929. Notes on the Gravel Terraces of the Bristol Avon. *Proceedings of the University of Bristol Spalaeological Society*, **3**, 162–172.

——, FLETCHER, C. J. N., WATERS, R. A., WILSON, D., WOODHALL, D. G. & ZALASIEWICZ. 1997. Geology of the country around Llanilar and Rhayader. *Memoir of the British Geological Survey.*

DAVIES, J. R., FLETCHER, C. J. N., WILSON, D., WOODHALL, D. G. & ZALASIEWICZ, J. A. 1997. *Geology of the Country around Llanilar and Rhayader.* Memoir, British Geological Survey.

DAVIES, K. H. 1983. Amino-acid analysis of Pleistocene marine molluscs from the Gower Peninsula. *Nature*, **302**, 137–139.

—— & KEEN, D. H. 1985. The age of Pleistocene marine deposits at Portland, Dorset. *Proceedings of the Geologists' Association*, **96**, 217–225.

DAVIS, A. G. 1953. On the geological history of some of our snails illustrated by some Pleistocene and Holocene deposits in Kent and Surrey. *Journal of Conchology*, **23**, 355–364.

DAVIS, W. M. 1895. The development of certain English rivers. *Geographical Journal*, **5**, 127–146.

—— 1899. The drainage of Cuestas. *Proceedings of the Geologists' Association*, **16**, 87–93.

—— 1909. The valleys of the Cotswold Hills. *Proceedings of the Geologists' Association*, **21**, 150–152.

DAWKINS, W. B. 1867. On the age of the lower brickearth of the Thames valley. *Quarterly Journal of the Geological Society, London*, **23**, 91–109.

—— 1868. On a new species of fossil deer from Clacton. *Quarterly Journal of the Geological Society, London*, **24**, 511–513.

—— 1869. On the distribution of the British post-glacial mammals. *Quarterly Journal of the Geological Society, London*, **25**, 192–217.

—— 1877. The exploration of the fossiliferous deposits at Windy Knoll, Castleton, Derbyshire. *Quarterly Journal of the Geological Society, London*, **31**, 246–255.

DAWSON, M. R. 1985. Environmental reconstruction of a Late Devensian terrace sequence. Some preliminary findings. *Earth Surface Processes and Landforms*, **10**, 237–246.

—— 1987. Sedimentological aspects of periglacial terrace aggradations: case study from the English Midlands. *In:* BOARDMAN, J. (ed.) *Periglacial Processes and Landforms in Britain and Ireland.* Cambridge University Press, 265–274.

—— 1988. Diamict deposits of pre-Late Devensian Glacial age underlying the Severn Main Terrace at Stourport, Worcestershire: their origins and stratigraphic implications. *Proceedings of the Geologists' Association*, **99**, 125–132.

—— 1989. Chelmarsh. *In:* KEEN, D. H. (ed.) *The Pleistocene of the West Midlands: Field Guide.* Quaternary Research Association, Cambridge, 80–85.

—— & BRYANT, I. D. 1987. Three-dimensional facies geometry in Pleistocene outwash sediments, Worcester, U. K. *In:* ETHRIDGE, F. G. (ed.) *Recent developments in fluvial sedimentology.* Society of Economic Paleontologists and Mineralogists Special Publication, **39**, 191–196.

DAY, M. H. 1977. *Guide to Fossil Man: A Handbook of Human Palaeontology*, 3rd edn, Cassell, London.

DELANEY, C. 1995. *Sedimentology of Late Devensian Deglacial Deposits in the Loyh Ree Area, Central Ireland.* PhD Thesis, Trinity College, Dublin.

DE RANCE, C. E. 1877. The superficial geology of the country adjoining the coasts of southwest Lancashire. *Memoir Geological Survey of Great Britain, London.*

DE ROUFFIGNAC, C., BOWEN, D. Q., COOPE, G. R., KEEN, D. H., LISTER, A. M., MADDY, D., ROBINSON, E., SYKES, G. A. & WALKER, M. J. C. 1995. Late Middle Pleistocene deposits at Upper Strensham, Worcestershire, England. *Journal of Quaternary Science*, **10**, 15–31.

DERBYSHIRE, E., FOSTER, C., LOVE, M. A. & EDGE, M. J. 1984. Pleistocene lithostratigraphy of north-east England: A sedimentological approach to the Holderness sequence. *In:* MAHANEY, W. C. (ed.) *Correlation of Quaternary Chronologies*, Geo Books, Norwich, 371–384.

DEVOY, R. J. N. 1977. Flandrian sea level changes in the Thames estuary and the implications for land subsidence in England and Wales. *Nature, London*, **270**, 712–715.

—— 1979. Flandrian sea level changes and vegetation history of the Lower Thames estuary. *Philosophical Transactions of the Royal society of London*, **B285**, 355–407.

—— 1987. The estuary of the western Yar, Isle of Wight: seal-level changes in the Solent region. *In:* BARBER, K. E. (ed.) *Wessex and the Isle of Wight.* Quaternary Research Association Field Guide, Cambridge, 115–122.

DEWEY, H. 1913. The raised beach of North Devon: its relation to others and to Palaeolithic Man. *Geological Magazine*, **10**, 154–163.

—— 1919. On some Palaeolithic flake implements from the high level terraces of the Thames valley. *Geological Magazine*, **6**, 49–57.

—— 1930. Palaeolithic Thames deposits. *Proceedings of the Prehistoric Society of East Anglia*, **6**, 147–155.

—— 1932. The Palaeolithic deposits of the Lower Thames valley. *Quarterly Journal of the Geological Society, London*, **88**, 35–56.

—— 1934. The excursion to the 100-foot terrace of the Thames at Swanscombe, Kent (4th August), *International Congress of Prehistoric and Protohistoric Science*, London, 70–72.

—— 1959. Palaeolithic deposits of the Thames at Dartford Heath and

Swanscombe, North Kent. Unpublished edited text of Henry Stopes memorial lecture, Geologists' Association, 1959.

—— & BROMEHEAD, C. E. N. 1915. The Geology of the Country around Windsor and Chertsey. Memoir of the Geological Survey of Great Britain.

—— & —— 1921. The Geology of South London. *Memoir of the Geological Survey of Great Britain.*

—— & SMITH, R. A. 1914. The Palaeolithic sequence at Swanscombe, Kent. *Proceedings of the Geologists' Association,* **25,** 90–97.

——, BROMEHEAD, C. E. N., CHATWIN, C. P., *et al.* 1924. The Geology of the Country around Dartford. Memoir of the Geological Survey of Great Britain.

——, WOOLDRIDGE, S. W., CORNES, H. W. & BROWN, E. E. S. 1925. The geology of the Canterbury district and report of excursion to Canterbury. *Proceedings of the Geologists' Association,* **36,** 257–290.

DIBLEY, G. E. & KENNARD, A. S. 1916. Excursion to Grays. *Proceedings of the Geologists' Association,* **27,** 103–105.

DICKSON, C. A., DICKSON, J. H. & MITCHELL, G. F. 1970. The Late Weichselian flora of the Isle of Man. *Philosophical Transactions of the Royal Society of London,* **B258,** 31–79.

DICKSON, J. H., STEWART, D. A., THOMPSON, R., TURNER, G., BAXTER, M. S., DRNDARSKY, N. D. & ROSE, J. 1978. Palynology, palaeomagnetism and radiometric dating of Flandrian marine aand freshwater sediments of Loch Lomond. *Nature,* **274,** 548–553.

DIEBEL, K. & WOLFSCHLAGER, H. 1975. Ostracoden sua dem junpleistozanen Travertin von Ehringsdorf bei Weimar. *Abhandlungen des Zentralen Geologischen Instituts* (Berlin), **23,** 91–136.

DINES, H. G. 1928. On the glaciation of the North Cotteswold area. *Summary of Progress, Geological Survey of Great Britain* (for 1927), 66–71.

—— & CHATWIN, C. P. 1930. Pliocene sandstone from Rothamstead (Hertfordshire), *Summary of Progress, Geological Survey of Great Britain* (for 1929), 1–7.

—— & EDMONDS, F. H. 1925. The Geology of the Country around Romford. *Memoir of the Geological Survey of Great Britain.*

—— & —— 1929. The Geology of the Country around Aldershot and Guildford. *Memoir of the Geological Survey of Great Britain.*

——, KING, W. B. R. & OAKLEY, K. P. 1938. A general account of the 100 ft terrace gravels of the Barnfield Pit, Swanscombe. *Journal of the Royal Anthropological Institute,* **68,** 21–27.

——, RICHARDSON, L. S. & ARKELL. 1946. The Geology of the Country around Witney. *Memoir of the Geological Survey of Great Britain.*

DIXON, E. E. L. 1921. The geology of the South Wales Coalfield. Part 8. The country around Pembroke and Tenby. *Memoir of the Geological Survey.*

——, MADEN, J., TROTTER, F. M., HOLLINGWORTH, S. E. & TONKS, L. H. 1926. The geology of the Carlisle, Longtown and Silloth districts. *Memoir of the Geological Survey.*

DIXON, R. G. 1978. Deposits marginal to the Red Crag basin. *Bulletin of the Geological Society of Norfolk,* **200,** 92–104.

DOCHERTY, J. 1967. The exhumed sub-Tertiary surface in north-west Kent. *South East Naturalist,* **70,** 19–31.

—— 1969. The geomorphology of some Late-Glacial deposits in the western part of the North Downs. *Area,* **2,** 24–264.

—— 1971. Chalk Karst: a synthesis of C. C. Faggs's theories of chalkland morphology in the light of recent hydrological research. *Proceedings of the Croydon Natrual History and Scientific Society,* **15,** 21–34.

D'OLIER, B. 1975. Some aspects of late Pleistocene-Holocene drainage of the River Thames in the eastern part of the London Basin. *Philosophical Transactions of the Royal Society of London,* **A279,** 269–277.

DONNER, J. J. 1960. Pollen analysis of the Burn of Benholm peat-bed, Kincardineshire, Scotland. *Societas Scientarum Fennica, Commentationes Biologicae,* **22,** 1–13.

—— 1979. The Early or Middle Devensian peat at the Burn of Benholm, Kincardineshire. *Scottish Journal of Geology,* **15,** 247–250.

DONOVAN, D. T. 1954. A bibliography of the Palaeolithic and Pleistocene sites of the Mendip, Bath and Bristol area. *Proceedings of the University of Bristol Spelaeological Society,* **7,** 23–34.

—— 1955. The Pleistocene deposits at Gough's Cave, Cheddar, including an account of recent excavations. *Proceedings of the University of Bristol Spelaeological Society,* **7,** 76–104.

—— 1964. A bibliography of the Palaeolithic and Pleistocene sites of the Mendip, Bath and Bristol area. First supplement. *University of Bristol Spelaeological Society,* **10,** 89–97.

DOUGLAS, T. D. 1980. The Quaternary deposits of western Leicestershire. *Philosophical Transactions of the Royal Society of London,* **B288,** 259–286.

—— 1991. The glacial deposits of Northumbria. *In:* EHLERS, J., GIBBARD, P. L. & ROSE, J. (eds) *Glacial Deposits in Great Britain and Ireland.* Balkema, Rotterdam. 151–168.

DUFF, K. L. 1985. (ed.) *The Story of Swanscombe Man,* Kent County Council and Nature Conservancy Council, 40.

DUIGAN, S. L. 1955. Plant remains from the gravels of the Summer-town-Radley Terrace near Dorchester, Oxfordshire. *Quarterly Journal of the Geological Society, London,* **111,** 225–238.

—— 1956. Pollen analysis of the Nechells interglacial deposits. *Quarterly Journal of the Geological Society, London,* **112,** 373–372.

DULLER, G. A. T., WINTLE, A. G. & HALL, A. M. 1995. Luminescence dating and its application to key pre-Late Devensian sites in Scotland. *Quaternary Science Reviews,* **14,** 495–519.

DUPHORN, K., GRUBE, F., MEYER, K. D., *et al.* 1973. Pleistocene and Holocene. *Eiszeitalter und Gegenwart,* **23/24,** 222–250.

DWERRYHOUSE, A. R. 1923. The glaciation of north-eastern Ireland. *Quarterly Journal of the Geological Society, London,* **79,** 352–422.

—— & MILLER, A. A. 1930. The glaciation of Clun Forest, Radnor Forest and some adjoining districts. *Quarterly Journal of the Geological Society, London,* **86,** 96–129.

DYER, K. R. 1972. Recent sedimentation in the Solent area. *Memoir du Bureau de la Recherche Géologique et Minéralogique,* 79, 271–280.

—— 1975. The buried channels of the 'Solent River', southern England *Proceedings of the Geologists' Association,* **86,** 239–245.

EARP, J. R., MAGRAW, D., POOLE, E. G., LAND. & WHITEMAN, A. J. 1961. Geology of the country around Clitheroe and Nelson. *Memoir Geological Survey.*

EASTWOOD, T., HOLLINGWORTH, S. E., ROSE, W. C. C. & TROTTER, F. M. 1968. Geology of the country around Cockermouth and Caldbeck. *Memoir Geological Survey.*

——, WHITEHEAD, T. H. & ROBERTSON, T. 1925. The geology of the country around Birmingham. *Memoir of the Geological Survey.*

EDDISON, J. & GREEN, C. (eds) 1988. Romney Marsh: evolution, occupation, reclamation. *Oxford University Committee for Archaeology Monograph* **24**, Oxford.

EDEN, D. N. 1980. The loess of north-east Essex, England. *Boreas,* **9,** 165–177.

EDMONDS, E. A. 1972. The Pleistocene history of the Barnstaple area. *Report of the Institute of Geological Sciences,* **72/2,** 12.

EDWARDS, C. A. 1981. The tills of Filey Bay. *In:* NEALE, J. & FLENLEY, J. (eds) *The Quaternary in Britain.* Oxford, Pergamon. 108–118.

EDWARDS, K. J. 1985. The anthropogenic factor in vegetational history. *In:* EDWARDS, J. K. & WARREN, W. P. (eds) *The Quaternary History of Ireland,* Academic, London, 157–220.

——, CASELDINE, C. J. & CHESTER, D. K. 1976. Possible interstadial and interglacial pollen floras from Teindland, Scotland. *Nature,* **264,** 742–744.

EDWARDS, W., MITCHELL, G. H. & WHITEHEAD, T. H. *1950.* Geology of the district north and south of Leeds. *Memoir of the Geological Survey.*

EHLERS, J. 1981. Problems of the Saalian stratigraphy in the Hamburg area. *Mededelingen Rijks Geologische Dienst,* **34,** 26–29.

——, GIBBARD, P. L. & WHITEMAN, C. A. 1987 Recent investigations of the Marly Drift of northwest Norfolk, England. *In:* VAN DER MEER, J. J. M. (ed.) *Tills and glaciotectonics.* Balkema, Rotterdam, 39–54.

——, —— & —— 1991 The glacial deposits of northwest Norfolk. *In:* EHLERS, J., GIBBARD, P. L. & ROSE, J. (eds) *Glacial deposits of Britain and Ireland.* Balkema, Rotterdam, 223–232.

ELLIS, C. 1986. The postglacial molluscan succession of the South Downs dry valleys *In:* SIEVEKING, G. de G. & HART, M. B. (eds) *The scientific study of flint and chert.* 175–184. Cambridge, Cambridge University Press.

ELLIS, T. S. 1882. On some features in the formation of the Severn valley as seen near Gloucester. *Transactions of the School of Science Philosophical Society, Gloucester* (for 1882), 3–15.

ELLIS-GRUFFYDD, I. D. 1972. *The glacial geomorphology of the upper Usk basin (South Wales) and its right bank tributaries.* PhD thesis, University of London.

—— 1977. Late Devensian glaciation in the Upper Usk basin. *Cambria*, **4**, 46–55.

ELLISON, R. A. 1982. Geology of sheet SO82. *Institute of Geological Sciences.*

—— & LAKE R. D. 1987. Geology of the country around Braintree. *Memoir of the British Geological Survey.*

——, MOORLOCK, B. S. P., WORSSAM, B. C., WYATT, R. J. & BARON, A. J. M. 1988. Tewkesbury 1:50,000 Solid and Drift Sheet 216. *British Geological Survey.*

EMILIANI, C. 1955. Pleistocene temperatures. *Journal of Geology,* **63**, 538–578.

—— 1957. Temperature and age analysis of deep-sea cores. *Science, New York,* **125**, 383–387.

ERDTMANN, G. 1925. Pollen statistics from the Curragh and Ballaugh, isle of Man. *Proceedings Liverpool Geological Society,* **14**, 158–163.

ERLENKEUSER, H. 1979. Environmental effects on radiocarbon in Coastal Marine Sediments. *In:* BERGER, R. & SUESS, H. E. (eds) Radiocarbon Dating. *Proceedings of the Ninth International Conference, Los Angeles and La Jolla 1976.* (London: University of California Press).

EVANS, C. D. R. 1990. United Kingdom offshore regional report: the geology of the western English Channel and its western approaches. *British Geological Survey.*

EVANS, D. 1993. Quaternary. *In:* GATLIFF, R. W., RICHARDS, P. C., SMITH, K., GRAHAM, C. C., McCORMAC, M., SMITH, N. J. P., LONG, D., CAMERON, T. D. J., EVANS, D., STEVENSON, A. G. BULAT, J. & RITCHIE, J. D. *United Kingdom offshore regional report: the geology of the central North Sea.*

—— 1994. Quaternary. *In:* GATLIFF, R. W., RICHARDS, P. C., SMITH, K., GRAHAM, C. C., McCORMAC, M., SMITH, N. J. P., LONG, D., CAMERON, T. D. J., EVANS, D., STEVENSON, A. G. BULAT, J. & RITCHIE, J. D. *United Kingdom offshore regional report: the geology of the central North Sea.* British Geological Survey, 79–93.

—— & HUGHES, M. J. 1984. The Neogene succession of the South West Approaches, Great Britain. *Journal of the Geological Society, London.* **141**, 315–326.

EVANS, D. J. A., OWEN, L. A. & ROBERTS, D. 1995. Stratigraphy and sedimentology of Devensian (Dimlington Stadial) glacial deposits, east Yorkshire, England. *Journal of Quaternary Science,* **10**, 241–265.

EVANS, H. 1975. The two till problem in west Norfolk. *Bulletin of the Geological Society of Norfolk,* **27**, 61–75.

EVANS, J. 1860. On the occurrence of flint implements in undisturbed beds of gravel, sand and clay. *Archaeologia,* **38**, 280–307.

—— 1872. *The Ancient Stone Implements, Weapons and Ornaments of Great Britain,* 1st edn, Longmans, Green and Co., London.

—— 1897. *The Ancient Stone Implements, Weapons and Ornaments of Great Britain,* 2nd edn, Longmans, Green and Co., London.

EVANS, J. G. C., FRENCH, C. & LEIGHTON, D. 1978. Habitat change in two Late-glacial and Post-glacial sites in southern Britain: the molluscan evidence. *In:* LIMBREY, S. & EVANS, J. G. (eds) *The effect of man on the landscape: the Lowland Zone,* 63–75. CBA Research Report Number 21. London. Council for British Archaeology.

EVANS, P. 1954. Field meeting in the Vale of St Albans. *Proceedings of the Geologists' Association,* **65**, 18–22.

—— 1971. Towards a Pleistocene timescale. Part 2 of *The Phanerozoic Time-Scale-A Supplement,* Geological Society, London, Special Publications, **5**, 123–356.

EVANS, W. B. & ARTHURTON, R. S. 1973. North-west England. *In:* MITCHELL, G. F., PENNY, L. F., SHOTTON, F. W & WEST, R. G. *A Correlation of Quaternary deposits in the British Isles. Geological Society of London Special Report No 4.* 28–31. London, Geological Society of London.

——, WILSON, A. A., TAYLOR, B. J. & PRICE, D. 1968. The geology of the country around Macclesfield, Congleton, Crewe and Middlewich. *Memoir Geological Survey.*

EVERARD, C. E. 1954. The Solent River: a geomorphological study. *Transactions of the Institute of British Geographers* **20**, 41–58.

EYLES, C. H. & EYLES, N 1984. Glaciomarine sediments of the Isle of Man as a key to late Pleistocene stratigraphic investigations in the Irish Sea Basin. *Geology,* **12**, 359–364.

EYLES, N. & McCABE, A. M. 1989*a.* The Late Devensian (22,000 B. P.) Irish Sea basin: The sedimentary record of a collapsed sheet margin. *Quaternary Science Reviews,* **8**, 304–351.

—— & —— 1989*b.* Glaciomarine facies within subglacial tunnel valleys: the sedimentary record of glacioisotope downwarping in the Irish Sea basin. *Sedimentology,* **36**, 431–448.

—— & —— 1991. Glaciomarine deposist of the Irish Sea basin: The role of Glacio-Isostatic disequilibrium. *In:* EHLERS, J., GIBBARD, P. L. & ROSE, J. (eds*) Glacial Deposits in Great Britain and Ireland.* Balkema, Rotterdam, 311–332.

—— & SLADEN, J. A. 1981. Stratigraphy and geotechnical properties of weathered lodgement till in Northumberland, England. *Quarterly Journal of Engineering Geology,* **14**, 129–141.

——, SLADEN, J. A. & GILROY, S. 1982. A depositional model for stratigraphic complexes and facies superimposition in lodgement tills. *Boreas,* **11**, 317–333.

——, McCABE, A. M. & BOWEN, D. Q. 1994. The stratigraphic and sedimentological significance of Late Devensian ice sheet surging in Holderness, Yorkshire, UK. *Quaternary Science Reviews,* **13**, 727–759.

FALCONER, H. 1868. *Palaeontological Memoirs and Notes, Compiled and Edited by Charles Murchison,* Vol 2, R. Hardwicke, London.

FARRINGTON, A. 1934. The glaciation of the Wicklow Mountains. *Proceedings of the Royal Irish Academy,* **42B**, 173–209.

—— 1936. The glaciation of the Bantry Bay district. *Scientific proceedings of the Royal Dublin Society,* **21**, 345–361.

—— 1938. The local glaciers of Mount Leinster and Blackstairs Mountain. *Proceedings of the Royal Irish Academy,* **45B**, 65–71.

—— 1942. The granite drift near Brittas, on the border between county Dublin and Wicklow. *Proceedings of the Royal Irish Academy,* **47B**, 279–291.

—— 1944. The glacial drifts of the district around Ennisberry, County Wicklow. *Proceedings of the Royal Irish Academy,* **50B**, 133–157.

—— 1947. Unglaciated areas in southern Ireland. *Irish Geography,* **1**, 89–97.

—— 1949. The glacial drifts of the Leinster Mountains. *Journal of Glaciology,* **1**, 220–225.

—— 1953. Local Pleistocene glaciation and the level of the snow line of Croaghaun Mountain, in Achill Island, Co. Mayo, Ireland. *Journal of Glaciology,* **2**, 262–267.

—— 1954. A note on the correlation of the Kerry–Cork glaciations with those of the rest of Ireland. *Irish Geography,* **3**, 47–53.

—— 1957. Glacial lake Blessington. *Irish Geography,* **3**, 216–222.

—— 1959. The Lee basin. Partone: glaciation. *Proceedings of the Royal Irish Academy,* **60B**, 135–166.

—— 1966. The early-glacial raised beach in County Cork. *Proceedings of the Royal Dublin Society,* **13**, 197–219.

—— & MITCHELL, G. F. 1973. Some glacial features between Pollaphuca and Balringlass, County Wicklow. *Irish Geography,* **6**, 543–560.

—— & SINGE, F. M. 1970. The eskers of the Tullamore district. *In:* Stephen, N. & Glasscock, R. E. (eds) *Irish Geographical Studies in honour of E Estyn Evans,* Belfast, 49–52.

FEDEROFF, N. 1971. Caracteres micromorphologiques des pedogeneses quaternaire en France. *Bulletin de l'Association Francaise pour l'Etude du Quaternaire,* Supplement, **4**, 341–349.

FEYLING-HANSSEN, R. W. 1982. Foraminiferal zonation of a boring in Quaternary deposits of the northern North Sea. *Bulletin of the Geological Society of Denmark,* **31**, 29–47.

—— & KNUDSEN, K L. 1986. Three North Sea Borings: Correlation between three borings in Quaternary deposits of the northern North Sea. *Aarhus Universitet Geoskrifter,* **24**, 125–143.

FIELD, M. H. 1992. *Azolla tegeliensis* Florschütz from the early Pleistocene of the British Isles. *Geological Magazine,* **129**, 363–365.

FINDLAY, D. C. 1977. Bourne (Avon): a temporary section in gravelly head. *In:* CRABTREE, K. (ed.) Field Handbook Easter Meeting 1977 Bristol, *Quaternary Research Association,* 21–25.

——, HAWKINS, A. B. & LLOYD, C. R. 1972. A gravel deposit on Bleadon Hill, Mendip, Somerset. *Proceedings of the University of Bristol Spelaeological Society,* **13**, 83–87.

FIRTH, C. R. 1990. Late Devensian relative sea-level changes associated with the deglaciation of the Inverness Firth and Beauly Firth. *In:* AUTON, C. A., FIRTH, C. R. & MERRITT, J. W. (eds) *Beauly to Nairn: Field Guide.* Quaternary Research Association, Cambridge, 5–9.

—— & HAGGART, B. A. 1989. Loch Lomond Stadial and Flandrian shorelines in the inner Moray Forth area, Scotland. *Journal of Quaternary Science,* **4,** 37–50.

FISHER, M. J., FUNNELL, B. M. & WEST, R. G. 1969. Foraminifera and pollen from a marine interglacial deposit in the western North Sea. *Proceedings Yorkshire Geological Society,* **37,** 311–320.

FISHER, O. 1868a. A few notes on Clacton, Essex. *Geological Magazine,* **5,** 213–215.

—— 1868b. The boulder clay at Witham and the Thames valley. *Geological Magazine,* **5,** 98–100.

FISHER, P. F. 1982. *A study of the plateau gravels in the western part of the London Basin.* PhD thesis, Kingston Polytechnic, 2 volumes.

FITZPATRICK, E. A. 1965. An interglacial soil at Teindland, Morayshire. *Nature,* **207,** 621–622.

—— 1969. Some aspects of soil evolution in north-east Scotland. *Soil Science,* **107,** 403–408.

FLOWER, J. W. 1869. On some recent discoveries of flint implements of the drift in Norfolk and Suffolk, with observations on the theories accounting for their distribution. *Quarterly Journal of the Geological Society, London,* **25,** 449–460.

FORD, T. D. 1976. *Caves of Derbyshire.* Buxton, Dalesman Books and Derbyshire Caving Association.

FOSTER, H. D. 1968. *The Glaciation of the Harlech Dome.* PhD thesis, University of London.

—— 1970a. Establishing the age aand geomorphological significance of sorted stone stripes in the Rhinog Mountains, North Wales. *Geografiska Annaler,* **52A,** 96–102.

—— 1970b. Sarn Badrig, a sub-marine moraine in Cardigan Bay, North Wales. *Zeitschrift fut Geomorphologie,* **14,** 475–486.

FOWLER, J. 1932. The 'One Hundred Foot' Raised Beach between Arundel and Chichester, Sussex. *Quarterly Journal of the Geological Society, London,* **88,** 84–99.

FOX-STRANGWAYS, C. 1905. The geology of the country between Derby and Burton-on-Trent, Ashby-de-la-Zouch and Loughborough. *Memoir Geological Survey.*

FRANCIS, E. A. 1970. Quaternary *In:* HICKLING, G. (ed.) *Geology of Durham County, Transactions of the Natural History Society of Northumberland,* **41,** 134–152.

FRANKS, J. W. 1960. Interglacial deposits at Trafalgar Square, London. *New Phytologist,* **59,** 145–152.

——, SUTCLIFFE, A. J., KERNEY, M. P., *et al.* 1958. Haunt of the elephant and rhinoceros: the Trafalgar Square of 100,000 years ago -new discoveries. *Illustrated London News,* 14th June, Vol. 232, 1011–1013.

FRENCH, C. A. I. 1982. An analysis of the molluscs from an Ipswichian interglacial river channel at Maxey, Cambridgeshire, England. *Geological Magazine,* **119,** 593–598.

FRENCH, H. H. 1888. Excursion to Gomshall, Netley Heath, and Clandon. *Proceedings of the Geologists' Association,* **10,** 182–186.

FRENCH, J. 1891. On the occurrence of Westleton Beds in part of north-western Essex. *Essex Naturalist,* **5,** 210–218.

FRIEDMAN, G. M. 1967. Dynamic processes and statistical parameters compared for size frequency distribution of beach and river sands. *Journal of Sedimentary Petrology,* **37,** 327–354.

FUNNELL, B. M. 1955. An account of the geology of the Bungay district. *Transactions Suffolk Naturalists' Society,* **9,** 115–126.

—— 1961. The Palaeogene and early Pleistocene of Norfolk. *Transactions of the Norfolk and Norwich Naturalists Society,* **19,** 340–364.

—— & WEST, R. G. 1962. The Early Pleistocene of Easton Bavents. *Quarterly Journal of the Geological Society, London,* **117,** 125–141.

—— & —— 1977. Preglacial Pleistocene deposits of East Anglia. *In:* SHOTTON, F. W. (ed.) *British Quaternary Studies: recent advances.* Clarendon, Oxford, 247–265.

GALE, S. J. & HUNT, C. O. 1985. Kirkhead Cave: biostratigraphy and magnetostratigraphy. *Archaeometry,* **26(2),** 192–198.

——, HOARE, P. G., HUNT, C. O. & PYE, K. 1988. The Middle and Upper Quaternary deposits at Morston, north Norfolk, U. K. *Geological Magazine,* **125,** 521–533.

GALLOIS, R. W. 1978. The Pleistocene history of West Norfolk. *Bulletin of the Geological Society of Norfolk,* **30,** 3–38.

GARRARD, R. A. & DOBSON, M. R. 1974. The nature and maximum extent of glacial sediments off the west coast of Wales. *Marine Geology,* **16,** 31–44.

GASCOYNE, M., CURRANT, A. P. & LORD, T. C. 1981. Ipswichian fauna of Victoria Cave and the marine palaeoclimatic record. *Nature, London,* **294,** 652–654.

——, SCHWARCZ, H. P. & FORD, D. C. 1983. Uranium series ages of speleotherm from north-west England: correlation with Quaternary climate. *Philisophical Transactions of the Royal Society of London,* **B301,** 143–164.

GAUNT, G. D. 1970. The occurrence of Pleistocene ventrifacts at Aldborough, near Boroughbridge, West Yorkshire. *Journal of Earth Science (Leeds),* **8,** 159–161.

—— 1974. A radiocarbon date relating to Lake Humber. *Proceedings of the Yorkshire Geological Society,* **40,** 631–637.

—— 1976. The Devensian maximum ice limit in the Vale of York. *Proceedings of the Yorkshire Geological Society,* **40,** 631–637.

—— 1981. Quaternary history of the southern part of the Vale of York. *In:* NEALE, J. & FLENLEY, J. (eds) *The Quaternary in Britain.* Pergamon Oxford, 82–97.

——, COOPE, G. R. & FRANKS, J. W. 1970. Quaternary deposits at Oxbow opencast coal site in the Aire Valley, Yorkshire. *Proceedings of the Yorkshire Geological Society,* **38,** 175–200.

——, COOPE, G. R., OSBORNE, P. J. & FRANKS, J. W. 1972. An interglacial deposit near Austerfield, southern Yorkshire. *Report of the Institute of Geological Sciences. 72/4.* London.

——, JARVIS, R. A. & MATHEWS, B. 1971. The late Weichselian sequence in the Vale of York. *Proceedings of the Yorkshire Geological Society,* **38,** 281–284.

GEIKIE, A. & REID, C. 1866. The Pliocene deposits of north-western Europe. *Nature, London,* **34,** 341–343.

GEORGE, T. N. 1932. The Quaternary beaches of Gower. *Proceedings of the Geologists' Association,* **43,** 291–324.

—— 1933a. The glacial deposits of Gower. *Geological Magazine,* **70,** 208–232.

GENNARD, D. E. 1984. A palaeoecological study of the interglacial deposit at Benburb, County Tyrone. *Proceedings of the Royal Irish Academy,* **84B,** 43–55.

GERRARD, A. J. W. 1983. *Periglacial landforms of the Cox Tor -Staple Tors area of western Dartmoor.* Department of Geography, University of Birmingham, Working Paper Series, No. 13, 36.

GIBBARD, P. L. 1974. *Pleistocene Stratigraphy and Vegetational History of Hertfordshire.* PhD thesis, University of Cambridge.

—— 1977. Pleistocene history of the Vale of St Albans. *Philosophical Transactions of the Royal Society of London,* **B280,** 445–483.

—— 1978a. Quaternary geology and landform development in the Vale of St Albans. *In:* ROSE, J. & GIBBARD, P. L. (eds) *Field Guide to the Vale of St Albans,* Quaternary Research Association, London, 9–29.

—— 1978b. Westmill. *In:* ROSE, J. & GIBBARD, P. L. (eds) *Field Guide to the Vale of St Albans,* Quaternary Research Association, London, 63–67.

—— 1978c. Hatfield Poly. *In:* ROSE, J. & GIBBARD, P. L. (eds) *Field Guide to the Vale of St Albans,* Quaternary Research Association, London, 79–85.

—— 1978d. Moor Mill. *In:* ROSE, J. & GIBBARD, P. L. (eds) *Field Guide to the Vale of St Albans,* Quaternary Research Association, London, 87–90.

—— 1979. Middle Pleistocene drainage in the Thames valley. *Geological Magazine,* **116,** 35–44.

—— 1982. Terrace stratigraphy and drainage history of the Plateau Gravels of north Surrey, south Berkshire, and north Hampshire, England. *Proceedings of the Geologists' Association,* **93,** 369-384.

—— 1983. The diversion of the Thames – a review. *In:* ROSE, J. & GIBBARD, P. L. (eds) *Field Guide to the Vale of St Albans,* Quaternary Research Association, London, 8–23.

—— 1985. *The Pleistocene History of the Middle Thames Valley,* Cambridge University Press, 155.

—— 1988a. Palynological problems and the vegetational sequence of the Pliocene -preglacial Pleistocene of East Anglia. *In:* GIBBARD, P. L. & ZALASIEWICZ (eds) *The Pliocene -Middle Pleistocene of East Anglia,* Field Guide, Quaternary Research Association, Cambridge, 42–49.

—— 1988b. The history of the great northwest European rivers during the past three million years. *Philosophical Transactions of the Royal Society of London,* **B318,** 559–602.

—— 1989. The geomorphology of a part of the Middle Thames forty years on: a reappraisal of the work of F. Kenneth Hare. *Proceedings of the Geologists' Asssociation,* **100,** 481–503.

—— 1994. *Pleistocene history of the Lower Thames Valley.* Cambridge University Press.

—— & ALLEN, L. G. 1995. Drainage evolution in south and east England during the Pleistocene. *Terra Nova,* **6,** 444–452.

—— & CHESHIRE, D. A. 1983. Hatfield Polytechnic (Roe Hyde Pit), *In:* ROSE, J. (ed.) *Diversion of the Thames,* Field Guide, Quaternary Research Association, Cambridge, 110–119.

—— & PEGLAR, S. M. 1989. Palynology of the fossiliferous deposits at Witham-on-the-Hill, Lincolnshire. *In:* KEEN, D. H. (ed.) *The Pleistocene of the West Midlands. Field Guide.* Quaternary Research Association, Cambridge, 131–133.

—— & PEGLAR, S. M. 1990. Palynology of the interglacial deposits at Little Oakley, Essex, and their correlation. *Philosophical Transactions of the Royal Society of London,* **B328,** 341–357.

—— & PETTIT, M. 1978. The palaeobotany of the interglacial deposits at Sugworth, Berkshire. *New Phytologist,* **81,** 465–477.

—— & STUART, A. J. 1974. Trace fossils from proglacial lake sediments. *Boreas,* **3,** 69–74.

—— & —— 1975. Flora and vertebrate fauna of the Barrington Beds. *Geological Magazine,* **112,** 493–501.

—— & TURNER, C. 1988. In defense of the Wolstonian stage. *Quaternary Newsletter,* **54,** 9–14.

—— & WYMER, J. J. 1983. Highlands Farm. *In:* ROSE, J. (ed.) *Diversion of the Thames,* Field Guide, Quaternary Research Association, Cambridge, 67–76.

—— & ZALASIEWICZ, J. A. 1988. *Pliocene-Middle Pleistocene of East Anglia: Field Guide.* Quaternary Research Association, Cambridge.

GIBBARD, P. L., COOPE, G. R., HALL, A. R., *et al.* 1982. Middle Devensian river deposits beneath the 'Upper Floodplain' terrace of the river Thames at Kempton Park, Sunbury, Surrey, England. *Proceedings of the Geologists' Association,* **93,** 275–290.

——, BRYANT, I. D. & HALL, A. R. 1986a. A Hoxnian interglacial doline infilling at Slade Oak Lane, Denham, Buckinghamshire, England. *Geological Magazine,* **123,** 27–43.

——, SWITSUR, V. R. & WINTLE, A. G. 1986b. A reappraisal of the age of silts in the Wrecclesham Gravel at Alton Road, Farnham, Surrey. *Quaternary Newsletter,* **50,** 6–13.

——, WINTLE, A. G. & CATT, J. A. 1987. Age and origin of clayey silt 'brickearth' in West London, England. *Journal Quaternary Science,* **2,** 3–9.

——, WHITEMAN, C. A. & BRIDGLAND, D. R. 1988. A preliminary report on the stratigraphy of the Lower Thames valley. *Quaternary Newsletter,* **56,** 1–8.

——, WEST, R. G., ANDREW, R. & PETTIT, M. 1991a. Tottenhill, Norfolk. *In:* LEWIS, S. G., WHITEMAN, C. A. & BRIDGLAND, D. R. (eds) *Central East Anglia and the Fen Basin. Field Guide.* Quaternary Research Association, London, 131–143.

——, WEST, R. G., ZAGWIJN, W. H., BALSON, P. S., BURGER, A. W., FUNNELL, B. M., JEFFERY, D. H., DE JONG, J., KOLFSCHOTEN, T. VAN, LISTER, A. M., MEIJER, T., NORTON, P. E. P., PREECE, R. C., ROSE, J., STUART, A. J., WHITEMAN, C. A. & ZALASIEWICZ, J. A. 1991b. Early and Middle Pleistocene correlations in the southern North Sea Basin. *Quaternary Science Reviews,* **10,** 23–52.

——, ——, ANDREW, R. & PETTIT, M. 1992. The margin of a Middle Pleistocene ice advance at Tottenhill, Norfolk, England. *Geological Magazine,* **129,** 59–76.

——, ALLEN, P., FIELD, M. H. & HALLAM, D. F. 1996. Early Pleistocene sediments at Great Blakenham, Suffolk, England. *Quaternary Science Reviews,* **15,** 413–424.

GIBBONS, W. & MCCARROLL, D. 1993. *Geology of the Country around Aberdaron, including Bardsey Island.* Memoir, British Geological Survey.

GILBERT, A. 1966. The raised shoreline sequence at Saunton in North Devon. *In:* CHARMAN, D. J., NEWNHAM, R. M. & CROOT, D. G. (eds) *The Quaternary of Devon and east Cornwall.* Field Guide, Quaternary Research Association, London, 40–47.

GILBERT, C. J. 1919a. On the occurrence of the extensive deposits of high-level sands and gravels resting upon the chalk at Little heath, near Berkhampstead. *Quarterly Journal of the Geological Society, London,* **75,** 32–43.

—— 1919b. Excursion to Berkhampstead and Little Heath. *Proceedings of the Geologists' Association,* **30,** 87–91.

GILBERTSON, D. D. 1976. Non-marine molluscan faunas of terrace gravels in the Upper Thames Basin. *In:* ROE, D. A. (ed.) *Field Guide to the Oxford Region* Quaternary Research Association, Oxford, 16–19.

—— 1979. The Burtle Sand Beds of Somerset: the significance of freshwater interglacial faunas. *Proceedings of the Somerset Archaeological and Natrual History Society,* **123,** 115–118.

—— 1980. The palaeoecology of the Middle Pleistocene Mollusca from Sugworth, Oxfordshire. *Philosophical Transactions of the Royal Society of London,* **B289,** 107–118.

—— & HAWKINS, A. B. 1974. Upper Pleistocene deposits and landforms at Holly Lane, Clevedon, Somerset (ST 419727). *Proceedings of the University of Bristol Spelaeological Society,* **13,** 349–360.

—— & —— 1977. The Quaternary deposits at Swallow Cliff, Middlehope, County of Avon. *Proceedings of the Geologists' Association,* **88,** 255–266.

—— & —— 1978. *The Pleistocene succession at Kenn, Somerset.* Bulletin of the Geological Survey of Great Britain, No. 66. Institute of Geological Sciences, London,

—— & —— 1978b. The col-gully and glacial deposits at Court Hill, Clevedon, near Bristol, England. *Journal of Glaciology,* **20,** 173–188.

—— & —— 1983. Periglacial slope deposits and frost structures along the southern margins of the Severn Estuary. *Proceedings of the University of Bristol Spelaeological Society,* **16, 3,** 175–184.

—— & MOTTERSHEAD, D. N. 1975. The Quaternary deposits at Doniford, west Somerset. *Field Studies,* **4,** 117–129.

GIPP, M. R. 1993. The orientation of buried iceberg scours and othe linear phenomena. *Marine Geology,* **114,** 263–272.

GIRLING, M. A. 1974. Evidence from Lincolnshire of the age and intensity of the mid-Devensian temperate episode. *Nature,* **250,** 270.

—— 1977. Tattershall Castle and Kirkby-on-Bain. *In:* CATT, J. A. (ed.) Guidebook *for Excursion C7. Yorkshire and Lincolnshire.* INQUAX Congress, U.K. Norwich: Geo Abstracts for International Union for Quaternary Research, 19–21.

—— 1980. *Late Pleistocene insect faunas from two sites.* PhD Thesis, University of Birmingham.

GLADFELTER, B. G. 1972. Cold-climate features in the vicinity of Clacton-on-Sea, Essex, England. *Quaternaria,* **16,** 121–135.

—— 1975. Middle Pleistocene sedimentary sequences in East Anglia (UK). *In:* BUTZER, K. W. & ISSAC, G. L. *After Australopithecines: Stratigraphy, Ecology and Culture Change in the Middle Pleistocene* Mouton, The Hague, 223–258.

—— 1993. The geostratigraphic context of the archaeology. *In:* SINGER, R., GLADFELTER, B. G. & WYMER, J. J. *The Lower Paleolithic site at Hoxne, England.* University of Chicago Press, Chicago, 23–66.

—— & SINGER, R. 1975. Implications of East Anglian glacial stratigraphy for the British Lower Palaeolithic. *In:* Quaternary Studies (eds SUGGATE, R. P. & CRESSWELL, M. M.), Selected papers from IX INQUA Congress, Christchurch, New Zealand, 2–10 December 1973. *Bulletin of the Royal Society of New Zealand,* **13,** 139–145.

GODWIN, H. 1940. A boreal transgression of the sea in Swansea Bay. Data for the study of post-glacial history. VI. *New Phytologist,* **39,** 308–321.

—— 1960. Radiocarbon dating and Quaternary history in Britain. *Proceedings of the Royal Society of London.* **B153,** 287–320.

—— 1962. Vegetational history of Kentish Chalk Downs as seen at Wingham and Frogholt. *Veröffentlichungen des Geobotanischen Institut Rübel,* **37,** 83–99.

—— 1964 Late Weichselian conditions in south-eastern Britain: organic deposits at Colney Heath, Hertfordshire. *Proceedings of the Royal Society of London,* **B160,** 258–275.

—— 1975. *The History of the British Flora: a factual basis for phytogeography.* Cambridge University Press

—— & MITCHELL, G. F. 1938. Stratigraphy and development of two raised bogs near Tregaron, Cardiganshire. *New Phytologist*, **37**, 425–454.

—— & NEWTON, L. 1938. The submerged forest at Borth and Ybyslas, Cardiganshire. Data for the study of Post-glacial history. *New Phytologist*, **37**, 333–344.

—— & WILLIS, E. H. 1961. Cambride University Natural Radiocarbon Measurements III. *Radiocarbon*, **3**, 60.

—— & —— 1964. Cambridge University Natural Radiocarbon Measurements VI. *Radiocarbon*, **6**, 123–125.

GORDON, J. E. 1993. Bigholm Burn. *In:* GORDON, J. E. & SUTHERLAND, D. G. (eds) *Quaternary of Scotland*. Chapman and Hall, London, 596–599.

GOSTELOW, T. P. & BROWNE, M. E. 1981. Engineering geology of the upper Forth Estuary. *Report of the British Geological Survey*, **16**, No. 8.

GOUDIE, A. S. 1976. The Oxford Region. *In:* ROE, D. A. (ed.) *Field Guide to the Oxford Region*, Quaternary Research Association, Oxford, 1–5.

GOUDIE, A. S. & HART, M. G. 1975. Pleistocene events and forms in the Oxford region. *In:* SMITH, C. G. & SCARGILL, D. I. *Oxford and its Region* Oxford University Press, 3–13.

GOWLETT, J. 1994. West Stow. *Proceedings of the Suffolk Institute of Archaeology and History*, **38**, 224–225.

GRACIANSKY, P. C. de & POAG, C. W. 1985. Geologic history of Goban Spur, northwest Europe continental margin, *In:* GRACIANSKY, P. C. de and fourteen others. *Initial Reports of the Deep Sea Drilling Project*, **80**. United States Government Printing Office, Washington, 1187–1216.

GRAY, J. M. 1975. The Loch Lomond Readvance and contemporaneous sea-levels in Loch Etive and neighbouring areas of western Scotland. *Proceedings of the Geologists' Association*, **86**, 227–238.

—— 1982. The last glaciers (Loch Lomond Advance) in Snowdonia, North Wales. *Geological Journal*, **17**, 111–133.

—— 1993. Moss of Achnacree and Achnaba Landforms. *In:* GORDON, J. E. & SUTHERLAND, D. G. (eds) *Quaternary of Scotland*, Chapman and Hall, London, 319–323.

—— & COXON, P. 1991. The Loch Lomond Stadial glaciation in Britain and Ireland. *In:* EHLERS, J., GIBBARD, P. L. & ROSE, J. *Glacial Deposits in Great Britain and Ireland*. Balkema, Rotterdam, 89–105.

—— & SUTHERLAND, D. G. 1977. The Oban-Ford moraine: a reappraisal. *In:* GRAY, J. M. & LOWE, J. J. (eds) *Studies in the Scottish Lateglacial Environment*. Pergamon, Oxford, 33–44.

GRAY, J. W. 1911. The north and mid-Cotteswolds and the Vale of Moreton during the Glacial Epoch. *Proceedings of the Cotteswolds Naturalists Field Club*, **17**, 257–274.

GRAYSON, R. 1972. *The buried bedrock topography between Manchester and the Mersey Estuary*. MSc thesis, University of Manchester.

GREEN, A. H. 1864. The Geology of Banbury, Woodstock, Bicester and Buckingham. *Memoir Geological Survey*.

GREEN, C. P. 1974. Pleistocene gravels of the River Axe in southwestern England, and their bearing on the southern limit of glaciation in Britain. *Geological Magazine*, **111**, 213–220.

—— 1988. The Palaeolithic site at Broom, Dorset, 1932–41: from the record of C. E. Bean, Esq. *Proceedings of the Geologists' Association*, **99**, 173–180.

—— & KEEN, D. H. 1987. Stratigraphy and palaeoenvironments of the Stone Point deposits: the 1975 investigation. *In:* BARBER, K. E. (ed.) *Wessex and the Isle of Wight*. Quaternary Research Association Field Guide, 17–22.

—— & McGREGOR, D. F. M. 1978a. Pleistocene gravel trains of the River Thames. *Proceedings of the Geologists' Association*, **89**, 143–156.

—— & McGREGOR, D. F. M. 1978b. Pleistocene gravel deposits of the Vale of St. Albans and the Middle Thames. *In:* ROSE, J. & GIBBARD, P. L. (eds) *Field Guide to the Vale of St. Albans*, Quaternary Research Association, London, 31–37.

—— & —— 1978c. Westwood. *In:* ROSE, J & GIBBARD, P. L. (eds) *Field Guide to the Vale of St. Albans*, Quaternary Research Association, London, 91.

—— & —— 1980. Quaternary evolution of the River Thames. *In:* JONES, D. K. C. (ed.) *The Shaping of Southern England*, Institute of British Geographers Special Publication **11**, Academic, London, 177–202.

—— & —— 1983. Lithology of the Thames Gravels. *In:* ROSE, J & GIBBARD, P. L. (eds) *Field Guide to the Vale of St. Albans*, Quaternary Research Association, London, 24–28.

—— & —— 1987. River terraces: a stratigraphic record of environmental change. *In:* GARDINER, V. (ed.) *International Geomorphology 1986 Part 1*, Wiley, Chichester, 977–987.

——, HEY, R. W. & McGREGOR, D. F. M. 1980. Volcanic pebbles in Pleistocene gravels of the Thames in Buckinghamshire and Hertfordshire. *Geological Magazine*, **117**, 59–64.

——, McGREGOR, D. F. M. & EVANS, A. 1982. Development of the Thames drainage system in early and Middle Pleistocene times. *Geological Magazine*, **119**, 281–290.

——, COOPE, G. R., CURRANT, A. P., HOLYOAK, D. T., IVANOVICH, M., JONES, R. L., KEEN, D. H., McGREGOR, D. F. M. & ROBINSON, J. E. 1984. Evidence of two temperate episodes in late Pleistocene deposits at Marsworth, U.K. *Nature*, **309**, 778–781.

——, ——, JONES, R. L., KEEN, D. H., BOWEN, D. Q., CURRANT, A. P., HOLYOAK, D. T., IVANOVICH, M., ROBINSON, J. E., ROGERSON, R. J. & YOUNG, R. C. 1996. Pleistocene deposits at Stoke Goldington, in the valley of the Great Ouse, UK. *Journal of Quaternary Science*, **11**, 59–87.

GREEN, G. W. & WELCH, F. B. 1965. Geology of the country around Wells and Cheddar. *Memoir Geological Survey*.

GREEN, H. S. 1981. The first Welshman: excavations at Pontnewydd. *Antiquity*, **55**, 184–195.

—— 1984. *Pontnewydd Cave. A Lower Palaeolithic hominid site in Wales:* The first report. National Museum of Wales, Cardiff.

—— 1986. Palaeolethic Settlement of Wales research project: a review of progress 1978–85. *In:* COLLCUTT, S. N. (ed.) *The Palaeolithic and its Nearest Neighbours*. University of Sheffield, 36–42.

—— & WALKER, E. A. 1991. *Ice Age Hunters: Neanderthals and Early Modern Hunters in Wales*. National Museum of Wales, Cardiff.

—— *et al.* 1981. Pontnewydd Cave in Wales -a new Middle Pleistocene hominid site, *Nature*, **294**, 707–713.

—— *et al.* 1989. Le site acheuleen de la Grotte de Pontnewyedd, Pays de Galles: geomorphologie, stratigraphie, chronologie, faune, hominides fossiles, geologie et industrie lithique dans le contexte paleoecologique. *L'Anthropologie*, **93**, 15–52.

GREEN, R. D. 1968. *Soils of Romney Marsh*. Soil Survey of Great Britain, Bulletin No. 4, Harpenden.

GREENLY, E. 1919. *The Geology of Anglesey*. Memoir Geological Survey.

—— 1921. The Pleistocene formations of Claverham and Yatton. *Proceedings of the Naturalists' Society*, Series **4, 5**, 145–147.

GREENSMITH, J. T. & GUTMANIS, J. C. 1990. Aspects of the late Holocene history of the Dungeness area, Kent. *Proceedings of the Geologists' Association*, **101**, 225–237.

—— & TUCKER, E. V. 1980. Evidence for differential subsidence on the Essex coast. *Proceedings of the Geologists' Association*, **91**, 169–175.

GREENWOOD, B. 1972. Modern analogues and the evaluation of a Pleistocene sedimentary sequence. *Transactions of the Institute of British Geographers*, **56**, 145–169.

GREGORY, D. M. & BRIDGE, V. A. 1979. On the Quaternary foraminiferal species *Elphidium ? ustulatum* Todd 1957: Its stratigraphic and palaeoecological implications. *Journal of Foraminiferal Research*, **19**, 70–75.

——, HARLAND, R., & WILKINSON, I. P. 1978. Palaeontology of a series of boreholes through the drift of Forth and the Forth Approaches. *In:* THOMSON, M. E. IGS studies of the geology of the Firth of Forth and its Approaches. *Report of the Institute of Geological Sciences*. No. 77/17, 52–56.

GREGORY, J. W. 1894. Evolution of the Thames. *Natural Science*, **5**, 97–108.

—— 1922. *Evolution of the Essex Rivers and of the Lower Thames*, Benham, Colchester, 64.

—— 1925. The Evishardran esker, County Tyrone. *Geological Magazine*, **62**, 451–458.

GRESSWELL, R. K. 1967. The geomorphology of the Fylde. *In:* STEEL, R. W. & LAWTON, R. (eds) *Liverpool Essays in geography: a Jubilee Collection*. London, Longman, 25–42.

GRIFFIN, K. 1984. Plant macrofossils from a Quaternary deposit in the North Sea. in: *Quaternary Stratigraphy of the North Sea* (Abstract volume), University of Bergen.

GRIFFITHS, J. C. 1939. The mineralogy of the glacial deposits of the region between the rivers Neath and Towy, South Wales. *Proceedings of the Geologists' Association*, **50**, 433–462.

GRINDLEY, H. E. 1954. The Wye Glacier. *In:* Herefordshire, its natural history, archaeology and history. Centenary Volume of the Transactions of the Woolhope Naturalists' Field Club. Gloucester: British Publishing Co., 36–47.

GRUBE, F., CHRISTENSEN, S. & VOLLMER, T. 1986. Glaciations in north west Germany. *Quaternary Science Reviews*, **5**, 347–357.

GRUHN, R., BRYAN, A. L. & MOSS, A. J. 1974. A contribution to Pleistocene chronology in south east Essex, England. *Quaternary Research*, **4**, 53–71.

——, SCHWARCZ, H. P. & CHADWIN, J. 1988. ESR dating of tooth enamel: coupled correlation for U-uptake and U-series disquilibrium. *Nuclear Tracks and Radiation Measures*, **14**, 237–241.

GUILCHER, A. 1950. Nivation, cryoplanation et solifluxtion quaternaires dans les collines de Bretagne occidentale et du nord du Devonshire. *Revue de Geomorphologie Dynamique*, **1**, 53–77.

HAGGART, B. A. 1986. Relative sea-level change in the Beauly Firth, Scotland. *Boreas*, **15**, 191–207.

—— 1987. Relative sea-level changes in the Moray Firth area, Scotland. *In:* TOOLEY, M. J. & SHENNAN, I. (eds) *Sea-Level Changes*. Blackwell Scientific, Oxford, 67–108.

—— 1989. Variations in the pattern and rate of isostatic uplift indicated by a comparison of Holocene sea-level curves from Scotland. *Journal of Quaternary Science*, **4**, 67–76.

HALD, M., STEINSUNS, P. L., DOITTEN, T., KORSON, S., POLYAK, L. & ASPELI, R. 1994. Recent and Late Quaternary distribution of Elphidium exclavation F. clavation in Arctic seas. *Cushman Foundation Special Publication*, **32**, 141–153.

HALL, A. M. 1984b. Introduction. *In:* HALL, M. A. (ed.) *Buchan Field Guide*. Quaternary Research Association, Cambridge, 1–26.

—— & CONNELL, E. R. 1986. A preliminary report on the Quaternary sediments at Leys gravel pit, Buchan, Scotland. *Quaternary Newsletter*, **48**, 17–28.

—— & —— 1991. The glacial deposits of Buchan, northeast Scotland. *In:* EHLERS, J., GIBBARD, P. L. & ROSE, J. (eds) *Glacial Deposits in Great Britain and Ireland*, Balkema, Rotterdam, 129–136.

—— & JARVIS, J. 1989. A preliminary report on the Late Devensian glaciomarine deposits around St Fergus, Grampian Region. *Quaternary Newsletter*, **59**, 5–7.

—— & —— 1993. Kirkhill. *In:* GORDON, J. E. & SUTHERLAND, D. G. (eds) *Quaternary of Scotland*. Chapman and Hall, London, 225–230.

—— & —— 1993. Bellscamphie. *In:* GORDON, J. E. & SUTHERLAND, D. G. (eds) *Quaternary of Scotland*. Chapman and Hall, London, 230–233.

—— & —— 1995. A multiple till sequence near Ellon, Grampian Region: T. F. Jamieson's 'indigo boulder clay' re-examined. *Scottish Journal of Geology*, **31**, 53–59.

——, WHITTINGTON, G. & GORDON, J. E. 1993a. Interglacial peat at Fugla Ness Shetland. *In:* BIRNIE, J., GORDON, J., BENNETT, K. & HALL, A. (eds) *The Quaternary of Shetland*. Quaternary Research Association, London, 62–76.

——, GORDON, J. E. & WHITTINGTON, G. 1993b. Early Devensian interstadial peat at Sel Ayre, Shetland. *In:* BIRNIE, J., GORDON, J. BENNETT, K. & HALL, A. (eds) *The Quaternary of Shetland*, Quaternary Research Association, London, 104–118.

——, DULLER, G., JARVIS, J. & WINTLE, A. G. 1995a. Middle Devensian ice-proximal gravels at Howe of Blyth, Grampian Region. *Scottish Journal of Geology*, **31**, 61–64.

——, WHITTINGTON, G., DULLER, A. T. & JARVIS, J. 1995b. Late Pleistocene environments in lower Strathspey, Scotland. *Transactions of the Royal Society of Edinburgh: Earth Sciences*, **85**, 253–273.

HAMBLIN, R. J. O. 1991. Comment on: The origin of major incisions within the Pleistocene deposits of the North Sea -Wingfield (1990). *Marine Geology*, **96**, 23–125.

—— 1992. Quaternary, including sea-bed sediments. *In:* HAMBLIN, R. et al. *United Kingdom offshore regional report: the geology of the English Channel*. British Geological Survey.

HANVEY, P. 1987. Sedimentology of lee-side stratification sequences in Late Pleistocene drumlins, northwest Ireland. *In:* MENZIES, J. & ROSE, J. (eds) *Drumlin Symposium*. Balkema, Rotterdam.

—— 1989. Stratified flow deposits in a Late Pleistocene drumlin in northwest Ireland. *Sedimentary Geology*, **62**, 211–221.

HARDING, P. & GIBBARD, P. L. 1984. Excavations at Northwold Road, Stoke Newington, north east London, 1981. *Transactions of the Middlesex Archaeological Society*, **34**, 1–18.

——, BRIDGLAND, D. R., MADGETT, P. A. et al. 1991. Recent investigations of Pleistocene sediments near Maidenhead, Berkshire, and their archaeological content. *Proceedings of the Geologists' Association*, **102**, 25–53.

——, KEEN, D. H., BRIDGLAND, D. R. & ROGERSON, R. J. 1991. A Palaeolithic site rediscovered at Biddenham, Bedfordshire. *Bedfordshire Archaeology*, **19**, 87–90.

HARE, F. K. 1947. The geomorphology of a part of the Middle Thames. *Proceedings of the Geologists' Association*, **58**, 294–339.

HARLAND, R., GREGORY, D. M., HUGHES, M. J. & WILKINSON, I. P. 1978. A late Quaternary bio-and climatostratigraphy for marine sediments in the north-central part of the North Sea. *Boreas*, **7**, 91–96.

HARMER, F. W. 1902. A sketch of the later Tertiary history of East Anglia. *Proceedings of the Geologists' Association*, **17**, 416–79.

—— 1907. On the origin of certain canon-like valleys associated with lake-like areas of depression. *Quarterly Journal of the Geological Society, London*, **63**, 470–514.

HARMER, F. W. 1909. The Pleistocene Period in the eastern counties of England. *Jubilee Volume of the Geologists' Association*, 103–123.

HARRIES, J. W. R. 1977. The Sand and Gravel Resources of the Country around Eynsham, Oxfordshire. *Mineral Assessment Report of the Institute of Geological Sciences* 28, 88.

HARRIS, C. & WRIGHT, M. D. 1980. Some glaciation drift deposits near Pontypridd, South Wales. *Geological Journal*, **15**, 7-20.

——, WILLIAMS, G., BRABHAM, P., EATON, G. & McCARROLL, D. 1997. Glaciotectonized Quaternary sediments at Dinas Dinlee, Gwynedd, North Wales and their bearing on the style of deglaciation in the Eastern Irish Sea Basin. *Quaternary Science Reviews*, **16**, 109–127.

HART, J. McA. 1960. Field meeting at Grays Thurrock. *Proceedings of the Geologists' Association*, **71**, 242–244.

HART, J. K. 1990. Lleiniog. *In:* ADDISON, K., EDGE, M. J. & WATKINS, R. (eds) *North Wales*. Quaternary Research Association Field Guide, Coventry, 116–119.

—— 1994. Till fabric associated with deformable beds. *Earth Surface Processes and Landforms*, **19**, 15–32.

—— & BOULTON, G. S. 1991 The glacial drifts of Norfolk. *In:* EHLERS, J., GIBBARD, P. L. & ROSE, J. (eds) *Glacial deposits of Britain and Ireland*. Balkema, Rotterdam, 233–243.

—— & PEGLAR, S. M. 1990. Further evidence for the timing of the Middle Pleistocene glaciation in Britain. *Proceedings of the Geologists' Association*, **101**, 187–196.

HARVEY, A. M. 1985. The river systems of North-west England. *In:* JOHNSON, R. J. (ed.) *The Geomorphology of North-West England*. *122–139*. Manchester. Manchester University Press.

HAWKINS, A. B. & KELLAWAY, G. A. 1971. Field Meeting at Bristol and Bath with Special Reference to New Evidence of Glaciation. *Proceedings of the Geologists' Association*, **82**, 267–291.

—— & TRATMAN, E. K. 1977. The Quaternary Deposits of the Mendip, Bath and Bristol areas; including a reprinting of Donovan's 1954 and 1964 Bibliographies. *Proceedings of the University of Bristol Spelaeological Society*, **14**, **3**, 197–232.

HAWKINS, H. L. 1922. The relation of the River Thames to the London Basin. *Report of the British Association for the Advancement of Science* (for 1922), 365–366.

—— 1928. Excursion to Kingsclere. *Proceedings of the Geological Society of London*, **39**, 98–102.

HAWKINS, M. P. 1981. The sand and gravel resources of the Bury St. Edmunds (Suffolk) area. Description of 1:25000 sheet TL86. *Mineral Assessment Report*, 72. Institute of Geological Sciences, Keyworth.

HAYES, J. D., IMBRIE, J. & SHACKLETON, N. J. 1976. Variations in the Earth's orbit: pacemaker of the ice ages. *Science*, **194**, 1121–1132.

HAYNES, J. R. & DOBSON, M. R. 1969. Physiography, foraminifera and sedimentation in the Dovey Estuary (Wales). *Geological Journal*, **6**, 217–256.

——, McCABE, A. M. & EYLES, N. 1995. Microfaunas from Late Devensian glaciomarine deposits in the Irish Sea basin. *Irish*

Journal of Earth Sciences, **14,** 81–103.

HEDBERG, H. D. 1976. *International Stratigraphic Guide.* Wiley, New York.

HEIJNIS, H. 1990. Dating of the Odhar Peat at the Allt Odhar site by the Uranium series disequilibrium dating method. *In:* AUTON, C. A., FIRTH, C. R. & MERRITT, J. W. (eds) *Beauly to Nairn: Field Guide.* Cambridge, Quaternary Research Association, 72–74.

—— & PLICHT, J. VAN DER. 1992. Uranium/thorium dating of Late Pleistocene deposits in NW Europe, uranium/thorium isotope systematics and open-system behaviour of peat layers. *Chemical Geology,* **94,** 161–171.

——, RUDDOCK, J. & COXON, P. 1993. A uranium-thorium dated Late Eemian or Early Midlandian organic deposit from near Kilfenora between Spa and Fenit, County Kerry, Ireland. *Journal of Quaternary Science,* **8,** 31–43.

HELM, D. G. & ROBERTS, B. 1975. A re-interpretation of the origin of sands and gravels around Banc-y-Warren, near Cardigan, west Wales. *Geological Journal,* **10,** 131–146.

—— & —— 1984. The origin of Late Devensian sands and gravels, south-east Anglesey. *Geological Journal,* **19,** 33–55.

HENRY, A. 1984. *The Lithostratigraphy, Biostratigraphy and chronostratigraphy of Coastal Pleistocene Deposits in Gower, South Wales.* PhD thesis, University of Wales.

HENWOOD, W. J. 1843. On the metalliferous deposits of Cornwall and Devon. *Transactions of the Royal Geological Society of Cornwall,* **5,** 1–512.

HESSION, M. A. I. 1988. *Quaternary geology of the south Irish Sea.* PhD thesis, University of Wales.

HEY, R. W. 1958. High-level gravels in and near the Lower Severn Valley. *Geological Magazine,* **95,** 161–168.

—— 1959. Pleistocene deposits on the west side of the Malvern Hills. *Geological Magazine,* **96,** 403–417.

—— 1963. The Pleistocene history of the Malvern Hills and adjacent areas. *Proceedings of the Cotteswold Naturalist's Field Club,* **33,** 185–191.

—— 1965. Highly quartzose pebble gravels in the London Basin. *Proceedings of the Geologists' Association,* **76,** 403–420.

—— 1967a. The Westleton Beds reconsidered. *Proceedings of the Geologists' Association,* **78,** 427–445.

—— 1967b. Sections in the beach plain of Dungeness. *Geological Magazine,* **104,** 361–370.

—— 1976a. The terraces of the Middle and Lower Thames. *Studia Societatis Scientiarum Torunensis.* Torun-Polonia, **8C,** 115–22.

—— 1976b. Provenance of far-travelled pebbles in the pre-Anglian Pleistocene of East Anglian Pleistocene of East Anglia. *Proceedings of the Geologists' Association,* **87,** 69–82.

—— 1980. Equivalents of the Westland Green Gravels in Essex and East Anglia. *Proceedings of the Geologists' Asssociation,* **91,** 279–290.

—— 1982. Composition of Pre-Anglian gravels in Norfolk. *Bulletin of the Geological Society of Norfolk,* **32,** 51–59.

—— 1983. Ferneux Pelham. *In: Diversion of the Thames* (ed. ROSE, J.), Field Guide, Quaternary Research Association, Canbridge, 94–95.

—— 1986. A re-examination of the Northern Drift of Oxfordshire. *Proceedings of the Geologists' Association,* **97,** 291–302.

—— 1991. Pleistocene gravels in the lower Wye valley. *Geological Journal,* **26,** 123–136.

—— & AUTON, C. A. 1988. Compositions of pebble-beds in the Neogene and pre-Anglian Pleistocene of East Anglia. *In:* GIBBARD, P. L. & ZALASIEWICZ, J. A. (eds) *Pliocene-Middle Pleistocene of East Anglia,* Field Guide, Quaternary Research Association, Cambridge, 35–41.

—— & BENCHLEY, P. J. 1977. Volcanic pebbles from Pleistocene gravels in Norfolk and Essex. *Geological Magazine,* **114,** 219–225.

——, KRINSLEY, D. H. & HYDE, P. J. W. 1971. Surface textures of sand grains from the Hertfordshire pebble gravels. *Geological Magazine,* **108,** 377–382.

HIBBERT, F. A. & SWITSUR, V. R. 1976. Radiocarbon dating of Flandrian pollen zones in Wales and Northern England. *New Phytologist,* **77,** 793–807.

HICKS, S. P. 1971. Pollen-analytical evidence for the effect of prehistoric agriculture on the vegetation of north Derbyshire. *New Phytologist,* **70,** 647–667.

HIGGINS, L. S. 1933. Coastal changes in South Wales – the excavation of an old beach (Merthyr Mawr Warren). *Geological Magazine,* **70,** 541–549.

HILL, A. R. & PRIOR, D. 1968. Directions of ice movement in north-east Ireland. *Proceedings of the Royal Irish Academy,* **66B,** 71–84.

HILLER, D. 1972. Untersuchungen zur Biologie und zur Okologie limnischer Ostracoden aus der Umbebung von Hamburg. *Archiv fur Hydrobiologie, Supplementband 40* (Stuttgart), **Heft 4,** 400–497.

HINCH, J. DE W. 1930. The shelly drift of Glanulra and Belderris, County Mayo. *Irish Naturalists' Journal,* **22,** 1–16.

HINTON, M. A. C. 1900a. The Pleistocene deposits of the Ilford and Wanstead District, Essex. *Essex Naturalist,* **11,** 161–165.

—— 1900b. The Pleistocene deposits of the Ilford and Wanstead district. *Proceedings of the Geologists' Association,* **16,** 271–281.

—— 1901. Excursion to Grays Thurrock. *Proceedings of the Geologists' Association,* **17,** 141–144.

—— 1910. A preliminary account of the British voles and lemmings; with some remarks on the Pleistocene climate and geography. *Proceedings of the Geologists' Association,* **21,** 489–507.

—— 1911. The British fossil shrews. *Geological Magazine,* **8,** 529–539.

—— 1923. Note on the rodent remains from Clacton-on-Sea. *Quarterly Journal of the Geological Society, London,* **79,** 626.

—— 1926a. The Pleistocene mammalia of the British Isles and their bearing upon the date of the Glacial Period. *Proceedings of he Yorkshire Geological Society New Series,* **20,** 325–348.

—— 1926b. *Monograph of the Voles and Lemmings (Microtinae), Living and Extinct,* Volume 1 (Volume 2 not published), British Museum, London, 488.

—— & KENNARD, A. S. 1990. Comtributions to the Pleistocene geology of the Thames valley, I. The Grays Thurrock area, Part I. *Essex Naturalist,* **11,** 336–370.

—— & —— 1905. The relative ages of the stone implements of the Lower Thames valley. *Proceedings of the Geologists' Association,* **19,** 76–100.

—— 1907. Contributions to the Pleistocene geology of the Thames valley I. The Grays Thurrock area, Part II (Revised), *Essex Naturalist,* **15,** 56–88.

HOARE, P. G. 1975. The pattern of glaciation of County Dublin. *Proceedings of the Royal Irish Academy,* **75B,** 207–224.

—— & CONNELL, E. R. 1981. The chalky till at Barrington, near Cambridge, and its connection with other Quaternary deposits in southern Cambridgeshire and adjoining areas. *Geological Magazine,* **118,** 463–476.

—— 1977. The glacial stratigraphy in Shangannagh and adjoining townlands, south-east County Dublin. *Proceedings of the Royal Irish Academy,* **77B,** 295–305.

HODGSON, E. 1862. On a deposit containing Diaomaceae, leaves, etc in the iron-ore mines near Ulverston. *Journal of the Geological Society, London,* **19,** 19–31.

HODGSON, J. M. 1964. The low-level Pleistocene marine sands gravels of the West Sussex coastal plain. *Proceedings of the Geologists' Association,* **75,** 547–561.

HODSON, F. & WEST, I. M. 1972. Holocene deposits of Fawley, Hampshire, and the development of Southampton Water. *Proceedings of the Geologists' Association,* **83,** 421–442.

HOLLAND, C. H., AUDLEY-CHARLES, M. G., BASSETT, M. G. *et al.* 1978. *A Guide to Stratigraphic Procedure.* Geological Society, London, Special Reports, **10.**

HOLLIN, J. T. 1971. *Ice-sheet Surges and Interglacial Sea Levels.* PhD thesis, Princeton University, 179.

—— 1977. Thames interglacial sites, Ipswichian sea levels and Antarctic ice surges. *Boreas,* **6,** 33–52.

* HOLLYER, S. E. & SIMMONS, M. B. 1978. The Sand and Gravel Resources of the Country around Southend-on-Sea, Essex. *Mineral Assessment Report of the Institute of Geological Sciences* **36,** 212.

HOLMAN, J. A. 1987. Middle Pleistocene herpetological 's from interglacial deposits at Sugworth near Oxford. *Bru.. gical Society Bulletin,* **21,** 5–7.

—— & CLAYDEN, J. D. 1988. Pleistocene interglacial herpetofauna from the Greenlands Pit, Purfleet, Essex. *British Herpetological Society Bulletin,* **26,** 26–27.

——, STUART, A. J. & CLAYDEN, J. D. 1990. A Middle Pleistocene herpetofauna from Cudmore Grove, Essex, England, and its paleogeographic and paleoclimatic implications. *Journal of Vertebrate Paleontology*, **10**, 86–94.

HOLMES, R., JEFFERY, D. H. & WINGFIELD, R. T. R. 1993. *Quaternary sediments around the United Kingdom (North Sheet 1:1000 000 Edinburgh, Scotland*. British Geological Survey.

—— 1977. Quaternary deposits of the central North Sea, 5. The Quaternary geology of the UK sector of the North Sea between 56° and 58°N. *Report of the Institute of Geological Sciences*, No. 77/14.

—— 1990. Rona Sheet 59N 06W. Quaternary Geology. 1:250 000 Map Series. *British Geological Survey*.

—— 1991. Foula Sheet 60N 04W. Quaternary Geology. 1:250 000 Map Series. *British Geological Survey*.

——, JEFFERY, D. H. & WINGFIELD, R. T. R. 1993. Quaternary sediments around the United Kingdom (North Sheet 1:1000 000 Edinburgh, Scotland, *British Geological Survey)*.

HOLMES, S. C. A. 1971. The geological mapper and the employment of his results, as illustrated in some areas of southern England. *Proceedings of the Geologists' Association*, **82**, 161–186.

HOLMES, T. V. 1890. Some sections between West Thurrock and Stifford on the Grays and Upminster railway. *Essex Naturalist*, **4**, 143–149.

—— 1892. The new railway from Grays Thurrock to Romford: sections between Upminster and Romford. *Journal of the Geological Society, London*, **48**, 365–372.

—— 1893. The new railway between Upminster and Romford. Boulder Clay between old river gravel at Hornchurch. Conclusions therefrom. *Essex Naturalist*, **7**, 1–14.

—— 1894. Further notes on some sections of the new railway from Romford to Upminster, and on the relations of the Thames valley beds to the boulder clay. *Quarterly Journal of the Geological Society, London*, **50**, 443–452.

—— 1896. Notes of the ancient physiography of south Essex. *Essex Naturalist*, **9**, 193–200.

HOLYOAK, D. T. 1983. A late Pleistocene interglacial flora and mollusca fauna from Thatcham, Berkshire, with notes on the Mollusca from the interglacial deposits at Aveley, Essex. *Geological Magazine*, **120**, 623–629.

—— & PREECE, R. C. 1983. Evidence of a high Middle Pleistocene sea-level from estuarine deposits at Bembridge, Isle of Wight, England. *Proceedings of the Geologists' Association*, **94**, 231–244.

—— & SEDDON, M. 1984. Devensian and Flandrian fossiliferous deposits in the Nene Valley, Central England. *Mercian Geologist*, **9**, 127–150.

—— & PREECE, R. C. 1985. Late Pleistocene interglacial deposits at Tattershall, Lincolnshire. *Philosophical Transactions of the Royal Society of London*, **B331**, 193–236.

——, IVANOVICH, M. & PREECE, R. C. 1983. Additional fossil and isotopic evidence for the age of the interglacial tufas at Hitchin and Icklingham. *Journal of Conchology*, **31**, 260–261.

HOPSON, P. M. 1981. The Sand and Gravel Resources of the Country around Stansted Mountfitchet, Essex, *Mineral Assessment Report of the Institute of Geological Sciences*, **104**, 110.

—— & BRIDGE, D. McC. 1987. Middle Pleistocene stratigraphy in the lower Waveney valley, East Anglia. *Proceedings of the Geologists' Association*, **98**, 171–185.

HOPSON, P. M., ALDISS, D. T. & SMITH, A. 1996. Geology of the country around Hitchin. *Memoir British Geological Survey*.

HORNE, J. 1923. *The Geology of the Lower Findhorn and Lower Strath Nairn: including part of the Black Isle near Fortrose*. Memoir of the Geological Survey.

——, ROBERTSON, D., JAMIESON, T. F., FRASER, J., KENDALL, P. F. & BELL, D. 1894. The character of the high-level shell-bearing deposits at Clava, Chapelhall and other locations. *Report of the British Association for the Advancement of Science for 1893*, 483–514.

——, ——, ——, ——, —— & —— 1897. The character of the high-level shell-bearing deposits in Kintyre. *Report of the British Association for the Advancement of Science for 1896*, 378–399.

HORTON, A. 1974. The sequence of Pleistocene deposits proved during the construction of the Birmingham motorways. *Institute of Geological Sciences Report*. **74/22**.

—— 1977. Nettlebed. *In:* SHEPHARD-THORN, E. R. & WYMER, J. J. (eds) *South East England and the Thames Valley*, Guide Book for

Excursion A5, X INQUA Congress, Birmingham, Geoabstracts, Norwich, 16–18.

—— 1983. Nettlebed. *In:* ROSE, J (ed.) *Diversion of the Thames*, Field Guide, Quaternary Research Association, Cambridge, 63–65.

—— 1989. Quinton. *In:* KEEN. D. H. (ed.) *The Pleistocene of the West Midlands: Field Guide*. Quaternary Research Association, Cambridge, 69–76.

——, WORSSAM, B. C. & WHITTOW, J. B. 1981. The Wallingford Fan Gravel. Philosophical Transactions of the Royal Society of London, **B293**, 215–255.

——, KEEN, D. H., ROBINSON, J. E., COOPE, G. R., CURRANT, A. P., GRAHAM, D. K., GREEN, C. P. & PHILLIPS, L. M. 1992. The Hoxnian Interglacial deposits at Woodston, Peterborough. *Philosophical Transactions of the Royal Society of London*, **B338**, 131–164.

HOWARD, A. J. 1993. The Quaternary geology and geomorphology of the area between Newark and Lincoln (Abstracts). *Quaternary Newsletter*, **69**, 59–60.

HOWARD, A. S., YOUNG, S. R. & PHARAOH, T. C. in prep. *The Geology of the Nottingham District*. Memoir of the British Geological Survey.

HOWELL, F. C. 1960. European and northwest African Middle Pleistocene hominids. *Current Anthropologist*, **1**, 195–232.

HOWELL, F. T. 1973. The sub-drift surface of the Mersey and Weaver catchments and adjacent areas. *Geological Journal*, **8(2)**, 285–296.

HOWELLS, M. F., FRANCIS, E. H., LEVERIDGE, B. E. & EVANS, C. D. R. 1978. *Capel Curig and Bettws-y-Coed*. British Geological Survey, 56–58.

——, LEVERIDGE, B. E., EVANS, C. D. R & NUTT, M. J. C. 1981. *Dolgarrog*. British Geological Survey, 71–75.

——, LEVERIDGE, B. E. & ADDISON, R. 1985. The geology of the Passes of Nant Ffrancon and Llanberis District. British Geological Survey.

HUBBARD, R. N. L. B. 1972. An interim report of the pollen record at Swanscombe. *Proceedings of the Royal Anthropological Institute* (for 1971), 79.

—— 1982. The environmental evidence from Swanscombe and its implications for Palaeolithic archaeology. *In:* LEACH, P. E. (ed.) *Archaeology in Kent to AD 1500* Council for British Archaeology, Research Report 48, 3–7.

HUDDART, D. 1977. *South East Ireland*. Guidebook for excursion A14, X INQUA Congress, (ed. BOWEN, D. Q.). *Norwich, Geoabstracts*, 1–56.

—— 1991. The glacial history and glacial deposits of the North and West Cumbrian lowlands. *In:* EHLERS, J., GIBBARD, P. L. & ROSE, J. (eds) *Glacial Deposits in Great Britain and Ireland*. Balkema, Rotterdam, 151–168.

——, TOOLEY, M. J. & CARTER, P. A. 1977. The coasts of northwest England. *In:* KIDSON, C. & TOOLEY, M. J. (eds) *The Quaternary History of the Irish Sea. Geological Journal Special Issue Number 7*. 119–154. Liverpool. Seel House Press.

HUGHES, C. E. 1980. *Interglacial Marine Deposits and Strandlines of the Somerset Levels*. PhD thesis, University of Wales.

HUGHES, M. J. 1978. Foraminifera from vibrocore G5 samples *In:* PANTIN, H. M. (ed.) Quaternary sediments from the north-east Irish Sea: Isle of Man to Cumbria. *Bulletin Geological Survey Great Britain*, **64**, 1–43.

HUGHES, S. 1987. *The aminostratigraphy of British Quaternary non-marine deposits*. PhD thesis, University of Wales.

HUGHES, T. McK. 1868. On the two plains of Hertfordshire and their gravels. *Quarterly Journal of the Geological Society, London*, **24**, 283–7.

HULL, E. 1855. On the physical geography and Pleistocene phenomena of the Cotteswold Hills. *Quarterly Journal of the Geological Society, London*, **11**, 475–496.

—— 1859. *The Geology of the Country around Woodstock, Oxfordshire*, Memoir Geological Survey.

—— 1864. *The geology of the country around Oldham and Manchester*. Memoir Geological Survey.

—— & WHITAKER, W. 1861. *The Geology of Parts of Oxfordshire and Berkshire*. Memoir Geological Survey.

HULME, P. D. 1980. The classification of Scottish peatlands. *Scottish Geographical Magazine*, **96**, 46–50.

HUNT, C. O. 1981. Pollen and organic-walled microfossils in

interglacial deposits from Kenn, Avon. *Proceedings of the Somerset Archaeological and natural History Society*, **125**, 73–76.

—— 1985. Pollen from the Eynsham Gravel at Magdalen College, Oxford. *In:* BRIGGS, D. J., COOPE, G. R. & GILBERTSON, D. D. The Chronology and Environmental Framework of Early Man in the Upper Thames Valley: A New Model. *British Archaeological Report, British Series*, **137**, 85–7.

—— 1987. *The Pleistocene History of the Langport-Chard area of Somerset.* PhD thesis, University College of Wales, Aberystwyth.

—— 1990a. An interglacial pollen assemblage from the Chadbrick Gravel at Hurcott Farm Somerset. *Proceedings of the Somerset Archaeological and Natural History Society*, **134**, 267–270.

—— 1990b. *A4/A36/A46 Swainswick-Batheaston Bypass: Geological survey of Hampton Rocks Railway Cutting.* Unpublished Report, Departments of Environment and Transport, Bristol.

—— 1992. Pollen and algal microfossils from the High Lodge clayey-silts. *In:* ASHTON, N. M., COOK, J., LEWIS, S. G. & ROSE, J. (eds) *High Lodge. Excavations by G. de G. Sieveking, 1962-8 and J. Cook, 1988.* British Museum Press, London, 109–115.

—— 1998. Quaternary of Somerset. *In:* CAMPBELL, S. *Quaternary of South West England.* Geological Conservation Review Series. London: Chapman & Hall.

——, GILBERTSON, D. D. & THEW, N. M. 1984. The Pleistocene Chadbrick Gravels of the Cary Valley, Somerset: amino-acid racemization and molluscan studies. *Proceedings of the Ussher Society*, **6**, 129–135.

HUTCHINSON, J. N. 1969. A reconsideration of the coastal landslides at Folkestone Warren, Kent. *Géotechnique* **19**, 6–38.

IMBRIE, J. *et al* 1992. On the structure and origin of major glaciation cycles I, Linear responses to Milankovitch forcing. *Paleoceanography*, **7**, 701–738.

—— *et al.* 1993. On the structure and origin of major glaciation cycles 2, The 100,000-year cycle. *Paleoceanography*, **8**, 699–736.

INCE, J. 1981. *Pollen Analysis and Radiocarbon Dating of Late-Glacial and Early Flandrian Deposits in Snowdonia, North Wales.* PhD thesis, City of London Polytechnic.

—— 1983. Two post-glacial pollen profiles from the uplands of Snowdonia, Gwynedd, North Wales. *New Phytologist*, **95**, 159–172.

INNES, J. & LONG, A. J. 1992. A preliminary investigation of the 'Midley Sand', Romney Marsh, Kent, UK. *Quaternary Newsletter*, **67**, 32–39.

JACKSON, I. 1977. The sand and gravel resources of the country west and south of Lincoln, Lincolnshire: Description of the 1 : 25 000 resources sheets SK 95, SK 96 and SK 97. *Mineral Assessment Report, Institute of Geological Sciences*, **27**.

—— 1982. The sand and gravel resources of the country north and west of Woodhall Spa, Lincolnshire: Description of 1 : 23 000 resource sheet TF16 and part of TF17. *Mineral Assessment Report, Institute of Geological Magazine*, 94.

JAMES, H. C. L. 1981b. Pleistocene sections at Gerrans Bay, south Cornwall. *Proceedings of the Ussher Society*, **5**, 239–240.

JAMIESON, T. F. 1874. On the last stage of the glacial period in North Britain. *Quarterly Journal of the Geological Society, London*, **30**, 317–338.

—— 1906. The glacial period in Aberdeenshire and the southern border of Moray Firth. *Quarterly Journal of the Geological Society, London*, **62**, 13–39.

JANOSSY, D. 1975. Mid-Pleistocene microfauna of Contintental Europe. *In:* BUTZER, K. W. & ISSAC, G. L. (eds) *After the Australopithecines: Stratigraphy, Ecology and Culture Change in the Middle Pleistocene* The Hague, 375–396.

—— 1987. *Pleistocene Vertebrate Faunas of Hungary,* Elsevier, Amsterdam, 208.

JANSEN, J. H. F. & HENSEY, A. M. 1981. Interglacial and Holocene sedimentation in the northern North Sea: an example of Eemian deposits in the Tartan Field. *In:* SHUTTENHELM, R. P. E. & VAN WEERING, Tj. C. E. (eds) Holocene Marine Sedimentation in the North Sea Basin. N10, S-D, *Special Publication of the International Association of Sedimentologists*, **5**, 323–334

——, VAN WEERING, T. C. E. & EISMA, D. 1979. Late Quaternary sedimentation in the North Sea, *In:* OELE, E., SCHÜTTENHELM, R. T. E. & WIGGERS, A. J. (eds) *The Quaternary History of the North Sea.* Uppsala (*Acta Universitatis Upsaliensis*), 175–187.

JANSEN, K. A. & KNUDSEN, K. L. 1988. Quaternary foraminiferal stratigraphy in boring 81/29 from the central North Sea. *Boreas*, **17**, 273–287.

JARDINE, W. G. 1962. Post-glacial sediments at Girvan, Ayrshire. *Transactions of the Geological Society of Glasgow*, **24**, 262–278.

—— 1964. Post-glacial sea-levels in south-west, Scotland. *Scottish Geographical Magazine*, **80**, 5–11.

—— 1971. Form and age of late-Quaternary shore-lines and coastal deposits of south-west Scotland: critical data. *Quaternaria*, **14**, 103–114.

—— 1975. Chronology of Holocene marine transgression and regression in south-western Scotland. *Boreas*, **4**, 173–196.

—— 1980a. *Field Guide to the Glasgow Region.* Quaternary Research Association, Cambridge, 70.

—— 1982, Sea-level changes in Scotland during the last 18,000 years. *Proceedings of the Geologists' Association*, **93**, 25–41.

—— 1986. The geological and geomorphological setting of the estuary and Firth of Clyde. *Proceedings of the Royal Society of Edinburgh*, **90B**, 25–41.

——, DICKSON, J. H., HAUGHTON, P. D. W., HARKNESS, D. D., BOWEN, D. Q. & SYKES, G. A. 1988. A late Middle Devensian interstadial site at Sourlie, near Irvine, Strathclyde. *Scottish Journal of Geology*, **24**, 288–295.

JEFFERY, D. H. 1991. Comment on: The origin of major incisions within the Pleistocene deposits of the North Sea -Wingfield (1990). *Marine Geology*, **96**, 125–126.

—— 1992 Quaternary. *In:* CAMERON, T. D. J., CROSBY, A., BALSON, P. S., JEFFERY, D. H., LOTT, G. K., BULAT, J. & HARRISON, D. J. 1992. United Kingdom offshore regional report: the geology of the southern North Sea. *British Geological Survey*, 101–115.

JEHU, T. J. 1904. The glacial deposits of northern Pembrokshire. *Transactions of the Royal Society of Edinburgh*, **41**, 53–87.

—— 1909. The glacial deposits of western Caernarvonshire. *Transactions of the Royal Society of Edinburgh*, **47**, 17–56.

JENKINS, D. G. 1982. The age and palaeoecology of the St. Erth Beds, southern England, based on planktonic foraminifera. *Geological Magazine*, **119**, 201–205.

——, WHITTAKER, J. E. & CARLTON, R. 1986. On the age and correlation of the St. Erth Beds, S. W. England, based on planktonic foraminifera. *Journal of Micropalaeontology*, **5**, 93–105.

JENKINSON, R. D. S. 1984. *Creswell Crags: Late Pleistocene sites in the East Midlands.* BAR British Series 122. Oxford. British Archaeological Reports.

——, HUNT, C. O. & BROOKS, I. 1985. Pin Hole Cave. *In:* BRIGGS, D. J., GILBERTSON, D. D. & JENKINSON, R. D. S. (eds) *Peak District and Northern Dukeries Field Guide.* Cambridge. Quaternary Research Association, 135–138.

JENNINGS, S. & SMYTH, C. 1987. Coastal sedimentation in East Susex during the Holocene. *Progress in Oceanography* **18**, 205–241.

JESSEN, A. 1905. On the shell-bearing clay in Kintyre. *Transactions of the Edinburgh Geological Society*, **13**, 76–86.

JESSEN, K., ANDERSON, S. T. & FARRINGTON, A. 1959. The interglacial deposit near Gort, County Galway, Ireland. *Proceedings of the Royal Irish Academy*, **60B**, 1–77.

—— & FARRINGTON, A. 1938. The bogs at Ballybelagh, near Dublin, with remarks on Late-Glacial conditions in Ireland. *Proceedings of the Royal Irish Academy*, **44B**, 205–260.

—— & MILTHERS, V. 1928. Stratigraphical and palaeontological studies of interglacial freshwater deposits in Jutland and north-west Germany.

JESSOP, R. F. 1930. *The Archaeology of Kent.* Methuen, London.

JOACHIM, K. 1978. *Late Glacial Coleopteron Assemblages from the West Coast of the Isle of Man.* PhD thesis, University of Birmingham.

JOHN, B. S. 1970a. Pembrokshire. *In:* Lewis, C. A. (ed.) *The glaciations of Wales and adjoining regions.* Longman, London, 229–265.

JOHN, D. T. 1980. The soils and superficial deposits on the North Downs of Surrey. *In:* JONES, D. K. C. (ed.) *The Shaping of Southern England,* Institute of British Geographers Special Publication **11**, Academic, London, 101–130.

—— & FISHER, D. F. 1984. The stratigraphical and geomorphological significance of the Red Crag fossils at Netley Heath, Surrey: a review and re-appraisal. *Proceedings of the Geologists' Association*, **95**, 235–247.

JOHNSON, J. P. 1901. Additions to the Palaeolithic fauna of the Uphall Brickyard, Ilford, Essex. *Essex Natrualist*, **11**, 209–212.

JOHNSON, R. H. 1969. The glacial geomorphology of the area around Hyde, Cheshire. *Proceedings of the Yorkshire Geological Society*, **37**, 189–230.

—— & WALTHALL, S. 1979. The Longdendale Landslide. *Geological Journal*, **14(2)**, 135–158.

JONES, D. K. C. 1974. The influence of the Calabrian transgression on the drainage evolution of south-east England. *In:* BROWN, E. H. & WATERS, R. S. (eds) *Progress in Geomorphology*, Institute of British Geographers, Special Publication **7**, Academic, London, 139–158.

—— 1981. *The Geomorphology of the British Isles: Southeast and Southern England*. Methuen, London and New York.

JONES, O. T. 1965. The glacial and post-glacial history of the lower Teifi valley. *Quarterly Journal of the Geological Society, London*, **121**, 247–281.

JONES, P. F. & STANLEY, M. F. 1974. Ipswichian mammalian fauna from the Beeston Terrace at Boulton Moor, near Derby. *Geological Magazine*, **111**, 515–520.

JONES, R. L. 1976. Late Quaternary vegetational history of the North York Moors. IV. Seamer Carrs. *Journal of Biogeography*, **3**, 397–406.

—— 1977a. Late Devensian deposits from Kildale, north-east Yorkshire. *Proceedings of the Yorkshire Geological Society*, **41**, 185–188.

—— 1977b. Late Quaternary vegetational history of the North York Moors. V. The Cleveland Dales. *Journal of Biogeography*, **4**, 353–362.

—— 1978. Late Quaternary vegetational history of the North York Moors. VI. The Cleveland Moors. *Journal of Biogeography*, **5**, 81–92.

—— & GAUNT, G. D. 1976. A dated Late Devensian organic deposit at Cawood near Selby. *The Naturalist*, **101**, 121–123.

——, KEEN, D. H., BIRNIE, J. F. & WATON, P. V. 1990. Past landscapes of Jersey -vegetation development and sea-level change during the Flandrian Stage. *Société Jersiaise*, St. Helier.

JONES, T. R. 1850. Description of the Entomostraca of the Pleistocene beds of Newbury, Copford, Clacton and Grays. *Annals and Magazine of Natural History, Series 2*, **6**, 25–71.

DE JONG, J. 1988. Climatic variability during the past threee million years, as indicated by vegetational evolution in northwest Europe and with emphasis on data from the Netherlands. *Philosophical Transactions of the Royal Society of London*, **B318**, 603–617.

JOON, B., LABAN, C. & VAN DER MEER, J. J. M. 1990. The Saalian glaciation in the Dutch part of the North Sea. *Geologie en Mijnbouw*, **69**, 151–158.

JUKES-BROWNE, A. J. 1885. *The geology of south west Lincolnshire*. Memoir Geological Survey.

—— & WHITE, H. J. O. 1908. *The Geology of the Country around Henley-on-Thames and Wallingford*. Memoir Geological Survey.

KAHLKE, H. D. (ed.) 1965. Das Pleistozan von Voigtstedt. *Palaeontologische Abhandlungen*, **A11 2/3**, 227–692.

—— 1969. Das Pleistozan von Sussenborn. *Palaeontologische Abhandlungen*, **A111 3/4**, 367–788.

—— 1975. The macrofaunas of continental Europe during the Middle Pleistocene: Stratigraphic sequence and problems of intercorrelation. *In:* BUTZER, K. W. & ISSAC, G. L. (eds) *After the Australopithecines: Stratigraphy, Ecology and Culture Change in the Middle Pleistocene* Mouton, The Hague, 309–374.

KEAR, B. S. 1976. Soils of the Isle of Man. *Proceedings, Isle of Man Natural History and Antiquarian Society*, **8**, 39–50.

KEEN, D. H. 1978. *The Pleistocene deposits of the Channel Islands*. Report of the Institute of Geological Sciences, **78/26**, 15.

—— 1980. The environment of deposition of the South Hampshire Plateau Gravels. *Proceedings of the Hampshire Field Club and Archaeological Society*, **36**, 15–24.

—— 1981. The Holocene deposits of the Channel Islands. *Institute of Geological Sciences Report*. **81/10**.

—— 1982. Late Pleistocene land Mollusca from the Channel Islands. *Journal of Conchology*, **31**, 57–61.

—— 1985. The Pleistocene deposits and Mollusca from Portland, Dorset. *Geological Magazine*, **122**, 181–186.

—— 1990. Significance of the record provided by Pleistocene fluvial deposits and their included molluscan faunas for palaeoenvironmental reconstruction and stratigraphy: case studies from the English Midlands. *Palaeogeography, Palaeoclimatology, Palaeoecology*, **80**, 25–34.

—— (ed.) 1993. *Quaternary of Jersey*. Quaternary Research Association, Cambridge.

—— 1995. Raised beaches and sea-levels in the English Channel in the Middle and Late Pleistocene: problems of interpretation and implications for the isolation of the British Isles. *In:* PREECE, R. C. (ed.) *Island Britain: a Quaternary perspective*. Geological Society, London, Special Publications, **96**, 63–74.

—— 1998. Portland Bill. *In:* CAMPBELL *et al. Quaternary of South-West England*. Geological Conservation Review Series. Chapman and Hall, London.

—— & BRIDGLAND, D. R. 1986. An interglacial fauna from Avon No. 3 Terrace at Eckington, Worcestershire. *Proceedings of the Geologists' Association*, **97**, 303–307.

——, HARMON, R. S. & ANDREWS, J. T. 1981. U series and amino acid dates from Jersey. *Nature*, **289**, 162–164.

——, JONES, R. L, EVANS, R. A. & ROBINSON, I. E. 1988. Faunal and floral assemblages from Bingley Bog, West Yorkshire, and their significance for Late Devensian and early Flandrian environmental changes. *Proceedings of the Yorkshire Geological Society*, **47**, 125–138.

——, ROBINSON, J. E., WEST, R. G., LOWRY, F., BRIDGLAND, D. R. & DAVEY, N. D. W. 1990. The fauna and flora of the March Gravels at Northam Pit, Eye, Cambridgeshire, England. *Geological Magazine*, **127**, 453–465.

——, VAN VLIET-LANOE, B. & LAUTRIDOU, J. P. 1993. Belcroute and Portelet. *In:* Keen, D. H. (ed.) *Quaternary of Jersey*. Quaternary Research Association, 62–67.

——, COOPE, G. R., JONES, R. L., FIELD, M. H., GRIFFITHS, H. I., LEWIS, S. G. & BOWEN, D. Q. 1997. Middle Pleistocene deposits at Frog Hall Pit, Stretton-on-Dunsmore, Warwickshire, English Midlands, and their implication for the age of the type Wolstonian. *Journal of Quaternary Science*, **12**, 183–208.

KEITH, A. 1939. A resurvey of the anatomical features of the Piltdown Skull with some observations on the recently discovered Swanscombe Skull. Parts I and II. *Journal of Anatomy, London*, **73**, 155–285 and 234–254.

KELLAWAY, G. A., HORTON, A. & POOLE, G. 1971. The development of some Pleistocene structures in the Cotswold and Upper Thames Basin. *Bulletin of the Geological Survey of Great Britain*, **37**, 1–28.

KELLY, M. R. 1964. The Middle Pleistocene of North Birmingham. *Philosophical Transactions of the Royal Society of London*, **B247**, 533–592.

—— 1968. Floras of Middle and Upper Pleistocene age from Brandon, Warwickshire. *Philosophical Transactions of the Royal Society of London*, **B254**, 401–415.

KEMP, D. D. 1976. Buried raised beaches on the northern side of the Forth Valley, central Scotland. *Scottish Geographical Magazine*, **92**, 120–128.

KEMP, R. A. 1983. Stebbing: the Valley Farm Palaeosols Layer. *In:* Rose, J. (ed.) *Diversion of the Thames*. Field Guide, Quaternary Research Association, Cambridge, 154–158.

—— 1984. *Quaternary Soils in Southern East Anglia and the Lower Thames Basin*. PhD thesis, University of London.

—— 1985a. The Valley Farm Soil in southern East Anglia. *In:* BOARDMAN, J. (ed.) *Soils and Quaternary Landscape Evolution*. Wiley, Chichester, 179–196.

—— 1985b. The decalcified Lower Loam at Swanscombe, Kent: a buried Quaternary soil. *Proceedings of the Geologists' Association*, **96**, 343–355.

—— 1987a. Genesis and environmental significance of a buried Middle Pleistocene soil in eastern England. *Geoderma*, **41**, 49–77.

—— 1987b. The interpretation and environmental significance of a buried soil near Ipswich airport, Suffolk. *Philosophical Transactions of the Royal Society of London*, **B317**, 365–391.

—— 1991. Micromorphology of the buried Quaternary soil within Burchell's 'Ebbsfleet Channel', Kent. *Proceedings of the Geologists' Association*, **102**, 275–287.

KENDALL, J. D. 1881. Interglacial deposits of west Cumberland and north Lancashire. *Quarterly Journal of the Geological Society, London*, 37, 130–165.

KENDALL, P. 1902. A system of glacial lakes in the Cleveland Hills. *Quarterly Journal of the Geological Society, London*, **58**, 471–571.

KENNARD, A. S. 1904. Notes on a palaeolith from Grays, Essex. *Essex Naturalist*, **13**, 112–113.

—— 1916. The Pleistocene succession in England. *Proceedings of the Prehistoric Society of East Anglia*, **2**, 249–267.

—— 1924. The Pleistocene non-marine Mollusca of England. *Proceedings of the Malacological Society of London*, **16**, 84–97.

—— 1938. Report on the non-marine Mollusca from the Middle Gravels of the Barnfield Pit. *Journal of the Royal Anthropological Institute of London*, **68**, 28–30.

—— 1942. Faunas of the High Terrace at Swanscombe. *Proceedings of the Geologists' Association*, **53**, 105.

—— 1944. The Crayford Brickearths. *Proceedings of the Geologists' Association*, **55**, 121–169.

—— & WOODWARD, B. B. 1897. The post-Pliocene non-marine Mollusca of Essex. *Essex Naturalist*, **10**, 87–109.

—— & —— 1900. The Pleistocene non-marine Mollusca of Ilford. *Proceedings of the Geologists' Association*, **16**, 282–286.

—— & —— 1907. Notes on the post-Pliocene Mollusca of the Milne collection. *Proceedings of the Malacological Society of London*, **7**, 261–263.

—— & —— 1923. On the non-marine Mollusca 0f Clacton-on-Sea. *Quarterly Journal of the Geological Society, London*, **79**, 629–634.

—— & —— 1924. Appendix 3: The Pleistocene non-marine mollusca. *In:* The river gravels of the Oxford district, *Quarterly Journal of the Geological Society, London*, **80**, 170–175.

KERNEY, M. P. 1959. An interglacial tufa near Hitchin, Hertfordshire. *Proceedings of the Geologists Association*, **70**, 322–337.

—— 1963. Late-glacial deposits on the Chalk of south-east England. *Philosophical Transactions of the Royal Society of London* B **246**, 203–254.

—— 1965. Weichselian deposits in the Isle of Thanet, East Kent *Proceedings of the Geologists' Association*, **76**, 269–274.

—— 1971. A Middle Weichselian deposit at Halling, Kent. *Proceedings of the Geologists' Association*, **82**, 1–11.

—— 1976. Mollusca from an interglacial tufa in East Anglia, with the description of a new species of Lyrodiscus Pilsbry (Gastropoda: Zonitidae). *Journal of Conchology*, **29**, 47–50.

——, BROWN, E. H. & CHANDLER, T. J. 1964. The Late-glacial and Post-glacial history of the chalk escarpment near Brook, Kent. *Philosophical Transactions of the Royal Society of London*, **B248**, 135–204.

——, PREECE, R. C. & TURNER, C. 1980. Molluscan and plant biostratigraphy of some Late Devensian and Flandrian deposits in Kent. *Philosophical Transactions of the Royal Society of London*, **B291**, 1–43.

KIDSON, C. 1970. The Burtle Beds of Somerset. *Proceedings of the Ussher Society*, **2**, 189–191.

—— 1974. The Quaternary of South-West England; Westward Ho!; Saunton Down; Burtle Beds of Somerset. *In:* STRAW, A. (ed.) *Exeter Field Meeting, Easter 1974.* Quaternary Research Association Field Handbook, Exeter, 2–4; 23–24; & 52–53.

—— 1977. The coast of South-West England. *In:* KIDSON, C. & TOOLEY, M. J. (eds) *The Quaternary History of the Irish Sea.* Geological Journal Special Issue No. 7, Seel House, Liverpool, 257–298.

—— & HAYNES, J. R. 1972. Glaciation in the Somerset Levels: the evidence of the Burtle Beds. *Nature*, **239**, 390–392.

——, —— & HEYWORTH, A. 1974 The Burtle Beds of Somerset -glacial or marine? *Nature*, **251**, 211–213.

—— & HEYWORTH, A. 1976. The Quaternary deposits of the Somerset Levels. *Quarterly Journal of Engineering Geology*, **9**, 217–235.

—— & WOOD, R. 1974. The Pleistocene stratigraphy of Barnstaple Bay. *Proceedings of the Geologists' Association*, **85**, 223–237.

——, GILBERTSON, D. D., HAYNES, J. R., HEYWORTH, A., HUGHES, C. E. & WHATLEY, R. C. 1978. Inter-glacial marine deposits of the Somerset Levels, South West England. *Boreas*, **7**, 215–228.

——, COLLIN, R. L. & CHISHOLM, N. W. T. 1989. Surveying a major dune system -Braunton Burrows, north-west Devon. *Geographical Journal*, **55**, 94–105.

KING, E. L, SEJRUP, H. P, HAFLIDASON, H, ELVERHOI, A. & AARSETH, I. 1996. Quaternary seismic stratigraphy of the North Sea Fan: glacially-fed gravity flow aprons, hemipelagic sediments and large submarine slides. *Marine Geology*, **130**, 293–315.

KING, W. B. R. & OAKLEY, K. P. 1936. The Pleistocene succession in the lower parts of the Thames Valley. *Proceedings of the Prehistoric Society*, **2**, 52–76.

KIRBY, R. & OELE, E. 1975. The geological history of the Sandettie - Fairy Bank area, southern North Sea. *Philosophical Transactions of the Royal Socety of London*, **A279**, 257–267.

KIRBY, R. P. 1968. The ground moraines of Midlothian and East Lothian. *Scottish Journal of Geology*, **4**, 209–220.

—— 1969a. Variation in glacial deposition in a sub-glacial environment: an example from Midlothian. *Scottish Journal of Geology*, **5**, 49–53.

—— 1969b. Till fabric analyses from the Lothians, central Scotland. *Geografiska Annaler*, **51**a, 48–60.

KNIGHT, D. J. 1977. Morecambe Bay feasability study -a sub-surface investigation. *Quarterly Journal of Engineering Geology*, **10**, 303–319.

KNIGHT, J. R. & MCCABE, A. M. 1996. Drumlin evolution and ice sheet asillations along the NE Atlantic fringe, Donegal Bay, western Ireland. *Sedimentary Geology*.

KNUDSEN, K. L. & ASBJÖRNSDOTTIR, L. 1991. Plio-Pleistocene foraminiferal stratigraphy and correlation in the Central North Sea. *Marine Geology*, **101**, 113–124.

—— & SERJUP, H. P. 1988. Amino acid geochronology of selected interglacial sites in the North Sea area. *Boreas*, **17**, 347–354.

—— & —— 1993. Pleistocene stratigraphy in the Devils Hole area, central North Sea: foraminiferal and amino-acid evidence. *Journal of Quaternary Science*, **8**, 1–14.

KUBALA, M. 1980. The sand and gravel resources of the country around Fordingbridge, Hampshire: description of 1 : 25 000 sheet SU 11 and parts of SU 00, SU 01, SU 10, SU 20 and SU 21. *Mineral Assessment Report Institute of Geological Sciences*, No. 50.

KUKLA, G. J. 1977. Pleistocene Land-Sea correlations. *Earth Science Reviews*, **13**, 307–374.

LACAILLE, A. D. 1936. The Palaeolithic sequence at Iver, Bucks. *Antiquaries Journal*, **16**, 420–443.

LAMBERT, C. A., PEARSON, R. G. & SPARKS, B. W. 1963. A flora and fauna from late Pleistocene deposits at Sidgwick Avenue, Cambridge. *Proceedings of the Linnean Society*, **174**, 13–29.

LAMPLUGH, G. W. 1890. Glacial sections near Bridlington. Part IV. *Proceedings of the Yorkshire Geological Society*, **11**, 275–307.

—— 1903. The Geology of the Isle of Man. *Memoir Geological Survey*.

—— 1925. Kelsey Hill, Kirmington and other drift problems. *Transactions of the Hull Geological Society*, **6**, 259–275.

LAURENT, M., FALGUERES, J. J., BAHAIN, ROUSSEAU, L. & VAN VLIET LANOE, B. 1998. ESR Dating of Quartz Extracted from Quaternary and Neogene sediments: method, potential and actual limits. *Quaternary International*, **17**, 1057–1062.

LAWSON, T. E. 1982. Geological notes and local details for 1 : 10,000 sheets TM28 NW, NE, SW, SE (Harleston, Norfolk), *Institute of Geological Sciences*.

LAXTON, J. L. & ROSS, D. L. 1983. The sand and gravel resources of the country west of Stirling, Central Region. Description of 1 : 25,000 sheet NS 69 & 79. *Mineral Assessment Report, Institute of Geological Sciences*, **31**, 82.

LEACH, A. L. 1933. The geology and scenerey of Tenby and the south Pembrokeshire coast. *Proceedings of the Geologists' Association*, **44**, 187–216.

LEAR, D. L. 1985. *The Quaternary deposits of the lower Teifi Valley.* PhD thesis, University of Wales.

LEHMAN, S. J., JONES, G. A., KEIGWIN, L. D., ANDERSEN, E. S., BUTENKO, G. and OSTMO, S. R. 1991. Initiation of Fennoscandian ice-sheet retreat during the last deglaciation. *Nature*, **349**, 513–516.

LESNE, P. 1920. Quelques insects du pliocene superieur du Compte de Durham. *Bulletin Musee Historie Natural du Paris*, **26**, 388–484.

—— 1926. Sur une faunule coleopterologique pliocene du nord de l'Angleterre. *Centre Recheres Acadamy Science Paris*, **182**, 495.

LETZER, J. M. 1973. The nature and origin of superficial sands at Headley Heath, Surrey. *Proceedings of the Croydon Natural History and Scientific Society*, **14**, 263–268.

LEVI, S., AUDUNSSON, H., DUNCAN, R. A., KRISTJANSSON, L., GILLOT, P-Y. & JAKOBSSON, S. P. 1990. Late Pleistocene geomagnetic excursion in Icelandic lavas: confirmation of the Laschamp excursion. *Earth and Planetary Science Letters,* **96,** 443–457.

LEWIS, C. A. 1967. The glaciations of the Behy valley, County Kerry, Ireland. *Irish Geography,* **5,** 293–301.

—— 1970. The Upper Wye and Usk regions. *In:* LEWIS, C. A. (ed.) *The Glaciations of Wales and Adjoining Regions.* London.

—— 1974. The glaciations of the Dingle peninsula, County Kerry, Ireland. *Scientific Proceedings of the Royal Dublin Society,* **A5,** 207–235.

—— 1976. The Knockmealdown mountains: a glacial nunatak. *Irish Geography,* **9,** 18–28.

—— 1977. *South and southwest Ireland.* INQUA field guide, (ed. BOWEN, D. Q.) X congress, 1977, Geoabstracts, Norwich. 1–52.

LEWIS, H. C. 1894. *Papers and notes on the glacial geology of Great Britain and Ireland.* Longman, London.

LEWIS, S. G. 1989. Witham-on-the-Hill, Lincolnshire. *In:* KEEN, D. H. (ed.) *The Pleistocene of the West Midlands. Field Guide.* Quaternary Research Association, 123–130.

—— 1991. Shouldham Thorpe, Norfolk. *In:* LEWIS, S. G., WHITEMAN, C. A. & BRIDGLAND, D. R. (eds) *Central East Anglia and the Fen Basin. Field Guide.* Quaternary Research Association, London, 127–130.

—— 1992. High Lodge -stratigraphy and depositional environments. *In:* ASHTON, N. M., COOK, J., LEWIS, S. G. & ROSE, J. (eds) *High Lodge. Excavations by G. de G. Sieveking, 1962–8 and J. Cook, 1988.* British Museum Press, London, 51–85.

—— 1993. *The status of the Wolstonian glaciation in the English Midlands and East Anglia.* PhD thesis, University of London.

—— & BRIDGLAND, D. R. 1991. Ingham and Timworth, Suffolk. *In:* LEWIS, S. G., WHITEMAN, C. A. & BRIDGLAND, D. R. (eds) *Central East Anglia and the Fen Basin. Field Guide.* Quaternary Research Association, London, 71–83.

—— & ROSE, J. 1991a. Tottenhill, Norfolk. *In:* LEWIS, S. G., WHITEMAN, C. A. & BRIDGLAND, D. R. (eds) *Central East Anglia and the Fen Basin. Field Guide.* Quaternary Research Association, London, 145–148.

—— & —— 1991b. Knettishall, Suffolk. *In:* LEWIS, S. G., WHITEMAN, C. A. & BRIDGLAND, D. R. (eds) *Central East Anglia and the Fen Basin. Field Guide.* Quaternary Research Association, London, 105–109.

LISTER, A. M. & BRANDON, A. 1991. A pre-Ipswichan cold stage mammalian fauna from the Balderton Sand and Gravel, Lincolnshire, England. *Journal of Quaternary Science,* **6,** 139–57.

——, GRUN, R., DOUGHTY, P. & YOUNG, P. in press. ESR-dated mammoth and musk-ox remains with associated pollen spectra from Early Midlandian sediments at Aghnadarragh, County Antrim, Northern Ireland. *Journal of Quaternary Science.*

LONG, A. J. & HUGHES, P. D. M. 1995. Mid-and late-Holocene evolution of the Dungeness foreland, UK. *Marine Geology,* **124,** 253–271.

—— & INNES, J. B. 1995a. The back-barrier and barrier depositional history of Romney Marsh, Walland Marsh and Dungeness, Kent, England. *Journal of Quaternary Science,* **10,** 267–283.

—— & INNES, J. B. 1995b. A palaeoenvironmental investigation of the' Midley Sand and associated deposits at the Midley Church Bank, Romney Marsh. *In:* EDDISON, J. (ed.) *Romney Marsh: The Debatable Ground.* Oxford University Committee for Archaeology Monograph No. 41, Oxford, 37–50.

——, PLATER, A. J., WALLER, M. P. & INNES, J. B. 1996. Holocene coastal sedimentation in the eastern English Channel: data from the Romney Marsh region, United Kingdom. *Marine Geology,* **136,** 97–120.

LONG, D. L. 1992a. Devensian Late-glacial gas escape in the central North Sea. *Continental Shelf Research,* **12,** 1097–1110.

—— 1992b. Quaternary. *In:* ANDREWS, I. J., LONG, D., RICHARDS, P. C., THOMSON, A. R., BROWN, S., CHESHER, J. A. & McCORMAC, M. 1990. United Kingdom offshore regional report: the geology of the Moray Firth. British Geological Survey.

—— 1993. Quaternary. *In:* JOHNSON, H., RICHARDS, P. C., LONG, D. & GRAHAM, C. C. 1993. United Kingdom offshore regional report: the geology of the northern North Sea. British Geological Survey, 74–85.

—— in press. *In:* GATLIFF, R. W., RICHARDS, P. C., SMITH, K., GRAHAM, C. C., McCORMAC, M., SMITH, N. J. P., LONG, D.,

CAMERON, T. D. J., EVANS, D., STEVENSON, A. G. BULAT, J. & RITCHIE, J. D. United Kingdom offshore regional report: the geology of the central North Sea. *British Geological Survey.*

—— & MORTON, A. C. 1987. An ash fall within the Loch Lomond Stadial. *Journal of Quaternary Science,* **2,** 97–101.

—— & STOKER, M. S. 1986. Channels in the North Sea: the nature of a hazard. *In: Advances in underwater technology, ocean science and offshore engineering, Volume 6: Oceanology.* Proceedings of Oceanology International '86. Graham & Trotman, London, 339–351.

——, SKINNER, A. C. & RISE, L. 1988. Halibut Bank Sheet 60mN–00mW. Quaternary Geology. 1:250 000 Map Series. *British Geological Survey.* LONGWORTH, D. 1985. The Quaternary history of the Lancashire Plain. *In:* JOHNSON, R. J. (ed.) *The Geomorphology of North-West England.* 178–200. Manchester. Manchester University Press.

LOVELL, J. H. & NANCARROW, P. H. A. 1983. The sand and gravel resources of the country around Chichester and north of Bognor Regis, Sussex. Description of 1:25000 resource sheet SU 80 and 90. *Mineral Assessments Reports Institute of Geological Science* 138.

LOWE, J. J. & WALKER, M. J. C. 1984. *Reconstructing Quaternary Environments.* Longman, London.

LUCKMAN, B. H., 1970, The Hereford Basin. *In:* LEWIS, C. A. (ed.) *The Glaciations of Wales,* London, 175–196.

LUNKKA, J. P. 1994. Sedimentation and lithostratigraphy of the North Sea Drift and Lowestoft Till Formations in the coastal cliffs of northeast Norfolk, England. *Journal of Quaternary Science,* **9,** 209–233.

McCABE, A. M. 1969a. The glacial deposits of the Maguiresbridge Area, County Fermanagh, Northern Ireland. *Irish Geography,* **6,** 63–77.

—— 1969b. A buried head deposit near Lisnaskea, County Fermanagh, Northern Ireland. *Irish Naturalists' Journal,* **16,** 232–233.

—— 1972. Directions of late-Pleistocene ice flows in eastern Counties Meath and Louth, Ireland. *Irish Geography,* **6,** 443–461.

—— 1973. The glacial stratigraphy of eastern Counties Meath and Louth. *Proceedings of the Royal Irish Academy,* **73B,** 355–382.

—— 1982. Quaternary deposits and glacial stratigraphy in Ireland. *Quaternary Science Reviews,* **6,** 259–299.

—— 1985. Glacial Geomorphology. *In:* EDWARDS, J. K. & WARREN, W. P. (eds) *The Quaternary History of The Irish Sea.* Academic, London, 67–93.

—— 1986. Glaciomarine facies deposited by retreating glaciers: An example from the Late-Pleistocene of Northern Ireland. *Journal of Sedimentary Petrology,* **56,** 880–894.

—— 1993. The 1992 Farrington Lecture: Drumlin bedforms and related ice-marginal depositional systems in Ireland. *Irish Geography,* **26,** 22–44.

—— 1995a. Quaternary Geology of Donegal. *In:* WILSON, P. (ed.) *North-west Donegal, Irish Association for Quaternary Studies,* Field Guide, **19,** 15–20.

—— 1995b. Marine mollusscan shell dates from two glaciomarine jet efflux deposits, eastern Ireland. *Irish Journal of Earth Sciences,* **14,** 37–45.

—— 1996. Dating and Rhythmicity from the last deglacial cycle in the British Isles. *Journal of the Geological Society, London,* **153,** 499–502.

—— & CLARK, P. U. 1998. Ice sheet variability around the North Atlantic Ocean during the last deglaciation. *Nature, London,* **392,** 373–377.

—— & COXON, P. 1993. A Carpinus-dominated interglacial peat ball within glaciomarine delta sediments, Blackwater, County Wexford: evidence for part of the last interglacial cycle? *Proceedings of the Geologists' Association,* **114,** 201–207.

—— & DARDIS, G. F. 1989a. Sedimentology and depositional setting of Late Pleistocene drumlins, Galway Bay, western Ireland. *Journal of Sedimentary Petrology,* **59,** 544–559.

—— & —— 1989b. A geological view of drumlins in Ireland *Quaternary Science Reviews,* **8,** 169–177.

—— & EYLES, N. 1988. Sedimentology of and ice-contact glaciomarine delta, Carey valley, Northern Ireland. *Sedimentary Geology,* **59,** 1–14.

—— & HAYNES, J. R. 1996. A late Pleistocene intertidal boulder pavement from an isostatically emergent coast, Dundalk Bay, Eastern Ireland. *Earth Surface Processes and Landforms*, **21**, 555–572.

—— & O'COFAIGH, C. 1994. Sedimentation in a subglacial lake, Enniskerry, eastern Ireland. *Sedimentary Geology*, **91**, 57–95.

—— & —— 1995. Late Pleistocene morainal bank facies at Greystones, eastern Ireland: an example of sedimentation during ice marginal re-equilibration in an isostatically depressed basin. *Sedimentology*, **42**, 647–663.

—— & —— 1996. Late Pleistocene facies sequences and relative sea level trends along the south coast of Ireland. *Journal of Sedimentary Research*, **66**, 376–390.

——, MITCHELL, G. F. & SHOTTON, F. W. 1978. An inter-till freshwater deposit at Hollymount, Maguiresbridge, County Fermanagh. *Proceedings of the Royal Irish Academy*, **78B**, 77–89.

——, DARDIS, G. F. & HANNEY, P. 1984. Sedimentology of a Late-Pleistocene submarine moraine complex, County Down, Northern Ireland. *Journal of Sedimentary Petrology*, **56**, 716–730.

——, HAYNES, J. R. & McMILLAN, N. F. 1986. Late Pleistocene tidewater glaciers and glaciomarine sequences from north County Mayo, Republic of Ireland. *Journal of Quaternary Science*, **1**, 73–84.

——, COOPE, G. R., GENNARD, D. E. & DOUGHTY, P. 1987*a*. Freshwater organic deposits and stratified sediments between Early and Late Midlandian (Devensian) till sheets, at Aghnadarragh, County Antrim, Northern Ireland. *Journal of Quaternary Science*, **2**, 11–33.

——, DARDIS, G. F. & HANVEY, P. 1987*b*. Sedimentation at the margins of a Late Pleistocene ice lobe terminating in shallow marine environments, Dundalk Bay, eastern Ireland. *Sedimentology*, **34**, 473–493.

——, EYLES, N., HAYNES, J. R. & BOWEN, D. Q. 1990. Biofacies and sediments in an emergent Late Pleistocene glaciomarine sequence, Skerries, east central Ireland. *Marine Geology*, **94**, 23–36.

——, DARDIS, G. F. & HANVEY, P. 1992. *Glacial Sedimentology in northern and western Ireland*, INQUA field excursion guidebook, University of Ulster.

——, PENNEY, D. N. & BOWEN, D. Q. 1993. Glaciomarine facies from from the western sector of the last British ice sheet, Malin Beg, County Donegal, Ireland. *Quaternary Science Reviews*, **12**, 35–45.

——, CARTER, R. W. G. & HAYNES, J. R. 1994. A shallow marine emergent sequence from the northwestern sector of the last British ice sheet, Portballintrae, Northern Ireland. *Marine Geology*, **117**, 19–34.

McCALL, J. & GOODLET, G. A. 1952. Indicator stones from the drift of south Midlothian and Peebles. *Transactions of the Edinburgh Geological Society*, **14**, 401–409.

McCANN, S. B. 1966. The limits of the Late-glacial Highland, or Loch Lomond, Readvance along the West Highland seaboard from Oban to Mallaig. *Scottish Journal of Geology*, **2**, 84–95.

—— 1968. Raised shore platforms in the Western Isles of Scotland. *In:* BOWEN, E. G., CARTER, H. & TAYLOR, J. A. (eds) *Geography at Aberystwyth. Essays Written on the Occasion of the Departmental Jubilee 1917–18–1967–68*. University of Wales, Cardiff, 22–34.

McKENNY-HUGHES, T. 1887. On the drifts of the Vale of Clwyd and their relation to the caves and cave deposits. *Quarterly Journal of the Geological Society, London*, **43**, 73–120.

McMILLAN, N. F. 1947. The molluscan faunas of some tufas in Cheshire and Flintshire. *Proceedings of the Liverpool Geological Society*, **19**, 240–248.

—— 1957. Quaternary deposits around Lough Foyle, Northern Ireland. *Proceedings of the Royal Irish Academy*, **58B**, 185–205.

—— 1964. The Mollusca of the Wexford Gravels (Pleistocene), southeast Ireland. *Proceedings of the Royal Irish Academy*, **63B**, 265–290.

—— & ZEISSLER, H. 1985. The tufa deposit at Caerwys, North Wales, and its molluscan fauna. *Amateur Geologist*, **11**, 3–11.

MACE, A. 1959. An Upper Palaeolithic open site at Hengistbury Head, Christchurch, Hants. *Proceedings of the Prehistoric Society*, **25**, 233–259.

MACKLIN, M. G. 1981. Prestwich's 'Southern Drift' in S. E. London: a re-evaluation. *Quaternary Newsletter*, **34**, 19–26.

—— & HUNT, C. O. 1988. Late Quaternary alluviation and valley floor development in the upper Axe valley, Mendip, southwest

England. *Proceedings of the Geologists' Association*, **99**, 49–60.

MADDY, D. 1989. *The Middle Pleistocene development of the Rivers Severn and Avon*. PhD thesis, University of London.

—— 1997. Uplift driven valley-incision and river terrace formation in southern England. *Journal of Quaternary Science*, **12**, 539–545.

—— & LEWIS, S. G. 1991. A revised stratigraphic model and regional correlation for the Pleistocene deposits at Snitterfield, Warwickshire. *Proceedings of the Geologists' Association*, **102**, 289–300.

——, KEEN, D. H., BRIDGLAND, D. R. & GREEN, C. P. 1991. A revised model for the Pleistocene development of the River Avon, Warwickshire. *Journal of the Geological Society, London*, **148**, 473–484.

——, GIBBARD, P. L., COOPE, G. R., GREEN, C. P. & LEWIS, S. G. 1994. Reappraisal of Middle Pleistocene fluvial deposits near Brandon, Warwickshire and their significance for the Wolston glacial sequence. *Journal of the Geological Society, London*, **151**, 221–233.

——, GREEN, C. P., LEWIS, S. G. & BOWEN, D. Q. 1995. Pleistocene Geology of the Lower Severn Valley, U. K. *Quaternary Science Reviews*, **14**, 209–222.

MADGETT, P. A. & CATT, J. A. 1978. Petrography, stratigraphy and weathering of Late Pleistocene tills in east Yorkshire, Lincolnshire and north Norfolk. *Proceedings of the Yorkshire Geological Society*, **42**, 55–108.

MARR, J. E. 1920. The Pleistocene deposits around Cambridge. *Quarterly Journal of the Geological Society*, **75**, 204–244.

—— & KING, W. B. R. 1932. Further notes on the Huntingdon Road gravels, Cambridge. *Geological Magazine*, **69**, 175–178.

MARTIN, J. H. 1981. *Quaternary glaciofluvial deposits in central Scotland: Sedimentology and Economic Geology*. PhD thesis, University of Edinburgh.

MATHERS, S. J. & ZALASIEWICZ, J. A. 1988. The Red Crag and Norwich Crag Formations of southern East Anglia. *Proceedings of the Geologists' Association*, **99**, 261–278.

—— & —— 1996. A gravel beach rip-channel system: the Westleton Beds (Pleistocene) of Suffolk, England. *Proceedings of the Geologists' Association*, **107**, 57–68.

——, ——, BLOODWORTH, A. J. & MORTON, A. C. 1987. The Banham Beds: a petrologically distinct suite of Anglian glacigenic deposits from central East Anglia. *Proceedings of the Geologists' Association*, **98**, 229–240.

MATHEWS, B. 1970. Age and origin of aeolian sand in the Vale of York. *Nature*, **227**, 1234–1236.

MAW, G. 1864. On a supposed deposit of boulder-clay in North Devon. *Quarterly Journal of the Geological Society, London*, **20**, 445–451.

MAYHEW, D. F. & STUART, A. J. 1986. Stratigraphic and taxonomic revision of the fossil vole remains (Rodentia: Microtinae) from the Lower Pleistocene deposits of Eastern England. *Philosophical Transactions of the Royal Society of London*, **B312**, 431–485.

MEIJER, T. & PREECE, R. C. 1995. Malacological evidence relating to the insularity of the British Isles during the Quaternary. *In:* PREECE, R. C. (ed.) *Island Britain: A Quaternary Perspective*. Geological Society, London, Special Publications, **96**, 89–110.

MELLARS, P. A. 1969. Radiocarbon dates for a new Creswellian site. *Antiquity*, **43**, 308–310.

—— 1974. The palaeolithic and mesolithic. *In:* RENFREW, C. (ed.) *British prehistory: a new outline*. 41–99. London. Duckworth.

MERRITT, J. W. 1992. The high-level marine shell-bearing deposits of Clava, Inverness-shire, and their origin as glacial rafts. *Quaternary Science Reviews*, **11**, 759–779.

—— & AUTON, C. A. 1990. The Dalcharn interglacial site, near Cawdor, Nairnshire: lithostratigraphy. *In:* AUTON, C. A., FIRTH, C. R. & MERRITT, J. W. (eds) *Beauly to Nairn: Field Guide*. Quaternary Research Association, Cambridge, 41–54.

——, —— & FIRTH, C. R. 1995. Ice-proximal glaciomarine sedimentation and sea-level change in the Inverness area, Scotland: a review of the deglaciation of a major ice stream of the British Late Devensian ice sheet. *Quaternary Science Reviews*, **14**, 289–329.

MIALL, L. C. 1880. The (Raygill) Cave and its contents. *Proceedings Yorkshire Geological Society*, **7**, 207–208.

MILLER, G. H., JULL, A. J. T., LINICK, T., SUTHERLAND, D., SEJRUP, H. P., BRIGHAM, J. K., BOWEN, D. Q. & MANGERUD, J. 1987. Racemizatiion-derived late Devensian temperature reduction in

Scotland. *Nature,* **326,** 593–595.

MILLER, M. 1987. *Laminated Sediments in Glen Roy, Inverness-shire.* MSc thesis, City of London Polytechnic.

MILLING, M. E. 1975. Geological appraisal of foundation conditions, northern North Sea. *Proceedings of Oceanology International, Brighton,* 310–319.

MILLWARD, D., ELLISON, R. A., LAKE, R. D. & MOORLOCK, B. S. P. 1987. The geology of the country around Epping. *Memoir British Geological Survey.*

MITCHELL, G. F. 1960. The Pleistocene history of the Irish Sea. *British Association for the Advancement of Science,* **17,** 313–325.

—— 1962. Summer field meeting in Wales and Ireland. *Proceedings of the Geologists' Association,* **73,** 197–213.

—— 1965. The Quaternary deposits of the Ballaugh and Kirk Michael districts. *Quarterly Journal of the Geological Society, London,* **121,** 358–381.

—— 1968. Glacial gravel on Lundy Island. *Proceedings of the Royal Geological Society of Cornwall,* **20,** 65–68.

—— 1970. The Quaternary deposits between Fenit and Spa on the north shore of Tralee Bay, County Kerry. *Proceedings of the Royal Irish Academy,* **70B,** 141–162.

—— 1972. The Pleistocene history of the Irish Sea: second approximation. *Scientific Proceedings of the Royal Dublin Society,* **A, 4,** 181–199.

—— 1976. *The Irish Landscape.* Collins, London.

—— 1979. Ballivor. *In:* McCABE, A. M. (ed.) *Field Guide to East Central Ireland,* Quaternary Research Association, Dublin, 31–34.

—— 1986. *The Shell Guide To Reading The Irish Landscape.* Michael Joseph/Country House, London.

—— 1992a. Notes on a raised beach between two deamicts, Beginish Island, Valencia harbour, County Kerry. *Irish Journal of Earth Sciences,* **11,** 151–163.

—— 1992b. A note on the presence of cryoturbated drift with silicified limestone at 570m in the Knockmealdown mountains. *Irish Geography,* **25,** 102–103.

—— & ORME, A. R. 1965. The Pleistocene deposits of the Scilly Isles. *Proceedings of the Ussher Society,* **1,** 190–192.

—— & —— 1967. The Pleistocene deposits of the Isles of Scilly. *Quarterly Journal of the Geological Society, London,* **123,** 59–92.

—— & WATTS, W. A. 1993. Notes on an interglacial deposit in Ballykeerogemoie townland and an interstadial deposit in Battles-town townland both in County Wexford. *Irish Journal of Earth Sciences,* **12,** 107–117.

MITCHELL, G. F., PENNY, L. F., SHOTTON, F. W. & WEST, R. G. 1973. *A Correlation of Quaternary Deposits in the British Isles.* Geological Society, London Special Reports, **4.**

——, COLHOUN, E. A., STEPHEN, N. & SYNGE, F. M. 1993. *In:* MITCHELL, G. F., PENNY, L. F., SHOTTON, F. W. & WEST, R. G. (eds) *A Correlation of Quaternary Deposits in The British Isles.* Geological Society, London, Special Reports, **4,** 67–80.

—— & MYKURA, W. 1962. *The Geology of the Neighbourhood of Edinburgh.* Memoir Geological Survey.

——, POCOCK, R. W. & TAYLOR, D. H. 1962. *Geology of the country around Droitwich, Abberley and Kidderminster.* Memoir of the Geological Survey.

MITCHUM Jr, R. M., VAIL, P. R. & THOMPSON, S. 1977. Seismic stratigraphy and global changes of sea level. Part 2: The depositional sequence as a basic unit for stratigraphic analysis. *In:* PAYTON, C. E. (ed.) *Seismic stratigraphy -Applications to Hydrocarbon Exploration.* AAPG Mem. No. 26, 53–62.

MOAR, N. T. 1969. Late Weichselian and Flandrian pollen diagrams from south-west Scotland. *New Phytologist,* **68,** 433–467.

MOFFAT, A. J. & CATT, J. A. 1986. A re-examination of of the evidence for a Plio-Pleistocene marine transgression on the Chiltern Hills, III. Deposits. *Earth Surface Processes and Landforms,* **11,** 233–247.

MOIR, J. REID & HOPWOOD, A. T. 1939. Excavations at Brundon, Suffolk (1935–37). 1. Stratigraphy and archaeology. 2. Fossil Mammals. *Proceedings of the Prehistoric Society,* **5,** 1–32.

MOORE, C. 1870. The mammalia and other remains from drift deposits in the Bath Basin. *Proceedings of the Bath natural History Field Club,* **2,** 37–55.

MOORE, P. D. 1968. Human influence upon Vegetational History in North Cardiganshire. *Nature,* **217,** 5133, 1006–1009.

—— 1978. Studies in the vegetational history of mid-Wales. V. Stratigraphy and pollen analysis of Llyn Mire in the Wye Valley. *New Phytologist,* **80,** 281–302.

—— & CHATER, E. H. 1969. The changing vegetation of west-central Wales in the light of human history. *Journal of Ecology,* **57,** 361–379. MOORLOCK, B. S. P., BARRON, A. J. M., AMROSE, K. & CANNELL, B. 1985. *Geology of sheet SO85.* British Geological Survey, Keyworth.

MORGAN, A. 1973. Late Pleistocene environmental changes indicated by insectfaunas of the English Midlands. *Boreas,* **2,** 173–212.

MORGAN, A. V. 1973. Pleistocene geology of the area north and west of Wolverhampton, Staffordshire, England. *Philosophical Trasac-tions of the Royal Society of London,* **B265,** 233–297.

—— & WEST, R. G. 1988. A pollen diagram from an interglacial deposit at, Trysull, Staffordshire, England. *New Phytologist,* **109,** 393–397.

MORRISON, J., SMITH, D. E., CULLINGFORD, R. A. & JONES, R. L. 1981. The culmination of the main postglacial transgression in the Firth of Tay area, Scotland. *Proceedings of the Geologists' Association,* **92,** 197–209.

MORRISON, M. E. S. & STEPHENS, N. 1965. A submerged Late-Quaternary deposit at Roddans Port on the north-east coast of Ireland. *Philosophical Transactions of the Royal Society of London,* **249,** 221–255.

MOTTERSHEAD, D. N. 1971. Coastal head deposits between Start Point and Hope Cove, Devon. *Field Studies,* **3,** 433–453.

—— 1977a. South west England. Guidebook for excursions A6 and C6. Geo Abstracts, Norwich, 60.

—— 1977b. The Quaternary evolution of the south coast of England. *In:* KIDSON, C. & TOOLEY, M. J. (eds) *The Quaternary History of the Irish Sea.* Geological Journal Special Issue, No. 7, Seel House Press, Liverpool, 299–320.

——, GILBERTSON, D. D. & KEEN, D. H. 1987. The raised beaches and shore platforms of Torbay: a re-evaluation. *Proceedings of the Geologists' Association,* **98,** 241–257.

MUNT, M. C. & BURKE, A. 1987. The Pleistocene geology and faunas at Newtown, Isle of Wight. *Proceedings of the Isle Wight Natural History and Archaeological Society,* **8,** 7–14.

MUNTHE, H. 1897. On the interglacial submergence of Great Britain. *Bulletin of the Geological Institute of Upsala,* **13,** 369–411.

MYKURA, W. & PHEMISTER, J. 1976. *The Geology of Western Shetland.* Memoir Geological Survey.

NICHOLS, H. 1967. Vegetatiional change, shoreline displacement and the human factor in the late Quaternary history of south-west Scotland. *Transactions of the Royal Society of Edinburgh,* **67,** 145–187.

NICHOLLS, R. J. 1987. Evolution of the upper reaches of the Solent River and the formation of Poole and Christchurch Bays. *In:* BARBER, K. E. (ed.) *The Quaternary of Wessex and the Isle of Wight.* Quaternary Research Association Field Guide, Cambridge, 99–114.

NORRIS, A., BARTLEY, D. D. & GAUNT, G. D. 1971. An account of the deposits of shell marl at Burton Salmon, West Yorkshire. *The Naturalist,* **56,** 57–63.

NORTON, P. E. P. & BECK, R. B. 1972. Lower Pleistocene mollusc assemblages and pollen form the Crag of Aldeby (Norfolk) and Easton Bavents (Suffolk). *Bulletin of the Geological Society of Norfolk,* **22,** 11–31.

OAKLEY, K. P. 1939. Geology and Palaeolithic studies. *In:* A survey of the prehistory of the Farnham district (Surrey). *Surrey Archae-ological Society.*

OLD, R. A., SUMBLER, M. G. & AMBROSE, K. 1987. *Geology of the Country around Warwick.* Memoir Geological Survey.

——, HAMBLIN, R. J. O., AMBROSE, K. & WARRINGTON, G. 1991. *Geology of the country around Redditch.* Memoir for 1:50 000 geological sheet 183 (England and Wales).

PALMER, L. S. 1931. On the Pleistocene succession of the Bristol District. *Proceedings of the Geologists' Association,* **42,** 345–361.

—— & COOKE, J. H. 1923. The Pleistocene deposits of the Portsmouth district and their relation to Early Man. *Proceedings of the Geologists' Association,* **34,** 253–282.

PANTIN, H. M. 1978. Quaternary sediments of the north-eastern Irish Sea. *Quaternary Newsletter,* **17,** 7–9.

—— & EVANS, C. D. R. 1984. The Quaternary history of the central and southwestern Celtic Sea. *Marine Geology*, **57**, 259–293.

PARKS, D. A. & RENDELL, H. M. 1992a. TL Geochronology of brickearth from South East England. *Quaternary Science Reviews*, **11**, 7–12.

—— & —— 1992b. Thermoluminescence dating and geochemistry of loessic deposits in southeast England. *Journal of Quaternary Science*, **7**, 99–107.

PARSONS, A. R. 1966. *Some aspects of the glacial geomorphology of Northeast Northumberland*. MSc thesis, University of Leicester.

PATERSON, T. T. & FAGG, B. E. B. 1940. Studies on the Palaeolithic succession in England: no II. The Upper Brecklandian Acheul (Elveden). *Proceedings of the Prehistoric Society*, **6**, 1–29.

PATERSON, I. B. 1981. The Quaternary geology of the Buddon Ness areas of Tayside, Scotland. *Report of the Institute of Geological Sciences*, **81/11**.

——, ARMSTRONG, M. & BROWNE, M. A. E. 1981. Quaternary estuarine deposits in the Tay-Earn area, Scotland. *Report of the Institute of Geological Sciences*, **81/1**, 35.

PAUL, M. A., PEACOCK, J. D. & BARRAS, B. F. 1995. Flandrian stratigraphy and sedimentation in the Bothkennar-Grangemouth area, Scotland. *Quaternary Newsletter*, **75**, 22–35.

PEACOCK, J. D. 1975. Scottish late and post-glacial marine deposits. *In:* GEMMEL, A. M. D. (ed.) *Quaternary Studies in North East Scotland*. Department of Geography, University of Aberdeen, 45–48.

—— 1981. Scottish late-galcial marine deposits and their environmental significance. *In:* NEAL, J. W. & HENLEY, J. R. (eds) *The Quaternary in Britain*. Oxford, 222–236.

—— 1984. Quaternary geology of the Outer Hebrides. *Report of the British Geological Survey*, **16(2)**, 26.

—— & HARKNESS, D. D. 1990. Radiocarbon ages and the full-glacial to Holocene transition in seas adjacent to Scotland and southern Scandinavia: a review. *Transactions of the Royal Society of Edinburgh: Earth Sciences*, **81**, 385–396.

—— & LONG, D. L. 1994. Late Devensian glaciation and deglaciation of Shetland. *Quaternary Newsletter*, **74**, 16–21.

——, BERRIDGE, N. G., HARRIS, A. L. & MAY, F. 1968. *The Geology of the Elgin District*. Memoir Geological Survey.

——, GRAHAM, D. K. & WILKINSON, I. P. 1978. Late-glacial and post-glacial marine environments at Ardyne, Scotland and their significance in the interpretation of the history of the Clyde sea area. *Report of the Institute of Geological Sciences*, **78/17**, 25.

——, —— & GREGORY, D. M. 1980. Late and post-glacial marine environments in part of the inner Cromarty Firth. *Report of the Institute of Geological Sciences*, **80/7**, 11.

PEAKE, D. S. 1971. The age of the Wandle Gravels in the vicinity of Croydon *Proceedings of the Croydon Natural History and Scientific Society*, **14**, 145–176.

—— 1982. A reappraisal of the Pleistocene history of the River Wandle and its basin. *Proceedings of the Croydon Natural History and Scientific Society*, **17**, 89–116.

PENNING, W. H. & JUKES-BROWNE, A. J. 1881. *The Geology of the Neighbourhood of Cambridge*. Memoir Geological Survey.

PENNINGTON, R. 1875. On the bone-caves in the neighbourhood of Casteleton, Derbyshire. *Quarterly Journal of the Geological Society, London*. **31**, 238–245.

PENNINGTON, W. 1969. *The History of the British Vegetation*. London. English Universities Press.

—— 1977. The Late Devensian flora and vegetation of Britain. *Philosophical Transactions of the Royal Society of London, B280*, 247–271.

—— 1978. Quaternary Geology. *In:* MOSELEY, F. (ed.) *The Geology of the Lake District*. Yorkshire Geological Society, Occasional Publication, **3**, 207–225.

—— & BONNEY, A. P. 1970. Absolute pollen diagram from the British late-glacial. *Nature*, **226**, 871–873.

PENNEY, D. N. 1990. Quaternary ostracod chronology of the central North Sea: the record from BH 81/29. *Courier Forschungsinstitut Senckenberg*, **123**, 97–109.

PENNY, L. F., COOPE, G. R. & CATT, J. A. 1969. Age and insect fauna of the Dimlington silts, East Yorkshire. *Nature*, **224**, 65–67.

——, STRAW, A., CATT, J. A., FLENLEY, J. R., BRIDGER, J. F. D., MADGETT, P. A., & BECKETT, S. C. 1972. East Yorkshire & North Lincolnshire. *Quaternary Research Association field guide*. Hull.

PERKINS, N. K. & RHODES, E. J. 1994. Optical dating of fluvial sediments from Tattershall, U. K. *Quaternary Geochronology (Quaterary Science Reviews)* **3**, 517–520.

PERRIN, R. M. S., DAVIES, H. & FYSH, M. D. 1973. Lithology of the Chalky Boulder Clay. *Nature, phys. sc.* **245**, 101–104.

——, & —— 1974. Distribution of late Pleistocene aeolian deposits in eastern and southern England. *Nature*, **248**, 320–324.

——, ROSE, J. & DAVIES, H. 1979. The distribution, variation and origins of pre-Devensian tills in eastern England. *Philosophical Transactions of the Royal Society of London*, **B287**, 535–570.

PHILLIPS, B. A. M. 1967. The post-glacial raised shoreline around the northern plain of the Isle of Man. *Northern Universities Geographical Journal*, **8**, 56–63.

PHILLIPS, F. M., BOWEN, D. Q., & ELMORE, D. 1994. Surface exposure dating of glacial features in Great Britain using cosmogenic chlorine-36: Preliminary Results. *Abstract V. M. Goldschmidt Geochemical Conference*, Edinburgh.

PHILLIPS, L. 1976. Pleistocene vegetational history and geology in Norfolk. *Philosophical Transactions of the Royal Society of London*, **B275**, 215–286.

PICKERING, R. 1957. The Pleistocene geology of the South Birmingham area.. *Quarterly Journal of the Geological Society, London*, **113**, 223–237.

PIGOTT, M. E. & PIGOTT, C. D. 1963. Stratigraphy and pollen analysis of Malham Tarn and Tarn Moss. *Field Studies*, **1(1)**, 84–101.

PILCHER, J. R. 1973. Pollen analysis and radiocarbon dating of a peat on Slieve Gallon, County Tyrone, Northern Ireland. *New Phytologist*, **72**, 681–689.

PITCHER, W. S., SHEARMAN, D. J. & PUGH, D. C. 1954. The loess of Pegwell Bay, Kent, and its associated frost soils. *Geological Magazine*, **91**, 308–314.

PLANT, J. 1859. Notice on the occurrence of mammalian remains ub the valley of the Soar, Leicestershire. *The Geologist*, **2**, 174–175.

PLATER, A. J. 1992. The late Holocene evolution of Denge Marsh, southeast England: a stratigraphic, sedimentological and micro-palaeontological approach. *The Holocene*, **2**, 63–70.

—— & LONG, A. J. 1995. The morphology and evolution of Denge Beach and Denge Marsh. *In:* EDDISON, J. (ed.) *Romney Marsh: The Debatable Ground*. Oxford University Committee for Archaeology Monograph No. 41, Oxford, 8–36.

POCOCK, T. I. 1925. Terraces and drifts of the Welsh border and their relations to the drifts of the English Midlands. *Zeitschrifft fur Gletscherkunde*, **13**, 10–38.

—— 1940. Glacial drift and river terraces of the Herefordshire Wye. *Zietschrift Gletscherk*, **27**, 98–117.

PORTLOCK, J. E. 1843. *Report on the geology of the County of Londonerry and parts of Tyrone and Fermanagh*. Dublin, Andrew Milliken and Hodges and Smith and London, Brown, Green and Longmans.

POSNANSKY, M. 1960. The Pleistocene succession in the middle Trent basin. *Proceedings of the Geologists' Association*, **71**, 285–311.

POTTS, A. S. 1971. Fossil cryonival features in central Wales. *Geografiska Annaler*, **53A**, 39–51.

POUNDER, E. J. & MACKLIN, M. G. 1985. The alluvial fan at Burrington Coombe, Mendip: a study of its morphology and development. *Proceedings of the Bristol Naturalists' Society*, **45**, 29–38.

PRAEGER, R. L. 1985. Report of the sub-committee appointed to investigate the gravels of Ballyrudder, County Antrim. *Proceedings Belfast Naturalists' Field Club*, 198–209.

PREECE, R. C. 1978. *The Biostratigraphy of the Flandrian Tufas in Southern Britain*. PhD thesis, University of London.

—— 1979. The molluscan fauna of an early Postglacial tufa at Totland, Isle of Wight. *Journal of Conchology*, **30**, 35–42.

—— 1980a. The biostratigraphy and dating of a Postglacial slope deposit at Gore Cliff, near Blackgang, Isle of Wight. *Journal of Archaeological Science*, **7**, 255–265.

—— 1980b. The biostratigraphy and dating of the tufa deposit at the Mesolithic site at Blashenwell, Dorset, England. *Journal of Archaeological Science*, **7**, 345–362.

—— 1990. The molluscan fauna of Late Devensian loess from Reculver, Kent. *Journal of Conchology*, **33**, 295–297.

—— 1992. Episodes of erosion and stability since the Late-glacial: the evidence from dry valleys in Kent. *In:* BELL, M. & BOARDMAN, J. (eds) *Past And Present Soil Erosion: Archaeological and Geogra-*

phical Perspectives. Oxbow Monograph, **22**, 175–183.

—— 1994. Radiocarbon dates from the 'Allerød soil' in Kent. *Proceedings of the Geologists' Association*, **105**, 111–123.

—— & BRIDGLAND, D. R. (eds) 1998a. *Late Quaternary Environmental Change in North-West Europe: Excavations at Holywell Coombe, South-East England.* Chapman & Hall, London.

—— & —— 1998b. Holywell Coombe, Folkestone: a 13,000 year history of an English chalkland valley. *Quaternary Science Reviews* (in press).

—— & VENTRIS, P. A. 1983. An interglacial site at Galley Hill, near St Ives. *Bulletin of the Geological Society of Norfolk*, **33**, 63–72.

——, TURNER, C. & GREEN, H. S. 1982. *Field excursion to the tufas of the Wheeler Valley and to Pontnewydd and Cefn Caves.* Quaternary Research Association Field Guide, 1–9.

——, SCOURSE, J. D., HOUGHTON, S. D., KNUDSEN, K. L. & PENNEY, D. N. 1990. The Pleistocene sea-level and neotectonic history of the eastern Solent, southern England. *Philosophical Transactions of the Royal Society of London*, B **328**, 425–477.

——, LEWIS, S. G., WYMER, J. J., BRIDGLAND, D. R. & PARFITT, S. 1991. Beeches Pit, West Stow, Suffolk. *In:* LEWIS, S. G., WHITEMAN, C. A. & BRIDGLAND, D. R. (eds) *Central East Anglia and the Fen Basin. Field Guide.* Quaternary Research Association, London, 94–104.

——, KEMP, R. A. & HUTCHINSON, J. N. 1995. A Late-glacial colluvial sequence at Watcombe Bottom, Ventnor, Isle of Wight, England. *Journal of Quaternary Science*, **10**, 107–121.

PRESTWICH, J. 1861. Notes on some further discoveries of flint implements in beds of post-Pliocene gravel and clay, with a few suggestions to search elsewhere. *Quarterly Journal of the Geological Society, London*, **17**, 362–368.

—— 1892. The raised beaches and head or rubble drift of the south of England. *Quarterly Journal of the Geological Society, London*, **48**, 263–343.

—— 1875. Notes on the phenomena of the Quaternary period in the Isle of Portland and around Weymouth. *Quarterly Journal of the Geological Society, London*, **31**, 29–54.

PRICE, D., WRIGHT, W. D., JAMES, R. C. B., TONKS, L. H. & WHITEHEAD, T. H. 1963. *Geology of the Country Around Preston.* Memoir Geological Survey of the Great Britain, London.

PROCTOR, C. J. & SMART, P. L. 1991. A dated cave sedimentary record of Pleistocene transgressions on Berry Head, South-west England. *Journal of Quaternary Science*, **6**, 233–245.

PUGH, M. E. & SHEARMAN, D. J. 1967. Cryoturbation structures at the south end of the Isle of Portland. *Proceedings of the Geologists' Association*, **78**, 463–471.

RACKHAM, D. J. 1978. Evidence for changing vertebrate communities in the Middle Devensian *Quaternary Newsletter*, **25**, 1–3.

—— 1981. *Mid-Devensian mammals in Britain.* MSc thesis, University of Birmingham.

RAMSAY, A. C. 1852. On the superficial accumulations and surface markings of North Wales. *Quarterly Journal of the Geological Society, London*, **8**, 371–376.

RAVIS, C. F. 1869. Supplementary notes of the late movements on the somersetshire coast. *Proceedings of the Bristol Naturalists' Society*, Series, **2, 3**, 89–94.

RAYMO, M. E., RUDDIMAN, W. F. & FROELICH, P. N. 1988. Influence of late Cenozoic mountain building on ocean geochemical cycles. *Geology*, **16**, 649–653.

—— 1997. The timing of major climate terminations. *Paleoceanography*, **12**, 577–585.

READE, T. M. 1885. Drift deposits of Colwyn Bay. *Quarterly Journal of the Geological Society, London*, **41**, 102–107.

—— 1893. The drift beds of the Moel Tryfan area of the North Wales coast. *Proceedings Liverpool Geological Society*, **7**, 36–39.

—— 1894. An ancient glacial shore. *Geological Magazine*, **1(2)**, 76–77.

—— 1895. Foraminiferal boulder clay at Great Crosby and at Blackpool. *Proceedings Liverpool Geological Society*, **7**, 387–390.

REID, C. 1882. *The geology of the country around Cromer.* Memoir Geological Survey.

—— 1892. The Pleistocene deposits of the Sussex coast, and their equivalents on other districts. *Quarterly Journal of the Geological Society, London*, **48**, 344–361.

—— 1893. A fossiliferous Pleistocene deposit at Stone on the Hampshire coast. *Quarterly Journal of the Geological Society,*

London, **49**, 325–329.

—— 1885. *The geology of Holderness and adjoining parts of Yorkshire and LIncolnshire.* Memoir Geological Survey.

—— 1903. *Geology of the country around Salisbury.* Memoir Geological Survey.

—— & REID, E. M. 1904. On a probable Palaeolithic floor at Prah Sands (Cornwall). *Quarterly Journal of the Geological Society, London*, **48**, 263–343.

—— & FLETT, J. S. 1907. *The geology of the Land's End district.* Memoir Geological Survey.

REID, E. M. 1920. On two preglacial floras from Castle Eden (County Durham). *Quarterly Journal of the Geological Society, London*, **76**, 104.

RENDELL, H., WORSLEY, P., GREEN, F. & PARKS, D. 1991. Thermoluminescence dating of the Chelford Interstadial. *Earth & Planetary Science Letters*, **103**, 182–189.

REYNOLDS, P. J. 1987a. Holbury Gravel Pit: deposition and weathering features of pre-Devensian brickearths. *In:* BARBER, K. E. (ed.) *Wessex and the Isle of Wight Field Guide* Quaternary Research Association, Cambridge, 12–14.

—— 1987b. Lepe Cliff: the evidence for a pre-Devensian brickearth. *In:* BARBER, K. E. (ed.) *Wessex and the Isle of Wight Field Guide* Quaternary Research Association, Cambridge pp. 21–22.

——, CATT, J. A., WEIR, A. H. & FISHER, G. C. 1996. Stratigraphy and origin of New Forest brickearths, England. *Journal of Quaternary Science*, **11**, 203–216.

RICE, R. J. 1968. The Quaternary deposits of central Leicestershire. *Philosophical Transactions of the Royal Soceity of London*, **A262**, 459–509.

—— 1981. The Pleistocene deposits of the area around Croft in south Leicestershire. *Philosophical Transactions of the Royal Society of London*, **B293**, 385–418.

—— 1991. Distribution and provenance of the Baginton Sand and Gravel in the Wreake Valley, northern Leicestershire, England: implications for inter-regional correlation. *Journal of Quaternary Science*, **6**, 39–54.

RICHARDS, A. E. 1994. *The Pleistocene stratigraphy of Herefordshire.* PhD thesis, University of Cambridge.

RICHMOND, G. M. 1996. The INQUA-approved provisional Lower-Middle Pleistocene boundary. *In:* TURNER, C. (ed.) *The Early Middle Pleistocene in Europe.* Balkema, Rotterdam, 319–327.

RINGROSE, P. S. 1989a. Palaeoseismic(?) liquefaction event in Late Quaternary lake sediment at Glen Roy, Scotland. *Terra Nova*, **1**, 57–62. RISE, L. & ROKOENGEN, K. 1984. Surficial sediments in the Norwegian sector of the North Sea between 60°30' and 62°N. *Marine Geology*, **58**, 287–317.

——, SKINNER, A. C. & LONG, D. 1984. Nordlige Nordsjf. Kvartaergeologisk kart mellom 60°30' og 62°N, og fst for 1°f (Northern North Sea. Quaternary geology map between 60°30' and 62°N, and east of 1°E). *1:500 000. (Trondheim: Institutt for kontinentalsokkelundersfkelser (IKU), Norway.)*

RITCHIE, W. 1979. Machair development and chronology of the Uists and adjacent islands. *Proceedings of the Royal Society Edinburgh*, **B77**, 107–122.

ROBINSON, M. 1993. Microfossil analyses and radiocarbon dating of depositional sequences related to Holocene sea-level change in the Forth valley, Scotland. *Transactions of the Royal Society of Edinburgh: Earth Sciences*, **84**, 1–60.

ROBERTS, M. B. 1986. Excavation of the Lower Palaeolithic site at Amey's Eartham Pit, Boxgrove, West Sussex: a preliminary report. *Proceedings of the Prehistoric Society*, **52**, 215–245.

—— 1994. Reply to Bowen & Sykes. *Nature*, **371**, 751.

—— & PARFITT, S. A. in press *The Middle Pleistocene site at ARC Eartham Quarry, Boxgrove, West Sussex, UK.* English Heritage Monograph Series: London.

——, STRINGER, C. B. & PARFITT, S. A. 1994. Hominid tibia from Middle Pleistocene sediments at Boxgrove, UK. *Nature*, **369**, 311–313.

ROBERTS, M. C. 1985. The geomorphology and stratigraphy of the Lizard Loess in south Cornwall, England. *Boreas*, **14**, 75–82.

ROE, D. A. 1968. A gazetteer of British Lower and Middle Palaeolithic sites. *Research Report, Council for British Archaeology*, **8**.

—— 1977. Fordwich and Sturry. *In:* SHEPHARD-THORN, E. R. & WYMER, J. J. (eds) *South East England and the Thames Valley.*

INQUA Field Guide. Geo Abstracts, Norwich.

ROE, H. M. 1994. *Pleistocene Buried Valleys in Essex*. PhD thesis, University of Cambridge.

—— 1995. The Cudmore Grove Channel site. *In:* BRIDGLAND, D. R., ALLEN P. & HAGGART, B. A. (eds) *The Quaternary of the Lower Reaches of the Thames*. Quaternary Research Association Field Guide, Durham, 258–269.

ROGERSON, R. J., KEEN, D. H., COOPE, G. R., ROBINSON, J. E., DICKSON, J. H. & DICKSON, C. A. 1992. The fauna, flora and palaeoenvironmental significance of deposits beneath the low terrace of the River Great Ouse at Radwell, Bedfordshire, England. *Proceedings of the Geologists' Association*, **103**, 1–13.

ROLFE, W. D. I. 1966. Woolly rhinoceros from the Scottish Pleistocene. *Scottish Journal of Geology*, **2**, 253–258.

ROKOENGEN, K., LOFALDI, M., RISE, L. LOKEN, T. & CARLSEN, R. 1982. Description and dating of a submerged beach in the northern North Sea. *Marine Geology*, **50**, M21–M28.

ROMANS, J. C. C. 1977. Stratigraphy of buried soil at Teinland Forest, Scotland. *Nature*, **268**, 622–623.

ROSE, J. 1981. Field Guide to the Quaternary geology of the south-eatern part of the Loch Lomond basin. *Proceedings of the Geological Society of Glasgow 1980–81, 1–19*.

—— 1985. the Dimlington Stadial/Dimlington Chronozone: A proposal for naming the main glacial episode of the Late Devensian Britain. *Boreas*, **14**, 225–230.

—— 1987. Status of the Wolstonian Glaciation in the British Quaternary. *Quaternary Newsletter*, **53**, 1–9.

—— 1988. Stratigraphic nomenclature for the British Middle Pleistocene -procedural dogma or stratigraphic common sense. *Quaternary Newsletter*, **54**, 15–20.

—— 1989. Tracing the Baginton -Lillington Sands and Gravels from the West Midlands to East Anglia. *In:* KEEN, D. H. (ed.) *The Pleistocene of the West Midlands: Field Guide*. Quaternary Research Association, Cambridge, 102–110.

—— 1991. Stratigraphic basis of the 'Wolstonian glaciation', and retention of the term 'Wolstonian' as a chronostratigraphic stage name -a discussion. *In:* LEWIS, S. G., WHITEMAN, C. A. & BRIDGLAND, D. R. (eds) *Central East Anglia and the Fen Basin*. Quaternary Research Association Field Guide, London, 15–20.

—— 1995. Major river systems of central and southern Britain during the Early and Middle Pleistocene. *Terra Nova*, **6**, 435–443.

—— & ALLEN, P. 1977. Middle Pleistocene stratigraphy in south-east Suffolk. *Journal of the Geological Society, London*, **133**, 83–102.

——, —— & HEY, R. W. 1976. Middle Pleistocene stratigraphy in southern East Anglia. *Nature*, London, **236**, 492–494.

——, ——, KEMP, R. A., WHITEMAN, C. A. & OWEN, N. 1985. The early Anglian Barham Soil in southern East Anglia. *In:* BOARDMAN, J. (ed.) *Soils and Quaternary Landscape Evolution*. Wiley, Chichester, 197–229.

——, LOWE, J. J. & SWITSUR, R. 1988. A radiocarbon date on plant detritus beneath till from the type area of the Loch Lomond Readvance. *Scottish Journal of Geology*, **24**, 113–124.

ROSS, H. 1996. *Last glaciation of Shetland*. PhD thesis, University of St Andrews.

ROUSSEAU, D. D. & KEEN, D. H. 1989. Malacological records from the Upper Pleistocene at Portelet (Jersey, Channel Islands): comparisons with western and central Europe. *Boreas*, **18**, 61–66.

ROWE, P. J. & ATKINSON, T. C. 1985. Uranium-Thorium dating results from Robin Hood's Cave. *In:* BRIGGS, D. J., GILBERTSON, D. D. & JENKINSON, R. D. S. (eds) *Peak District and Northern Dukeries Field Guide*. Quaternary Research Association, Cambridge, 200–207.

——, RICHARDS, D. A., ATKINSON, T. C., BOTTRELL, S. H. & CLIFF, R. A. 1997. Geochemistry and radiometric dating of a Middle Pleistocene peat. *Geochemica et Cosmochimica Acta*, **61**, 4201–4211.

ROWLANDS, B. M. 1970. *The glaciation of the Arenig region*. PhD thesis, University of Liverpool.

—— 1971. Radiocarbon evidence of the age of an Irish Sea glaciation in the Vale of Clwyd. *Nature*, **230**, 9–11.

RUDDIMAN, W. F. 1987. Synthesis of the ocean/ice-sheet record. *In:* RUDDIMAN, W. F. & WRIGHT, H. E. (eds) *North America and adjacent oceans during the last deglaciation*. **3**, Geological Society of America.

RUSSELL, G. 1978. The structure and vegetation history of the Manx hill peats. *In:* DAVEY, P. (ed.) *Man and Environment in the Isle of Man*. British Archaeological Reports, **54**. Oxford.

SALISBURY, C., WHITLEY, P. J., LITTON, C. D. & FOX, J. L. 1984. Flandrian courses of the River Trent at Colwick, Nottingham. *Mercian Geologist*, **9**, 189-207.

SALVADOR, A. (ed.) 1994. *International Stratigraphic Guide*. Geological Society of America (2nd edition).

SANDERS, W. 1841. Account of a raised sea beach at Woodspring Hill, near Bristol. *Report of the British Association for the Advancement of Science, Transactions Section*, **102**–103.

SANDFORD, K. S. 1924 The river gravels of the Oxford district. *Quarterly Journal Geological Society of London*, **80**, 113–179.

SAUNDERS, G. E. 1968a. A reappraisal of Glacial Drainage Phenomena in the Lleyn Peninsula. *Proceedings of the Geologists' Association*, **79**, 305–324.

—— 1968b. A fabric analysis of the ground moraine deposits of the Lleyn Peninsula of south-west Caernarvonshire. *Geological Journal*, **6**, 105–118.

SCAIFE, R. G. 1982. Late-Devensian and Early Flandrian vegetation changes in southern England. *In:* BELL, M. & LIMBREY, S. (eds) *Archaeological aspects of woodland ecology*. Symposia of the Association for Environmental Archaeology No 2. *BAR International Series* **146**, 57–74.

—— 1987. The Late-Devensian and Flandrian vegetation of the Isle of Wight. *In:* BARBER, K. E. (ed.) *Wessex and the Isle of Wight*. Quaternary Research Association Field Guide, Cambridge, 156–180.

SCHADLA-HALL, R. T. 1987. Early man in the eastern Vale of Pickering. *In:* ELLIS, S. (ed.) *East Yorkshire Field Guide*. Cambridge. Quaternary Research Association, 22–30.

SCOURSE, J. D. 1984. The Pleistocene gravels of the Axe Valley (Appendix). *Report and Transactions of the Devonshire Association for the Advancement of Science*, **116**, 77–88.

—— 1985. *Late Pleistocene stratigraphy of the Isles of Scilly and adjoining regions*. PhD thesis, University of Cambridge.

—— 1987. Periglacial sediments and landforms in the Isles of Scilly and West Cornwall. *In:* BOARDMAN, J. (ed.) *Periglacial Processes and Landforms in Britain and Ireland*. Cambridge University Press, Cambridge, 225–236.

—— 1990. Glacial deposits of the Isles of Scilly. *In:* EHLERS, J., GIBBARD, P. L. & ROSE, J. (eds) *Glacial Deposits of Great Britain and Ireland*. Balkema, Rotterdam, 291–300.

—— 1991. Late Pleistocene stratigraphy and palaeobotany of the Isles of Scilly. *Philosophical Transactions of the Royal Society of London*, **B334**, 405–448.

—— 1996. Late Pleistocene stratigraphy and palaeobotany of north and west Cornwall. *Transactions of the Royal Geological Society of Cornwall*, **22**, 2–56.

——, AUSTIN, W. E. N., BATEMAN, R. M., CATT, J. A., EVANS, C. D. R., ROBINSON, J. E. & YOUNG, J. R. 1990. Sedimentology and micropalaeontology of glacimarine sediments from the Central and South Western Celtic Sea. *In:* DOWDESWELL, J. A. & SCOURSE, J. D. (eds) *Glacimarine Environments: Processes and Sediments*. Geological Society, London, Special Publications, **53**, 329–347.

——, ROBINSON, E. & EVANS, C. 1991. Glaciation of the central and south-western Celtic Sea. *In:* EHLERS, J., GIBBARD, P. L. & ROSE, J. (eds) *Glacial deposits in Great Britain and Ireland*. Balkema, Rotterdam, 301–310.

——, ALLEN, J. R. N., AUSTIN, W. E. N., COXON, P., DEVOY, R. J. N. & SEJRUP, H. P. 1992. New evidence on the age and significance of the Gortian Temperate Stage: A preliminary report on the Cork Harbour site. *Proceedings of the Royal Irish Academy*, **92B**, 21–43.

——, ANSARI, M. H., AUSTIN, W. E. N., SEJRUP, H. P. & BALSON, P. S. 1993. Terrestrial -marine correlation of Middle Pleistocene interglacial deposits in the southern North Sea (UK sector). *Terra Abs.* **5**, 608.

SEALY, K. R. & SEALY, C. E. 1956. The terraces of the Middle Thames, *Proceedings of the Geologists' Association*, **67**, 369–392.

SEAGRIEF, S. C. & GODWIN, H. 1960. Pollen diagrams from southern England: Elstead, Surrey. *New Phytologist*, **59**, 84–91.

SEDDON, B. 1957. Late-glacial cwm glaciers in Wales. *Journal of Glaciology*, **3**, 94–99.

—— 1962. Late-glacial deposits at Llyn Dwythwch and Nant

Ffrancon, Caernarvonshire. *Philosophical Transactions of the Royal Society of London*, Series **B244**, 459–481.

SEDDON, M. & HOLYOAK, D. T. 1985. Evidence of sustained regional permafrost during deposition of fossiliferous Late Pleistocene sediments at Stanton Harcourt, Oxfordshire, England. *Proceedings of the Geologists' Association*, **96**, 53–73.

SEJRUP, H. P. & KNUDSEN, K. L. 1993. Paleoenvironments and correlations of interglacial sediments in the North Sea. *Boreas*, **22**, 223–235.

——, AARSETH, I., ELLINGSEN, E., REITHER, E., JANSEN, E., LOVLIE, R., BENT, A., BRIGHAM-GRETTE, J., LARSEN, E. & STOKER, M. 1987. Quaternary stratigraphy of the Fladen area, central North Sea: a multidisciplinary study. *Journal of Quaternary Science*, **2**, 35–58.

——, NAGY, J. & BRIGHAM-GRETTE, J. 1989. Foraminiferal stratigraphy and amino acid geochronology of Quaternary sediments in the Norwegian Channel, northern North Sea. *Norsk Geologisk Tidsskrift*, **69**, 111–124.

——, HAFLIDASON, H., AARSETH, I., FORSBERG, C. F., KING, E., LONG, D. & ROKOENGEN, K. 1994. Late Weichselian glaciation history of the northern North Sea. *Boreas*, **5**, 1–13.

——, AARSETH, I., HAFLIDASON, H., LOVLIE, R., BRATTEN, A., TJOSTHEIM, G., FORSBERG, C. F. & ELLINGSEN, K. L., 1995. Quaternary of the Norwegian Channel; paleoceanography and glaciation history. *Norsk Geologisk Tidsskrift*, **75**, 65–87.

SHACKLETON, N. J. & OPDYKE, N. D. 1973. Oxygen isotope and palaeomagnetic stratigraphy of Equatorial Pacific core V28-238: oxygen isotope temperatures and ice volumes on a 10^5 year and a 10^6 year scale. *Quaternary Research*, **3**, 39–55.

——, BERGER, A. & PELTIER, W. R. 1990. An alternative astronomical calibration of the lower Pleistocene timescale based on ODP Site 677. *Transactions of the Royal Society of Edinburgh: Earth Sciences*, **81**, 251–261.

SHACKLEY, M. L. 1973. A contextual study of the Mousterian industry from Great Pan Farm, Isle of Wight. *Proceedings of the Isle of Wight Natural History and Archaeological Society*, **6**, 542–554.

SHAKESBY, R. A. & STEPHENS, N. 1984. The Pleistocene gravels of the Axe Valley, Devon. *Report and Transactions of the Devonshire Association for the Advancement of Science*, **116**, 77–88.

SHAW, J. & CARTER, R. W. G. 1980. Late Midlandian sedimentation and glaciotectonics of the North Antrim End Moraine. *Irish Naturalists' Journal*, **20**, 67–69.

SHEPHARD-THORN, E. R. 1975. The Quaternary of the Weald - a review. *Proceedings of the Geologists' Association*, **86**, 537–548.

——, BERRY, F. G. & WYATT, R. J. 1982. Geological notes and local details for 1:10000 sheets SU 80 NW, NE, SW and SE, SU 90 NW, NE, SW and SE, TQ 00 NW, SW (West Sussex Coastal Plain between Chichester and Littlehampton). *Institute of Geological Sciences*.

SHIMWELL, D. W. 1985. The distribution and origin of the lowland mosslands. *In:* JOHNSON, R. J. (ed.) *The Geomorphology of North-West England.* Manchester University Press, 299–312.

SHOTTON, F. W. 1953. The Pleistocene deposits of the area between Coventry, Rugby and Leamington, and their bearing upon the topographic development of the Midlands. *Philosophical Transactions of the Royal Society of London*, **B237**, 209–260

—— 1976. Amplification of the Wolstonian Stage of the British Pleistocene. *Geological Magazine*, **113**, 241–250.

—— 1968. The Pleistocene succession around Brandon, Warwickshire. *Philosophical Transactions of the Royal Society of London*, **B254**, 387–400.

—— 1983. The Wolstonian Stage of the British Pleistocene in and around its type area of the English Midlands. *Quaternary Science Reviews*, **2**, 261–280.

—— 1989. The Wolston Sequence and its position within the Pleistocene. *In:* KEEN, D. H. (ed.) *The Pleistocene of the West Midlands: Field Guide.* Quaternary Research Association, Cambridge, 1–4.

—— & COOPE, G. R. 1983. Exposures in the Power House Terrace of the River Stour, Wilden, Worcestershire, England. *Proceedings of the Geologists' Association*, **94**, 33–44.

—— & WILLIAMS, R. E. G. 1971. Birmingham radiocarbon dates: V. *Radiocarbon*, **13**, 141–156.

—— & —— 1973. Birmingham radiocarbon dates: VII. *Radiocarbon*, **15**, 451–468.

——, SUTCLIFFE, A. J. & WEST, R. G. 1962. The fauna and flora from the brick pit at Lexden, Essex, *Essex Naturalist*, **31**, 15–22.

——, BLUNDELL, D. J. & WILLIAMS, R. E. G. 1973. Birmingham radiocarbon dates: VI. *Radiocarbon*, **15**, 385–399.

——, GOUDIE, A. S., BRIGGS, D. J. & OSMASTON, H. A. 1980. Cromerian interglacial deposits at Sugworth, near Oxford, England, and their relation to the Plateau Drift of the Coteswolds and the terrace sequence of the Upper and Middle Thames. *Philosophical Transactions of the Royal Society of London*, **B289**, 55–86.

——, SUTCLIFFE, A. J., BOWEN, D. Q., CURRANT, A. P., COOPE, G. R., HARMON, R. S., SHACKLETON, N. J., STRINGER, C. B., TURNER, C., WEST, R. G. & WYMER, J. J. 1983. Interglacials after the Hoxnian in Britain. *Quaternary Newsletter*, **39**, 19–25.

——, KEEN, D. H., COOPE, G. R., CURRANT, A. P., GIBBARD, P. L., ALTO, M., PEGLAR, S. M. & ROBINSON, J. E. 1993. The Pleistocene deposits at Waverley Wood Pit, Warwickshire, England. *Journal of Quaternary Science*, **8**, 293–325.

SIBRAVA, V., BOWEN, D. Q. & RICHMOND, G. M. 1986. Quaternary Glaciations in the Northern Hemisphere. *In: Quaternary Science Reviews*, **5**, 1–511.

SIMKINS, K. 1968. *Aspects of the Quaternary History in Central Caernarvonshire, Wales.* PhD thesis, University of Reading.

—— 1974. The Late-glacial deposits at Glanllynnau, Caernarvonshire. *New Phytologist*, **73**, 605–618.

SIMMONS, I. G., ATHERDEN, M. A., CUNDILL, P. R., INNES, J. B. & JONES, R. L. 1982. Prehistoric environments. *In:* SPRATT, D. A. (ed.) *Prehistoric and Roman archaeology of north-east Yorkshire.* 33–99. BAR British Series 104. Oxford. British Archaelogical Reports.

—— & CUNDILL, P. R. 1974. Late Quaternary vegetational history of the North York Moors. VIII Correlation of Flandrian II litho and pollen stratigraphy at North Gill, Glaisdale Moor. *Journal of Biogeography*, **15**, 249–272.

SIMPSON, I. M. & WEST, R. G. 1958. On the stratigraphy and palaeobotany of a late-Pleistocene organic deposit at Chelford, Cheshire. *New Phytologist*, **57**, 239–250.

SIMPSON, S. 1948. The glacial deposits of Tullos and Bay of Nigg, Aberdeen. *Transactions of the Royal Society of Edinburgh*, **61**, 687–697.

SINGER, R., GLADFELTER, B. G. & WYMER, J. J. 1993. *The Lower Paleolithic Site at Hoxne, England.* University of Chicago Press.

SINGH, G. 1970. Late-glacial vegetational history of Lecale, County Down. *Proceedings of the Royal Irish Academy*, **69B**, 189–216.

—— & SMITH, A. G. 1973. Post-glacial vegetational history and relative land-and sea-level changes in Lecale, County Down. *Proceedings of the Royal Irish Academy*, **73B**, 1–51.

SISSONS, J. B. 1966. Relative sea-level changes between 10,300 and 8300 BP in part of the Carse of Stirling. *Transactions of the Institute of British Geographers*, **39**, 19–29.

—— 1967. *The Evolution of Scotland's Scenery.* Oliver and Boyd, Edinburgh.

—— 1969. Drift stratigraphy and buried morphological features in the Grangemouth-Falkirk-Airth area, central Scotland. *Transactions of the Institute of British Geographers*, **48**, 19–50.

—— 1971. The geomorphology of central Edinburgh. *Scottish Geographical Magazine*, **87**, 185–196.

—— 1972. The last glaciers in part of the south-east Grampians. *Scottish Geographical Magazine*, **88**, 168–181.

—— 1974. Lateglacial marine erosion in Scotland. *Boreas*, **3**, 41–48.

—— 1980. The Loch Lomond advance in the Lake District, northern England. *Transactions of the Royal Society of Edinburgh: Earth Sciences*, **71**, 13–27.

—— 1981. Lateglacial marine erosion and a jokulhlaup deposit in the Beauly Firth. *Scottish Journal of Geology*, **17**, 7–19.

—— 1983. Shorelines and isostasy in Scotland. *In:* SMITH, D. E. & DAWSON, A. G. (eds) *Shorelines and Isostasy.* Academic, London, 209–225.

—— & BROOKS, C. L. 1971. Dating of early postglacial land and sea-level changes in the Western Forth Valley. *Nature Physical Science*, **234**, 124–127.

—— & SMITH, D. E. 1965. Peat bogs in a postglacial sea and a buried raised beach in the western part of the Carse of Stirling. *Scottish Journal of Geology*, **1**, 247–255.

SKINNER, A. C. & GREGORY, D. M. 1983. Quaternary stratigraphy in the northern North Sea. *Boreas*, **12**, 145–152.

——, McELVENNEY, E., RUCKLEY, N., RISE, L. & ROKOENGEN, K. 1986. Cormorant Sheet 61mN–00m. *Quaternary Geology. 1 : 250 000 Map Series. British Geological Survey.*

SMART, J. G. O., BISSON, G. & WORSSAM, B. C. 1966. *Geology of the Country Around Canterbury and Folkestone.* Memoirs of the Geological Survey of England & Wales.

SMITH, A. & ROSE, J. 1997. A new find of Quaternary quartzite-rich gravels near Letchworth, Hertfordshire, southeastern England. *Proceedings of the Geologists' Association*, **108**, 317–326.

SMITH, A. G. 1958. Post-glacial deposits in south Yorkshire and north Lincolnshire. *New Phytologist*, **57**, 19–49.

SMITH, A. J. 1985a. A catastrophic origin for the palaeovalley system of the eastern English Channel. *Marine Geology*, **64**, 65–75.

—— 1985b. The English Channel: response to geological events after the Variscan orogeny. *Annales de la Société Géologique Polonaise*, **55**, 3–22.

—— 1989. The English Channel by geological design or catastrophic accident? *Proceedings of the Geologists' Association*, **100**, 325–327.

SMITH, B. 1930. Borings through the glacial drifts of the northern plain of the Isle of Man. *Summary of Progress Geological Survey*, **3**, 14–23.

SMITH, D. B. 1981. The Quaternary Geology of the Sunderland District, North-east England *In:* NEALE, J. & FLENLEY, J. (eds) *The Quaternary in Britain.* Pergamon, Oxford, 146–167.

—— & FRANCIS, E. A. 1967. Geology of the country between Durham and West Hartlepool. *Memoir Geological Survey.*

——, BEAUMONT, P., GAUNT, G. D., FRANCIS, E. A. & PENNY, L. F. 1973. North-east England. *In:* MITCHELL, G. F., PENNY, L. F., SHOTTON, F. W & WEST, R. G. *A Correlation of Quaternary Deposits in the British Isles.* Geological Society, London, Special Reports, **4**, 22–28.

SMITH, D. E. 1993. Western Forth Valley. *In:* GORDON, J. E. & SUTHERLAND, D. G. (eds) *Quaternary of Scotland.* Chapman and Hall, London, 456–464.

——, DAWSON, A. G., CULLINGFORD, R. A. & HARKNESS, D. D. 1985b. The stratigraphy of Flandrian relative sea-level changes at a site in Tayside. *Earth Surfaces Processes and Landforms*, **10**, 17–25.

——, THOMPSON, K. S. R. & KEMP, D. D. 1978. The Late Devensian and Flandrian history of the Teith Valley, Scotland. *Boreas*, **7**, 97–107.

SMITH, J. 1896b. The geological position of the Irvine whale bed. *Transactions of the Geological Society of Glasgow*, **10**, 29–50.

SMITH, R. F. & BOARDMAN, J. 1989. The use of soil information in the assessment of the incidence and magnitude of historical flood events in upland Britain. *In:* BEVAN, K. & CARLING, P. (eds.) *Floods: Hydrological, Sedimentological and Geomorphological Implications.* Longman, London, 185–197.

SMITHSON, F. 1953. The micro-mineralogy of North Wales soils. *Journal of Soil Science*, **4**, 194–209.

SMYTH, C. T. 1986. A palaeoenvironmental investigation of Flandrian valley deposits from the Combe Haven Valley, East Sussex. *Quaternary Studies*, **2**, 22–33.

SOUTHGATE, G. A. 1984. Thermoluminescence dating of beach and dune sands: potential of single-grain measurements. *Nuclear Tracks*, **10**, 743–747.

SOLOMON, J. D. 1931. Palaeolithic and Mesolithic sites at Morston, Norfolk. *Man*, **31**, 275–278.

—— 1932. The glacial succession in the North Norfolk coast. *Proceedings of the Geologists' Association*, **43**, 241–271.

SPARKS, B. W. 1955. Notes on four Quaternary deposits in the Cambridge region. *Journal of Conchology*, **24**, 47–53.

—— 1957. The non-marine Mollusca of the interglacial deposits at Bobbitshole, Ipswich. *Philosophical Transactions of the Royal Society of London*, **B241**, 1–31.

—— & WEST, R. G. 1959. The palaeoecology of the interglacial deposits at Histon Road, Cambridge. *Eiszeitalter und Gegenwart*, **10**, 123–143.

—— & WEST, R. G. 1963. The interglacial deposits at Stutton, Suffolk. *Proceedings of the Geologists' Association*, **74**, 419–432.

—— & —— 1968. Interglacial deposits at Wortwell, Norfolk. *Geological Magazine*, **105**, 471–481.

——, ——, WILLIAMS, R. B. G. & RANSOM, M. 1969 Hoxnian interglacial deposits near Hatfield, Herts. *Proceedings of the Geologists' Association*, **80**, 243–267.

——, WILLIAMS, R. B. G. & BELL, F. G. 1972. Presumed ground-ice depressions in East Anglia. *Proceedings of the Royal Society of London*, **A327**, 329–343.

SPENCER, H. E. P. 1967. A contribution to the geological history of Suffolk. Part 2. The geological history of the Orwell-Gipping system. *Transactions of the Suffolk Natural History Society*, **3**, 290–313.

—— 1971. A contribution to the geological history of Suffolk. Pary 5. The early Pleistocene. *Transactions of the Suffolk Natural History Society*, **15**, 279–363.

—— & MELVILLE, R. V. 1974. The Pleistocene mammalian fauna of Dove Holes, Derbyshire. *Bulletin of the Geological Survey of Great Britain* **48**, 43–53.

STEPHENS, N. 1963. Late glacial sea levels in north-east Ireland. *Irish Geography*, **4**, 345–359.

—— 1966a. *Geomorphological studies in Ireland and Western Britain with special reference to Pleistocene period.* PhD thesis, The Queens University, Belfast.

—— 1966b. Some Pleistocene deposits in North Devon. *Biuletyn Peryglacjalny*, **15**, 103–114.

—— 1968. Late-glacial and post-glacial shorelines in Ireland and south-west Scotland. *In:* MORRISON, R. B. (ed.) *Means of Correlation of Quaternary Successions,* Studies on the Quaternary, VII Congress, International Association Quaternary Research, Boulder, Colorado, 437–456.

—— 1970. The west country and southern Ireland *In:* LEWIS, C. A. (ed.) *The glaciations of Wales and adjoining regions.* Longman, London, 267–314.

—— 1973. South-west England. *In:* MITCHELL, G. F. *et al. A correlation of Quaternary deposits in the British Isles.* Geological Society, London, Special Reports, **4**, 36–45.

—— & McCABE, A. M. 1977. Late-Pleistocene ice movements and patterns of Late-and post-glacial shorelines on the coast of Ulster. *In:* KIDSON, C. & TOOLEY, M. J. (eds) *Quaternary History of the Irish Sea. Geological Journal, special issue no. 7*, 179–198.

—— & SYNGE, F. M. 1965. Late-Pleistocene shorelines and drift limits in north Donegal. *Proceedings of the Royal Irish Academy*, **64B**, 131–153.

——, CREIGHTON, J. R. & HANNON, M. A. 1975. The Late Pleistocene period in north-eastern Ireland: an assessment 1975. *Irish Geography*, **8**, 1–23.

STEVENSON, A. C. & MOORE, P. D. 1982. Pollen analysis of an interglacial deposit at West Angle, Dyfed, Wales. *New Phytologist*, **90**, 327–338.

STEVENSON, A. G. 1991a. Flett Sheet 61N 04W. Quaternary Geology. 1 : 250 000 Map Series. *British Geological Survey.*

—— 1991b. Miller Sheet 61N 02W. Quaternary Geology. 1 : 250 000 Map Series. *British Geological Survey.*

STEVENSON, A. S. 1991c. Miller Sheet 61mN–02mW. Quaternary Geology. 1 : 250 000 Map Series. *British Geological Survey.*

STEWART, A., WALKER, A. & DICKSON, J. H. 1984. Pollen diagrams from Dubh Lochan, near Loch Lomond. *New Phytologist*, **98**, 531–549.

STEWART, F. S. 1991. *A Reconstruction of the Eastern Margin of the Late Weichselian Ice Sheet in Northern Britain.* PhD thesis, University of Edinburgh.

STOKER, M. S. & BENT, A. J. A. 1985. Middle Pleistocene glacial and glaciomarine sediments in the west central North Sea. *Boreas*, **14**, 325–332.

—— & —— 1987. Lower Pleistocene deltaic and marine sediments in boreholes from the central North Sea. *Journal of Quaternary Science*, **2**, 87–96.

—— & HOLMES, R. 1991. Submarine end moraines as indicators of Pleistocene ice-limits off north-west Britain. *Journal of the Geological Society, London*, **148**, 431–434.

——, SKINNER, A. C., FYFE, J. A., & LONG, D. 1983. Palaeomagnetic evidence for early Pleistocene in the central and northern North Sea. *Nature*, London, **304**, 332–334.

——, LONG, D. & FYFE, J. A. 1985a. The Quaternary succession in the central North Sea. *Newsletters on Stratigraphy*, **14**, 119–128.

——, —— & —— 1985b. A revised Quaternary stratigraphy for the central North Sea. *Report of the British Geological Survey*, **17**, No.

2.

——, HITCHEN, K. & GRAHAM, C. C. 1993. United Kingdom offshore regional report: the geology of the Hebrides and West Shetland shelves, and adjacent deep-water areas. *British Geological Survey.*

STRAHAN, A. 1886. On the glaciation of South Lancashire, Cheshire and the Welsh borders. *Quarterly Journal of the Geological Society, London,* **42,** 369–391.

—— 1890. The geology of the neighbourhoods of Flint, Mold and Ruthin. *Memoir Geological Survey.*

—— 1907a. The geology of the South Wales Coalfield Part VIII. The country around Swansea. *Memoir of the Geological Survey of Great Britain.*

—— 1907b. The geology of the South Wales Coalfield Part IX. West Gower and the country around Pembrey. *Memoir Geological Survey*

—— & CANTRILL, T. C. 1904. The geology of the South Wales Coalfield Part VI. The country around Bridgend. *Memoir Geological Survey.*

——, ——, DIXON, E. E. L. & THOMAS, H. H. 1909. The geology of the South Wales Coalfield Part X. The country around Carmarthen. *Memoir Geological Survey.*

STRAW, A. 1958. The glacial sequence in Lincolnshire. *East Midland Geographer,* **1,** 29–40.

—— 1960. The limit of the 'Last' glaciation in North Norfolk. *Proceedings of the Geologists' Association,* **71,** 379–390.

—— 1966. The development of the Middle and Lower Bain Valley, East Lincolnshire. *Transactions Institute of British Geographers,* **40,** 145–154.

—— 1979. The geomorphological significance of the Wolstonian glaciation of eastern England. *Transactions of the Institute of British Geographers, New Series,* **4,** 540–549.

—— 1983. Pre-Devensian glaciation of Lincolnshire (Eastern England) and adjacent areas. *Quaternary Science Reviews,* **2,** 239–260.

STRICKLAND, H. E. 1936. Chapter VI in the *Memoirs of Hugh Edwin Strickland* by Sir William Jardine. J. van Voorst, London.

STRINGER, C. B., CURRANT, A. P., SCHWARCZ, H. P. & COLLCUTT, S. N. 1986. Age of Pleistocene faunas from Bacon Hole, Wales. *Nature,* **320,** 59–62.

STUART, A. J. 1982. *Pleistocene vertebrates in the British Isles.* London. Longman.

—— 1992. The High Lodge mammalian fauna. *In:* ASHTON, N. M., COOK, J., LEWIS, S. G. & ROSE, J. (eds) *High Lodge. Excavations by G. de G. Sieveking, 1962–8 and J. Cook, 1988.* British Museum Press, London, 120–123.

SUMBLER, M. G. 1983a. A new look at the type Wolstonian glacial deposits of central England. *Proceedings of the Geologists' Association,* **94,** 23–31.

—— 1983b. The type Wolstonian sequence some further comments. *Quaternary Newsletter,* **40,** 36–39.

—— 1989. The Froghall Sand and Gravel: a post-'Wolstonian' fluvial deposit near Coventry. *Quaternary Newsletter,* **58,** 3–8.

—— 1995. The terraces of the rivers Thame and Thames and their bearing on the chronology of glaciation in central and eastern England. *Proceedings of the Geologists' Association,* **106,** 93–106.

SUTCLIFFE, A. J. 1995. Insularity of the British Isles 250 000 -30 000 years ago: the mammalian, including human evidence. *In:* PREECE, R. C. (ed.) *Island Britain: a Quaternary perspective.* Geological Society, London, Special Publications, **96,** 127–140.

—— & BOWEN, D. Q. 1973. Preliminary report on excavations in Minchin Hole, April-May, 1973. *Newsletter of the William Pengelly Cave Studies Trust,* **21,** 12–25.

——, CURRANT, A. P. & STRINGER, C. B. 1987. Evidence of sea-level change from coastal caves with raised beach deposits, terrestial faunas and dated stalagmites. *Progress in Oceanography,* **18,** 243–271.

——, LORD, T. C., HARMON, R. S., IVANOVICH, M., RAR, A. & HESS, J. W. 1984. A mammalian fauna of northern character in Yorkshire at *ca.* 83,000 years BP. *Quaternary Newsletter,* **43,** 9–12.

——, ——, ——, ——, —— & —— 1985. Wolverine in northern England at about 83, 000 yrs BP: faunal evidence for climatic change during Isotope Stage 5. *Quaternary Research,* **24,** 73–86.

SUTHERLAND, D. G. 1981. The high-level marine shell beds of Scotland and the build-up of the last Scottish ice sheet. *Boreas,* **10,** 247–254.

—— 1984. The Quaternary deposits and landforms of Scotland

and the neighbouring shelves: a review. *Quaternary Science Reviews,* **3,** 157–254.

—— 1993. Tangy Glen. *In:* GORDON, J. E. & SUTHERLAND, D. G. (eds) *Quaternary of Scotland.* Chapman and Hall, London, 310–313.

—— & WALKER, M. J. C. 1984. A late Devensian ice-free area and possible interglacial site on the Isle of Lewis, Scotland. *Nature,* **309,** 701–703.

——, BALLANTYNE, C. K. & WALKER, M. J. C. 1984. Late Quaternary glaciation and environmental change on St Kilda, Scotalnd, and their palaeoclimatic significance. *Boreas,* **13,** 261–272.

SWINNERTON, H. H. 1937. The problem of the Lincoln Gap. *Transactions of the Lincolnshire Naturalists' Union,* **9,** 145–153.

SYNGE, F. M. 1950. The glacial deposits around Trim, County Meath. *Proceedings of the Royal Irish Academy,* **53B,** 99–110.

—— 1956. The glaciation of north-east Scotland. *Scottish Geographical Magazine,* **72,** 129–143.

—— 1963a. A correlation between the drifts of south-east Ireland and those of west Wales. *Irish Geography,* **4,** 360–366.

—— 1963b. The glaciation of the Nephin Beg range, County Mayo. *Irish Geography,* **4,** 397–403.

—— 1964. Some problems concerned with the glacial succession in south-east Ireland. *Irish Geography,* **5,** 73–82.

—— 1966. Glacial geology. *In:* FINCH, T. F. & RYAN, P. (eds) *Soils of County Limerick, Soil Survey Bulletin* **16,** *Dublin,* 12–20.

—— 1968. The glaciation of west Mayo. *Irish Geography,* **5,** 372–386.

—— 1969. The Wirm ice limit in the west of Ireland. *In: Quaternary Geology and Climate,* publication 1701, National Academy of Sciences, Washington, 89–92.

—— 1971. The glacial deposits of Glenasmole, County Dublin, and the neighbouring uplands. *Geological Survey of Ireland Bulletin,* **1,** 87–97.

—— 1973. The glaciation of south Wicklow and the adjoining parts of the neighbouring counties. *Irish Geography,* **6,** 561–569.

—— 1977. Introduction. *In:* HUDDARD, D. (ed.) *South East Ireland ,* Guidebook for excursion A14, (ed. BOWEN, D. Q.) X INQUA Congress, Geoabstracts, Norwich, 5–8.

—— 1978. Pleistocene events. *In:* DAVIES, G. L. H. & STEPHENS, N., *Ireland,* London, Methuen, 115–180.

—— 1979a. Quaternary glaciation in Ireland. *Quaternary Newsletter,* **28,** 1–18.

—— 1979b. Killabee. *In:* McCABE, A. M. (ed.) *East Central Ireland,* Field Guide, Quaternary Research Association, Dublin.

—— 1981. Quaternary glaciation and changes of sea level in the south of Ireland. *Geologie en Mijnbouw,* **60,** 305–315.

—— & STEPHENS, N. 1960. The Quaternary period in Ireland -an assessment, 1960. *Irish Geography,* **4,** 121–130.

—— & —— 1966. Late-and Post-glacial shorelines and ice limits in Argyll and northeast Ulster. *Transactions of the Institute of British Geographers,* **39,** 101–125.

SZABO, B. J. & COLLINS, D. 1975. Ages of fossil bones from British interglacial sites. *Nature,* **254,** 680–682.

TALLIS, J. H. 1964. The pre-peat vegetation of the southern Pennines. *New Phytologist,* **63,** 363–373.

—— & SWITZER, V. R. 1983. Forest and moorland in the south Pennine upland in the mid-Flandrian period: I Macro-fossil evidence of the former forest cover. *Journal of Ecology,* **71,** 585–600.

TAYLOR, R. T. & BEER, K. E. 1981. Raised beach and mined fluvial deposits near Marazion, Cornwall. *Proceedings of the Ussher Society,* **5,** 247–250.

TE PUNGA, M. T. 1957. Periglaciation in southern England. *Tydsk. K. Nederlandsch Aardrykskundig Genoots,* **74,** 400–412.

THOMAS, G. S. P. 1976. The Quaternary Stratigraphy of the Isle of Man. *Proceedings of the Geologists Association,* **87,** 307–323.

—— 1977. The Quaternary of the Isle of Man. *In:* KIDSON, C & TOOLEY, M. J. (eds) *The Quaternary of the Irish Sea. Geological Journal Special Issue* 7, 155–179. Liverpool. Seel House Press.

—— 1984a. A Late Devensian glaciolacustrine fan-delta at Rhosesmor, Clwyd, North Wales. *Geological Journal,* **19,** 125–141.

—— 1984b. The origin of the glacio-dynamic structure of the Bride Moraine, Isle of Man. *Boreas,* **13,** 355–364.

—— 1985a. The Late Devensian Glaciation along the border of north-east Wales. *Geological Journal,* **20,** 319–340.

—— 1985*b*. The Quaternary of the northern Irish Sea. *In:* JOHNSON, R. J. (ed.) *The Geomorphology of North-West England*. Manchester University Press, 143–158.

—— 1989. The Late Devensian glaciation along the western margin of the Cheshire-Shropshire lowland. *Journal of Quaternary Science*, **4** (2), 167–181.

—— & SUMMERS, A. J. 1981. Pleistocene foraminifers from south-east Ireland -a reply. *Quaternary Newsletter*, **34**, 15–18.

—— & —— 1982. Drop-stone and allied structures from Pleistocene waterlain till at Ely House, County Wexford. *Journal of Earth Sciences Royal Dublin Society*, **4**, 109–119.

—— & —— 1983. The Quaternary stratigraphy between Blackwater Harbour and Tinnaberna, County Wexford. *Journal of Earth Sciences Royal Dublin Society*, **5**, 121–134.

——, —— & DACKOMBE, R. V. 1982. The Late-Quaternary deposits of the middle Dyfi Valley, Wales. *Geological Journal*, **17**, 297–309.

——, DACKOMBE, R. V. & CONNAUGHTON, M. 1985. Facies variation in a Late Pleistocene supraglacial outwash sandur from the Isle of Man. *Geological Journal*, **20**, 193–213.

THOMAS, M. F. 1961. River terraces and drainage development in the Reading area. *Proceedings of the Geologists' Association*, **72**, 415–426.

THOMAS, K. W. 1965. The stratigraphy and pollen analysis of a raised bog at Llanllwch near Carmarthen. *New Phytologist*, **64**, 101–117.

THOMPSON, D. B. & WORSLEY, P. W. 1968. A Late Pleistocene molluscan fauna from the drifts of the Cheshire Plain. *Geological Journal*, **5**, 197–207.

THOMPSON, R., CAMERON, T. D. J., SCHWARZ, C., JENSEN, K. A., MAENHAUT VAN LEMBERGE, V. & SHA, L. P. 1992. The magnetic roperties of Quaternary and Tertiary sediments in the southern North Sea. *Journal of Quaternary Geology*, 19–334.

THOMSON, M. E. 1978. IGS studies of the geology of the Firth of Forth and its pproaches. *Report of the Institute of Geological Sciences*, No. 77/17.

THORLEY, A. 1981. Pollen analytical evidence relating to the vegetation history of the Chalk. *Journal of Biogeography*, **8**, 93–106.

THURRELL, R. G., WORSSAM, B. C. & EDMONDS, E. A. 1968. *Geology of the Country Around Haslemere*. Memoir Geological Survey of England and Wales.

TIPPING, R., CARTER, S. & HAGGART, B. A. 1994. Late Quaternary valley floor evolution in the lower reaches of Carradale, Kintyre. *Scottish Journal of Geology*, **30**, 131–145.

TOMLINSON, M. E. 1925. River terraces of the lower valley of the Lower Valley of the Warwickshire Avon. *Quarterly Journal of the Geological Society, London*, **81**, 137–169.

—— 1929. The drifts of the Stour-Evenlode watershed and their extension into the valleys of the Warwickshire Stour and Upper Evenlode. *Proceedings Birmingham Natural History Society*. **15**, 157–196.

—— 1935. The superficial deposits of the country north of Stratford-upon-Avon. *Quarterly Journal of the Geological Society, London*, **91**, 423–462.

—— 1941. Pleistocene gravels of the Cotswold sub-edge plain from Mickleton to the Frome Valley. *Quarterly Journal of the Geological Society, London*, **96**, 385–421.

—— 1963. The Pleistocene chronology of the Midlands. *Proceedings of the Geologists' Association*, **74**, 187–202.

TOOLEY, M. J. 1974. Sea-level changes during the last 9000 years in north-west England. *Geographical Journal*, **140**, 18–42.

—— 1977. The Quaternary history of north-west England and the Isle of Man. *In:* TOOLEY, M. J. (ed.) *Guidebook for Excursion A4. the Isle of Man, Lancashire coast and Lake District*. INQUA X Congress, United Kingdom. Norwich. Geo Abstracts.

—— 1978. *Sea-level changes: north-west England during the Flandrian Stage*. Clarendon, Oxford.

—— 1982. Sea-level changes in northern England. *Proceedings of the Geologists' Association*, **93**, 43–51.

—— 1985. Sea-level changes and coastal morphology in North-West England. *In:* JOHNSON, R. J. (ed.) *The Geomorphology of North-West England*. Manchester University Press, 94–121

—— & SWITSUR, V. R. 1988. Water level changes and sedimentation during the Flandrian Age in the Romney Marsh area. *In:* EDDISON, J. & GREEN, C. (eds) *Romney Marsh, Evolution. Occupation. Reclamation*. Oxford University Committee for Archaeology Monograph No. 34, Oxford, 53–71.

TRENCHMAN, C. T. 1920. On a deposit of interglacial loess and some transported preglacial freshwater clays on the Durham coast. *Quarterly Journal of the Geological Society of London*, **75**, 173–303.

TRIMMER, J. 1831. On the diluvial deposits of Caernarvonshire between the Snowdon chain and the Menai Strait. *Proceedings of the Geological Society*, **1**, 331–332.

—— 1851. Generalisations respecting the erratic Tertiaries or Northern Drift. *Quarterly Journal of the Geological Society, London*, **7**, 19–31.

—— 1853. On the Southern Termination of the Erratic Tertiaries; annd on the Remains of a Bed of Gravel on the Summit of Clevedon Down, Somerset. *Quarterly Journal of the Geological Society, London*, **9**, 282–286.

TROTTER, F. M. 1929. The glaciation of eastern Edenside, Alston Block and the Carlisle Plain. *Quarterly Journal of the Geological Society, London*, **88**, 549–607.

—— & HOLLINGWORTH, S. E. 1932. The glacial sequence in the north of England. *Geological Magazine*, **69**, 374–380.

TUCHOLKA, P., FONTUGNE, M., GUICHARD, F. & PATERNE, M. 1987. The Blake magnetic polarity episode in cores from the Mediterranean Sea. *Earth and Planetary Science Letters*, **86**, 320–326.

TURNER, J., 1964. The anthropogenic factor in vegetational history I: Tregaron and Whixall Mosses. *New Phytologist*, **63**, 73–90.

TURNER, C. 1970. The Middle Pleistocene deposits at Mark's Tey, Essex. *Philosophical Transactions of the Royal Society of London*, **B257**, 373–440.

—— 1983. Nettlebed. *In:* ROSE, J. (ed.) *Diversion of the Thames*. Field Guide. Quaternary Research Association. Cambridge, 66–68.

USSHER, W. A. E. 1879. *The post-Tertiary geology of Cornwall*. Stephen Austin & Sons, Hertford (privately published).

—— 1914. A geological sketch of Brean Down and its environs, with special reference to the marsh deposits of Somerset. *Proceedings of the Somerset Archaeological and Natural History Society*, **40**, **2**, 17–40.

——, JUKES-BROWNE, A. J. & STRAHAN, A. 1888. The geology of the country around Lincoln. *Memoir of the Geological Survey of England and Wales*. Old Series Sheet 83.

VAIL, P. R. 1987. Seismic stratigraphy interpretation using sequence stratigraphy, Part 1: seismic stratigraphy interpretation procedure. *In:* BALLY, A. W. (ed.) *Atlas of Seismic Stratigraphy*. *Association American Petroleum Geologists Studies in Geology*, **27**, 1–10.

VALENTIN, H. H. 1957. Glazial morphologische untersochungen in Ostengland. *Abhandlungen der Geographische Institut der Freien Universitat*, Berlin, **4**, 1–86.

VENTRIS, P. A. 1985. *Pleistocene environmental history of the Nar Valley, Norfolk*. PhD Thesis, University of Cambridge.

—— 1986. The Nar Valley. *In:* WEST, R. G. & WHITEMAN, C. A. (eds) *The Nar Valley and North Norfolk, Field Guide*. Quaternary Research Association, Coventry, 7–55.

—— 1996. Hoxnian Interglacial freshwater and marine deposits in Northwest Norfolk, England and their implications for sea-level reconstruction. *Quaternary Science Reviews*, **15**, 437–451.

VINCENT, P. J. 1976. Some periglacial deposits near Aberystwyth, Wales, as seen with a scanning electron microscope. *Biuletyn Peryglacjalny*, **25**, 59–64.

—— 1982. Some observations on the so-called relic karst of the Morecambe Bay region, north-west England. *Revue Geologiei Dynamique et Geographie Physique*, **23**, 143–150.

—— & LEE, M. P. 1981. Some observations on the loess around Morecambe Bay, north-west England. *Proceedings of the Yorkshire Geological Society*, **43**, 281–294.

—— & LEE, M. P. 1982. Snow patches on Farleton Fell, south-east Cumbria. *Geographical Journal*, **148**, 337–342.

VON WEYMARN, J. 1979. A new concept of glaciation in Lewis & Harris, Outer Hebrides. *Proceedings of the Royal Society of Edinburgh*, **B77**, 97–105.

—— & EDWARDS, K. J. 1973. Interstadial site on the Island of Lewis. *Nature*, **246**, 473–474.

WALDER, P. S. 1967. The composition of the Thames gravels near Reading, Berkshire. *Proceedings of the Geologists' Association*, **78**, 107–120.

WALKER, D. 1955. Late-glacial deposits at Lunds, Yorkshire. *New Phytologist*, **54**, 343–349.

WALKER, M. J. C. 1980. Late-glacial history of the Brecon Beacons, South Wales. *Nature*, **287**, 133–135.

—— 1982. The Late-glacial and early Flandrian deposits at Traeth Mawr, Brecon Beacons, South Wales. *New Phytologist*, **90**, 177–194.

—— 1984. Craig-y-fro and Craig Cerrig-gleisiaid, Brecon Beacons/Fforest Fawr. *In:* BOWEN, D. Q. & HENRY, A. (eds) *Wales: Gower, Preseli, Fforest Fawr.* Quaternary Research Association field guide, Aberystwyth, 91–96.

——, MERRITT, J. W., AUTON, C. A., COOPE, G. R., FIELD, M. H., HEIJNIS, H. & TAYLOR, B. J. 1992. Allt Odhar and Dalcharn: two pre-Late Devensian (Late Weichselian) sites in northern Scotland. *Journal of Quaternary Science*, **7**, 69–86.

WALLACE, T. D. 1883. Shells in glacial clay at Fort George, Inverness-shire. *Transactions of the Edinburgh Geological Society*, **4**, 143–144.

WALLER, M. P. 1993. Flandrian vegetational history of south-eastern England. Pollen data from Pannel Bridge, East Sussex. *New Phytologist*, **124**, 345–369.

—— 1994. Flandrian vegetational history of south-eastern England. Stratigraphy of the Brede valley and pollen data from Brede Bridge. *New Phytologist*, **126**, 369–392.

——, BURRIN, P. J. & MARLOW, A. 1988. Flandrian sedimentation and palaeoenvironments in Pett Level, the Brede and Lower Rother valleys and Walland Marsh. *In:* EDDISON, J. & GREEN, C. (eds) *Romney Marsh. Evolution, Occupation. Reclamation.* Oxford University Committee for Archaeology Monograph No. 34, Oxford, 3–30.

WARREN, P. T., PRICE, D., NUTT, M. J. C. & SMITH, E. G. 1984. *Geology of the Country around Rhyl and Denbigh.* Memoir, British Geological Survey.

WARREN, S. H. 1900. Palaeolithic flint implements from the Chalk Downs of the Isle of Wight and the valleys of the Western Yar and Stour. *Geological Magazine* (NS), **7**, 406–412.

—— 1916. Further observations on the Late Glacial or Ponder's End Stage of the Lea Valley. *Quarterly Journal of the Geological Society, London*, **71**, 164–182.

—— 1923. The Late-glacial Stage of the Lea Valley (Third report). *Quarterly Journal of the Geological Society, London*, **79**, 603–605.

WARREN, W. P. 1979. Moraines on the northern slopes and foothills of the MacGillycuddy's Reeks, south-west Ireland. *In:* SCHLUCHTER, Ch. (ed.) *Moraines and Varves,* Balkema, Rotterdam, 223–236.

—— 1985. Stratigraphy. *In:* EDWARDS, K. J. & WARREN, W. P. (eds) *The Quaternary History of Ireland*, Academic, London, 39–65.

WATERS, R. S. 1964. The Pleistocene legacy to the geomorphology of Dartmoor. *In:* SIMMONS, I. G. (ed.) *Dartmoor Essays.* Devonshire Association for the Advancement of Science, Literature and Art, Exeter, 73–96.

WATON, P. V. & BARBER, K. E. 1987. Rimsmoor, Dorset: biostratigraphy and chronology of an infilled doline. *In:* BARBER, K. E. (ed.) *Wessex and the Isle of Wight.* Quaternary Research Association Field Guide, Cambridge, 75–80.

WATSON, E. 1965. Periglacial structures in the Aberystwyth region. *Proceedings of the Geological Society*, **76**, 443–462.

—— 1966. Two Nivation cirques near Aberystwyth, Wales. *Biul peryglac*, **15**, 79–101.

—— 1968. The periglacial laandscape in the Aberystwyth region. *In:* BOWEN, E. G. *et al.* (eds) *Geography at Aberystwyth.* Cardiff.

—— 1970. Remains of pingos in Wales and the Isle of Man. *Geological Journal* **7**, 381–387.

—— 1976. Field excursions in the Aberystwyth region. *Biuletyn Peryglacjalny.* **26**, 79–112.

—— 1977. The periglacial environment of Great Britain during the Devensian. *Philosophical Transactions of the Royal Society of London*, **B280**, 183–198.

—— & WATSON, S. 1967. The periglacial origin of the drifts at Morfa-Bychan, near Aberystwyth. *Geological Journal*, **5**, 419–440.

WATTS, W. A. 1959a. Pollen spectra from the interglacial deposits at Kirmington, Lincolnshire. *Proceedings of the Yorkshire Geological Society*, **32**, 145–151.

—— 1959b. Interglacial deposits at Kilbeg and Newtown, County Waterford. *Proceedings of the Royal Irish Academy*, **60B**, 73–134.

—— 1963. Late glacial pollen zones in western Ireland. *Irish Geography*, **4**, 367–376.

—— 1964. Interglacial deposits at Baggotstown, near Bruff, County Limerick. *Proceedings of the Royal Irish Academy*, **63B**, 167–189.

—— 1967. Interglacial deposits in Kildromin townland, near Herbertstown, County Limerick. *Proceedings of the Royal Irish Academy*, **65B**, 339–348.

—— 1977. The Late Devensian vegatation in Ireland. *Philosophical Transactions of the Royal Society of London*, **280B**, 273–293.

—— 1985. Quaternary vegetation cycles. *In:* EDWARDS, K. J. & WARREN, W. P. (eds) *The Quaternary History of Ireland*, Academic, London, 155–185.

WEDD, C. B. SMITH, B. & WILLIS, L. J. 1928. The geology of the country around Wrexham Part 2: Coal Measures and newer formations. *Memoir of the Geological Survey.*

WEIR, A. H., CATT, J. A. & MADGETT, P. A. 1971. Postglacial soil formation in the loess of Pegwell Bay, Kent (England). *Geoderma*, **5**, 131–149.

WELIN, E., ENGSTRAND, L. & VACZY, S. 1971. Institute of Geological Sciences radiocarbon dates I. *Radiocarbon* **13**, 26–28.

WELCH, F. B. A. 1955. Note on gravels at Kenn, Somerset. *Proceedings of the University of Bristol Spelaeological Society*, **7**, 137.

—— & TROTTER, F. M. 1961. *Geology of the Country Around Monmouth and Chepstow.* Memoir Geological Survey.

WEST, R. G. 1956. The Quaternary deposits at Hoxne, Suffolk. *Philosophical Transactions of the Royal Society of London*, **B239**, 265–356.

—— 1957. Interglacial deposits at Bobbitshole, Ipswich. *Philosophical Transactions of the Royal Society of London*, **B241**, 33–44.

—— 1958. The Pleistocene Epoch in East Anglia. *Journal of Glaciology*, **3**,

—— 1961a. Vegetational history of the Early Pleistocene of the Royal Society borehole at Ludham, Norfolk. *Proceedings of the Royal Society*, **B155**, 437–453.

—— 1961b. The glacial and interglacial deposits of Norfolk. *Transactions of the Norfolk and Norwich Naturalists' Society*, **19**, 365–375.

—— 1963. Problems of the British Quaternary. *Proceedings of the Geologists' Association*, **74**, 147–186.

—— 1969. Note on the pollen analysis from the Speeton Shell Bed. *Proceedings of the Geologists' Association*, **80**, 217–221.

—— 1977. *Pleistocene Geology and Biology* (second edition). Longman, London.

—— 1980. *The Pre-glacial Pleistocene of the Norfolk and Suffolk coasts.* Cambridge University Press.

—— 1981. A contribution to the Pleistocene of Suffolk: an interglacial site at Sicklesmere, near Bury St Edmunds. *In:* NEALE, J. & FLENLEY, J. (eds) *The Quaternary in Britain: essays in honour of Lewis Penny on his retirement.* Pergamon, Oxford, 43–48.

—— & DONNER, J. J. 1956. The glaciations of East Anglia and the East Midlands: a differemtiation based on stone orientation measurements of the till. *Quarterly Journal of the Geological Society, London*, **112**, 69–91.

—— & SPARKS, B. W. 1960. Coastal interglacial deposits of the English Channel. *Philosophical Transactions of the Royal Society of London B* **243**, 95–133.

—— & WILSON, D. G. 1966. Cromer Forest bed Series. *Nature*, London, **209**, 497–498.

——, DEVOY, R. J. N., FUNNELL, B. M. & ROBINSON, J. E. 1984. Pleistocene deposits at Earnley, Bracklesham Bay, Sussex. *Philosophical Transactions of the Royal Society of London*, **B306**, 137–157.

——, KNUDSEN, K. L., PENNY, D. N., PREECE, R. C. & ROBINSON, J. E. 1994. Palaeontology and taphonomy of Late Quaternary fossil assemblages at Somersham, Cambridgeshire, England, and the problem of reworking. *Journal of Quaternary Science*, **9**, 357–366.

——, ANDREWS, R., KNUDSEN, K. L., PEGLAR, S. M. & PETTIT, M. E. 1995. Late Pleistocene deposits at Chatteris, March and Wimblington, Cambridgeshire, U.K. *Proceedings of the Geologists' Association*, **106**, 195–210.

WESTON, C. H. 1850. On the Diluvia and Valleys in the Vicinity of Bath. *Quarterly Journal of the Geological Society, London*, **6**, 449–451.

WHITAKER, W., WOODWARD, H. B., BENNETT, F. J., SKERTCHLY, S. B. J.

& JUKES-BROWNE, A. J. 1891. The geology of parts of Cambridgeshire and of Suffolk (Ely, Mildenhall, Thetford). *Memoir, Geological Survey.*

WHITE, H. J. O. 1902. On a peculiarity in the course of certain streams in the London and Hampshire Basins. *Proceedings of the Geologists' Association,* 17, 107–120.

—— 1921. *A Short Account of the Geology of the Isle of Wight.* Memoirs of the Geological Survey of England & Wales.

—— 1924. *Geology of the Country Around Brighton and Worthing.* Memoir Geological Survey.

WHITEHEAD, P. F. 1989. Development and deposition of the Avon Valley Terraces. *In:* KEEN, D. H. (ed.) *The Pleistocene of the West Midlands: Field Guide.* Quaternary Research Association, Cambridge, 37–41.

WHITEHEAD, T. H. & POCOCK, R. W. 1947. *Memoir Geological Survey.*

WHITEMAN, C. A. 1987. Till lithology and genesis near the southern margin of the Anglian ice-sheet in Essex, England. *In:* VAN DER MEER, J. J. M. (ed.) *Tills and Glaciotectonics.* Balkema, Rotterdam, 55–66.

—— 1990. *Early and Middle Pleistocene stratigraphy in central Essex, England.* PhD thesis, London University.

—— 1992. The palaeogeography and correlation of pre-AnglianGlaciation terraces of the River Thames in Essex and the London Basin. *Proceedings of the Geologists' Association,* 103, 37–56.

—— & ROSE, J. 1992. Thames River Sediments of the British Early and Middle Pleistocene. *Quaternary Science Reviews,* 11, 363–376.

WHITTAKER, W. 1889. *The Geology of London and Part of the Thames Valley.* Memoir, Geological Survey.

WHITTINGTON, G. 1994. Bruckenthalia spiculifolia (Salsib.) Reichenb. (Ericaceae) in the Late Quaternary of Western Europe. *Quaternary Science Reviews,* 13, 761–768.

——, HALL, A. M. & JARVIS, J. 1993. A pre-Late Devensian pollen site from Camp Fauld, Buchan, north-east Scotland. *New Phytologist,* 125, 867–874.

WHITTINGTON, R. J. 1977. A Late-glacial drainage pattern in the Kish Bank area and post-glacial sediments in the central Irish Sea. *In:* KIDSON, C. & TOOLEY, M. J. (eds) *Quaternary History of the Irish Sea,* Seel House, Liverpool, 55–68.

WHITTOW, J. B. & BALL, D. F. 1970. North-west Wales. *In:* LEWIS, C. A. (ed.) *The glaciations of Wales and adjoining regions.* Longman, London, 21–58.

WILCOX, C. & STANCZYSZYN, R. 1983. The sand and gravel resources of the country around Diss, Norfolk. Description of 1:25000 sheet TM 17 and part of TM 18. *Mineral Assessment Report,* 137. Institute of Geological Sciences.

WILKS, P. J. 1979. Mid-Holocene sea-level and sedimentation interactions in the Dovey estuary area, Wales. *Palaeooogeography, Palaeoclimatology, Palaeoecology,* 26, 17–36.

WILLIAMS, G. J. 1968a. The buried channel and superficial deposits of the lower Usk and their correlation with similar features in the lower Severn. *Proceedings of the Geologists' Association,* 79, 325–348.

—— 1968b. *Contributions to the Pleistocene Geomorphology of the Middle and Lower Usk.* PhD thesis, University of Wales.

WILLIAMS, K. E. 1927. The glacial drifts of western Cardiganshire. *Geological Magazine,* 64, 205–227.

WILLS, L. J. 1924. The development of the Severn Valley in the neighbourhood of Iron-Bridge and Bridgnorth. *Quarterly Journal of the Geological Society, London,* 80, 274–314.

—— 1926. The geology and soils of Hartlebury Common. *Proceedings of the Birmingham Natural History and Philosophical Society,* 15, 95–101.

—— 1937. *The Pleistocene History of the West Midlands.* British Association for the Advancement of Science Presidential Address to Section C (Geology) London: British Association.

—— 1938. The Pleistocene development of the Severn from Bridgnorth to the sea. *Quarterly Journal of the Geological Society, London,* 94, 161–242.

—— 1948. *The palaeogeography of the Midlands.* Liverpool. Hodder & Stoughton.

—— 1951. *A Palaeogeographical Atlas of the British Isles and adjacent parts of Europe.* Blackie. London. (2nd edition 1952).

WILSON, D., DAVIES, J. R, FLETCHER, C. J. N. & SMITH, M. 1990. *Geology of the South Wales Coalfield Part VI. The Country around Bridgend.* Memoir, British Geological Survey.

WILSON, P. 1990a. Morphology, sedimentological characteristics and origin of a fossil rock glacier on Muckish Mountain, northwest Ireland. *Geografiska Annaler,* 72A, 237–247.

—— 1990b. Characteristics and significance of protatus ramparts and fossil rock glaciers on Errigal mountain, County Donegal. *Proceedings of the Royal Irish Academy,* 90B, 1–21.

—— 1992. Small-scale patterned ground, Comeragh mountains, southeast Ireland. *Permafrost and periglacial Processes,* 3, 63–70.

—— 1993. Description and origin of some talus-foot delvis accumulations, Ceghla mountains, County Donegal, Ireland. *Permafrost and Periglacial Processes,* 4, 231–244.

WILSON, S. J. 1991. The correlation of the Speeton Shell Bed, Filey Bay, Yorkshire, to an oxygen isotope stage. *Proceedings of the Yorkshire Geological Society,* 48(3), 223–226.

WINGFIELD, R. T. R. 1989. Glacial incisions indicating Middle and Upper Pleistocene ice limits off Britain. *Terra Nova,* 1, 538–548.

—— 1990. The origin of major incissions within the Pleistocene deposits of the North Sea. *Marine Geology,* 91, 31–52.

—— 1994. Pleistocene and Holocene. *In:* TAPPIN, D. R. *et al. United Kingdom offshore regional report: the geology of Cardigan Bay and the Bristol Channel.* British Geological Survey, 76–93.

—— 1995. Pleistocene and Holocene. *In:* JACKSON, D. I. *et al. United Kingdom offshore regional report: the geology of the Irish Sea.* British Geological Survey, 85–102.

WINTLE, A. G. 1981. Thermoluminescence dating of late Devensian loesses in southern England. *Nature* 289, 479–480.

—— 1981. Thermoluminescence dating of Late Devensian loesses in southern England. *Nature,* 289, 479–481.

WINWOOD, H. H. 1875. Notes on some Railway sections near Bath. *Proceedings Bath History and Antiquarian Field Club,* 3, 2, 129–130.

—— 1889. Recent 'finds' in the Victoria gravel pit. *Proceedings Bath History and Antiquarian Field Club,* 6, 3, 327–332.

—— & CATT, J. A. 1985. Thermoluminescence dating of soils developed in late Devensian loess at Pegwell Bay, Kent. *Journal of Soil Science,* 36, 293–298.

WIRTZ, D. 1953. Zur Stratigraphie des Pleistocans in westen der Britischen Inseln. *Neves Jahrbuch fur Geologie und Palaeontologie,* 96, 267–303.

WOOD, A. 1959. The erosional history of the cliffs around Aberystwyth. *Geological Journal,* 2, 271–279.

WOODLAND, A. W. 1970. The buried tunnel-valleys of East Anglia. *Proceedings of the Yorkshire Geological Society,* 37, 521–578.

—— & EVANS, W. B. 1968. The geology of the South Wales Coalfield, Part 4. The country around Pontypridd and Maesteg. *Memoir Geological Survey.*

WOODWARD, H. H. 1876. Geology of East Somerset and the Bristol Coal-Fields. *Memoir Geological Survey.*

—— 1905. Geology of the railway cuttings between Langport and Castle Cary. Summary of the Progress of the Geological Survey for 1904.

WOOLACOTT, D. 1905. The superficial deposits and pre-glacial valleys of the Northumberland and Durham Coalfields. *Quarterly Journal of the Geologyal Society, London,* 61, 64–95.

WOOLDRIDGE, S. W. 1927. The Pliocene history of the London Basin. *Proceedings of the Geologists' Association,* 38, 49–132.

—— 1938. The glaciation of the London Basin and the evolution of the Lower Thames drainage system. *Quarterly Journal Geological Society of London,* 94, 627–667.

—— 1960. The Pleistocene succession in the London Basin. *Proceedings of the Geologists' Association,* 71, 113–129.

—— & LINTON, D. L. 1955. *Structure, Surface and Drainage in South East England.* London (published in 1939 as Publication No. 10, Institute of British Geographers.

WORSLEY, P. 1966. Some Weichellian fossil frost wedges from north east Cheshire. *The Mersian Geologist,* 1, 357–365.

—— 1967. Problems in naming the Pleistocene deposits of the north east Cheshire Plain. *The Mercian Geologist,* 2, 51–55.

—— 1970. The Cheshire-Shropshire Lowlands. *In:* LEWIS, C. A. (ed.) *The glaciations of Wales and adjoining regions.* Longman, London, 83–106.

—— 1980. Problems in radiocarbon dating the Chelford Interstadial of England. *In:* CULLINGFORD, R. A., DAVIDSON, D. A. & LEWIN, J.

(eds) *Timescales in Geomorphology*. Chichester: Wiley, 289–304.
—— 1986. On the age of wood in till at Broughton Bay. *Quaternary Newsletter*, **49**, 17–19.
—— 1991. Glacial deposits of the lowlands between the Mersey and Severn Rivers. *In:* EHLERS, J., GIBBARD, P. L. & ROSE, J. (eds*)* *Glacial Deposits in Great Britain and Ireland*, Balkema, Rotterdam, 203–211.
—— 1992. A pre-Devensian mammoth from Arclid, Cheshire. *Proceedings of the Geologists' Association*, **103**, 75–77.
—— in press. The glacial geology of Condover. *In:* LISTER, A. M., SCOURSE, J. & COOPE, G. R. (eds) *The Last Mammoths in Britain: discoveries at Condover, 1986–7*. Oxford: Oxford University Press.
—— & COLLINS, P. E. F. 1995. The geomorphological context of the Brimpton Late Pleistocene succession (south central England). *Proceedings of the Geologists' Association*, **106**, 39–45.
——, COOPE, G. R., GOOD, T. R., HOLYOAK, D. T. & ROBINSON, J. E. 1983. A Pleistocene succession from beneath the Chelford Sands at Oakwood Quarry, Chelford, Cheshire. *Geological Journal*, **18**, 307–324.
WORSSAM, B. C. 1963. Geology of the country around Maidstone. *Memoirs of the Geological Survey of England & Wales*.
—— 1982. Geological notes and local details for 1:10 000 sheet SO82 NE (Deerhurst). *Institute of Geological Sciences*.
—— & OLD, R. A. 1988. Geology of the Country around Coalville. *Memoir of the British Geological Survey*. HMSO.
——, ELLISON, R. A. & MOORLOCK, B. S. P. 1989. *Geology of the country around Tewkesbury*. Memoir of the British Geological Survey.
WRAY, D. A., & COPE, F. W. 1948. *Geology of Southport and Formby*. Memoir Geological Survey.
WRIGHT, W. B. 1914. *The Quaternary Ice Age*. London (2nd edition, 1937).
—— & MUFF, H. B. 1904. The Pre-glacial raised beach of the south coast of Ireland. *Scientific Proceedings of the Royal Dublin society*, **10**, 250–324.
WYATT, R. J. 1971. New evidence for drift-filled valleys in north-east Leicestershire and south Lincolnshire. *Bulletin of the Geological Survey of Great Britain*, **37**, 29–56.

WYATT, R. J., HORTON, A. & KENNA, R. J. 1971. Drift-filled channels on the Leicestershire-Lincolnshire border. *Bulletin of the Geological Survey of Great Britain*, **37**, 57–80.
WYMER, J. J. 1968. *Lower Palaeolithic Archaeology in Britain*. John Baker, London.
—— 1981. The Palaeolithic. *In:* SIMMONS, I. G. & TOOLEY, M. J. (eds*)* *The Environment in British Prehistory*. Duckworth, London, 49–81.
—— 1985. *Palaeolithic Sites of East Anglia*. Geobooks, Norwich.
—— & STRAW, A. 1977. Hand axes from beneath glacial till at Welton-le-Wold, Lincolnshire, and the distribution of palaeoliths in Britain. *Proceedings of the Prehistoric Society*, **43**, 355–360.
ZAGWIJN, W. H. 1974. The Pliocene-Pleistocene boundary in western and southern Europe. *Boreas*, **3**, 75–97.
—— 1979. Early and Middle Pleistocene coastlines in the southern North Sea Basin. *In:* OELE, E., SCHÜTTENHELM, R. T. E. & WIGGERS, A. J. (eds) *The Quaternary History of the North Sea*. Uppsala (*Acta Universitatis Upsaliensis*), 31–42.
—— 1985. An outline of the Quaternary stratigraphy of the Netherlands. *Geologie en Mijnbouw*, **64**, 17–24.
—— 1989. The Netherlands during the Tertiary and the Quaternary: a case history of Coastal Lowland evolution. *Geologie en Mijnbouw*. **68**, 107–120.
ZALASIEWICZ, J. A. & MATHERS, S. J. 1985. Lithostratigraphy of the Red and Norwich Crags of the Aldeburgh-Orford area, south-east Suffolk. *Geological Magazine*, **122**, 287–296.
——, ——, HUGHES, M. J., GIBBARD, P. L., PEGLAR, S. M., HARLAND, R., NICHOLSON, R. A., BOULTON, G. S., CAMBRIDGE, P. & WEALTHALL, G. P. 1988. Stratigraphy and palaeoenvironments of the Red Crag and Norwich Crag formations between Aldeburgh and Sizewell, Suffolk, England. *Philosophical Transactions of the Royal Society of London*, **B322**, 221–272.
ZEUNER, F. E. 1945. *The Pleistocene Period*. Hutchinson, London.
—— 1959. *The Pleistocene Period*. Hutchinson, London (second edition).